International Flight Operations
2nd Edition

James Albright

Acknowledgments

Thanks to Steven Foltz who proved invaluable with fact checking.

James' Lawyer Advises:

Always remember that James, when you get right down to it, is just a pilot. He tries to give you the facts from the source materials but maybe he got it wrong, maybe he is out of date. Sure, he warns you when he is giving you his personal techniques, but you should always follow your primary guidance (Aircraft manuals, government regulations, etc.) before listening to James.

Contents

IV – Communicate

V – Surveillance

VI – Abnormals

VII Tutorial

VIII - Appendices

Introduction

International flight operations can be a daunting challenge for any pilot, even more so for the very first few trips away from one's home country. Most operators require their pilots complete a recognized course and then simply turn them loose. This is a recipe for trouble.

Having a good source of written material to act at first as a tutorial and later as reference material would seem a necessity for any international pilot's bag of tricks. Sadly, most international flight operations textbooks are poorly written, based on unreferenced folklore, poorly organized as reference material, and unsuitable as introductory tutorials. I've written several international flight operations manuals over the years for various business aviation management companies. Each one was better than the one before, and I think I finally have the previously mentioned complaints solved.

Organization

This manual is organized into sections to making finding topics more logical:

I - Negotiate	-	the regulatory material and where to find them.
II - Aviate	-	the nuts and bolts of defining our location, airspace, how to plot, Reduced Vertical Separation Minima, and Global Navigation Satellite Systems.
III - Navigate	-	airspace rules throughout the world.
IV - Communicate	-	radio and data link systems.
V - Surveillance	-	automatic dependent surveillance and transponder systems.
VI - Abnormals	-	lost communications, loss of navigation capability, loss of altitude keeping accuracy, volcanic ash, and weather deviation.
VII - Tutorial	-	a sample trip, from preparation, departure, en route, to arrival.
VIII - Appendices	-	Everything else.

Tutorial

Section VII presents a tutorial on how to prepare, plan, and execute a multiple leg journey, with exact details about the many steps involved. It would be a good place to start for those who have not done this before, or for those who haven't done so in a while.

A Word About Typography

Just about everything in this manual comes from primary source material that is indicated in [brackets] where the source material can be found in the last section of the manual, the chapter called "References."

I use italics in every section except the tutorial to indicate personal techniques and opinion, those items that can't be found in the references. The tutorial is pretty much all technique and in that section italics are used when referring to the example trip.

A Few Words About Currency

One of the challenges for every pilot is keeping abreast of the many national and international rules and regulations. Even the most basic procedures can be modified, replaced, or rendered completely useless by advances in technology and technique. Nothing remains the same, it would seem.

Even with all the reference materials cited, there is a danger that the material has become outdated. As soon as it is published, it is out of date. Some of the reference material, it would seem, is never current. Try finding CPDLC rules for continental Europe, for example.

So this is just a best effort as of January, 2021. It will get you started and give you hints about where to look for updates.

As pilots we are responsible for an unmanageable amount of information and we are left to rely on those that have gone before us. Keep up with the news, look for reliable pilot message boards and blogs, and keep "plugged in." So please be careful out there. I hope I have given you a good head start on the most challenging aspect of aviation.

— James Albright

Chapter 1

Aircraft Regulatory Compliance

*A*s strange as it may sound, many pilots who started their aviation careers in the United States do not understand that most of the world flies by a different set of rules. Stranger still, there are pilots who venture beyond their borders without a clue about the International Civil Aviation Organization (ICAO) and continue to get away with ignorance of the law. These pilots are endangering their lives and the lives of all around them. So we must begin with the legal framework that binds the U.S. pilot to the rules of the ICAO and the countries they visit.

It is often said that the sheer volume of U.S. aviation regulations is more than any one pilot can really comprehend. The number of ICAO rules is even more daunting. So step two is to learn which regulations are most important, to learn how to best access the rules that matter, and to know where to find the primary source documents when needed.

Finally, just because you know the rules as they apply to a U.S. aircraft and those that are dictated by international standards, you still have to understand what the country you are visiting (or even simply overflying) expects. These rules are sometimes posted on the Internet and in English, making life much easier. But more often than not, a copy of the rules is only available in the host country's language and often only available at great cost. You should have a method of ensuring you will be in compliance with host nation rules before you venture forward.

Why do we have an international system in the first place?

World War II highlighted the need for some standardization in the way nations operate in the airspace of other nations and in the airspace over the high seas. In 1944, 52 nations met in Chicago to agree on a set of rules that have become known as the "Chicago Convention" and on the establishment of the International Civil Aviation Organization (ICAO). The document was signed on December 7, 1944 and ratified in 1947. As of 2019 there are 193 nations who have signed on. The convention itself has 96 articles and has later become supported by 19 Annexes. Every signatory, including the United States, have agreed to comply with the convention and the annexes; but every signatory can deviate so long as they publish where the rules in their state differ.

How do I get a copy of this? While the ICAO charges for many of its Annexes and some of its documents, they do offer this one for free at: https://www.icao.int/publications/pages/doc7300.aspx.

1944 Chicago Convention on Civil Aviation

Where does it say I have to do any of this?

Title 14 of the United States Code of Federal Regulations, Part 91, §91.703 removes all doubt in the matter.

[14 CFR 91] §91.703   Operations of civil aircraft of U.S. registry outside of the United States.

(a) Each person operating a civil aircraft of U.S. registry outside of the United States shall—

(1) When over the high seas, comply with annex 2 (Rules of the Air) to the Convention on International Civil Aviation and with §§91.117(c), 91.127, 91.129, and 91.131;

(2) When within a foreign country, comply with the regulations relating to the flight and maneuver of aircraft there in force;

(3) Except for §§91.117(a), 91.307(b), 91.309, 91.323, and 91.711, comply with this part so far as it is not inconsistent with applicable regulations of the foreign country where the aircraft is operated or annex 2 of the Convention on International Civil Aviation; and

(4) When operating within airspace designated as Minimum Navigation Performance Specifications (MNPS) airspace, comply with §91.705. When operating within airspace designated as Reduced Vertical Separation Minimum (RVSM) airspace, comply with §91.706.

(5) For aircraft subject to ICAO Annex 16, carry on board the aircraft documents that summarize the noise operating characteristics and certifications of the aircraft that demonstrate compliance with this part and part 36 of this chapter.

(b) Annex 2 to the Convention on International Civil Aviation, Tenth Edition—July 2005, to which reference is made in this part, is incorporated into this part and made a part hereof as provided in 5 U.S.C. §552 and pursuant to 1 CFR part 51.

*H*ow do I get a copy of this? As of 2020, all "Federal Aviation Regulations, which are more properly known as Title 14 to the U.S. Code of Federal Regulations (14 CFR), are available at: http://www.faa.gov/regulations_policies/.*

Chapter 2

Primary Source Materials (ICAO)

*A*s a pilot licensed by a country that is a signatory to the ICAO, basically *every pilot, you are constrained to operate under the rules of the ICAO except as noted by the country you happen to be flying in.*

In other words, you should know the ICAO rules if you ever plan on venturing outside your own borders. Using a secondary source, such as the Jeppesen Airways Manuals, is perfectly acceptable for routine operations. When things are not routine, however, it helps to know where to look in the primary source materials.

ICAO Annexes

ICAO Annex 1 – Personnel Licensing

Standards and Recommended Practices for Personnel Licensing were first adopted by the Council on 14 April 1948 pursuant to the provisions of Article 37 of the Convention on International Civil Aviation (Chicago 1944) and designated as Annex 1 to the Convention.

This annex includes things like licenses and ratings for pilots (Chapter 2), other crew members (Chapter 3), non-crewmembers (Chapter 4), and the medical requirements for each category (Chapter 6).

ICAO Annex 2 – Rules of the Air

In October 1945, Standards, Practices and Procedures (SARPS) for the rules of the air were published as Recommendations for Standards, Practices and Procedures — Rules of the Air in the first part of Doc 2010 and later adopted as Annex 2 on 1 September 1952.

Article 38 of the Convention requires states to notify the Organization of any differences between their national regulations and practices and the International Standards contained in this Annex and any amendments.

This annex includes things like general rules (Chapter 3), visual flight rules

(Chapter 4), instrument flight rules (Chapter 5), signals (Appendix 1), aircraft intercept rules (Appendix 2), and unlawful interference (Attachment B).

ICAO Annex 3 – Meteorological Service for International Air Navigation

Standards and Recommended Practices relating to meteorology were first adopted by the Council on 16 April 1948, pursuant to the provisions of Article 37 of the Convention on International Civil Aviation (Chicago, 1944), and designated as Annex 3 to the Convention with the title Standards and Recommended Practices — Meteorological Codes.

This annex outlines a world area forecast system and standards when it comes to things like meteorological observations and reports (Chapter 4), aircraft observations and reports (Chapter 5), forecasts (Chapter 6), and other ways weather reports are made. If you've ever wondered why your weather charts are formatted the way they are, see Appendix 1. All those codes, like DZ for drizzle and GR for hail? See Appendix 3. TAF formats are in Appendix 5.

ICAO Annex 4 – Aeronautical Charts

Standards and Recommended Practices for Aeronautical Charts were first adopted by the Council on 16 April 1948, pursuant to the provisions of Article 37 of the Convention on International Civil Aviation (Chicago, 1944), and were designated as Annex 4 to the Convention.

This annex gives the specifications to be used for aerodrome, en route, area, approach, and even plotting charts. Symbols, notes, and even the colors to be used are specified.

ICAO Annex 5 – Units of Measurement to be used in Air and Ground Operations

International Standards and Recommended Practices for Dimensional Units to be used in Air-Ground Communications were first adopted by the Council on 16 April 1948 pursuant to Article 37 of the Convention on International Civil Aviation (Chicago, 1944) and were designated as Annex 5 to the Convention.

This annex outlines the International System of Units (SI), gives conversion factors (Attachment C), and defines Coordinated Universal Time (Attachment D).

ICAO Annex 6 – Operation of Aircraft

Part I – International Commercial Air Transport Aeroplanes

Part II – International General Aviation Aeroplanes

Standards and Recommended Practices for the Operation of Aircraft — International Commercial Air Transport were first adopted by the Council on 10 December 1948 pursuant to the provisions of Article 37 of the Convention on International Civil Aviation (Chicago, 1944) and designated as Annex 6 to the Convention.

This annex includes things like flight operations, airplane performance limitations, equipment, maintenance, crew, manuals, logs, and records. You will also find the requirement for a journey log, an air operator certificate, and even the framework for a safety management system here. Part I applies to commercial aircraft and Part II to general aviation.

ICAO Annex 7 – Aircraft Nationality and Registration Marks

Annex 7 contains Standards adopted by the International Civil Aviation Organization on 8 February 1949 as the minimum Standards for the display of marks to indicate appropriate nationality and registration which have been determined to comply with Article 20 of the Convention.

This annex specifies how aircraft are marked to designate registry, what the certificate of registration should look like, and the requirement for an identification plate.

ICAO Annex 8 – Airworthiness of Aircraft

Standards and Recommended Practices for the Airworthiness of Aircraft were adopted by the Council on 1 March 1949 pursuant to the provisions of Article 37 of the Convention on International Civil Aviation (Chicago 1944) and designated as Annex 8 to the Convention.

This annex includes things like type certification, production approval, the certificate of airworthiness, and the continuing airworthiness of aircraft.

ICAO Annex 9 - Facilitation

Standards and Recommended Practices on Facilitation were first adopted by the Council on 25 March 1949, pursuant to the provisions of Article 37 of the Convention on International Civil Aviation (Chicago 1944) and designated as Annex 9 to the Convention.

This annex includes things like the documentation needed for entry and departure of aircraft, disinfection, inspection, and other passenger and cargo concerns. It also includes the need to land at an airport designated as an international airport, as well as the measures when landing someplace not so designated.

ICAO Annex 10 – Aeronautical Telecommunications

Volume I – Radio Navigtion Aids

Standards and Recommended Practices for Aeronautical Telecommunications were first adopted by the Council on 30 May 1949 pursuant to the provisions of Article 37 of the Convention on International Civil Aviation (Chicago 1944) and designated as Annex 10 to the Convention.

This annex includes specifications for ILS, VOR, NDB, marker beacons, GNSS, and MLS.

Volume II – Communication Procedures including those with PANS status

Standards and Recommended Practices for Aeronautical Telecommunications were first adopted by the Council on 30 May 1949 pursuant to the provisions of Article 37 of the Convention on International Civil Aviation (Chicago 1944) and designated as Annex 10 to the Convention. Volume II contains material that has the status of Procedures for Air Navigation Services (PANS).

This annex includes procedures for voice, Aeronautical Fixed Telecommunications Network (AFTN), distress, and data link.

Volume III – Communication Systems (Digital Data and Voice Communications)

Standards and Recommended Practices for Aeronautical Telecommunications were first adopted by the Council on 30 May 1949 pursuant to the provisions of Article 37 of the Convention on International Civil Aviation (Chicago 1944) and designated as Annex 10 to the Convention.

This annex includes things like Mode S, VHF air-ground digital link (VDL), HF data link, SELCAL, and Emergency Locator Transmitter (ELT).

Volume IV – Surveillance and Collision Avoidance Systems

Standards and Recommended Practices for Aeronautical Telecommunications were first adopted by the Council on 30 May 1949 pursuant to the provisions of Article 37 of the Convention on International Civil Aviation (Chicago 1944) and designated as Annex 10 to the Convention.

This annex includes things like Secondary Surveillance Radar (SSR), Airborne Collision Avoidance System (ACAS), and Mode S.

Volume V – Aeronautical Radio Frequency Spectrum Utilization

Standards and Recommended Practices for Aeronautical Telecommunications were first adopted by the Council on 30 May 1949 pursuant to the provisions of Article 37 of the Convention on International Civil Aviation (Chicago 1944) and designated as Annex 10 to the Convention.

This annex maps out the acceptable use of various frequencies, including those used for distress.

ICAO Annex 11 – Air Traffic Services

Air Traffic Control procedures were first adopted by the Council on 18 May 1950, pursuant to Article 37 of the Convention on International Civil Aviation (Chicago, 1944), and designated as Annex 11 to the Convention.

This annex includes things like the designation of air traffic control services, flight information services, contingencies, and Traffic Information Broadcasts by Aircraft (TIBA).

ICAO Annex 12 – Search and Rescue

Standards and Recommended Practices for Search and Rescue were adopted by the Council on 25 May 1950 and designated as Annex 12 to the Convention on International Civil Aviation.

This annex includes things like the organization of search and rescue services, cooperation between the states, operating procedures, and standardized signals.

ICAO Annex 13 – Aircraft Accident and Incident Investigation

Standards and Recommended Practices for Aircraft Accident Inquiries were first adopted by the Council on 11 April 1951 pursuant to Article 37 of the Convention on International Civil Aviation (Chicago, 1944) and were designated as Annex 13 to the Convention.

This annex includes things like notification, investigation, and reporting aircraft mishaps.

ICAO Annex 14 – Aerodromes

Volume I – Aerodrome Design and Operations

Volume II - Heliports

Standards and Recommended Practices for Aerodromes were first adopted by the Council on 29 May 1951 pursuant to the provisions of Article 37 of the Convention on International Civil Aviation (Chicago 1944) and designated as Annex 14 to the Convention.

This annex includes things like pavement strength, declared distances, rescue and fire fighting, obstacle restrictions, visual markings, lights, electrical systems, and aerodrome maintenance. It also includes an attachment covering obstacle limitation surfaces.

ICAO Annex 15 – Aeronautical Information Services

Standards and Recommended Practices for Aeronautical Information Services were first adopted by the Council on 15 May 1953, pursuant to the provisions of Article 37 of the Convention on International Civil Aviation (Chicago 1944), and were designated as Annex 15 to the Convention.

This annex includes things like Aeronautical Information Publications (AIPs), Notices to Airmen (NOTAMs), Aeronautical Information Circulars (AICs), and electronic terrain and obstacle data.

ICAO Annex 16 – Environmental Protection

Volume I – Aircraft Noise

Standards and Recommended Practices for Aeronautical Information Services were first adopted by the Council on 15 May 1953, pursuant to the provisions of Article 37 of the Convention on International Civil Aviation (Chicago 1944), and were designated as Annex 15 to the Convention.

This annex is where we get our noise level standards, Chapters 2, 3, and 4 have become known as the criteria for what is called Stage 2, 3, and 4 in the United States. The higher chapters are given to propeller-driven aircraft, helicopters, and for supersonic airplanes.

Volume II – Aircraft Engine Emissions

The Council agreed in 1980 to add environmental aspects into Volume II — Aircraft Engine Emissions.

This annex includes the criteria for vented fuel and engine emissions.

Volume III - CO_2 Certification Requirement

The Council agreed in 2010 to develop International Standards and Recommended Practices for Aeroplane CO_2 Emissions.

Once known as the "Carbon Trading Scheme," this program has been somewhat controversial and even as late as 2020 is in a state of flux. It could impact you now or in the future and should be watched carefully for changes.

ICAO Annex 17 - Security

Standards and Recommended Practices for Aeronautical Information Services were first adopted by the Council on 15 May 1953, pursuant to the provisions of Article 37 of the Convention on International Civil Aviation (Chicago 1944), and were designated as Annex 15 to the Convention.

This annex includes things like the prevention and management of acts of unlawful interference. You will also find the special SSR codes here.

ICAO Annex 18 – The Safe Transport of Dangerous Goods by Air

The provisions of Annex 18 govern the international transport of dangerous goods by air. The broad provisions of this Annex are amplified by the detailed specifications of the Technical Instructions for the Safe Transport of Dangerous Goods by Air (Doc 9284).

This annex includes things like packing, labeling, training programs, and limitations of transporting dangerous goods by air.

ICAO Annex 19 - Safety Management

The Council agreed in 2013 to develop International Standards and Recommended Practices for Safety Management.

This annex outlines Safety Management System (SMS) framework, to include safety data collection, analysis, and exchange.

ICAO Documents

There are many ICAO documents that may or may not apply to what you are doing. The following are the documents that are probably the most applicable.

ICAO Doc 4444 ATM/501 – Procedures for Air Navigation Services – Air Traffic Management

The Procedures for Air Navigation Services — Air Traffic Management

(PANS-ATM) are the result of the progressive evolution of the Procedures for Air Navigation Services — Air Traffic Control (PANS-ATC).

This document outlines air traffic services, including speed control, wake turbulence, position reporting, separation methods and minima, radar services, phraseologies, Automatic Dependent Surveillance (ADS), Controller-Pilot Data Link Communications (CPDLC), emergency procedures and contingencies, flight plans, and incident reports.

ICAO Doc 7030 – Regional Supplementary Procedures

The ICAO Regional Supplementary Procedures (SUPPS) form the procedural part of the Air Navigation Plans to meet those needs of specific areas that are not covered in the worldwide provisions. They complement the statement of requirements for facilities and services contained in the Air Navigation Plan publications.

This document outlines the major differences found in regions of the world with the ICAO standard. Regions are defined as Africa-Indian Ocean (AFI), Caribbean (CAR), European (EUR), Middle East/Asia (MID/ASIA), North America (NAM), North Atlantic (NAT), Pacific (PAC), and South America (SAM). In theory this could be the "go to" source for flying away from home, but has never been kept up-to-date and as of 2020, the current edition is 12 years old.

ICAO Doc 7300/8 – The Convention on International Civil Aviation signed at Chicago on 7 December 1944

This document contains the text of the Convention on International Civil Aviation, signed at Chicago on 7 December 1944 (hereinafter referred to as the "Convention"), in the English, French, Russian and Spanish languages as amended.

This document is simply the Chicago Convention in a format more easily read and searched than the original, which is available only as a Photostat copy and has not been updated.

ICAO Doc 7910/133 – Location Indicators

This document is the official source of ICAO location identifiers.

ICAO Doc 8168 OPS/611 – Procedures for Air Navigation Services – Aircraft Operations

The division of the PANS-OPS into the two volumes was accomplished in

1979 as a result of an extensive amendment to the obstacle clearance criteria and the construction of approach-to-land procedures.

Volume I – Flight Procedures

Flight Procedures describes the operational requirements for flying the procedures designed in Volume II.

Volume II – Construction of Visual and Instrument Flight Procedures

Construction of Visual and Instrument Flight Procedures is intended for the guidance of procedures specialists and describes the essential areas and obstacle clearance requirements for the achievement of safe, regular instrument flight operations. It provides the basic guidelines to States, and those operators and organizations producing instrument flight charts that will result in uniform practices at all aerodromes where instrument flight procedures are carried out.

This document contains what in the United States is known as the U.S. Standard for Terminal Instrument Procedures (TERPS), that is, airspace construction for departure, en route, and arrival.

Volume III - Aircraft Operating Procedures

This volume was broken out from Volume I in 2018 to consolidate the operational procedures recommended for flight operations personnel and flight crew.

This volume is dedicated to how you fly the aircraft: altimeter setting, operating on parallel or near-parallel runways, secondary surveillance radar, operational flight information, standard operating procedures, voice and data communiations, airborne surveillance, and noise abatement procedures.

ICAO Doc 8400 – ICAO Abbreviations and Codes

This document is the official source of ICAO abbreviations.

ICAO Doc 9574 - Manual on Implementation of a 300m (1,000 ft) Vertical Separation Minimum Between FL290 and FL410 Inclusive

This document contains the foundation for Reduced Vertical Separation Minima (RVSM).

ICAO Doc 9613 AN/937 – Performance-Based Navigation (PBN) Man-

ual

Volume I – Concept and Implementation Guidance

Volume II – Implementing RNAV and RNP

This manual identifies the relationship between RNAV and RNP applications and the advantages and limitations of choosing one or the other as the navigation requirement for an airspace concept. It also aims at providing practical guidance to States, air navigation service providers and airspace users on how to implement RNAV and RNP applications, and how to ensure that the performance requirements are appropriate for the planned application.

This document is a primer on the concepts, which continue to be in a state of change. As of 2020 the latest revision was in 2013 and there have been a lot of changes since.

ICAO Doc 9859 AN/460 – Safety Management Manual

ICAO's Standards and Recommended Practices (SARPs) require that States establish a safety programme to achieve an acceptable level of safety in aviation operations. The acceptable level of safety shall be established by the State(s) concerned. While the concept of safety programmes and SMS is restricted to Annexes 6, 11 and 14 at present, it is possible that the concept will be expanded to include additional operational Annexes in the future.

You need a safety management system to fly in some parts of the world and you need to consider this manual to do that correctly.

ICAO Doc 9869 - Performance-Based Communication and Surveillance (PBCS) Manual

This manual is used to comply with Required Communication Performance (RCP) and Required Surveillance Performance (RSP) airspace requirements around the world.

You will need this to obtain PBCS authorizations.

ICAO Doc 10037 - Global Operational Data Link Document (GOLD)

The GOLD provides guidance and information concerning data link operations and is intended to facilitate the uniform application of Standards and Recommended Practices contained in Annex 2 — Rules of the Air, Annex 10 — Aeronautical Telecommunications and Annex 11 — Air Traffic Services, the provisions in the Procedures for Air Navigation Services — Air

Traffic Management (PANS-ATM, Doc 4444) and, when necessary, the Regional Supplementary Procedures (Doc 7030).

This manual gives you an excellent overview of data link operations.

Satellite Voice Guidance Material (SVGM)

The SVGM provides a comprehensive update of various regional and State guidance material for Air Navigation Service Providers (ANSPs) and aircraft operators to use SATVOICE for ATS communications. This includes the incorporation of performance-based specifications to be applied, where appropriate (i.e. RCP for controller intervention and RSP for position reporting), as well as associated guidance on data collection, monitoring, and analysis.

This manual covers SATVOICE and SATCOM, which are not the same. It also covers Required Communications Performance (RCP) and Required Surveillance Performance (RSP).

How do I get a copy of these? As of 2020, you can get most of them at: https://www.bazl.admin.ch/bazl/en/home.html, select your language, select "Portal for Specialists" then "National and international legislation" and then "Annexes to the ICAO Convention" or "Manuals to ICAO Annex 14" -- these are not always up-to-date but they are free. You can have the latest at http://www.icao.int but they provide documents for a fee and are very expensive. You can also try creative variations of the document numbers, titles, or descriptions in your Internet search engine.

Chapter 3

Primary Source Materials (U.S.)

U.S. pilots can access various advisory circulars, the U.S. Aeronautical Information Publication (AIP) which is about the same as the Aeronautical Information Manual (AIM), various Federal Aviation Administration (FAA) orders, and Federal Aviation Regulations which are more properly known as Title 14 to the U.S. Code of Federal Regulations (14 CFR). Non-U.S. pilots can best learn the differences between ICAO and U.S. rules by looking at the U.S. AIP.

Advisory Circulars

There is a debate among some U.S. pilots about the enforceability of anything written in an advisory circular because of the word "advisory" and a statement in most of these that says "This AC is not mandatory and is not a regulation. This AC describes an acceptable means, but not the only means, to comply with applicable regulations." What these pilots are missing is the fact that any other means they choose to comply needs to be at least as well thought out as what appears in the advisory circular. No matter which means you choose, you need to be familiar with the AC.

AC 20-138D, Airworthiness Approval of Positioning and Navigation Systems

This advisory circular provides guidance material for the airworthiness approval of installed positioning and navigation equipment. Positioning and navigation equipment may be used for a variety of functions such as navigation, automatic dependent surveillance, and/or terrain awareness and warning systems.

While this AC is targeted toward manufacturers it provides background information about GNSS, GPS, SBAS, RNAV, DME/DME, RNP, Baro-VNAV, and other topics of interest to the international pilot.

AC 90-96A, Approval of U.S. Operators and Aircraft to Operate Under Instrument Flight Rules (IFR) in European Airspace Designated for Basic Area Navigation (B-RNAV) and Precision Area Navigation (P-RNAV)

This advisory circular provides operational approval and airworthiness guidance material regarding RNAV requirements for operators of U.S.-registered civil aircraft, operating in a B-RNAV or P-RNAV environment in European RNAV airspace.

European navigation requirements are changing and B-RNAV and P-RNAV are giving way to RNAV 1 and, to a lesser extent, RNAV 2. Many of the procedures will specifically state "P-RNAV OR RNAV 1 REQUIRED" in recognition that some operators have the older P-RNAV authorization. ICAO Doc 9613 says this is good enough and this AC outlines how you prove you are B-RNAV and P-RNAV qualified.

AC 91-70B, Oceanic and International Operations

This advisory circular contains general information and guidance for operators planning oceanic flights, including authorizations needed for operations outside the continental United States. This includes Special Areas of Operation (SAO) such as North Atlantic Minimum Navigation Performance Specifications (NAT/MNPS), Reduced Vertical Separation Minimum (RVSM), Area Navigation (RNAV), and Required Navigation Performance (RNP) airspace.

This is your best source of how to conduct remote and oceanic airspace operations from the perspective of a U.S. operator. It tells you how to prepare, how to plot, when you need to worry about Extended Operations (ETOPS), all about the Strategic Lateral Offset Procedure (SLOP), communications procedures, polar route procedures, and much, much more. An update is due to cover innovations in paperless operations, but as of 2020 it hasn't been published.

AC 91-85B, Authorization of Aircraft and Operators for Flight in Reduced Vertical Separation Minimum Airspace

This advisory circular AC contains information on airworthiness, continuing airworthiness, and operations programs for Reduced Vertical Separation Minimum (RVSM) operations.

This AC gives you an excellent primer on what it takes to get an aircraft RVSM certified, how maintenance affects that, and the monitoring requirements.

AC 120-42B, Extended Operations (ETOPS and Polar Operations)

This advisory circular (AC) provides certificate holders with guidance for obtaining operational approval to conduct Extended Operations (ETOPS) under 14 CFR part 121, § 121.161.

Despite that description, ETOPS concerns more than just pilots operating under 14 CFR 121. If you are operating under 14 CFR 135 you are bound by ETOPS too, see 14 CFR 135.364. Even if you are not flying under commercial rules, this AC gives you lots to think about if you are flying outside of 180 minutes from a suitable airport or near the poles.

AC 120-47, Survival Equipment for use in Overwater Operations

The purpose of this AC is to provide information regarding the survival items that should be carried during aircraft extended overwater operations.

The scope of the AC is directed to 14 CFR 121 and 135 but provides best practices for other operators too.

How do I get a copy of these? As of 2020, you can get these advisory circulars at http://www.faa.gov/regulations_policies/advisory_circulars/, which has turned out to be one of the best parts of the www.faa.gov website. If you search for an AC that has been superseded or has expired, it will tell you.

Aeronautical Information Publications

United States Aeronautical Information Publication (AIP)

The AIP is prepared in accordance with the Standards and Recommended Practices (SARP) of Annex 15 to the Convention on International Civil Aviation and the Aeronautical Information Services Manual (ICAO Doc 8126). Charts contained in the AIP are produced in accordance with Annex 4 to the Convention on International Civil Aviation and the Aeronautical Chart Manual (ICAO Doc 8697). Differences from ICAO Standards, Recommended Practices and Procedures are given in subsection GEN 1.7.

Aeronautical Information Manual (AIM)

The AIM is designed to provide the aviation community with basic flight information and ATC procedures for use in the National Airspace System (NAS) of the United States. This manual contains the fundamentals required in order to fly in the United States NAS. It also contains items of interest to pilots concerning health and medical facts, factors affecting flight safety, a pilot/controller glossary of terms used in the ATC System, and information on safety, accident, and hazard reporting.

The AIM is well written and often updated. U.S. pilots should be cautioned, however, to note that the procedures given in the AIM are not always applicable when flying outside the U.S.

*H*ow do I get a copy of these? As of 2020, you can get the U.S. AIP at *https://www.faa.gov/air_traffic/publications/atpubs/aip_html/ and the AIM at http://www.faa.gov/air_traffic/publications/.*

FAA Orders

The Flight Standards Information Management System (FSIMS) is established by FAA Order 8900.1 and contains a lot of what determines what we can and cannot do as international pilots. There are quite a few that are worth reading.

Order 8900.1 Volume 4, Aircraft Equipment, Communications and Surveillance

Don't be fooled by the title, this volume contains a lot of information on international operations but it appears to be directed to the process of getting operations specification approval. These approval processes also pertain to getting letters of authorization and along the way reveal a lot of regulatory information.

*H*ow do I get a copy of these? As of 2021, you can find most of these at *http://fsims.faa.gov but navigation is fairly difficult. The best method seems to be clicking on "8900.1 Contents" and then exploring the volumes. There is a wealth of information under Volume 4.*

Federal Aviation Regulations

You could argue that all federal aviation regulations apply to a U.S. international pilot, but here are a few to consider specifically:

§ 1.1	Definitions
§ 45.21	Nationality and Registration Marks
§ 45.31	Marking of Export Aircraft
§ 47.3	Registration Required

§ 47.5   Applicants for Aircraft Registration

§ 47.7   Certificate of US Citizenship

§ 47.11   Evidence of Ownership

§ 47.39   Effective Date of Aircraft Registration

§ 47.43   Invalid Registration

§ 91.207   Emergency Locator Transmitters

§ 91.509   Survival Equipment for Overwater Operations

§ 91.511   Radio Equipment for Overwater Operations

§ 91.703   Operation of Civil Aircraft of U.S. Registry Outside of the United States

§ 91.707   Flights Between Mexico or Canada and the United States

§ 91.709   Operations to Cuba

§ 135.43   Crewmember Certificate, International Operations: Application and Issue

§ 135.98   Operations in the North Polar Area

§ 135.145   Aircraft Proving Tests

§ 135.165   Radio and Navigation Equipment: Extended Overwater or IFR Operations

§ 135.167   Emergency Equipment: Extended Overwater Operations

§ 135.183   Performance Requirements: Land Aircraft Operated Overwater

§ 135.381   En route limitations: one engine inoperative

How do I get a copy of these? As of 2020, you can find most of these at *http://www.faa.gov/regulations_policies/faa_regulations/.*

Chapter 4

Primary Source Materials (Regional)

*B*efore venturing to another country you should, the theory goes, consult each Aeronautical Information Publication for every country you visit and whose airspace you frequent. There are more than a few problems with this, chief among which is language. (Many are not written in English.) Another issue is you just can't find a lot of them easily. A few examples follow. If you subscribe to an international airway manual service, you have a distinct advantage.

Canada

The AIP Canada (ICAO) contains Part 1- General (GEN), Part 2 - Enroute (ENR), Part 3 - Aerodromes (AD) as well as AIP Supplements (AIP SUP) and Aeronautical Information Circulars (AIC).

*H*ow do I get a copy? As of 2020, you can find EASA regulations at: http://www.navcanada.ca/EN/products-and-services/Pages/AIP.aspx

European Aviation Safety Agency

The European Aviation Safety Agency (EASA) is the European Union authority in aviation safety. Most countries in Europe are member states and many other organizations use EASA rules and regulations.

*H*ow do I get a copy of these? As of 2020, you can find EASA regulations at: http://easa.europa.eu/document-library/regulations#basic-regulation

Jeppesen Airway Manuals

Jeppesen offers a variety of manual options, some of which include international rules and regulations translated and outlined by region. In the absence of a particular country's AIP, the Jeppesen Airway Manual text pages should suffice under most circumstances.

United Kingdom

The UK integrated AIP is available online in two files.

How do I get a copy? As of 2020, you can find this regulation at: http:// www.nats-uk.ead-it.com/public/index.php.html.

The North Atlantic Track System

The airspace over the North Atlantic is perhaps the most congested in the world. You should download and study ICAO NAT Doc 007, the North Atlantic Operations and Airspace Manual. You will need special authorization to fly in what has become known as the North Atlantic High Level Airspace (NAT HLA), and some of the procedures are more exacting than you will find in other parts of the world.

How do I get a copy? As of 2020, you can find this regulation and others at: https://www.icao.int/EURNAT/Pages/EUR-and-NAT-Document.aspx.

Chapter 1

Coordinates

A s a brand new Air Force pilot in 1979, the height of my navigation skills involved holding a terrain chart in one hand while cradling the stick of a T-38 flying at "the speed of heat" 500 feet off the deck trying not to get lost. Coordinates were not important in my day-to-day flying. Years later, flying in flight levels and not feet, navigating between continents and not mountains, the coordinates that pinpoint positions on the globe are important again.

The History of Lines of Latitude and Longitude

[Sobel, page 2]

Lines of latitude and longitude began crisscrossing our world view in ancient times, at least three centuries before the birth of Christ. By A.D. 150, the cartographer and astronomer Ptolemy had plotted them on the twenty-seven maps of his first world atlas.

The Equator marked the zero-degree parallel of latitude for Ptolemy. He did not choose it arbitrarily but took it on higher authority from his predecessors, who had derived it from nature while observing the motions of the heavenly bodies. The sun, moon, and planets pass almost directly overhead at the Equator. Likewise, the Tropic of Cancer and the Tropic of Capricorn, two other famous parallels, assume their positions at the sun's command. They mark the northern and southern boundaries of the sun's apparent motion over the course of the year.

Ptolemy was free, however, to lay his prime meridian, the zero-degree longitude line, wherever he liked. He chose to run it through the Fortunate Islands (now called the Canary & Madeira Islands) off the northwest coast of Africa. As the world turns, any line drawn from pole to pole may serve as well as any other for a starting line of reference. The placement of the prime meridian is a purely political decision.

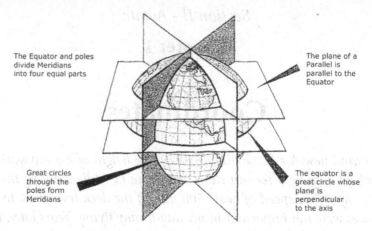

The Equator and poles divide Meridians into four equal parts

The plane of a Parallel is parallel to the Equator

Great circles through the poles form Meridians

The equator is a great circle whose plane is perpendicular to the axis

Figure: Planes of the Earth, from AFM 51-40, figure 2-3.

Great Circles

[AFM 51-40, pages 2-1 to 2-2.]

For most navigational purposes, the earth is assumed to be a perfect sphere, although in reality it is not. Inspection of the earth's crust reveals that there is a height variation of approximately 12 miles from the top of the tallest mountain to the bottom of the deepest point in the ocean.

Measured at the equator, the earth is approximately 6,887.91 nautical miles in diameter, while the polar diameter is approximately 6,864.57 nautical miles, and this difference may be used to express the ellipticity of the earth.

A great circle is defined as a circle on the surface of a sphere whose center and radius are those of the sphere itself. The arc of a great circle is the shortest distance between two points on a sphere, just as a straight line is the shortest distance between two points on a plane.

Circles on the surface of the sphere other than great circles may be defined as small circles. A small circle is a circle on the surface of the earth whose center and/or radius are not that of the sphere. A special set of small circles, called latitude, is discussed later.

From a pilot's perspective, a great circle is simply the shortest route between two points on the globe.

Latitude

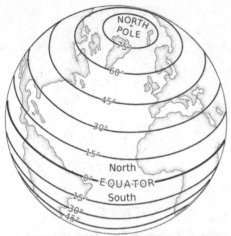

Figure: Latitude lines, from Wikimedia Commons, Pearson Scott Foresman.

[Sobel, page 2]

The zero degree parallel of latitude is fixed by the laws of nature.

Any sailor worth his salt can gauge his latitude well enough by the length of the day, or by the height of the sun or known guide stars above the horizon. Christopher Columbus followed a straight path across the Atlantic when he "sailed the parallel" on his 1492 journey, and the technique would doubtless have carried him to the Indies had not the Americas intervened.

[AFM 51-40, page 2-3.]

Once a day, the earth rotates on its north-south axis which is terminated by the two poles. The equator is constructed at the midpoint of this axis at right angles to it. A great circle drawn through the poles is called a meridian, and an infinite number of great circles may be constructed in this manner. Each meridian is divided into four quadrants by the equator and the poles. Since a circle is arbitrarily divided into 360 degrees, each of those quadrants therefore contains 90 degrees.

Take a point on one of these meridians 30 degrees north of the equator. Through this point pass a plane perpendicular to the north-south axis of rotation. This plane will be parallel to the plane of the equator as shown [in the figure] and will intersect the earth in a small circle called a parallel or parallel of latitude. The particular parallel of latitude chosen is 30° N, and every point on this parallel will be at 30° N. In the same way, other parallels can be constructed at any desired latitude, such as 10 degrees, 40 degrees, etc.

Longitude

[Sobel, page 2]

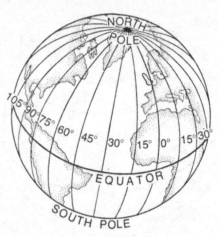

To learn one's longitude at sea, one needs to know what time it is aboard ship and also the time at the home port or another place of known longitude. Since the earth takes 24 hours to complete one full revolution of three hundred sixty degrees, one hour marks one twenty-fourth of a spin, or fifteen degrees. And so each hour's time difference between the ship and the starting point marks a progress of

Figure: Longitude lines, from Wikimedia Commons, Pearson Scott Foresman.

fifteen degrees of longitude to the east or west. Every day at sea, when the navigator resets his ship's clock to local noon when the sun reaches its highest point in the sky, and then consults the home-port clock, every hour's discrepancy between them translates into another fifteen degrees of longitude.

Those same fifteen degrees of longitude also correspond to a distance traveled. At the Equator, where the girth of the Earth is greatest, fifteen degrees stretch fully one thousand miles. North or south of that line, however, the mileage value of each degree decreases.

[AFM 51-40, page 2-4.]

The latitude of a point can be shown as 20° N or 20° S of the equator, but there is no way of knowing whether one point is east or west or another. This difficulty is resolved by the use of the other component of the coordinate system, longitude, which is the measurement of this east-west distance.

There is not, as with latitude, a natural starting point for numbering, such as the equator. The solution has been to select an arbitrary starting point. A great many places have been used, but when the English speaking people began to make charts, they chose the meridian through their principal observatory in Greenwich, England, as the origin for counting longitude, and this point has now been accepted by most other countries of the world. This Greenwich meridian is sometimes called the prime or first meridian, though actually it is the zero meridian. Longitude is counted east and west from this meridian, through 180 degrees.

Chapter 2

Direction

*W*hile *"direction" seems to be the most basic fundamental of getting from Point A to Point B, there are quite a few pitfalls in terminology. It is quite easy to get by for years and not really understand why some directions are true and others aren't. Well let's put an end to that right now.*

The Numerical System for Determining Direction

[AFM 51-40, pages 2-5 to 2-6.]

- The numerical system, divides the horizon into 360 degrees starting with north 000 degrees, east 090 degrees, south 180 degrees, west 270 degrees, and back to north.

- The circle, called a compass rose, represents the horizon divided into 360 degrees.

True Course

[AFM 51-40, pages 2-5 to 2-6.]

- Course is the intended horizontal direction of travel.

- Heading is the horizontal direction in which an aircraft is pointed. Heading is the actual orientation of the longitudinal axis of the aircraft at any instant, while course is the direction intended to be made good.

- Track is the actual horizontal direction made by the aircraft over the earth.

- Bearing is the horizontal direction of one terrestrial point from another.

A "True Course" is the relative bearing between your course and true north. It is usually found by placing a plotter over a chart and reading the angular difference to any meridian.

Variation

[AFM 51-37, page 1-12.] The magnetic compass points to magnetic north. The angular difference between true and magnetic north is known as variation and it changes for different locations on the earth. Variation must be considered when converting true course, true headings, or true winds to magnetic direction.

This can be considered an academic exercise in understanding the difference between TRUE and MAGNETIC, except for anyone who flies at high latitudes where magnetic navigation is unreliable, or anyone who flies in airspace where plotting procedures are required. If you ever need to plot a position, variation is critical.

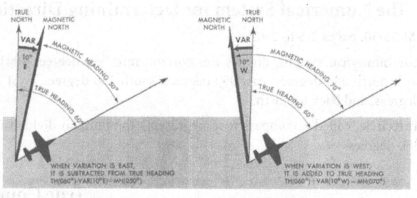

Figure: Variation, from AFM 51-37, page 1-13.

Deviation

[AFM 51-37, page 1-12.] Deviation [is] an error in compass indications caused by magnetic disturbances originating within the aircraft. The magnitude of deviation varies with operation of different electrical equipment. Periodically, the compass is checked and compensations are made to reduce the amount of deviation. Deviation errors remaining after the compass has been checked are recorded on a compass correction card in the cockpit. The STEER column on the compass correction card is the compass heading you should indicate to maintain the TO FLY magnetic heading.

At Air Force Instrument Instructor's school we were taught to fly IFR off nothing more than an attitude indicator and a magnetic compass. I came to the conclusion it would be safer to declare an emergency and get no gyro vectors. These days the chances of needing to fly off one of these cards are remote, but you should know how.

Deviation is given as degrees to steer to accomplish a desired heading, but can be thought of as positive and negative numbers to apply a magnetic heading.

True / Magnetic / Course

The navigator's text above hints at complications we pilots didn't want, so they gave us an old sailor's mnemonic: "True virgins make dull company" to which others added "Add Whiskey." Crude or not, the idea was to remember the order in which things are added to a true course to end up with what the sailor (and pilot) wanted, which was a course to sail (and fly):

TO FLY	STEER	TO FLY	STEER
N	001	180	179
15	016	195	194
30	031	210	209
45	046	225	224
60	062	240	238
75	077	255	253
90	092	270	268
105	107	285	283
120	122	300	298
135	135	315	314
150	149	330	330
165	164	345	346

B-16 COMPASS — SWUNG 12 APR 76 BY MJR

Figure: Compass correction card, from AFM 51-37, figure 1-15.

- *Start with a TRUE course using your handy plotter, to that you add*
- *magnetic VARIATION (explained: above) to get a*
- *MAGNETIC course; to that add*
- *DEVIATION (explained: above) to get a*
- *COMPASS heading to steer.*

The "Add Whiskey" part was to help us remember we add west variation and deviation while subtracting east variation and deviation. Another technique is to remember "East is least, west is best."

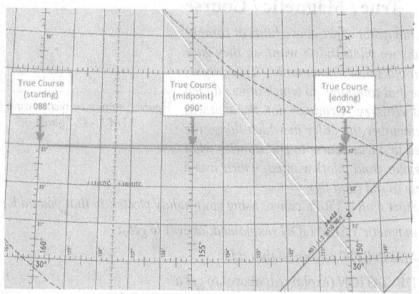

Figure: True Course initial vs. midpoint vs. ending

Chapter 3

Initial vs. Midpoint Course

*Y*our plotting chart is based on a Lambert Conformal projection, the lines of longitude converge near the poles. Except for the equator, the lines of latitude are not straight, they curve toward the equator. The measurement of your true course depends on where you place the center of your plotter and it does make a difference. In the figure shown, flying from 33°N 160°W to 33°N 150°W should, intuitively, require a 090° true course. The actual course, however, depends on what you want: the starting, mid, or ending course.

Why is this important? Most flight planning services offer either the starting or midpoint courses. Some pilots want to know what their initial course will be, others want the average course on the entire leg. It is a matter of personal preference. (If I didn't have an FMS, I think the midpoint course would be more useful, since it gives you the most line for your plotter and gives you the easiest, most accurate plot. But I have our flight plan reflect the initial course, since that gives me an easy way to crosscheck my heading after waypoint passage.)

Course Line

In the example we draw a line from 50°N 030°W and 51°N 020°W.

Initial Course

Placing the center of the plotter compass on our initial point and the course line on top of the endpoint we see our initial true course is 077°.

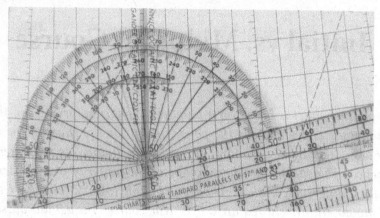

Midpoint Course

Placing the center of the plotter compass on the midpoint, 025°W in our example, we see the true course will be 081°.

We can check this mathematically using ten-degree tables at 50°N. See the Appendices, Chapter 39, True Course Ten-Degree Tables.

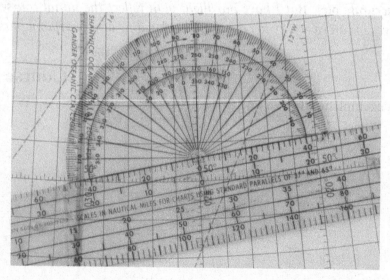

Chapter 4

Class I versus Class II

*S*o what is the difference between Class I and Class II airspace and why *should you care? The difference boils down to your proximity to navigational aids and being in one or the other determines your ATC separation standards. While many pilots think it determines your plotting requirements that is not true.*

Some in the FAA will tell you there is no Class I or Class II airspace anymore, since the terminology was deleted in the latest update to AC 91-70, with AC 91-70B issued in 2016. In fact, I had an LOA application kicked back in 2020 for this very reason. When I pointed out that it is still used in FAA Order 8900.1, they said they just haven't gotten around to it yet. As of November 2020, Class I and Class II still exist in FAA Order 8900.1 (Vol 3, Sec 4, Chapter 18) for authorizations B036 and B054 but retains Class II for B031, B032, B037, B038, B040, B041, B043, and B344. If you here "Class II" navigation, that means "oceanic or remote airspace" navigation in most cases.

Class I Navigation

[Order 8900.1, Vol 4, Ch. 1, Sect. 3, ¶4-56] There are two generic types of IFR Class I navigation:

• Navigation by direct reference to ICAO standard ground-based NAVAIDs.

• Navigation by use of RNAV systems.

A. ICAO Standard NAVAIDs. The primary means of conducting IFR Class I navigation has historically been station-referenced by using ICAO standard ground-based NAVAIDs (VOR, VOR/DME, NDB). The route structure and the ATC separation standards in most countries are based on the use of these ground-based NAVAIDs. When operating within the operational service volumes of these ground-based NAVAIDs, these standard systems may be used to satisfy the objectives of IFR Class I navigation.

1) Standard NAVAIDs may be used to conduct Class I navigation when flying any published IFR route or procedure, provided these operations are conducted at or above the published minimum IFR altitudes. The following are examples of published IFR routes:

• Victor airways.

• Colored airways.

• Jet/high-level routes.

• Standard Instrument Departures (SID).

• Standard Terminal Arrivals (STAR).

• Instrument departures.

2) In many foreign countries and in oceanic/remote areas, the situation is more complex, as NAVAID operational service volumes may differ. IFR Class I navigation can be conducted using standard VOR, VOR/DME, or automatic direction finder (ADF) equipment. Some published fixed route systems (also known as air traffic services (ATS) routes) are based on NDBs.

3) IFR Class I navigation can be conducted over unpublished point-to-point routes (off airways), provided all of the following conditions are met:

• Positive course guidance is available.

• The operation is conducted at or above the IFR minimum altitude published or approved for that route by the ICAO contracting state having jurisdiction over that airspace.

• The required airborne, ground-based, and/or space-based navigational facilities are available and operational to enable navigation to the degree of accuracy required for the control of air traffic.

B. RNAV Systems.

1) Appropriate RNAV systems can be used to conduct IFR Class I navigation. Any RNAV system used for IFR flight must provide present position information and navigation guidance to maintain the assigned track and arrive at the designated waypoints. RNAV may be based on the following:

• VOR- and DME-source-referenced.

• Global Navigation Satellite System (GNSS) (/GPS) earth-referenced in accordance with World Geodetic System 1984 (WGS84) or equivalent.

• Self-contained in the aircraft (INS, IRS).

2) IFR Class I navigation can be conducted with IFR-approved RNAV systems suitable for the area of operations. RNAV systems must be evaluated to ensure that the system and the operator are capable of navigating to the degree of accuracy required for the control of air traffic within the proposed area of operation.

Class II Navigation

[Order 8900.1, Vol 4, Ch. 1, Sect. 3, ¶4-77] INSTRUMENT FLIGHT RULES (IFR) CLASS II NAVIGATION. IFR Class II navigation is any Class II navigation operation conducted under IFR. The primary generic IFR Class II navigation requirements are identical to generic IFR Class I navigation requirements. However, in many cases, the means of navigation and the procedures/techniques necessary to satisfy these generic requirements are significantly different for IFR Class II navigation.

Standard High Altitude Service Volumes

Many years ago the regulations required plotting a certain distance away from the service volumes of qualified navigation aids. Things got messier when AC 91-70A included GNSS as a qualified navigation aid. That led pilots to reason plotting was never required. But all of that language was removed in AC 91-70B. In case you are wondering what the service volume of ground-based navigation aid is, here it is:

[Aeronautical Information Manual, ¶1-1-8]:

• Standard High Altitude Service Volume between 18,000 and 45,000 ft: 130 nm

• Standard Low Altitude Service Volume between 1,000 and 18,000 ft: 40 nm

• Standard Terminal Service Volume between 1,000 and 12,000 ft: 25 nm

• NDB HH Service Volume: 75 nm

• NDB MH Service Volume: 25 nm

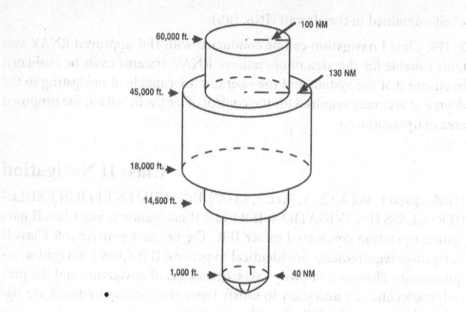

Figure: Standard High Altitude Service Volumes, from Aeronautical Information Manual, Figure 1-1-1.

Chapter 5

Plotting

W*e plot to avoid the classic one-degree error, to double-check the other pilot's FMS entries, to ensure the flight plan uplink was accurate, and to make sure the database itself is accurate.*

But wait, you say. The database itself has been QC'd, you've already checked the waypoints in the FMS, and your aircraft's graphical presentation makes any kind of graphical plotting completely pointless!

Well, you might have a point. But the system used to program your computers have errors now and then, Air Traffic Controllers make mistakes, and we pilots have been known to take shortcuts. Gross Navigational Errors still happen.

Do You Have to Plot?

Legally speaking

This used to be a pretty easy case to make because it once said so in AC 91-70 and FAA Order 8900.1, Vol 4, Ch 1, ¶4-80. They both said "there is a requirement to plot the route of flight on a plotting chart and to plot the aircraft position, approximatley 10 minutes after waypoint passage." This was based on being outside the service volume of "ICAO standard ground-based NAVAIDS" by 725 nm for turbojets, 250 nm for turboprops.

These requirements have been deleted and now AC 91-70B, ¶6.3.1.11.1 says "You should use a chart, of appropriate scale, to provide yourself with a visual presentation of your intended route, regardless of your type(s) of long-range navigation system (LRNS)."

If you have to do a "table top" with the FAA — one where they are considering giving you the authorization to fly oceanic through LOAs B036 or B039 — they will ask you to plot. ICAO rules do not mandate plotting, but they are written assuming you are plotting.

Why you should plot

In the old days — when we were entering latitude and longitude into an inertial navigation system that didn't understand named waypoints — the typical reason given for plotting was the one degree error. If you type a seven instead of a six when intending 56° North, for example, the aircraft will be headed into someone else's airspace.

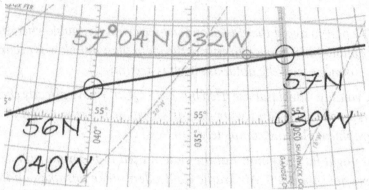

Other reasons:

- *Oceanic Reroute — Reroutes are common and except in rare combinations of aircraft/controller CPDLC capabilities, will require crews to manually enter FMS waypoints. I often read about crews that somehow mishandled the data entry. Plotting could have saved them.*

- *An FMS error — yes, these happen. A few years ago the FMS makers didn't all agree on what nomenclature was needed for half-degree latitude separation and the result was chaos. The pilots who plotted caught the error. Another cause, albeit rare, is a coding error that waited until the database was updated. The first airplane to fly the route when the new database went into effect was caught.*

- *Other "technical" errors. Navigation databases are incredibly complicated and with the complication comes the chance for errors.*

But what if I'm doing everything perfectly?

Just because you are doing everything "by the book" doesn't mean another aircraft's errors can't impact you. Here is a scenario for you. Let's say you filed Mach 0.80 as did the airplane in front of you, but the airplane behind you filed M0.83. Shanwick Oceanic planned on all this by placing the minimum spacing between you and the lead aircraft and allowed extra space between you and the third. Now let's say there is an unforecast increase in the tailwind and all three airplanes start to miss their next forecast ETA. (You are early.) You and the third aircraft revise your ETAs, as required, while maintaining your filed Mach Numbers. The lead aircraft, however, slows down to avoid having to revise his ETA and there is a loss of separation between you and the lead aircraft. Shanwick will be asking for all three aircraft to provide their paperwork and having shoddy paperwork may implicate the wrong crew.

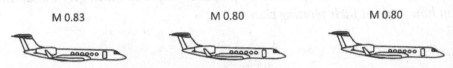

M 0.83   M 0.80   M 0.80

No matter the reason, I like to think of it this way. When you are flying domestically all of your airplane's wizardry is keeping you separated from other airplanes and air traffic control's radar is backing everything up. When you are flying oceanic you don't have ATC's radar to help you out. It is up to you to back up the airplane's computers.

How to plot (the old fashioned way)

As we shall see later on, there are other methods that make all of this very easy, but you should know how to plot the old fashioned way because it will help you understand what your automatic methods are doing and to detect any errors from those systems.

[AC 91-70B, ¶6.3.1.11.2] Your chart should include, at a minimum:

- The route of your filed flight plan or currently effective route clearance.
- Clearly depicted waypoints using standardized symbology.
- Graphic depictions of all ETPs.
- Alternate airports.
- Proximity of other adjacent tracks.

Note: For certificated operators, if OpSpec/MSpec A061 has been issued authorizing use of an Electronic Flight Bag (EFB) and the principal inspector (PI) has authorized "interactive plotting for oceanic and remote continental navigation," the EFB application may be used in place of a paper plotting/orientation chart. The current edition of AC 120-76, Guidelines for the Certification, Airworthiness, and Operational Approval of Electronic Flight Bags, provides guidance for operators to develop associated EFB procedures. For part 91 operators, an EFB may be used, provided the criteria and considerations of the current edition of AC 91-78, Use of Class 1 or Class 2 Electronic Flight Bag (EFB), are observed.

How is a Common Plotting Chart Laid Out?

Apart from the following, the chart printers are pretty much given discretion on how to print their plotting charts.

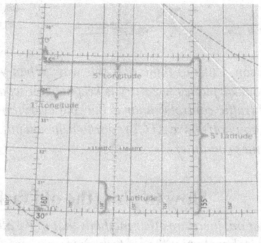

[ICAO Annex 4]

2.1.7 Recommendation.— The charts should be True North orientated.

2.15.1 True North and magnetic variation shall be indicated. The order of resolution of magnetic variation shall be that as specified for a particular chart.

2.15.2 Recommendation.— When magnetic variation is shown on a chart, the values shown should be those for the year nearest to the date of publication that is divisible by 5, i.e. 1980, 1985, etc.

2.18.1.1 World Geodetic System — 1984 (WGS-84) shall be used as the horizontal (geodetic) reference system. Published aeronautical geographical coordinates (indicating latitude and longitude) shall be expressed in terms of the WGS-84 geodetic reference datum.

2.18.2.1 Mean sea level (MSL) datum, which gives the relationship of gravity-related height (elevation) to a surface known as the geoid, shall be used as the vertical reference system.

There are some basic guidelines you should know for the chart you are using:

The horizontal lines are "parallels of latitude," usually a line for every degree with a major line every five degrees.

The vertical lines are "meridians of longitude," with a line for every degree with a major line every five degrees.

Longitude and latitude are subdivided into 60 parts known as minutes and labeled with a single quote mark (').

Minutes are further subdivided into 60 parts known as seconds and labeled with double quote marks (").

Bedford (KBED) airport, for example is at 42°28'11.8" N, 71°17'20.4" W; which is pronounced "forty-two degrees, twenty-eight minutes, eleven point eight seconds north, seventy-one degrees, seventeen minutes, twenty point four seconds west.

How to Plot a Position

There are many techniques on how to do this correctly, here is mine:

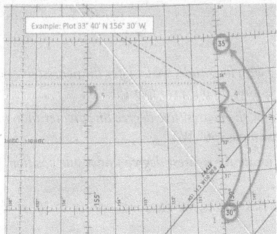

- *Ensure you are in the correct quadrant: In the north the latitudes increase as you go up, in the south they increase as you go down. In the west the longitudes go up as you head west, in the east the go up as you head further east. Locate the nearest five degree line in the general area of your point, in the example 30° N.*

- *Locate the five degree line just above your latitude, in our example 35° N.*

- *If your chart has one degree markings locate the nearest degree below your point, otherwise count the degree lines. In our example 33° N.*

- *Count the tick marks between degree lines on the chart you are using. In our example there are six so we conclude each tick mark represents 10 minutes of latitude. Counting up four tick marks we identify 30°40' N latitude.*

- *Notice that a line connecting 33°40' N 150° W and 33°40' N 160° W does not cross 33°40' N 155° W, it runs high. That's because the chart is a Lambert Conformal Projection which bends toward the poles. To get a more accurate position, we need to find the 33°40' point on the scale closest to our position.*

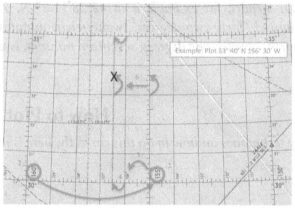

- *When dealing with longitude, we look for the nearest five degree line under our desired position, in our example 155° W.*

- *Then we look for the nearest five degree line greater than our desired position, in our example 160° W.*

- *We can now locate the nearest degree under our position, in our example 156° W.*

- *Counting the tick marks, we see there are six so 30' of longitude will be three greater.*

- *Unlike latitude, lines of longitude appear parallel between lines of latitude, so we can draw a line at 156°30' W between tick marks and it will remain accurate.*

- *We then transpose our mark identifying 33°40' N to this line of longitude and viola, we have our position.*

How to Plot a True Course

Understanding True versus Magnetic heading

Part of the plotting process is to check the courses in your FMS (which are almost always in Magnetic) against those on your charts (which are in True). To convert from True to Magnetic you need Variation.

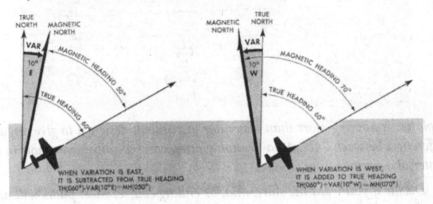

Figure: Variation, (AFM 51-37, page 1-13)

[AFM 51-37, page 1-12.] The magnetic compass points to magnetic north. The angular difference between true and magnetic north is known as variation and it changes for different locations on the earth. Variation must be considered when converting true course, true headings, or true winds to magnetic direction.

If you need to convert, the formula is:

True + Variation = Magnetic

Where West Variation is positive and East Variation is negative

If, for example, you measure a True course of 090 on the chart and the nearest line of Variation is 10° East, the Magnetic course will be 090 - 10 = 080° (Because you subtract East Variation.)

Measuring Course

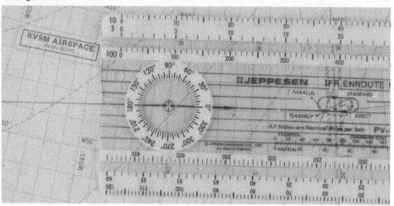

A plotter is nothing more than a circular instrument designed to give angular differences between lines. A navigation plotter, will typically have a hole in the center of a compass rose. To use:

- *Decide if you want the start, mid, or ending course. Most pilots will need the start course.*

- *Place the hole in the center of the compass rose over a line of longitude near the desired point, in our example we've used 40°W which is also the longitude of our start point.*

- *Align the line along the 0° mark to your desired course. You may find it helpful to insert your pencil or pen point in the hole while rotating the plotter to line up with your course.*

- *Read the true course along the line of selected longitude, 085° in our example.*

Note: You will have two choices aligned with the line of longitude, 085° and 275° in our example. In most cases it will be the number on top, but when dealing with courses near vertical it can be confusing. Always remember to give your answer a common sense check. In our example, we are headed to Europe and the answer should be generally easterly.

Measuring Distance

[AFM 51-40, Page 5-8.]

One of the disadvantages of the Lambert Conformal chart is the lack of a constant scale. If the two points between which the distance is to be measured are approximately in a north-south direction and the total distance between them can be spanned, the distance can be measure on the latitude scale opposite the midpoint. However, the total distance between any two points that do not lie approximately north or south of each other should be be spanned unless the distance is short. All distances should be measured as near the mid latitude as possible.

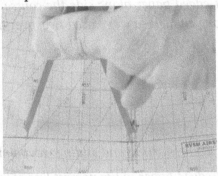

In the measurement of long distances, select a mid latitude lying approximately half-way between the latitudes of the two points. By using dividers set to a convenient, reasonably short distance, such as 60 nautical miles picked off at the mid latitude scale, you may determine an approximate distance by marking off units along the line to be measures as shown [in the figure].

The scale at mid latitude is accurate enough if the course line does not cover er more than 5 degrees of latitude (somewhat less at high latitudes). If the course line exceeds this amount or if it is crosses the equator, divide it into two or more legs and measure the length of each leg with the scale of its own mid latitude

If you have a set of dividers and a flat surface you aren't afraid to scratch, find the distance between waypoints is quite easy. First, place the points of the dividers on the start and end waypoints.

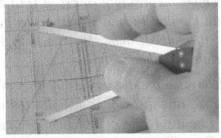

Next, find a line of longitude near the course line. It is important to use a line of longitude about the same latitude as the course, since these will change over

great distances. Each degree of latitude equals 60 nautical miles.

If you don't have a set of dividers — do you really want to have such a sharp instrument in the cockpit? — you can construct your own with a PostIt note or other straight-edged paper.

- Place the straight-edged paper along side the course. In our example, the PostIt note isn't long enough so we've used two, overlapping, notes.

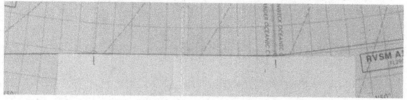

- Place a tick mark at the starting and ending waypoints.

- Move the straight-edged paper to the nearest line of longitude at about the same latitude. Place one tick mark over a convenient line of latitude, 49°N in our example.

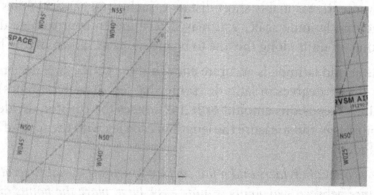

- Read the distance from the ending tick mark, using 60 nautical miles per degree. In our example the distance covers at least 6° of latitude, which comes to 360 nautical miles. The mark goes further by a tenth of a degree, meaning another 10 nautical miles. We conclude the distance between waypoints is therefore 370 nautical miles.

Note: You can also determine the distance using a set of "10 Degree Tables," where we would see the exact distance is actually 369 nautical miles. (Our PostIt note was off by 1 nautical mile, or had an error rate of 0.27 percent, not bad. [See the Appeendices, Chapter 37, True Course Ten-Degree Tables.]

Start / Mid / End Point Differences

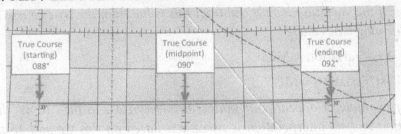

Your plotting chart is based on a Lambert Conformal projection, the lines of longitude converge near the poles. Except for the equator, the lines of latitude are not straight, they curve toward the equator. The measurement of your true course depends on where you place the center of your plotter and it does make a difference. In the figure shown, flying from 33°N 160°W to 33°N 150°W should, intuitively, require a 090° true course. The actual course, however, depends on what you want: the starting, mid, or ending course.

Most flight planning services offer either the starting or midpoint courses. Some pilots want to know what their initial course will be, others want the average course on the entire leg. It is a matter of personal preference.

I prefer using the starting course, since that is what the FMS will be showing prior to crossing the waypoint. (Following waypoint passage the course will update to reflect the "current" great circle route to the next waypoint. This course will constantly update as you progress, only reaching the midpoint course when you are actually at the midpoint.)

How to Determine a Magnetic Course

To determine the magnetic course, you will need to add or subtract the variation:

Look for the nearest lines of magnetic variation on the chart before and after the midpoint and interpolate if necessary.

59

If the variation is West, add this value to the true course to determine magnetic course. If the variation is East, subtract this value from the true course to determine magnetic course:

TC + West Variation = MC

TC - East Variation = MC

In our example, it appears our midpoint is very close to the "16°W" line of variation and no interpolation is necessary. Based on this we add 16 to our 270 true course and verify that our FMS and flight plan show a 286° magnetic course plus or minus a few degrees.

Note: It is not uncommon to find differences of 2 or 3 degrees in the magnetic course determined from a plotting chart and that reported in a computer flight plan. The magnetic variation changes over the years and your chart may be dated or hasn't been updated with the correct variation.

How to Determine the Position of a VOR Radial/DME

There are many ways to turn a VOR radial/DME into a latitude and longitude, the best of these may very well be inside your FMS. If you need to do this on a plotting chart, this method works well:

- Place the plotter hole over the VOR in question and your pencil point in the hole to hold the plotter centered over the VOR. (CON in our example.)

- Find the nearest line of variation. (6° West in our example.)

- Rotate the edge of the plotter to 360* in the northern hemisphere, 180* in the southern hemisphere, and then rotate toward the magnetic pole by the amount of the variation. (Rotate 6* to the west, in our example.)

- Move your pencil from the center hole to the straight line of the plotter that *describes the line to the magnetic pole, move the plotter so the straight edge connects that point to the VOR. Draw a line with a flag on it from the VOR in the direction of the pole. Label this line "360° Mag" if you like. (In our example the flag points slightly left.*

- *Now return the plotter center hole to the VOR and rotate it in relation to your 360° Mag line by the number of degrees in the VOR radial. Draw a line as you did earlier by placing a tick mark, moving the plotter, and drawing the line. (In our example the line is 15° clockwise from the Magnetic north line.)*

- *Determine the distance using the Distance Measuring techniques shown above. Place a tick mark on the VOR line. (015°/85 DME in our example.)*

- *The latitude and longitude can be read directly from the chart. (55°15'N 8°25'W in our example.)*

When to plot

There used to be an actual answer in writing:

[FAA Order 8900.1 OUTDATED VERSION Volume 4, Chapter 1, Paragraph 4-80.A] Plotting procedures are required for all turbojet operations where the route segment between the operational service volume of ICAO standard ground-based navigational aids exceeds 725 NM.

Plotting procedures are required for all turboprop operations where the route segment between the operational service volume of ICAO standard ground-based navigational aids exceeds 450 NM.

This language no longer appears anywhere. I think the practical answer to the "when do I have to plot?" question is whenever you don't have a backup to the space-based and inertial-based navigation.

Alternatives to Paper

A liberal reading of AC 91-70B would lead you to believe that doing all of your "plotting" on the aircraft's navigation display should be adequate:

[AC 91-70B, ¶6.3.2.6.3] You can use various additional techniques in order to verify that the correct points are loaded for your planned route. Verify the total route distance in your FMS against your master document to help find embedded mistakes. You should also cross-check course/headings and distances between each waypoint to ensure the FMS routing matches your master document. Referencing your plotting or orientation chart here can also be beneficial.

[AC 91-70B, ¶D.2.9.2] Ten Minutes After Waypoint Passage. Cross-check navigational performance and course compliance by one of the following methods:

D.2.9.1 The "plotting" method is appropriate for all aircraft navigation configurations.

1. Verify your plotting/orientation chart reflects the currently effective route clearance.

2. Plot your present latitude/longitude and record the time on your chart.

3. You should plot your position using coordinates from the nonsteering LRNS.

4. Investigate/take corrective action if your plotted position does not agree with your currently effective route clearance.

5. Using the steering LRNS, verify the next waypoint is consistent with the currently effective route clearance.

6. Verify your autopilot steering mode is in LNAV/VNAV or other appropriate mode to ensure steering to the next intended waypoint.

D.2.9.2 The "navigation display" method is appropriate for and available for use in aircraft equipped with an operable FMS:

1. Confirm the aircraft symbol is on the programmed route on the navigation display (at smallest scale).

2. Check system-generated cross-track deviation or similar indication of any deviation from the programmed route of flight.

3. Using the steering LRNS verify the "TO" waypoint is consistent with your currently effective route clearance.

4. Investigate/take correction action to address any anomalies or unexpected deviations.

5. Verify your autopilot steering mode is LNAV/VNAV or other appropriate mode to ensure steering to the next intended waypoint.

After investigating a GNE in response to an FAA inquiry in 2005, I asked if this method of plotting was adequate and was told no. As late as 2018 I asked members of the FAA navigation branch and was told the same thing. You should not simply look at the navigation displays and see that your airplane is where it is supposed to be and consider your plotting chores complete. But you don't have to resort to a paper plotting chart, a plotter, and a sharp pencil. There are other methods that are easier and more accurate . . .

Plotting with an iPad

There are a few different ways to plot with an iPad, some good and some bad. But before we cover that, we need to cover something most of us have ignored since we got our very first iPad . . .

Is that iPad really legal for use in a cockpit?

Operating an iPad and a portable GPS receiver that is independent of the aircraft systems would seem to be the ideal crosscheck of your aircraft avionics. But is it legal? The basic regulation seems to indicate that it is, provided you can determine the device in question "will not cause interference with the navigation or communication system" of your aircraft. But how can you make that determination?

These rules were established in 1961 but were relaxed considerably in 2000 and in 2006 with the release of AC 91-21.1B which gave operators the latitude to allow the use of non-transmitting Personal Electronic Devices (PEDs) and gave some guidance on Transmitting PEDs and Medical PEDs. Operators were also given guidance on how to make these determinations. But no guidance was given for PEDs that receive GPS signals.

The latest version of AC 91.21-D cleared a lot of this up. The basic rule is that if your aircraft was certified with an onboard WiFi system, you are considered "PED Tolerant." Otherwise, you either have to get them tested (very hard to do) or restrict your use to ground taxi operations and cruise flight above 10,000 feet (easy to do).

So for the purpose of oceanic operations and plotting, the iPad and portable GPS units are generally okay. (Operating commercially, you will need OpSpec/MSpec/LOA A061.) If you are using your iPad (or other Electronic Flight Bag hardware) to view your airfield diagram during taxi, that's okay too. But if you want to use these devices for takeoff and landing, you have more work to do.

Aircraft Type Data Certification Sheet . . . Good to go.

If you are flying something that was certified relatively recently, you may find the aircraft's PED tolerance explicitly stated. This for the Gulfstream GVII-G500:

Personal Electronic Devices (PEDs):

The GVII-G500 is a PED tolerant aircraft and compliance with PS-ANM-25-13 and sections 5.2 and 5.3 of DO-307A has been demonstrated; however, operators must establish compliance with 14 CFR 91.21, 121.306, 135.144 requirements. Any changes to aircraft doors, windows and other apertures, interior furnishings, or antenna/receiver locations can affect the spurious emissions tolerance and must be assessed per section 8.34 of the GVII-G500 Interior Certification Requirements Document (GVII-GER-0149).

Figure: GVII-G500 PED Tolerance, from its Type Data Certification Sheet.

So if you are flying a GVII-G500, you are good to go. Most aircraft certified more than 5 years ago will not have this statement. But that doesn't mean you are not PED tolerant, as we shall now see.

Airplane certified with a demonstrated tolerance for PEDs . . . Good to go.

[AC 91.21-1D, ¶7.2.1] Aircraft Designed and Certified PED Tolerant. Aircraft manufacturers with access to aircraft electronic system qualifications and aircraft radio receiver antenna installation data can easily demonstrate an aircraft meets the requirements of RTCA DO-307A. Operators may obtain statements of such demonstrations from an aircraft manufacturer to substantiate PED tolerance of the aircraft. Operators can also use the RTCA DO-307A methods in demonstrating PED tolerance of their aircraft. RTCA DO-307A separates demonstration methods for tolerance to intentional transmissions from PEDs versus tolerance to spurious emissions from PEDs. Aircraft with an FAA-approved system—such as an Onboard Mobile Telecommunications System (OMTS), Wireless Fidelity (WiFi), airborne access systems (AASs), or Network Control Units (NCUs)—are considered PED-tolerant for PEDs used with the installed system. If an aircraft model has demonstrated tolerance for both transmitting and non-transmitting PEDs, the operator may allow PED use during all phases of flight on this aircraft model.

If your aircraft is certified with one of the listed systems (OMTS, WiFi, or AAS), then you are "PED Tolerant" and can use PEDs during all phases of flight. Of course you will have a few precautions to take, like turning the cellu-

lar system off by using "Airplane" mode and making sure it is properly stowed for takeoff and landing, but you can use it in the cockpit for all phases of flight.

Airplane passes risk assessment ... Good to go.

[AC 91.21-1D, ¶7.2.2] Aircraft Not Designed and Certified PED Tolerant. An operator may choose to conduct a safety risk assessment following the process in RTCA DO-363 if it 1) does not have a designed and certified PED-tolerant aircraft, and 2) chooses not to test its aircraft fleet types according to RTCA DO-307A or obtain supporting documentation from an aircraft manufacturer. The operator's assessment must evaluate the avionics configuration of its fleet and failure modes of communication, navigation, surveillance, and other electronic systems with respect to electromagnetic interference. This assessment ultimately outlines mitigations and controls the operator needs to adopt to expand PED use into various phases of flight.

There are two phases to the risk assessment, as outlined in InFO 13010 Sup: "Back door" and "front door" assessment. "Back door coupling" refers to intentional radio frequency emissions from transmitting PEDs which can interfere with aircraft systems. Appendix B of InFO 13010 Sup provides instructions on how to determine if an analysis must be performed. Many aircraft have the necessary statement in their Type Certificate Data Sheet (TCDS) that allow them to assume the back door assessment is already completed. The front door assessment is much harder to determine and most operators will not be able to obtain such an assessment on their own.

Aircraft missing demonstrated tolerance or required assessment ... Good to go for cruise flight only.

[AC 91.21-1D, ¶7.2.3] Aircraft Not Demonstrated PED Tolerant. If the operator has not demonstrated PED tolerance for their aircraft, they may allow PED operation during cruise flight. If interference to aircraft systems from PEDs is experienced during cruise flight, the devices causing interference should be isolated, and applicable conditions recorded. The device responsible for the interference should be turned off.

Unless your aircraft is PED tolerant or you have done an RTCA DO-363 risk assessment, you can only allow PED use during cruise flight.

[AC 91.21-1D, ¶8.1] Operator Procedures. If an operator allows PEDs aboard its aircraft or the aircraft being operated, procedures should be established to control PED use during aircraft operations. RCTA DO-363 section 7.5 and InFO 13010SUP provide further guidance on what to include in the operator's policies, procedures, and training programs. In general, the procedures should address:

1. PEDs approved for use onboard the aircraft;

2. Times of approved PED operation;

3. How and when PEDs must be secured or stowed;

4. PED modes of operation used and not used;

5. How and when to inform passengers of the aircraft operator's PED policies and procedures; and

6. How to manage scenarios such as suspected or confirmed electro-magnetic interference, PED unit or battery smoke or fire, or other scenarios.

[AC 91.21-1D, ¶8.2] Passenger Communication. This paragraph outlines methods to inform passengers of permissible times, conditions, and limitations of PED usage. These methods may be accomplished through the departure briefing; passenger information cards; flightcrew, flight attendant (F/A), or prerecorded announcements; or other methods deemed appropriate by the operator. Operators should inform passengers of PED use restrictions, such as prior to departure, after takeoff (at 10,000 feet), prior to landing (at 10,000 feet), and after landing. For air carrier operations conducted under part 121 or 135, the limitations, at a minimum, should state the use of all such devices—except medical electronic devices such as heart pacemakers or portable oxygen concentrators (POC)—is prohibited during phases of operation when they could interfere with communication or navigation equipment onboard the aircraft or the ability of the flightcrew to give instructions in the event of an emergency. Methods of passenger communication may include:

1. Procedures to terminate operation of PEDs suspected of causing interference with aircraft systems.

2. Procedures for reporting PED interference to a responsible Flight Standards office.

3. Procedures for cockpit-to-cabin coordination and cockpit flightcrew monitoring procedures.

4. Procedures for determining acceptability of PEDs for operation

aboard its aircraft. Acceptable PED identification should be clearly spelled out in oral departure briefings and by written material provided to passengers.

5. Procedures for takeoff and landing preparation must be considered when allowing the PED operation during these phases of flight. Operators must recognize that the potential for personal injury to passengers is a crucial consideration, as well as the possibility of missing significant safety announcements during takeoff and landing. InFO 13010 and InFO 13010SUP provide guidance to address these considerations.

[AC 120-76D, ¶12] A part 91K, 121, 125, or 135 operator must have an EFB program authorized by the FAA in order to use EFB applications on either portable or installed equipment in flight operations. EFB program specifics (i.e., operating procedures, maintenance procedures, administrative procedures, and training modules) must be developed, as applicable, and be available to the FAA. FAA authorization for an EFB program will be granted upon successful evaluation of an applicant's program operation.

Bottom Line:

It is up to the operator to determine if you can use that iPad and portable GPS during cruise flight, taxi before takeoff, and taxi after landing. Under 14 CFR 91K, 121, and 135, the operator is the company that controls the operation and have a program "authorized by the FAA" usually with OpSpec/MSpec/LOA A061. Under 14 CFR 91, it is you, the pilot.

Plotting on an electronic image of a chart (PDF or other photo-like image)

There are various vendors out there that will sell you a PDF chart the day of your flight that already has the relevant oceanic tracks plotted. Alternatively, some vendors will sell you a chart without the tracks for a little less money. In either case, it is up to you to plot your course, ETPs, and all other items just as you would on paper. This would seem to be the easiest way to transition from paper to plastic since you are doing the same thing only on an iPad. It is actually very difficult and frustrating for reasons that I hope to make clear.

- *You can use a plastic plotter on an iPad but the second you touch the screen with your hands, the position and scale of the map can change. Try a larger plotter and place it on the iPad in the correct position before making contact with the screen.*

- *Measuring distance is even harder because the scale is prone to change the second you make contact with the screen. We had our best luck with a pair of dividers with the pointy ends dulled with a file.*

- *Finding the exact longitude and latitude can be easier if you draw straight lines from the nearest scale, pick the intersection, then erase the lines.*

This method of plotting on a PDF works but it isn't very accurate. Getting courses and distances will take a fair amount of time and can be frustrating. Placing your finger or stylus on exactly an exact latitude/longitude isn't easy. If you have access to a charting application, that is definitely easier, faster, and more accurate.

The remaining steps, such as plotting your position or doing a navigation accuracy check, are completed as you would with paper, just using the same steps to plot your route. We used this method for a few months in parallel with paper procedures. Paper was consistently faster.

Using an application-based plotting tool

I first looked into this in 2015.. The software I used was ForeFlight, Garmin Pilot, and JeppFD. Since then, several others have come on market that are quite good. I'll detail the process for ForeFlight to show general procedures. You should look for application-specific instructions.

Understanding Latitude and Longitude Units of Measurement

As international pilots we all have an intuitive understanding of geographic coordinates from the days of Ferdinand Magellan:

The globe is divided by 360 degrees of latitude and longitude, measured from 0 to 180 going east and west starting at the prime meridian, and 0 to 90 degrees going north and back to 0 degrees going south starting at the equator in one direction and south back to north in the other.

Each one of those degrees is divided another 60 times into "minutes."

Each of those minutes is further divided another 60 times into "seconds."

HDDD°MM'SS" — You often see these coordinates where the H is N, S, E, or W, the DDD are the degrees, a degree symbol, MM are the minutes with a single quote, and the SS are the seconds with a double quote. For example, N39°53'41" means 39 degrees, 53 minutes, 41 seconds North latitude. Your FMS doesn't do it this way and your application software probably doesn't either.

HDD°MM.dd — Your FMS probably uses a format that uses decimal minutes instead of seconds. For example, the earlier latitude would translate to N39°53.68 and might appear as N39.5368. Confused? You can tell it is using decimal minutes and not seconds because the seconds are never higher than 59. Some applications also use this format, which makes your plotting life easier.

HDD.dddd — Some applications use degrees and decimal degrees.

It is important to know which method your FMS, your Master Document, and your plotting software are using. You can not mix one method with the other without first doing some translation. Let's say your Master Document shows your ETP is at N53°05.30, using the same format that your FMS uses, HDD°MM.dd. But now let's say your plotting software uses HDD.dddd. If you type in N53.0530, that will translate to N53°08.83.

You can do the math on your own. To convert decimal values into minutes or seconds, multiply by 60. For example, the .83 minutes in the last example be-

comes (0.83) x (60) = 50 seconds. To convert seconds or minutes into decimal values, divide by 60. So 50 seconds becomes (50) / (60) = .83 minutes.

If your plotting application uses HDD.dddd, there is probably a way to automatically convert your inputs. In ForeFlight, for example, you can have it automatically change all your inputs into the needed NDD.dddd through the settings tab. Or you can have it make the conversion if you follow a particular format. Typing in your coordinate in the format HDDDMMS tells it your are using degrees, minutes, and decimal minutes. ForeFlight will do the translation for you, but when you examine the same point it will be in HDD.dddd format.

Plotting your route

FLIGHT PLAN

RTE: KBED DCT LBSTA ALLEX N437A TUDEP 5250N 5440N 5530N 5520N
     RESNO NETKI LIPGO UL18 BADSI WCO ASKE5A EGGW

ALT: FL 410

If you are using an interactive application to produce your plotting chart, you can cut and paste the route from either the application's master document or the PDF version of the master document. Press and hold any portion of the route until at least a portion of the route appears in inverse video. Then drag the start and end handles until the entire route is highlighted. Then select "Copy." You then go to the plotting application to the route entry appears, press and hold until you see a "paste" button.

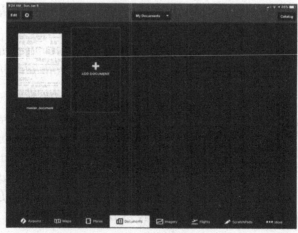

Photo: ForeFlight, the documents page

To cut and paste your routing into ForeFlight you will first have to export the master document PDF file into ForeFlight. From that point you select the file from the bottom Documents tab.

At this point you select and copy the route by pressing on a part of the route, extending the copy handles until the route is highlighted, and the select "Copy" from the pop up menu.

Photo: ForeFlight, entering the route

Now select "FPL" from the top menu, "Clear" the old route if necessary, and then press and hold the Search window on top. You should be presented with the text you just copied, press to select.

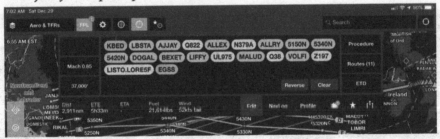

Photo: ForeFlight, entering the route

The result should be your copied route.

Checking courses and distances

Once you've entered the route, pressing the FPL button brings up the flight plan which includes headings and distances:

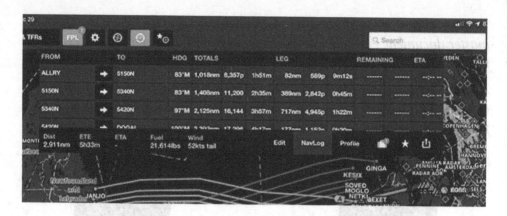

Photo: ForeFlight example flight plan page.

Notice that this brings up headings not the courses. If ForeFlight has or has recently had access to the Internet, it will automatically download the winds and you will not be able to display courses. To get around this, tap the "Edit" button below the legs, then look for either "ETD" or a time which indicates the ETD. Tap the ETD and you will see a calendar. If you select a date at least 7 days away, the winds are zeroed and the NavLog will then display "CRS" which is the Magnetic Course:

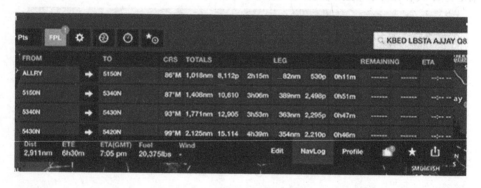

Photo: ForeFlight example distance/heading check.

This works, but remember it isn't the True course, it is Magnetic. That should not be a problem since your FMS will most likely be using Magnetic as well.

ETPs and PSRs

You will need to enter at least one Equal Time Point (ETP), possibly a Point of Safe Return (PSR), and you may want to enter other points onto the chart that should not appear as routing waypoints.

Photo: ForeFlight, plotting an ETP, step 1

Press and hold a point on the route near the desired point. Select "More" on the location line and then "Save."

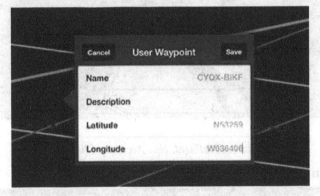

Photo: ForeFlight, plotting an ETP, step 2

From the next menu give the ETP a suitable name, correct the latitude and longitude. The default format probably isn't what you want: degrees.decimal degrees. To automatically enter degrees, minutes, and decimal minutes, use the format HDDDMMS, i.e., N53259 or W036406. (Latitude degrees must be in two digits, longitude degrees must be three digits.) However you enter it, it will be converted to degrees and decimal degrees.

Photo: ForeFlight, plotting an ETP, step 3

The resulting point is given within a triangle above a flag.

Navigation Accuracy Check

Using two fingers (using two hands makes this easier), simultaneously press the applicable VOR and the approximate aircraft position, fine tune the VOR position so it is exact, adjust the other until the radial and DME agree with your raw data, release both fingers. The resulting point should be on the course line.

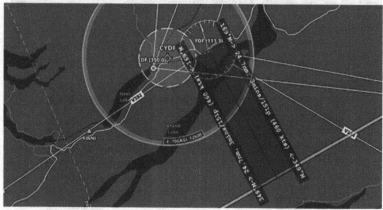

Photo: ForeFlight, Nav Accuracy Check

Post Position Plot

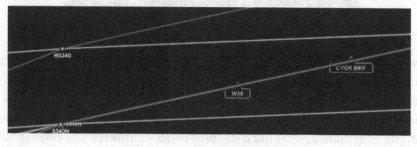

Photo: ForeFlight, post-position plot

Post-position plots in ForeFlight are entered just as you would any other user non-routing point with a suitable name, as shown earlier with ETPs or PSRs.

Plotting with a Portable GPS

Will a portable GPS unit help? Most definitely.

Photo: *The Dual XGPS near a cockpit window.*

Is it legal? Yes, a portable GPS is allowed as just another PED. Commercial operators will need A061 OpSpec/MSpec/LOA approval, see: Personal Electronic Devices (PEDs). Some models can be linked to multiple iPads via a Bluetooth connection. These provide the best possible post-position plots and can be invaluable backups when things go wrong.

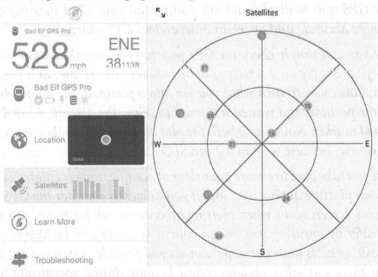

Photo: *Bad Elf App display*

For the Bad Elf, as an example, Bluetooth pairing procedures are convention-al. Simply turn the unit on, go to the Settings / Bluetooth menu on the iPad and pair. You may have to wait a few minutes for the unit to find the required number of satellites. Once that is done, you should see an airplane symbol on your charting applications.

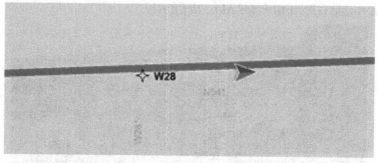

Photo: Example post-position plot using JeppFD and a portable GPS unit.

I've heard the argument that using a completely independent GPS violates the intent of AC 91-70B, ¶D.2.9.1, which says the plotting procedures should be made by using the "nonsteering LRNS." In my opinion this is nonsense. First, if your LRNS uses blended positions from GPS-updated IRUs, this is hardly an independent source. Second, how can you check the performance of one GPS using another GPS which uses much of the same hardware? I think using a portable GPS unit to display aircraft position on your iPad charting applica-tion is more accurate and offers an independent GPS source.

I believe you can simply check the GPS position on your iPad as an adequate position plot. Simply do a screen grab by pressing the "Home" and power but-tons simultaneously to turn what you see into a photo. In the photo above, we plotted the position and waited a minute to allow the aircraft symbol to pass the plotted marker. Notice how both the plot and aircraft symbol are two miles right of course, because we had a 2 nm SLOP.

I think if you take care to ensure your cleared oceanic route is entered accurate-ly into your plotting application, and if you diligently monitor the GPS symbol while doing screen grabs when plotting procedures call for them, you will not only be safer by ensuring you are on course, you will also be able to produce better position plots than manual methods will provide. You just need to make sure you carry out other oceanic record keeping duties, specifically with the Master Document. . . .

Chapter 6

Reduced Vertical Separation Minimums (RVSM)

It is becoming next to impossible to fly just about anywhere in the world without RVSM. You need to know more than just where it is in effect, the rules for getting you and your aircraft RVSM qualified, and how to keep your aircraft eligible to fly through RVSM airspace by conducting regular performance checks. You also need to know the country-specific rules that may not be what you are expecting in terms of flight level selection and contingency procedures. Do you need an LOA/OpSpec/MSpec to operate in RVSM airspace? It depends on where you are going and if you have ADS-B Out.

RVSM Description

[AC 91-85B, ¶B.2.1] RVSM airspace was designed to allow 1,000 ft vertical separation between aircraft operating at flight levels (FL) at or above FL 290. At 0901 universal coordinated time (UTC) on January 20, 2005, the FAA implemented RVSM between FL 290–410 (inclusive) in the following airspace: the airspace of the lower 48 states of the United States, Alaska, Atlantic, and Gulf of Mexico High Offshore Airspace, and the San Juan flight information region (FIR). On the same time and date, RVSM was also introduced into the adjoining airspace of Canada and Mexico to provide a seamless environment for aircraft traversing those borders. In addition, RVSM was implemented on the same date in the Caribbean and South American regions.

Location

Most of the world. The exceptions are becoming rarer and you will have to check the Jeppesen State pages prior to every trip to be sure. Implementation varies by country:

- *Africa / Indian Ocean. Between FL 290 and FL 410, inclusive, in selected FIRs. Consult AIPs, Jeppesen State Pages, and ICAO Document 7030, Regional Supplementary Procedures.*

- *Caribbean. Between FL 290 and FL 410, inclusive.*

- *European. Between FL 290 and FL 410, inclusive, except some portions of Eastern Europe. Consult AIPs, Jeppesen State Pages, and ICAO Document 7030, Regional Supplementary Procedures.*

- *North Atlantic. Between FL 290 and FL 410, inclusive.*

- *Middle East/Asia. Normally between FL 290 and FL 410, inclusive, in selected FIRs. In China, between FL8,900m (FL 291) and FL 12,500m (FL 411), inclusive, in selected FIRs. Consult AIPs, Jeppesen State Pages, and ICAO Document 7030, Regional Supplementary Procedures.*

- *North America. Between FL 290 and FL 410, inclusive.*

- *Pacific. Between FL 290 and FL 410, inclusive, though FL 410 is available for non-RVSM approved flights. There are exceptions; consult AIPs, Jeppesen State Pages, and ICAO Document 7030, Regional Supplementary Procedures.*

- *South America. Between FL 290 and FL 410, inclusive.*

Aircraft Eligibility / Approval

Do you need an LOA/OpSpec to fly in RVSM airspace? If all you are doing is flying in the U.S. domestic airspace and you have a qualified ADS-B Out system the answer is no, you do not. But if you plan on leaving U.S. domestic airspace or you do not have a qualified ADS-B Out system, you will indeed need a written authorization. Why?

If you don't have a qualified ADS-B Out system, AC 91-85B says you need one.

If you are leaving the U.S., ICAO Annex 6, Part I, §2.5.2 and ICAO Doc 9574, §4.3 say you need record of approval from your state of registry. These rules apply to you whenever you leave domestic U.S. airspace.

ICAO Equipment Requirements

[ICAO Doc 9574, ¶5.1.1.(g)] Before entering RVSM airspace, the pilot should review the status of equipment required. The following equipment should be operating normally:

1) two altitude measurement systems, as defined by the RVSM MASPS;

2) automatic altitude-keeping device(s);

Note.—Redundancy requirements for altitude-keeping devices should be established by regional agreement after an evaluation of such criteria as mean time between failures, length of flight segments and availability of direct pilot-controller communications and radar surveillance.

3) at least one altitude-reporting transponder (if required for operation in that specific RVSM airspace) capable of being switched to operate from either of the two altimetry systems required by the RVSM MASPS; and

4) one altitude-alerting device;

Should any of this equipment fail prior to the aircraft entering RVSM airspace, the pilot should request a new clearance so as to avoid flight in this airspace.

ICAO Approval Requirement

[ICAO Doc 9574, ¶4.3.3] Implementation of RVSM is dependent on the establishment of an aircraft approval confirmation process, which is intended to exclude unqualified aircraft and operators from operating in RVSM airspace unless the appropriate separation is applied. The process may have regional variations, but the primary responsibility for confirmation of the approval status of an aircraft/operator must rest with the State of the Operator/State of Registry. The confirmation process will be facilitated by the following measures:

    a.   maintaining a comprehensive record of all approvals granted for operations in RVSM airspace;

    b.   providing the approvals records in 4.3.3 a) to the regional monitoring agency (RMA) for inclusion in its regional RVSM-approvals database; and

    c.   including a check of the approval status of aircraft/operators in the schedule of routine in-flight inspections.

U.S. Eligibility

[AC 91-85B, Ch. 2]

2.2 Aircraft Eligibility. An aircraft is an "RVSM-Compliant Aircraft" when:

1. The aircraft design ensures the aircraft will meet RVSM performance requirements; and

2. The aircraft has been properly maintained on an ongoing basis to conduct such operations.

2.2.1 Aircraft may be produced RVSM-compliant or brought into compliance through the application of appropriate Service Bulletins (SB), Service Letters (SL), Engineering Change Orders (EO), or Supplemental Type Certificates (STC). For airworthiness guidance, see Appendix A, RVSM Airworthiness Certification.

2.2.2 To determine eligibility for RVSM operations, the limitations section of the Airplane Flight Manual (AFM) or AFM Supplement (AFMS) should indicate the aircraft has been determined to be capable of meeting the RVSM performance requirements of 14 CFR part 91 appendix G.

Note: For operators and pilots authorized under part 91 appendix G, section 9, the aircraft may have qualified as Group or Non-Group aircraft described in Appendix A.

U.S. Regulatory

[14 CFR 91, §91.180] Operations within airspace designated as Reduced Vertical Separation Minimum airspace.

(a) Except as provided in paragraph (b) of this section, no person may operate a civil aircraft in airspace designated as Reduced Vertical Separation Minimum (RVSM) airspace unless:

(1) The operator and the operator's aircraft comply with the minimum standards of appendix G of this part; and

(2) The operator is authorized by the Administrator or the country of registry to conduct such operations.

(b) The Administrator may authorize a deviation from the requirements of this section.

U.S. Aircraft Approval

[14 CFR 91, Appendix G, Section 2]

(a) Except as specified in Section 9 of this appendix, an operator may be authorized to conduct RVSM operations if the Administrator finds that its aircraft comply with this section.

(b) The applicant for authorization shall submit the appropriate data package for aircraft approval. The package must consist of at least the following:

(1) An identification of the RVSM aircraft group or the nongroup aircraft;

(2) A definition of the RVSM flight envelopes applicable to the subject aircraft;

(3) Documentation that establishes compliance with the applicable RVSM aircraft requirements of this section; and

(4) The conformity tests used to ensure that aircraft approved with the data package meet the RVSM aircraft requirements.

(c) Altitude-keeping equipment: All aircraft. To approve an aircraft group or a nongroup aircraft, the Administrator must find that the aircraft meets the following requirements:

(1) The aircraft must be equipped with two operational independent altitude measurement systems.

(2) The aircraft must be equipped with at least one automatic altitude control system that controls the aircraft altitude—

(i) Within a tolerance band of ±65 feet about an acquired altitude when the aircraft is operated in straight and level flight under nonturbulent, nongust conditions; or

(ii) Within a tolerance band of ±130 feet under nonturbulent, nongust conditions for aircraft for which application for type certification occurred on or before April 9, 1997 that are equipped with an automatic altitude control system with flight management/performance system inputs.

(3) The aircraft must be equipped with an altitude alert system that signals an alert when the altitude displayed to the flight crew deviates from the selected altitude by more than:

(i) ±300 feet for aircraft for which application for type certification was made on or before April 9, 1997; or

(ii) ±200 feet for aircraft for which application for type certification is made after April 9, 1997.

(d) Altimetry system error containment: Group aircraft for which application for type certification was made on or before April 9, 1997. To approve group aircraft for which application for type certification was made on or before April 9, 1997, the Administrator must find that the altimetry system error (ASE) is contained as follows:

(1) At the point in the basic RVSM flight envelope where mean ASE reaches its largest absolute value, the absolute value may not exceed 80 feet.

(2) At the point in the basic RVSM flight envelope where mean ASE plus three standard deviations reaches its largest absolute value, the absolute value may not exceed 200 feet.

(3) At the point in the full RVSM flight envelope where mean ASE reaches its largest absolute value, the absolute value may not exceed 120 feet.

(4) At the point in the full RVSM flight envelope where mean ASE plus three standard deviations reaches its largest absolute value, the absolute value may not exceed 245 feet.

(5) Necessary operating restrictions. If the applicant demonstrates that its aircraft otherwise comply with the ASE containment requirements, the Administrator may establish an operating restriction on that applicant's aircraft to restrict the aircraft from operating in areas of the basic RVSM flight envelope where the absolute value of mean ASE exceeds 80 feet, and/or the absolute value of mean ASE plus three standard deviations exceeds 200 feet; or from operating in areas of the full RVSM flight envelope where the absolute value of the mean ASE exceeds 120 feet and/or the absolute value of the mean ASE plus three standard deviations exceeds 245 feet.

(e) Altimetry system error containment: Group aircraft for which application for type certification is made after April 9, 1997. To approve group aircraft for which application for type certification is made after April 9, 1997, the Administrator must find that the altimetry system error (ASE) is contained as follows:

(1) At the point in the full RVSM flight envelope where mean ASE reaches its largest absolute value, the absolute value may not exceed 80 feet.

(2) At the point in the full RVSM flight envelope where mean ASE plus three standard deviations reaches its largest absolute value, the absolute value may not exceed 200 feet.

(f) Altimetry system error containment: Nongroup aircraft. To approve a nongroup aircraft, the Administrator must find that the altimetry system error (ASE) is contained as follows:

(1) For each condition in the basic RVSM flight envelope, the largest combined absolute value for residual static source error plus the avionics error may not exceed 160 feet.

(2) For each condition in the full RVSM flight envelope, the largest combined absolute value for residual static source error plus the avionics error may not exceed 200 feet.

(g) Traffic Alert and Collision Avoidance System (TCAS) Compatibility With RVSM Operations: All aircraft. After March 31, 2002, unless otherwise authorized by the Administrator, if you operate an aircraft that is equipped with TCAS II in RVSM airspace, it must be a TCAS II that meets TSO C-119b (Version 7.0), or a later version.

(h) If the Administrator finds that the applicant's aircraft comply with this section, the Administrator notifies the applicant in writing.

U.S. Authorization — Aircraft without a Qualfied ADS-B Out System
[14 CFR 91, Appendix G, Section 3]

(a) Except as specified in Section 9 of this appendix, authority for an operator to conduct flight in airspace where RVSM is applied is issued in operations specifications, a Letter of Authorization, or management specifications issued under subpart K of this part, as appropriate. To issue an RVSM authorization under this section, the Administrator must find that the operator's aircraft have been approved in accordance with Section 2 of this appendix and the operator complies with this section.

(b) Except as specified in Section 9 of this appendix, an applicant seeking authorization to operate within RVSM airspace must apply in a form and manner prescribed by the Administrator. The application must include the following:

(1) [Reserved]

(2) For an applicant who operates under part 121 or 135 of this chapter or under subpart K of this part, initial and recurring pilot training requirements.

(3) Policies and procedures: An applicant who operates under part 121 or 135 of this chapter or under subpart K of this part must submit RVSM policies and procedures that will enable it to conduct RVSM operations safely.

(c) In a manner prescribed by the Administrator, an operator seeking authorization under this section must provide evidence that:

(1) It is capable to operate and maintain each aircraft or aircraft group for which it applies for approval to operate in RVSM airspace; and

(2) Each pilot has knowledge of RVSM requirements, policies, and procedures sufficient for the conduct of operations in RVSM airspace.

U.S. Authorization — Aircraft with a Qualfied ADS-B Out System

[AC 91-85B, §4.1.1] Operators and pilots seeking to operate in RVSM airspace under the provisions of part 91 appendix G, section 9 are not required to apply for authorizations. The operator or pilot needs to ensure all applicable requirements in part 91 appendix G to operate in RVSM airspace are met. The operator or pilot should:

1.   Determine the aircraft is RVSM-compliant (see Chapter 2, Aircraft Eligibility);

2.   Ensure pilots are knowledgeable (see Chapter 3, Knowledge and Training);

3.   Ensure the aircraft meets RVSM performance and the aircraft has been height monitored in accordance with paragraph 4.3 (see paragraph 4.3.5 when an operator is conducting the initial flight in RVSM airspace); and

4.   Properly file a flight plan and understand the policies and procedures for the RVSM airspace in which the aircraft will operate.

[14 CFR 91, Appendix G, Section 9] Aircraft Equipped With Automatic Dependent Surveillance—Broadcast Out

An operator is authorized to conduct flight in airspace in which RVSM is applied provided:

(a) The aircraft is equipped with the following:

(1) Two operational independent altitude measurement systems.

(2) At least one automatic altitude control system that controls the aircraft altitude—

(i) Within a tolerance band of ±65 feet about an acquired altitude when the aircraft is operated in straight and level flight under nonturbulent, nongust conditions; or

(ii) Within a tolerance band of ±130 feet under nonturbulent, nongust conditions for aircraft for which application for type certification occurred on or before April 9, 1997, that are equipped with an automatic altitude control system with flight management/performance system inputs.

(3) An altitude alert system that signals an alert when the altitude displayed to the flightcrew deviates from the selected altitude by more than—

(i) ±300 feet for aircraft for which application for type certification was made on or before April 9, 1997; or

(ii) ±200 feet for aircraft for which application for type certification is made after April 9, 1997.

(4) A TCAS II that meets TSO C-119b (Version 7.0), or a later version, if equipped with TCAS II, unless otherwise authorized by the Administrator.

(5) Unless authorized by ATC or the foreign country where the aircraft is operated, an ADS-B Out system that meets the equipment performance requirements of §91.227 of this part. The aircraft must have its height-keeping performance monitored in a form and manner acceptable to the Administrator.

(b) The altimetry system error (ASE) of the aircraft does not exceed 200 feet when operating in RVSM airspace.

Performance Monitoring

Your RVSM performance needs to be checked at least once every 24 months. This is getting easier to do.

[AC 91-85B, §2.5.1] RVSM aircraft must participate in altitude-keeping performance monitoring programs to ensure safe and efficient operations in RVSM airspace.

- Operators and pilots conducting RVSM operations under the provisions of part 91 appendix G, section 9 must ensure their aircraft meet the RVSM altitude-keeping performance monitoring requirements as described in Chapter 4, paragraph 4.3. Under these provisions, aircraft with qualified ADS-B OUT systems will be monitored during normal operations whenever operating at RVSM altitudes where sufficient ADS-B data is available to the FAA to determine RVSM performance. All aircraft in an operator's fleet must have been monitored within the previous 24 months and found to be in compliance with the performance requirement specified in part 91 appendix G, section 9(b).

- Operators conducting RVSM operations under the provision of part 91 appendix G, section 3 must meet the RVSM Minimum Monitoring Requirements (MMR) and have their aircraft monitored as specified in Appendix E, RVSM Altitude-Keeping Performance Monitoring When Operating With an RVSM OpSpec, MSpec, or LOA.

You can verify your aircraft's approval at: http://faa.gov/air_traffic/separation_standards/naarmo/rvsm_approvals/

Operating Procedures

We will soon look upon these procedures as simply the way you fly airplanes and I suspect all this will end up as a paragraph or two in the Aeronautical Information Manual. But until then ...

Flight planning.

[AC 91-85B, §B.3.1] Flight Planning. During flight planning, the flightcrew and dispatchers, if applicable, should pay particular attention to conditions which may affect operation in RVSM airspace. These include, but may not be limited to:

1.   Verifying the aircraft and operator meet RVSM requirements.

2.   Annotating the flight plan to be filed with the Air Traffic Service Provider (ATSP) to show compliance for RVSM operations. The International Civil Aviation Organization (ICAO) flight plan, FAA Form 7233-4, Pre-Flight Pilot Checklist and International Flight Plan, Item 10, Equipment, should be annotated with the letter W for filing in RVSM airspace.

- When using FAA Form 7233-4, operators should ensure that the aircraft's registration number (Reg/) is listed in Item 18 (Other Information), if different than that listed in Item 7 (Aircraft Identification).

- For exceptions to the use of FAA Form 7233-4, refer to the FAA AIM, Chapter 5, Air Traffic Procedures, for the proper flight codes

Note: An aircraft or operator not meeting the requirements for RVSM operations including an aircraft without operable RVSM equipment is referred to as non-RVSM. If either the flightcrew or aircraft do not meet the requirements for RVSM, the operator or dispatcher will not file the RVSM equipment code in the flight plan and follow the procedures for a non-RVSM status, including the appropriate pilot-air traffic control (ATC) phraseology in Table B-1, RVSM Phraseology.

3. Reported and forecast weather conditions on the route of flight.

4. Minimum equipment requirements pertaining to altitude-keeping systems.

5. Traffic Alert and Collision Avoidance System (TCAS) equipage. TCAS equipage requirements are contained in part 121, § 121.356; part 125, § 125.224; part 129, § 129.18; and part 135, § 135.180. Part 91 appendix G does not contain TCAS equipage requirements specific to RVSM; however, part 91 appendix G does require that aircraft equipped with TCAS II and flown in RVSM airspace be modified to incorporate TCAS II Version 7.0 or a later version.

6. If required for the specific aircraft Group, accounting for any aircraft operating restrictions related to RVSM airworthiness approval. (See Appendix A, RVSM Airworthiness Certification, paragraph A.10.1.3.)

Preflight procedures.

[AC 91-85B, §B.3.2] Preflight Procedures. Accomplish the following actions during preflight:

1. Review maintenance logs and forms to ascertain the condition of equipment required for flight in the RVSM airspace. Ensure maintenance action has been taken to correct defects to required equipment.

2. During the external inspection of aircraft, pay particular attention to the condition of static sources, the condition of the fuselage skin near each static source, and any other component affecting altimetry system accuracy. (A qualified and authorized person other than the pilot (e.g., a Flight Engineer (FE) or maintenance personnel) may perform this check.)

3. Before takeoff:

• The aircraft altimeters should be set to the barometric pressure for local altimeter setting (QNH) and should display a known elevation (e.g., field elevation) within the limits specified in aircraft operating manuals.

The difference between the known elevation and the elevation displayed on the altimeters should not exceed 75 ft.

- The two primary altimeters should also agree within limits specified by the aircraft operating manual/Airplane Flight Manual (AFM), as applicable. An alternative procedure using atmospheric pressure at aerodrome elevation (QFE) may also be used.

Note: Both checks should be an emphasis item for training materials.

4.   Equipment required for flight in RVSM airspace should be operational, and indications of malfunction should be resolved.

Procedures before RVSM entry.

[AC 91-85B, §B.3.3] Procedures Before RVSM Airspace Entry. If any of the required equipment fails prior to the aircraft entering RVSM airspace, the pilot should request a new clearance to avoid flight in this airspace. The following equipment must be operating normally at entry into RVSM airspace:

1.   Two primary altitude measurement systems.

2.   One automatic altitude control system.

3.   One altitude alerting device.

Note: The operator or pilot should ascertain the requirement for an operational transponder and TCAS in each RVSM area where operations are intended.

In-flight procedures.

[AC 91-85B, §B.3.4] In-Flight Procedures. Incorporate the following policies into flightcrew training and procedures, as applicable:

1.   Flightcrews should comply with aircraft operating restrictions (if required for the specific aircraft Group) related to RVSM airworthiness approval. (See paragraph A.10.1.3.)

2.   Place emphasis on promptly setting the sub-scale on all primary and standby altimeters to 29.92 inches of mercury (in Hg)/1013.25 hectopascals (hPa) when climbing through the transition altitude and rechecking for proper altimeter setting when reaching the initial cleared flight level (CFL).

3.   In level cruise, it is essential the aircraft is flown at the CFL. This requires particular care is taken to ensure ATC clearances are fully

understood and followed. Except in contingency or emergency situations, the aircraft should not intentionally depart from CFL without a positive clearance from ATC.

4. During cleared transition between FLs, the aircraft should not be allowed to overshoot or undershoot the CFL by more than 150 ft (45 m).

Note: It is recommended the level-off be accomplished using the altitude capture feature of the automatic altitude control system, if installed.

5. An automatic altitude control system must be operative and engaged during level cruise, except when circumstances such as the need to retrim the aircraft or turbulence require disengagement. In any event, adherence to cruise altitude should be done by reference to one of the two primary altimeters.

6. The altitude alerting system must be operational.

7. At cruise FL, the two primary altimeters should agree within 200 ft (60 m) or a lesser value if specified in the aircraft operating manual. (Failure to meet this condition will require that the altimetry system be reported as defective and notified to ATC.) Note the difference between the primary and standby altimeters for use in contingency situations.

8. At intervals of approximately 1 hour, make cross-checks between the primary altimeters and the standby altimeter.

• The normal pilot scan of flight deck instruments should suffice for altimeter cross-checking on most flights.

• When operating in surveillance airspace (Radar/Automatic Dependent Surveillance-Broadcast (ADS-B)), the initial altimeter cross-check should be performed after level-off.

• In oceanic and remote continental (procedural) airspace, a cross-check should be performed and recorded in the vicinity of the point where oceanic and remote continental navigation begins (e.g., on coast out). The readings of the primary and standby altimeters should be recorded and available for use in contingency situations.

• Some aircraft have automatic comparators that compare the two primary altimetry systems. The comparators include a monitoring, warning, and fault function. The faults may be recorded automatically by the system, but a record of the differences in the primary altimetry systems may not be easily derived.

Note: In oceanic and remote continental (procedural) airspace, even if the aircraft is equipped with automatic comparators, the crew should be recording the altimeter cross-checks for use in a contingency situation.

9. Normally, the altimetry system being used to control the aircraft should be selected to provide the input to the altitude-reporting transponder transmitting information to ATC.

10. If ATC notifies the pilot of an assigned altitude deviation (AAD) error equal to or exceeding 300 ft (90 m), then the pilot should take action to return to CFL as quickly as possible.

Contingency procedures after entering RVSM airspace.

[AC 91-85B, §B.3.6] Contingency Procedures After Entering RVSM Airspace. The flightcrew, after realizing that they no longer can comply with RVSM requirements (aircraft system failure, weather, lost com, etc.), must request a new clearance from the controller/radio operator as soon as the situation allows. If a new clearance is not available or the nature of the emergency requires rapid action, the pilot should notify ATC of their action and contingency procedures. Operators should refer to the RVSM section of the AIM when experiencing abnormal situations and implementing contingency procedures. It is also the responsibility of the crew to notify ATC when the implementation of the contingency procedures is no longer required.

Postflight.

[AC 91-85B, §B.3.7] Postflight. In making maintenance logbook entries against malfunctions in altitude-keeping systems, the pilot should provide sufficient detail to enable maintenance to effectively troubleshoot and repair the system. The pilot should detail the actual defect and the crew action taken to try to isolate and rectify the fault. Note the following information when appropriate:

1. Primary and standby altimeter reading.

2. Altitude selector setting.

3. Subscale setting on altimeter.

4. Autopilot used to control the airplane and any differences when the

alternate system was selected.

5. Differences in altimeter readings if alternate static ports selected.

6. Use of air-data computer (ADC) selector for fault diagnosis procedure.

7. Transponder selected to provide altitude information to ATC and any difference if alternate transponder or altitude source is manually selected.

Hourly Checks

[ICAO Doc 9574, ¶5.1.1.(e)] Regular (hourly) cross-checks between the altimeters should be made, and a minimum of two RVSM MASPS-compliant systems must agree within 60 m (200 ft). Failure to meet this condition will require that the system be reported as defective and notified to ATC.

Standby Altimeter Performance

While there are no in-flight standby altimeter tolerances which would necessitate an in-flight abort, the standby altimeter should be evaluated against 14 CFR 43, Appendix E tolerances for subsequent maintenance action. The tolerances are altitude dependent.

Altitude	Equivalent pressure (inches of mercury)	Tolerance ±(feet)
0	29.921	20
1,000	28.856	20
2,000	27.821	30
4,000	25.842	35
6,000	23.978	40
8,000	22.225	60
10,000	20.577	80
12,000	19.029	90
14,000	17.577	100
16,000	16.216	110
18,000	14.942	120
20,000	13.750	130
22,000	12.636	140
25,000	11.104	155
30,000	8.885	180
35,000	7.041	205
40,000	5.538	230
45,000	4.355	255

Table: Standby Altimeter Tolerance, from 14 CFR 43, Appendix E., Table 1.

Chapter 7

Global Navigation Satellite System (GNSS)

A lot of rules for using GPS have changed over the years and what you can and cannot do also depends on where in the world you are.

For example, can you fly the "VOR Rwy 23" to a U.S. airport using GPS? No, the U.S. overlay program that said you could a few years ago was in Advisory Circular 90-94 which was cancelled in 2009. In the U.S., the approach has to have the term "GPS" in the title. What about the "VOR DME Rwy 31" to Sibu, Malaysia? Yes, they are WGS-84 compliant and ICAO rules say you can. In the case of the U.S. approach, it would be a good idea to have the GPS up for position awareness and in Malaysia you should probably have the VOR tuned for back up.

What about an approach that references GNSS and not GPS? Well, it depends. If your airplane lists it as a viable approach, if the country is WGS-84 compliant, and if the country's rules allow you to, then probably. It is a confusing world out there.

Overview

[FAA-H-8083-15B, pg. 9-25]

- The Department of Defense (DOD) developed and deployed GPS as a space-based positioning, velocity, and time system. The DOD is responsible for the operation of the GPS satellite constellation and constantly monitors the satellites to ensure proper operation. The GPS system permits Earth-centered coordinates to be determined and provides aircraft position referenced to the DOD World Geodetic System of 1984 (WGS-84). Satellite navigation systems are unaffected by weather and provide global navigation coverage that fully meet the civil requirements for use as the primary means of navigation in oceanic airspace and certain remote areas. Properly certified GPS equipment may be used as a supplemental means of IFR navigation for domestic en route, terminal operations, and certain IAPs. Navigational values, such as distance and bearing to a waypoint and groundspeed, are computed from the aircraft's current position (latitude and longitude) and the location of the next waypoint. Course guidance is provided as a linear deviation from the desired track of a great circle route between defined waypoints.

- The space element [of GPS] consists of 24 Navstar satellites. This group of satellites is called a constellation. The satellites are in six orbital planes (with four in each plane) at about 11,000 miles above the Earth. At least five satellites are in view at all times. The GPS constellation broadcasts a pseudo-random code timing signal and data message that the aircraft equipment processes to obtain satellite position and status data. By knowing the precise location of each satellite and precisely matching timing with the atomic clocks on the satellites, the aircraft receiver/processor can accurately measure the time each signal takes to arrive at the receiver and, therefore, determine aircraft position.

How GPS Works

There is obviously much more to it than what follows, but this gives you what you need to understand how GPS has changed the way we fly airplanes. . .

The Transmitted Signal

[AFAIS Performance-Based Navigation Presentation] Each Navstar satellite transmits on two frequencies:

- L1: 1575.42 MHz — C/A and P codes
- L2: 1227.6 MHz — P code only

Coarse Acquisition (C/A) code is available to all users without limitations and includes

- Ephemeris (position, altitude, speed information from the satellite)
- Time (from the onboard atomic clock, including a time correction factor to make up for the clock's internal errors)
- Satellite health status
- GPS Almanac (predicted positions for entire GPS constellation, often

good for months). A receiver that keeps the almanac in memory can predict from a cold start where to look for satellites, speeding acquisition times.

P-Code provides navigation/targeting data for U.S. government users with an encryption key:

- Position data

- Broadcast on both frequencies, allowing qualified receivers to compare both frequencies and correct for any ionospheric delays.

- Once decrypted P-code becomes Y-code.

[FAA-H-8083-15, pg. 7-22] The aircraft GPS receiver measures distance from a satellite using the travel time of a radio signal. Each satellite transmits a specific code, called a coarse/acquisition (CA) code, which contains information on the satellite's position, the GPS system time, and the health and accuracy of the transmitted data. Knowing the speed at which the signal traveled (approximately 186,000 miles per second) and the exact broadcast time, the distance traveled by the signal can be computed from the arrival time. The distance derived from this method of computing distance is called a pseudo-range because it is not a direct measurement of distance, but a measurement based on time. In addition to knowing the distance to a satellite, a receiver needs to know the satellite's exact position in space; this is know as its ephemeris. Each satellite transmits information about its exact orbital location. The GPS receiver uses this information to precisely establish the position of the satellite.

Each GPS satellite transmits these two frequencies and chances are your receiver captures the L1. There are no limits to the number of receivers since there is no interaction from these receivers back to the satellites. You will need four satellites to determine your position . . .

One satellite

Each satellite sends out a signal that includes its own position and the time. The receiver calculates the time it took the signal to travel and multiplies that by the speed of light) to compute the distance. That distance ("r" in the figure) defines a sphere. The receiver could be at any point on that sphere; more than just the black line, it is the entire outer shell of the sphere. This is true in theory but there is an issue with the time synchronization when dealing with only one satellite. (The problem goes away with more than one satellite since they can be synchronized. But we are just illustrating a point here.)

Two satellites

With two satellites you have an intersection of two spheres and the receiver could be in any position along those intersecting spheres. It is more than just the black lines in the diagram, your position could be at any point inside the three-dimensional shape described by the black line.

Three satellites

With three satellites you narrow the possible location down to one of two points (the two black points).

Four satellites

With one more satellite, you have narrowed the universe of possible intersections to just one (the single black point). Errors, of course, are possible.

Position Errors

[AFAIS Performance-Based Navigation Presentation] Errors are possible due to:

- Minor disturbances in satellite orbits from gravitational variations from the sun and the moon or solar wind.

- Ionospheric signal delays caused by water vapor in the atmosphere; this is the biggest source of signal error.

- Slight fluctuations in the satellite atomic clocks.

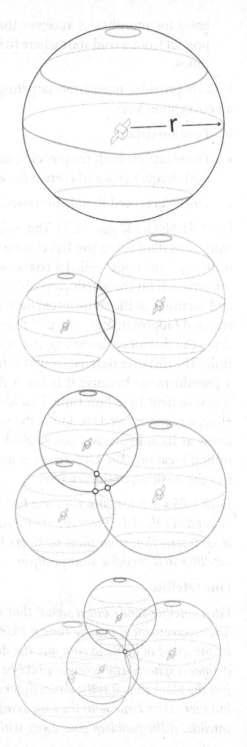

- Receiver quality (faulty clocks or internal noise).

- Multi-path signal reflections off structures.

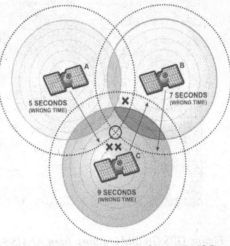

Any errors from even a single satellite can throw off the estimated distance computations and therefore your estimated position. The drawing makes light of a 5 second error, but at the speed of light that would be 930,000 miles, exceeding the satellite's orbit. We must obviously be talking about very small time errors.

Figure: GPS Position errors, from AFAIS Performance-Based Navigation Presentation.

The performance of each satellite is measured and corrected to ensure accuracy . . .

GPS Ground Stations

[AFAIS Performance-Based Navigation Presentation] There are 6 monitoring stations, including the master station at Colorado Springs.

- Collect position and timing data from satellites every 12 hours.

- Send information to master control station.

- Master control station computes corrections and uploads to satellites.

Some receivers are capable of greater accuracy than others, but the issue isn't as extreme as some would have you believe . . .

Positioning Services

[AFAIS Performance-Based Navigation Presentation]

Standard Positioning Service (SPS)

- Uses C/A code – for all users

- Single frequency (L1)

Precise Positioning Service (PPS)

- Uses P-code – for military

- Two frequencies (L1 and L2) – more accurate

- Requires Decryption Key do use it

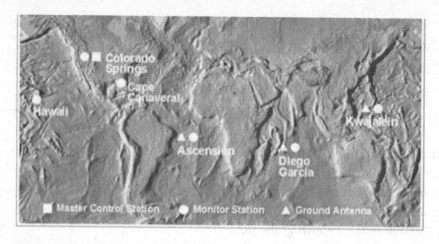

Figure: GPS Ground Stations, from AFAIS Performance-Based Navigation Presentation.

Selective Availability

[AFAIS Performance-Based Navigation Presentation]

- Selective Availability was designed into the system to provide non-military or non-governmental users intentionally limited accuracy.
- The system was turned off in 2000 and we are told the newer satellites don't even have the capability.

As the world became more dependent on GPS they became more worried that one day the U.S. government would turn on selective availability and send airplanes into mountains. The U.S. government promises us that they've abandoned the concept entirely.

Satellite Tracks

The signal coverage is supposed to be worldwide, but the satellites do not cover the world. How can that be?

[http://www.colorado.edu/geography/gcraft/notes/gps/gps_f.html]   The nominal GPS Operational Constellation consists of 24 satellites that orbit the earth in 12 hours. There are often more than 24 operational satellites as new ones are launched to replace older satellites. The satellite orbits repeat almost the same ground track (as the earth turns beneath them) once each day. The orbit altitude is such that the satellites repeat the same track and configuration over any point approximately each 24 hours (4 minutes earlier each day). There are six orbital planes (with nominally four SVs in each), equally spaced (60 degrees apart), and inclined at about fifty-five degrees with respect to the equatorial plane. This constellation provides the user with between five and eight SVs visible from any point on the earth.

There are some who say you cannot get a GPS signal at either pole because they are inclined at 55° from the equator, they even have anecdotal evidence. NASA offers a website to track each satellite and it is true they never get higher than 55° but there are lots of reports of excellent GPS signals at each pole. What gives?

Each GPS satellite traces a track over the earth from 55° North to 55° South every twelve hours. At their maximum latitudes they are actually "looking down" on the poles:

Height Above Pole=10998cos(55)−6887=2122

Of course you have no guarantee you will have at least one satellite that high in its orbit. In order to have line of sight on the pole, a satellite would have to be at least 39° latitude:

Minimum Latitude to See Pole=arc-sin(6887/10998)=39

I've not found anything in writing that tells you there will always be at least four satellites above 39° North and 39° South, but it appears so. You should have a good GPS position at either pole.

GNSS versus GPS

[AC 20-138D, ¶1-4.f.(2)(a)] GNSS is used internationally to indicate any satellite-based positioning system or augmentation system. The acronym 'GNSS' includes satellite constellations, such as GPS, GLONASS, Galileo, or Beidou, along with augmentation systems such as 'SBAS' and 'GBAS'; all of which provide a satellite-based positioning service.

The Global Navigation Satellite System (GNSS) includes navigation satellites and ground systems that monitor satellite signals and provide corrections and integrity messages, where needed, to support specific phases of flight. GPS is a subset of GNSS which means all GPS approaches are GNSS but not all GNSS approaches are GPS. If the approach is marked RNAV (GNSS) you might be okay, but you have some homework to do first: Is GNSS in your flight manual's list of allowed approaches? If you are a commercial operator, do you have the necessary OpSpec? Are there any host-nation prohibitions?

U.S. Requirements to Use GPS

General IFR Requirements

[Aeronautical Information Manual ¶1-1-17.b.2.]

(a) General Requirements. Authorization to conduct any GPS operation under IFR requires:

(1) GPS navigation equipment used for IFR operations must be approved in accordance with the requirements specified in Technical Standard Order (TSO) TSO-C129(), TSO-C196(), TSO-C145(), or TSO-C146(), and the installation must be done in accordance with Advisory Circular AC 20-138, Airworthiness Approval of Positioning and Navigation Systems. Equipment approved in accordance with TSO-C115a does not meet the requirements of TSO-C129. Visual flight rules (VFR) and hand–held GPS systems are not authorized for IFR navigation, instrument approaches, or as a principal instrument flight reference.

(2) Aircraft using un-augmented GPS (TSO-C129() or TSO-C196()) for navigation under IFR must be equipped with an alternate approved and operational means of navigation suitable for navigating the proposed route of flight. (Examples of alternate navigation equipment include VOR or DME/DME/IRU capability). Active monitoring of alternative navigation equipment is not required when RAIM is available for integrity monitoring. Active monitoring of an alternate means of navigation is required when the GPS RAIM capability is lost.

(3) Procedures must be established for use in the event that the loss of RAIM capability is predicted to occur. In situations where RAIM is predicted to be unavailable, the flight must rely on other approved navigation equipment, re-route to where RAIM is available, delay departure, or cancel the flight.

(4) The GPS operation must be conducted in accordance with the FAA–approved aircraft flight manual (AFM) or flight manual supplement. Flight crew members must be thoroughly familiar with the particular GPS equip-

ment installed in the aircraft, the receiver operation manual, and the AFM or flight manual supplement. Operation, receiver presentation and capabilities of GPS equipment vary. Due to these differences, operation of GPS receivers of different brands, or even models of the same brand, under IFR should not be attempted without thorough operational knowledge. Most receivers have a built–in simulator mode, which allows the pilot to become familiar with operation prior to attempting operation in the aircraft.

(5) Aircraft navigating by IFR–approved GPS are considered to be performance–based navigation (PBN) aircraft and have special equipment suffixes. File the appropriate equipment suffix in accordance with TBL 5–1–3 on the ATC flight plan. If GPS avionics become inoperative, the pilot should advise ATC and amend the equipment suffix. (6) Prior to any GPS IFR operation, the pilot must review appropriate NOTAMs and aeronautical information. (See GPS NOTAMs/Aeronautical Information).

IFR Oceanic

[Aeronautical Information Manual ¶1-1-17.b.3.(a)] Conduct GPS IFR operations in oceanic areas only when approved avionics systems are installed. TSO–C196() users and TSO–C129() GPS users authorized for Class A1, A2, B1, B2, C1, or C2 operations may use GPS in place of another approved means of long–range navigation, such as dual INS. (See TBL 1–1–5 and TBL 1–1–6.) Aircraft with a single installation GPS, meeting the above specifications, are authorized to operate on short oceanic routes requiring one means of long–range navigation (reference AC 20-138, Appendix 1).

You might also need authorization B054 to do that.

ICAO Requirements to Use GPS

WGS-84

[ICAO Doc 9613, Attachment 2, ¶3.4 a)] Navigation data may originate from survey observations, from equipment specifications/settings or from the airspace and procedure design process. Whatever the source, the generation and the subsequent processing of the data must take account of the following: (a) all coordinate data must be referenced to the World Geodetic System — 1984 (WGS-84).

Not every country uses the same system to map coordinates. While the differences are minor for en route navigation, they can be significant on approach.

See the Appendices, Chapter 43, World Geodetic System 84 (WGS-84). You can determine a country's WGS-84 status here: https://ww1.jeppesen.com/main/corporate/company/publications/wgs-84.jsp

Operational Approval

[ICAO Doc 8168 Vol 1 ¶1.7.6.1] Pilots shall verify, before operating on any PBN route or procedure, that they have approval to operate on the navigation specification used. Where there are additional restrictions, for example, sensor use or optional functionality [. . .], the pilot shall also verify that these restrictions are complied with.

Navigation Database

[ICAO Doc 8168 Vol 1 ¶1.7.5] Departure procedure information is contained in a navigation database using the WGS-84 coordinate system. If the navigation database does not contain the departure procedure, the procedure shall not be used.

[ICAO Doc 8168 Vol 1 ¶1.4.3.2] Arrival waypoint information is contained in a navigation database using the WGS-84 coordinate system. If the navigation database does not contain the arrival procedure, the procedure shall not be used.

Receiver Autonomous Integrity Monitoring (RAIM)

[AFAIS Performance-Based Navigation Presentation] For a GPS receiver to be certified for IFR navigation, it must have RAIM or an equivalent function. RAIM is simply a computer algorithm that evaluates the integrity of the GPS signal. That means it judges whether enough satellites are in view and in a good geometry to compute a sufficiently accurate position. RAIM checked now evaluates the current satellites in view. Predictive RAIM is based solely on the Almanac. In other words, RAIM uses the Almanac data to estimate where satellites are supposed to be for the future time entered. Sometimes, the number and position of satellites may result in an accuracy good enough only for certain phases of flight, ie, en route, terminal, or approach.

- RAIM — requires 5 satellites in view (1 extra) to provide the extra geometry needed to check the integrity of each satellite being used.

- Predictive RAIM — Uses almanac data or NOTAMS to determine in advance if any satellites should be excluded.

- Fault Detection and Exclusion (FDE) — With an additional satellite, an FDE system can not only detect but can automatically exclude a failed satellite. FDE is required for oceanic or remote operations.

- Baro-Aiding — Some systems can take an altimeter input to replace 1 satellite, so that RAIM only requires 4 satellites (versus 5) and FDE only requires 5 satellites (versus 6).

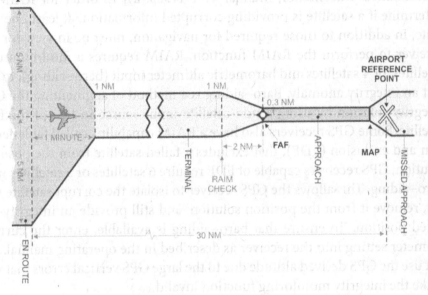

Figure: GPS CDI and RAIM Scaling, from AFAIS PBN Presentation.

[Aeronautical Information Manual ¶1-1-17.a.]

3. RAIM is the capability of a GPS receiver to perform integrity monitoring on itself by ensuring available satellite signals meet the integrity requirements for a given phase of flight. Without RAIM, the pilot has no assurance of the GPS position integrity. RAIM provides immediate feedback to the pilot. This fault detection is critical for performance-based navigation (PBN) [...] because delays of up to two hours can occur before an erroneous satellite transmission is detected and corrected by the satellite control segment.

(b) There are generally two types of RAIM fault messages. The first type of message indicates that there are not enough satellites available to provide RAIM integrity monitoring. The GPS navigation solution may be acceptable, but the integrity of the solution cannot be determined. The second type indicates that the RAIM integrity monitor has detected a potential error and that there is an inconsistency in the navigation solution for the given phase of flight. Without RAIM capability, the pilot has no assurance of the accuracy of the GPS position.

Fault Detection and Exclusion (FDE)

[Aeronautical Information Manual ¶1-1-17.a.3.(a)] In order for RAIM to determine if a satellite is providing corrupted information, at least one satellite, in addition to those required for navigation, must be in view for the receiver to perform the RAIM function. RAIM requires a minimum of 5 satellites, or 4 satellites and barometric altimeter input (baro–aiding), to detect an integrity anomaly. Baro–aiding is a method of augmenting the GPS integrity solution by using a non-satellite input source in lieu of the fifth satellite. Some GPS receivers also have a RAIM capability, called fault detection and exclusion (FDE), that excludes a failed satellite from the position solution; GPS receivers capable of FDE require 6 satellites or 5 satellites with baro–aiding. This allows the GPS receiver to isolate the corrupt satellite signal, remove it from the position solution, and still provide an integrity-assured position. To ensure that baro–aiding is available, enter the current altimeter setting into the receiver as described in the operating manual. Do not use the GPS derived altitude due to the large GPS vertical errors that will make the integrity monitoring function invalid.

Availability / NOTAMS

[Aeronautical Information Manual, §1-1-17, ¶a.2.(a)] The status of GPS satellites is broadcast as part of the data message transmitted by the GPS satellites. GPS status information is also available by means of the U.S. Coast Guard navigation information service: (703) 313–5907, Internet: http://www.navcen.uscg.gov/. Additionally, satellite status is available through the Notice to Airmen (NOTAM) system.

Satellite-Based Augmentation System (SBAS)

[AC 20-138D, ¶1-4.f.(2)(b)] The acronyms 'SBAS' and 'GBAS' are the respective international designations for satellite-based and ground-based augmentation systems complying with the International Civil Aviation Organization (ICAO) standards and recommended practices (SARPs). Several countries have implemented their own versions of 'SBAS' and 'GBAS' that have specific names and acronyms. For example, WAAS is the U.S. implementation of an 'SBAS' while EGNOS is the European implementation.

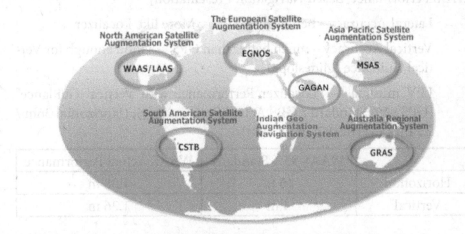

Figure: SBAS, from AFAIS PBN Presentation

Wide Area Augmentation System (WAAS)

The U.S. implementation of SBAS is WAAS. The U.S. system is compatible with the European (EGNOS) and Asia Pacific (MSAS) systems.

[AC 90-107 ¶6.b.] WAAS improves the accuracy, integrity, availability and continuity of GPS signals. Additionally, the WAAS geostationary satellites provide ranging sources to supplement the GPS signals. If there are no airworthiness limitations on other installed navigation equipment, WAAS avionics enable aircraft navigation during all phases of flight from takeoff through vertically guided approaches and guided missed approaches. WAAS avionics with an appropriate airworthiness approval can enable aircraft to fly to the LPV, LP, LNAV/VNAV and LNAV lines of minima on RNAV (GPS) approaches. One of the major improvements WAAS provides is the ability to generate glide path guidance independent of ground equipment. Temperature and pressure extremes do not affect WAAS vertical guidance unlike when baro-VNAV is used to fly to LNAV/VNAV line of minima. However, like most other navigation services, the WAAS network has service volume limits, and some airports on the fringe of WAAS coverage may experience reduced availability of WAAS vertical guidance. When a pilot selects an approach procedure, WAAS avionics display the best level of service supported by the combination of the WAAS signal-in-space, the aircraft avionics, and the selected RNAV (GPS) instrument approach.

Accuracy

[AFAIS Performance-Based Navigation Presentation]

a.   Lateral Accuracy - better than GPS — More like Localizer

b.   Vertical Accuracy – much better than GPS — Good enough for Vertical Guidance (glideslope)

c.   LPV minima — "Localizer Performance with Vertical Guidance" (GPS 95% Standard / GPS Actual Performance), (Horizontal 36m / 2.74m), (Vertical 77m / 3.89m)

	WAAS 95% Standard	WAAS Actual Performance
Horizontal	16 m	1.08 m
Vertical	4 m	1.26 m

Chapter 1

Area Navigation (RNAV)

So what is area navigation (RNAV), when you get right down to it? It started out as pilots flying with basic compass cards and doing fix-to-fix navigation and ended with global navigation satellites making everything much easier. RNAV airspace generally mandates a certain level of equipment and assumes you have a 95% chance of keeping to a stated level of navigation accuracy. Unlike Required Navigation Performance (RNP) standards, in the next chapter, RNAV will not alert you when there is a problem.

Examples of RNAV airspace include B-BRAV, P-RNAV, and the RNAV 1 and RNAV 2 routes found in the United States. MNPS is not exactly RNAV airspace, but is often thought of as just that. RNP-10, despite the name, is RNAV airspace. It can be confusing.

The Big Picture

[AC 90-100A, ¶4.b.] Area Navigation (RNAV). A method of navigation which permits aircraft operation on any desired flight path within the coverage of station-referenced navigation aids or within the limits of the capability of self-contained aids, or a combination of these.

[ICAO Doc 9613, pg. I-(iii)] RNAV and RNP systems evolved in a manner similar to conventional ground-based routes and procedures. A specific RNAV or RNP system was identified and its performance was evaluated through a combination of analysis and flight testing. For domestic operations, the initial systems used VOR and DME for estimating their position; for oceanic operations, INS were employed. These "new" systems were developed, evaluated and certified. Airspace and obstacle clearance criteria were developed based on the performance of available equipment; and specifications for requirements were based on available capabilities. In some cases, it was necessary to identify the individual models of equipment that could be operated within the airspace concerned.

In the old days we would navigate IFR from navaid to navaid and when we had to, we would fly fix-to-fix by mentally visualizing the airspace and estimating a course to fly. Then various boxes appeared that did this better than we could and "area navigation" was born. It is simply a method of navigation that allows us to fly along any desired flight path.

Equipment Requirements

RNAV routes typically specify minimum equipment levels needed to satisfy navigation accuracy. For example:

[AC 90-100A, ¶8.b.] U.S. RNAV operations are based upon the use of RNAV equipment that automatically determines aircraft position in the horizontal plane using inputs from the following types of positioning sensors (no specific priority).

(1) Global Navigation Satellite System (GNSS) in accordance with TSO-C145a, TSO-C146a, and TSO-C129/C129a. Positioning data from other types of navigation sensors may be integrated with the GNSS data provided it does not cause position errors exceeding the total system error requirements. The use of GPS equipment approved to TSO-C129() is limited to those which include the minimum system functions specified in Appendix 3. As a minimum, integrity should be provided by ABAS [Aircraft-Based Augmentation System]. In addition, GPS stand-alone equipment should include the following additional functions:

- Pseudorange step detection
- Health word checking

For procedures requiring GPS and/or aircraft approvals requiring GPS, if the navigation system does not automatically alert the flight crew of a loss of GPS, the operator must develop procedures to verify correct GPS operation.

(2) DME/DME RNAV equipment complying with the criteria in appendix 1. Based on current DME availability evaluations, coverage is not sufficient to support DME/DME RNAV operations without additional IRU augmen-

tation or using GPS.

(3) DME/DME/IRU RNAV equipment complying with the criteria in appendix 2.

An example of a suitable Aircraft-Based Augmentation System (ABAS) is receiver autonomous integrity monitoring (RAIM).

Total System Error

Total System Error (TSE) is simply a measure of how far off course the airplane can be. In RNP-1 or RNAV-1 airspace, for example, the TSE = 1. Is RNP more accurate than RNAV? No.

[AC 20-138D, ¶1-4.g.(2)]

RNAV systems conform to the ICAO performance-based navigation specification for total system error (TSE). RNAV total system error is the 95% probability that the navigation system accuracy remains within the limits defined for the RNAV operation. For example, during an RNAV-1 operation the TSE remains within one nautical mile of the desired path 95% of the time.

Looking at the figure, you see that RNAV-1 keeps the aircraft within 1 nautical mile of centerline 95% of the flight time.

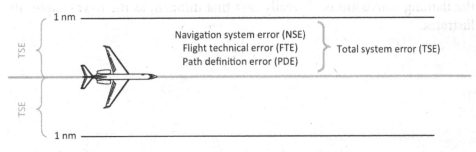

RNAV: Aircraft remains within Total System Error (ex: +/- 1 nm) for 95% of flight time

RNAV 1   *Idea is the same for RNAV 2, RNAV 5, etc.*

RNAV Airspace

Basic Area Navigation (B-RNAV) — *± 5 nm for 95% of flight time, will eventually be replaced but remains a requirement in European Civil Aviation Conference member States.*

Precision Area Navigation (P-RNAV) — *+/- 1 nm for 95% of flight time, will eventually be replaced but remains a requirement in many parts of the world.*

Required Navigation Performance-10 (RNP-10) — *+/- 10 nm for 95% of the flight flight; despite the name, RNP-10 is an RNAV system without performance monitoring and alert capability. The ICAO elected to retain "RNP-10" when in fact it should be "RNAV-10" because many areas of the world adopted "RNP-10" before the RNP specification was made. The affected regions complained it would be too costly to change all the manuals and charts, so the ICAO made this exception.*

RNAV-1 and RNAV-2

[90 AC-100A, ¶4.b.] For the purposes of this AC, the specified RNAV accuracy must be met 95% of the flight time.

- RNAV 1 requires a total system error of not more than 1 nm for 95% of the total flight time.

- RNAV 2 requires a total system error of not more than 2 nm for 95% of the total flight time.

The line between what is RNAV airspace and what is more properly called Required Navigation Performance (RNP) airspace gets blurred because of the naming conventions. It really isn't that difficult, as the next chapter illustrates.

Chapter 2

Required Navigation Performance (RNP)

*W*hich is better: RNAV or RNP? Because the equipment requirements tend to be higher and the certification rules are certainly stricter, we tend to think of Required Navigation Performance (RNP) as the higher standard. But which is more accurate? Their accuracy standards are the same. Surprised? The key difference is that RNP includes the concept of containment.

The Big Picture

[ICAO Doc 9613, pg. I-(iii)]

- Performance-based navigation (PBN). The PBN concept specifies that aircraft RNAV system performance requirements be defined in terms of the accuracy, integrity, availability, continuity and functionality, which are needed for the proposed operations in the context of a particular airspace concept. The PBN concept represents a shift from sensor-based to performance-based navigation. Performance requirements are identified in navigation specifications, which also identify the choice of navigation sensors and equipment that may be used to meet the performance requirements. These navigation specifications are defined at a sufficient level of detail to facilitate global harmonization by providing specific implementation guidance for States and operators.

- Under PBN, generic navigation requirements are defined based on operational requirements. Operators then evaluate options in respect of available technology and navigation services, which could allow the requirements to be met. An operator thereby has the opportunity to select a more cost-effective option, rather than a solution being imposed as part of the operational requirements. Technology can evolve over time without requiring the operation itself to be reviewed, as long as the expected performance is provided by the RNAV system. As part of the future work of ICAO, it is anticipated that other means for meeting the requirements of the navigation specifications will be evaluated and may be included in the applicable navigation specifications, as appropriate.

Performance based navigation incorporates RNAV and adds the ability to continuously monitor the accuracy and utility of the system, alerting the pilot when the system isn't as good as it is supposed to be.

Equipment Requirements

True RNP, that using Performance Based Navigation, does not specify equipment but may require more than just navigation capability:

[ICAO Doc 9613, page I-(iii)]

PBN offers a number of advantages over the sensor-specific method of developing airspace and obstacle clearance criteria, i.e.:

- reduces the need to maintain sensor-specific routes and procedures, and their associated costs;
- avoids the need for developing sensor-specific operations with each new evolution of navigation systems, which would be cost-prohibitive;
- allows for more efficient use of airspace (route placement, fuel efficiency and noise abatement);
- clarifies how RNAV systems are used; and
- facilitates the operational approval process for operators by providing a limited set of navigation specifications intended for global use.

Within an airspace concept, PBN requirements will be affected by the communication, surveillance and ATM environments, the navaid infrastructure, and the functional and operational capabilities needed to meet the ATM application. PBN performance requirements also depend on what reversionary, non-RNAV means of navigation are available and what degree of redundancy is required to ensure adequate continuity of functions.

Total System Error

Total System Error (TSE) is simply a measure of how far off course the airplane can be. In RNP-1 or RNAV-1 airspace, for example, the TSE = 1. Is RNP more accurate than RNAV? No.

[AC 20-138D, ¶1-4.g.(2)]

- RNAV systems conform to the ICAO performance-based navigation specification for total system error (TSE). RNAV total system error is the 95% probability that the navigation system accuracy remains within the limits defined for the RNAV operation. For example, during an RNAV-1 operation the TSE remains within one nautical mile of the desired path 95% of the time.

- RNP systems conform to a performance-based navigation specification based on RNAV capability that also includes requirements for on-board performance monitoring and alerting. For example, during an RNP 1.0 operation, the TSE remains within one nautical mile of the desired path 95% of the time, and on-board performance monitoring provides the pilot with an alert when the probability that TSE exceeds 2xRNP is greater than 10^{-5}.

- RNP is an RNAV subset that also includes a requirement to provide on-board navigation system accuracy performance monitoring and alerting which means an RNP system is also an RNAV system. GNSS equipment provides accuracy performance monitoring and alerting which, by definition, makes it both an RNAV and RNP capable system.

Both RNAV-1 and RNP-1 keep the aircraft within 1 nautical mile of centerline 95% of the flight time. The difference is that under RNP-1, the pilot is notified when the system thinks there is a greater than 0.00001 probability (.001%) that the airplane could wander outside of 2 nautical miles.

- *RNAV says you should be on course,*

- *RNP says you should be on course, monitors system performance, and alerts you when it thinks there is a problem.*

Containment

So what makes RNP different than RNAV?

Let's first look at what makes them the same:

- *The system defines navigation accuracy as being able to stay within the total system error at least 95% of the total flight time. This applies to BOTH RNAV and RNP.*

- *In our example, with RNAV-1 or RNP-1, the airplane will be within 1 nautical mile 95% of the flight time.*

The following applies ONLY to RNP

- *The system considers itself adequately contained as long as the probability of the airplane being inside an area twice the total system error value at least 99.999% of the time. The regulations seem to confuse the term "containment" as either the 95% navigation accuracy limit or the 99.999% alert limit.*

- *Regardless of terminology, remember that twice the stated number is where the airplane will be 99.999% of the time before issuing an alert.*

- *In our example, with RNP-1, the airplane will alert the pilot if there is greater than a 0.001% chance the airplane could be more than 2 nautical miles off course.*

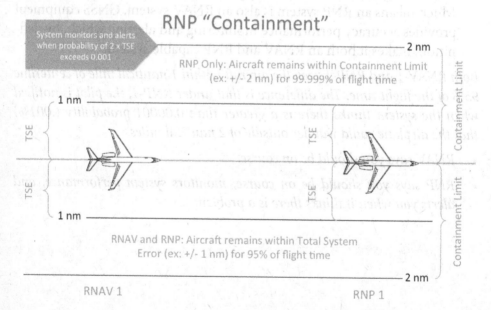

RNP "Containment"

System monitors and alerts when probability of 2 x TSE exceeds 0.001

RNP Only: Aircraft remains within Containment Limit (ex: +/- 2 nm) for 99.999% of flight time

RNAV and RNP: Aircraft remains within Total System Error (ex: +/- 1 nm) for 95% of flight time

RNAV 1   RNP 1

[ICAO Doc 9613, §II-A-2-4, ¶2.3.7] The PBN concept uses the term on-board performance monitoring and alerting instead of the term containment. This is to avoid confusion between existing uses of containment in various documents by different areas of expertise. For example:

a.   "Containment" refers to the region within which the aircraft will remain 95 percent of the time. The associated terms have been "containment value" and "containment distance" and the related airspace protection on either side of an RNAV ATS route.

b.   Within the industry standards of RTCA/DO-236 and EUROCAE/ED-75, "containment" refers to the region that the aircraft will remain when there is no alert (0.99999 probability), and defines a requirement for how often an alert occurs (0.9999). The associated terms are "containment limit," "containment integrity," "containment continuity," and "containment region."

c.   Within PANS-OPS material, "containment" has referred to the region used to define the obstacle clearance, and the aircraft is expected to remain within or above that surface (regardless of alerting) with very high probability. The associated terms have been "containment area," "airspace containment," "obstacle clearance containment," and related obstacle protection areas.

[ICAO Doc 9613, §II-A-2-4, ¶2.3.8] The previous ICAO expressions of "containment value" and "containment distance" have been replaced by the navigation accuracy of TSE.

RNP Airspace

Required Navigation Performance-4 (RNP-4) — ±4 nm for 95% of flight time plus integrity, continuity, performance and alerting requirements. Intended for oceanic and remote operations.

There is more to RNP than navigation accuracy, it may also require specific communications and surveillance capabilities such as CPDLC and ADS-C.

GNSS and RNAV (or) RNP

[AC 20-138D, ¶5-1.a.] There have been questions on whether GNSS is an RNAV or RNP system. The answer is GNSS is both an RNAV and RNP system because RNP is a subset of RNAV that also includes a requirement to provide on-board navigation system accuracy performance monitoring and alerting. Therefore, an RNP system is also capable of RNAV. GNSS equipment provides accuracy performance monitoring and alerting which, by definition, makes it an RNP-capable system.

Comparisons

Criteria	B-RNAV (aka RNAV 5)	NAT HLA	P-RNAV (aka RNAV 1)	RNAV 1	RNAV 2	RNP-4	RNP-10
Location	Europe en route arrival	Atlantic Caribbean * Parts of Canada *	Europe * en route arrival approach departure	U.S. en route arrival approach departure	U.S. en route arrival departure	Asia * Pacific * oceanic remote	Worldwide * oceanic remote
Accuracy	+/- 5 nm 95% time	6.3 nm lateral *	+/- 1 nm 95% time	+/- 1 nm 95% time	+/- 2 nm 95% time	+/- 4 nm 95% time	+/- 10 nm 95% time
Performance	N/A	N/A	N/A	N/A	N/A	Integrity Continuity Monitoring Alert	N/A
Aircraft Apvl	AFM Statement	State Apvl *	AC 90-96A JAA TGL-10	AFM Statement	AFM Statement	AFM * STC *	AFM
Operator Apvl (91)	None Req.	LOA	LOA	None Req.	None Req.	LOA	LOA
Operator Apvl (Commercial)	B034	B039	B034	B035	B035	B036	B036
Regulatory	AC 90-96A	ICAO Doc 7030 FAA Order 8900	AC 90-96A	AC 90-100A	AC 90-100A	ICAO Doc 7030 FAA Order 8900	ICAO Doc 7030 FAA Order 8900

* Note: the table simplifies various items; for a more complete explanation, see the regulatory references.

LOAs:

NAT HLA: B039

P-RNAV: B034, though some FSDOs say it is no longer needed

RNP-4: B036

RNP-10: B036

Chapter 3

Future Air Navigation System (FANS)

I was a staff officer at the Pentagon when I first heard about FANS and thought it was madness. It was envisioned as a system that completely revolutionized communications, navigation, and surveillance when flying anywhere in the world and, in 1992, it sounded like science fiction. Three years later the Boeing Aircraft Company came up with a way to do the communications part and that became FANS-1. A few years later Airbus did their version and that was known as FANS-A. Now we have a few variants but they are basically called FANS-1/A and you must have FANS-1/A to fly in some parts of the world. So what is FANS-1/A?

It is basically nothing more than a CPDLC system that uses the ICAO Aeronautical Telecommunications Network (ATN) over Satcom or VHF and Automatic Dependent Surveillance – Contract (ADS-C) as specified by the ICAO.

Definition

[ICAO Doc 10037, table 1-1]

- FANS 1/A — Initial future air navigation system (FANS 1/A) ATS applications, AFN, CPDLC and ADS-C, supported by FANS 1/A over ACARS. Note.— FANS 1/A typically involve communication (CPDLC), navigation (RNAV/RNP) and surveillance (ADS-C). This document refers to the FANS 1/A for the data link system, which includes the CPDLC and ADS-C applications. Refer to Doc 9613 for guidance material on navigation (RNAV/RNP) qualification and use.

- FANS 1/A+ — Same as FANS 1/A, except with additional features, such as the message latency monitor function, described in DO-258A/ED-100A, 4.6.6.9.

- FANS 1/A ADS-C — ATS applications, AFN and ADS-C, supported by

FANS 1/A over ACARS. FANS 1/A ADS-C - complies with AFN and ADS-C applications, No CPDLC.

- ATN B1 — ATS applications, CM and CPDLC, supported by aeronautical telecommunication network – baseline 1 (ATN B1): a) Context management (CM) application for data link initiation capability (DLIC); b) CPDLC for ATC communications management (ACM), ATC clearance (ACL), and ATC microphone check (AMC), except that: 1) CONFIRM ASSIGNED LEVEL and SYSU-5 USE OF LOGICAL ACKNOWLEDGEMENT PROHIBITED will not be used by the ATSU; and 2) ASSIGNED LEVEL (level) is not required by the aircraft. Note.— Interoperability for departure clearance (DCL), downstream clearance (DSC), data link – automatic terminal information service (D-ATIS), and flight plan consistency (FLIPCY) data link services, which are defined in DO-280B/ED-110B, are not supported.

- FANS 1/A –ATN B1 — Enables the use of CPDLC along a route of flight where data link services are provided by FANS 1/A technology in some airspaces and ATN B1 in other airspaces.

FANS mandates were a big deal about ten years ago, with everyone fretting on how they were going to comply. Most of the mandatory dates have come to pass and you will be denied some airspace throughout the world if you are not FANS compliant. But you hardly ever see that terminology any more. The mandatory requirements are given for CPDLC and ADS-C. Some parts of Europe require ATN B1 for data link and having any version of FANS that doesn't include ATN B1 will exclude you from data link.

For more about the two parts of FANS, see:

Section IV, Chapter 5 - Controller-Pilot Data Link Communications (CPDLC)

Section V, Chapter 3 - Automatic Dependent Surveillance - Contract (ADS-C)

Chapter 4

Performance Based Navigation

*T*he *Performance-Based Navigation (PBN) system is a concept of how we*
ensure our aircraft are where we say they are, when we say they are. The
designation is mostly consistent, but not completely. How you qualify and how
you prove your qualification is pretty much up to the State. But that approval
isn't listed as "PBN" but as the individual levels of compliance, i.e., RNP-4.

The Concept

[ICAO Doc 9613, p. I-(iii)]

- The PBN concept specifies that aircraft RNAV and RNP system performance requirements be defined in terms of the accuracy, integrity,
continuity and functionality, which are needed for the proposed operations in the context of a particular airspace concept. The PBN concept
represents a shift from sensor-based to PBN. Performance requirements
are identified in navigation specifications, which also identify the choice
of navigation sensors and equipment that may be used to meet the performance requirements. These navigation specifications are defined at a
sufficient level of detail to facilitate global harmonization by providing
specific implementation guidance for States and operators.

- Under PBN, generic navigation requirements are defined based on operational requirements. Operators then evaluate options in respect of
available technology and navigation services, which could allow the requirements to be met. Technology can evolve over time without requiring the operation itself to be reviewed, as long as the expected performance is provided by the RNAV or RNP system.

This isn't to say PBN systems cannot use a particular type of sensor, only that
the sensor isn't the defining characteristic of the specification. An acceptable
solution could be GPS-based or even DME/DME-based. But approval for that
solution for the specification depends on more than just what sensor is used.

The Navigation Specification

[ICAO Doc 9613, ¶1.2.] The navigation specification is used by a State as a basis for the development of their material for airworthiness and operational approval. A navigation specification details the performance required of the RNAV system in terms of accuracy, integrity, availability and continuity; which navigation functionalities the RNAV system must have; which navigation sensors must be integrated into the RNAV system; and which requirements are placed on the flight crew.

[ICAO Doc 9613, ¶1.2.3.1] On-board performance monitoring and alerting is the main element that determines if the navigation system complies with the necessary safety level associated to an RNP application; it relates to both lateral and longitudinal navigation performance; and it allows the aircrew to detect that the navigation system is not achieving, or cannot guarantee with 10–5 integrity, the navigation performance required for the operation.

The 10^{-5} integrity is the 0.9999 probability concept. The monitoring and alerting is the key component of a PBN specification.

[ICAO Doc 9613, ¶1.2.4.1] Both RNAV and RNP specifications include requirements for certain navigation functionalities. At the basic level, these functional requirements may include:

a. continuous indication of aircraft position relative to track to be displayed to the pilot flying on a navigation display situated in his primary field of view;

b. display of distance and bearing to the active (To) waypoint;

c. display of ground speed or time to the active (To) waypoint;

d. navigation data storage function; and

e. appropriate failure indication of the RNAV system, including the sensors.

[ICAO Doc 9613, ¶1.2.5]

For oceanic, remote, en-route and terminal operations, an RNP specification is designated as RNP X, e.g. RNP 4. An RNAV specification is designated as RNAV X, e.g. RNAV 1. If two navigation specifications share the same value for X, they may be distinguished by use of a prefix.

For both RNP and RNAV designations, the expression "X" (where stated) refers to the lateral navigation accuracy in nautical miles, which is expected to be achieved at least 95 per cent of the flight time by the population of aircraft operating within the airspace, route or procedure.

Approach navigation specifications cover all segments of the instrument approach. RNP specifications are designated using RNP as a prefix and an abbreviated textual suffix, e.g. RNP APCH or RNP AR APCH. There are no RNAV approach specifications.

Because functional and performance requirements are defined for each navigation specification, an aircraft approved for an RNP specification is not automatically approved for all RNAV specifications. Similarly, an aircraft approved for an RNP or RNAV specification having a stringent accuracy requirement (e.g. RNP 0.3 specification) is not automatically approved for a navigation specification having a less stringent accuracy requirement (e.g. RNP 4).

If your airplane is approved for RNP 0.3 and RNP 10, you might think RNP 4 is automatically included. But it isn't. RNP 0.3 does not have the same communications and surveillance requirements of RNP 4, specifically CPDLC and ADS-C. RNP 10 isn't a PBN specification at all. So you cannot infer you are RNP 4 qualified.

If you have an RNP 4 qualification you are good to go for RNP 10. In fact, if you had an LOA that said RNP 10 and got approval for RNP 4, the RNP 10 disappears. Be careful about RNP 4. Some U.S. FSDOs are granting RNP 4 LOAs based on the mistaken notion that aircraft with P-RNAV approval are more accurate than RNP 4. That might be true and it will work in the Caribbean. But it won't work in the rest of the world where RNP 4 also requires CPDLC and ADS-C.

- The existing RNP 10 designation is inconsistent with PBN RNP and RNAV specifications. RNP 10 does not include requirements for on-board performance monitoring and alerting. For purposes of consistency with the PBN concept, RNP 10 is referred to as RNAV 10 in this manual. Renaming current RNP 10 routes, operational approvals, etc., to an RNAV 10 designation would be an extensive and expensive task, which is not cost-effective. Consequently, any existing or new operational approvals will continue to be designated RNP 10, and any charting annotations will be depicted as RNP 10.

Airworthiness Approval

[ICAO Doc 9613, ¶3.4.2]

- The airworthiness approval process assures that each item of the RNAV equipment installed is of a type and design appropriate to its intended function and that the installation functions properly under foreseeable operating conditions. Additionally, the airworthiness approval process identifies any installation limitations that need to be considered for operational approval. Such limitations and other information relevant to the approval of the RNAV system installation are documented in the AFM, or AFM Supplement, as applicable. Information may also be repeated and expanded upon in other documents such as pilot operating handbooks or flight crew operating manuals. The airworthiness approval process is well established among States of the Operators and this process refers to the intended function of the navigation specification to be applied.

- Approval of RNAV systems for RNAV-X operations. The RNAV system installed should be compliant with a set of basic performance requirements as described in the navigation specification, which defines accuracy, integrity and continuity criteria. It should also be compliant with a set of specific functional requirements, have a navigation database, and support each specific path terminator as required by the navigation specification.

- Approval of RNP systems for RNP operations. Aircraft must be equipped with an RNP system able to support the desired navigation application, including the on-board performance monitoring and alerting function. It should also be compliant with a set of specific functional requirements, have a navigation database, and should support each specific path terminator as required by the navigation specification.

- *You do not get approved for PBN, rather you get approved for each specification, such as for RNP-4.*

Chapter 5

Class A through Class G Airspace

*T*he U.S. airspace classification method changed many years back to more closely align with the International Civil Aviation Organization (ICAO). They are close but not exact.

[ICAO Annex 11, Air Traffic Services §2.6.1] ATS airspaces shall be classified and designated in accordance with the following:

- Class A. IFR flights only are permitted, all flights are provided with air traffic control service and are separated from each other.

- Class B. IFR and VFR flights are permitted, all flights are provided with air traffic control service and are separated from each other.

- Class C. IFR and VFR flights are permitted, all flights are provided with air traffic control service and IFR flights are separated from other IFR flights and from VFR flights. VFR flights are separated from IFR flights and receive traffic information in respect of other VFR flights.

- Class D. IFR and VFR flights are permitted and all flights are provided with air traffic control service, IFR flights are separated from other IFR flights and receive traffic information in respect of VFR flights, VFR flights receive traffic information in respect of all other flights.

- Class E. IFR and VFR flights are permitted, IFR flights are provided with air traffic control service and are separated from other IFR flights. All flights receive traffic information as far as is practical. Class E shall not be used for control zones.

- Class F. IFR and VFR flights are permitted, all participating IFR flights receive an air traffic advisory service and all flights receive flight information service if requested.

Note.— Where air traffic advisory service is implemented, this is considered normally as a temporary measure only until such time as it can be replaced by air traffic control. (See also PANS-ATM, Chapter 9.)

Section III - Navigate

- Class G. IFR and VFR flights are permitted and receive flight information service if requested.

Class	Type of flight	Separation provided	Service provided	Speed limitation*	Radio communication requirement	Subject to an ATC clearance
A	IFR only	All aircraft	Air traffic control service	Not applicable	Continuous two-way	Yes
B	IFR	All aircraft	Air traffic control service	Not applicable	Continuous two-way	Yes
	VFR	All aircraft	Air traffic control service	Not applicable	Continuous two-way	Yes
C	IFR	IFR from IFR IFR from VFR	Air traffic control service	Not applicable	Continuous two-way	Yes
	VFR	VFR from IFR	1) Air traffic control service for separation from IFR; 2) VFR/VFR traffic information (and traffic avoidance advice on request)	250 kt IAS below 3 050 m (10 000 ft) AMSL	Continuous two-way	Yes
D	IFR	IFR from IFR	Air traffic control service, traffic information about VFR flights (and traffic avoidance advice on request)	250 kt IAS below 3 050 m (10 000 ft) AMSL	Continuous two-way	Yes
	VFR	Nil	IFR/VFR and VFR/VFR traffic information (and traffic avoidance advice on request)	250 kt IAS below 3 050 m (10 000 ft) AMSL	Continuous two-way	Yes
E	IFR	IFR from IFR	Air traffic control service and, as far as practical, traffic information about VFR flights	250 kt IAS below 3 050 m (10 000 ft) AMSL	Continuous two-way	Yes
	VFR	Nil	Traffic information as far as practical	250 kt IAS below 3 050 m (10 000 ft) AMSL	No	No
F	IFR	IFR from IFR as far as practical	Air traffic advisory service; flight information service	250 kt IAS below 3 050 m (10 000 ft) AMSL	Continuous two-way	No
	VFR	Nil	Flight information service	250 kt IAS below 3 050 m (10 000 ft) AMSL	No	No
G	IFR	Nil	Flight information service	250 kt IAS below 3 050 m (10 000 ft) AMSL	Continuous two-way	No
	VFR	Nil	Flight information service	250 kt IAS below 3 050 m (10 000 ft) AMSL	No	No

* When the height of the transition altitude is lower than 3 050 m (10 000 ft) AMSL, FL 100 should be used in lieu of 10 000 ft.

Figure: Airspace Classification, from ICAO Annex 11, Air Traffic Services, Appendix 4

124

Chapter 6

Basic Area Navigation (B-RNAV)

*I*n the days before Performance Based Navigation (PBN), countries would specify a track keeping accuracy needed to fly a route and you would certify that you had the equipment to do just that. The standard was "sensor based." PBN systems must be able to monitor their own performance and alert the crew when there are problems. B-RNAV comes from before PBN but is still in use in parts of Europe; you need to have it if you fly there. Under 14 CFR 91 you will need an AFM statement, under 14 CFR 135 you will need OpSpec B034.

Location

Europe

The problem with ICAO Doc 7030 is they set out to give us a regional differences document but they haven't updated it in over ten years. So it tells us we need to have B-RNAV, though many of these areas have moved on to PBN standards.

[ICAO Doc 7030, §EUR, ¶4.1.1.5.2] Precision RNAV (P-RNAV) and basic RNAV (B-RNAV)

4.1.1.5.2.1 The provisions in respect of en-route operations, as specified in 4.1.1.5.2.6 and 4.1.1.5.2.7, shall apply to all such operations conducted under IFR on the entire ATS route network as notified by the appropriate authorities in the following flight information regions (FIRs)/upper flight information regions (UIRs):

Amsterdam, Ankara, Athinai, Barcelona, Berlin, Bodø, Bordeaux, Bratislava, Bremen, Brest, Brindisi, Bruxelles, Bucuresti, Budapest, Canarias (AFI area of applicability), Casablanca, Chisinau, Düsseldorf, France, Frankfurt, Hannover, Istanbul, Kharkiv, København, Kyiv, Lisboa, Ljubljana, London, L'viv, Madrid, Malta, Marseille, Milano, München, Nicosia, Odessa, Oslo, Paris, Praha, Reims, Rhein, Riga, Roma, Rovaniemi, Scottish, Shannon, Simferopol, Skopje, Sofia, Stavanger, Sweden, Switzerland, Tallinn, Tampere, Tbilisi, Tirana, Trondheim, Tunis (FL 245 and above), Varna, Vilnius, Warszawa, Wien, Yerevan, Zagreb.

4.1.1.5.2.6 Only aircraft approved for B-RNAV operations may plan for operations under IFR on the ATS routes of the FIRs/UIRs identified in 4.1.1.5.2.1. Aircraft not equipped with RNAV but having a navigation accuracy meeting RNP 5 will be restricted to operations on ATS routes which States may designate within their lower airspace in accordance with 4.1.1.5.2.7.

4.1.1.5.2.7 Until such time as VOR facilities cease to be available, the carriage of a single RNAV system not meeting an average continuity of service of 99.99 percent of flight time may be approved for B-RNAV operations if the aircraft is also carrying VOR and distance-measuring equipment (DME) equipment.

Accuracy / Performance Standards

Accuracy

[AC 90-96A, ¶4.b.] Basic Area Navigation (B-RNAV). B-RNAV is defined as RNAV that meets a track keeping accuracy equal to or better than ±5 nm for 95 percent of the flight time. This value includes signal source error, airborne receiver error, display system error, and flight technical error. This navigation performance assumes the necessary coverage provided by satellite or ground-based navigation aids is available for the intended operation.

Accuracy versus Performance

[ICAO Doc 9613 ¶1.1.1.1] The PBN concept specifies that aircraft RNAV or RNP system performance requirements be defined in terms of accuracy, integrity, continuity and functionality required for the proposed operations in the context of a particular airspace concept, when supported by the appropriate NAVAID infrastructure. Compliance with WGS 84 and data quality prescribed in Annex 15 are integral to PBN.

[ICAO Doc 9613 ¶1.2.3.1] On-board performance monitoring and alerting is the main element that determines if the navigation system complies with the necessary safety level associated to an RNP application; it relates to both lateral and longitudinal navigation performance; and it allows the aircrew to detect that the navigation system is not achieving, or cannot guarantee with 10–5 integrity, the navigation performance required for the operation.

What we have grown up with, accuracy standards, specify what it takes to fly the airspace in question and permit properly equipped aircraft and trained crews to fly there. Performance Based Navigation, on the other hand, mandates a performance standard that includes navigation accuracy but also includes other parameters, such as the ability to self monitor and alert the crew of integrity issues.

B-RNAV is an accuracy standard that lives in a middle ground, as the PBN manual states:

[ICAO Doc 9613 ¶1.2.5.5.2] In the past, the United States and member States of the European Civil Aviation Conference (ECAC) used regional RNAV specifications with different designators. The ECAC applications (P-RNAV and B-RNAV) will continue to be used only within those States. Over time, ECAC RNAV applications will migrate towards the international navigation specifications of RNAV 1 and RNAV 5. The United States migrated from the USRNAV Types A and B to the RNAV 1 specification in March 2007.

Documentation / Certification

Aircraft System Eligibility

[AC 90-96A, Appendix 1 ¶1.b.(1)] The aircraft should be considered eligible for B-RNAV operations, if the AFM or POH shows the appropriate instrument flight rules (IFR) navigation system installation has received airworthiness approval in accordance with this advisory circular (AC) or with one of the following Federal Aviation Administration (FAA) ACs: AC 90-45A, AC 20-121A, AC 20-130, AC 20-138, or AC 25-15.

Part 91 Aircraft/Operator Approval

[AC 90-96A, Appendix 1 ¶1.b.(2)] U.S. part 91 operators should review their AFM or POH to ensure aircraft system eligibility as detailed in Appendix 1, paragraph 1b(1). Once aircraft system eligibility has been established, the operator should take steps to ensure B-RNAV operations are conducted in accordance with the guidance contained in Appendix 1, paragraph 1d, 2, 3, and 4, as well as any other established operational or airspace requirements. Operators must ensure the required functions of Appendix 1 are met. Once these actions are completed, the operator may begin to conduct B-RNAV operations. A letter of authorization (LOA) is not required when eligibility is based on the AFM or POH. See Appendix 1, paragraph 1c, for actions to take if the operator is unable to determine from the AFM or POH whether the aircraft system has been approved and installed in accordance with an appropriate FAA AC.

LOA B034 (B-RNAV and P-RNAV operations) is no longer required or offered for Part 91 operators. I am told that no action is required for operators who already have an approved B034 but they are encouraged to get LOA C063, if they have not already done so. LOA C063 authorizes RNAV-1 and RNP-1 and serves as a partial replacement for B034 in airspaces where still required.

U.S. Air Carrier Aircraft/Commercial Operator Approval

[AC 90-96A, Appendix 1 ¶1.b.(3)] Part 121, 125, or 135 operators should present the following documentation to their certificate-holding district office (CHDO): sections of the AFM that document airworthiness approval in accordance with an appropriate FAA AC as detailed in Appendix 1, paragraph 1b(1) and training and operations manuals that reflect the operating policies of Appendix 1, paragraph 1d, 2, 3, 4 as well as any other operational or airspace requirements established by European authorities. Operators must ensure the required functions of Appendix 1 are met.

[FAA Order 8900.1, Vol 3, Chapter 18, OPSEC B034, ¶B.] B034 also authorizes an operator to conduct IFR operations in designated European Basic RNAV (B-RNAV) and European Precision RNAV (P-RNAV) airspace.

If your AFM or POH has the necessary statement, you have what you need to apply for OpSpec B034 under 14 CFR 135. Otherwise, there are other means listed in AC 90-96A to get approval.

Chapter 7

North Atlantic High Level Airspace (NAT HLA)

All of us who fly the North Atlantic for a living are in a continuing battle to keep up with the changing requirements. The North Atlantic System Planning Group (NAT SPG) does an excellent job of publishing the rules of the airspace in ICAO Nat Doc 007, their airspace manual. The problem is that it is 177 pages and there are a lot of ops bulletins out there to keep track of. I think the easiest way to keep abreast of life in the North Atlantic High Level Airspace (NAT HLA) is to subscribe to Ops.Group. Nobody does a better job of keeping this complicated airspace understandable. They approach this from the standpoint of "What I've got" versus "What I don't have" and translate that to "Where can I go?" I think that works very well, so I'll copy them and add specific references.

Location

[ICAO NAT Doc 007 § 1.1.1] NAT HLA is that volume of airspace between flight level (FL) 285 and FL 420 within the oceanic control areas of Bodo Oceanic, Gander Oceanic, New York Oceanic East, Reykjavik, Santa Maria and Shanwick, excluding the Shannon and Brest Ocean Transition Areas. State approvals for NAT MNPSA operations granted prior to that date will be valid for NAT HLA operations.

Without HLA Approval . . .

. . . you cannot fly in NAT HLA airspace, which is from FL285 - FL420. Going around HLA isn't really feasible, because it extends from about 20N to the North Pole. You can fly in the NAT region at FL280 westbound, FL270 eastbound, or FL430 in either direction.

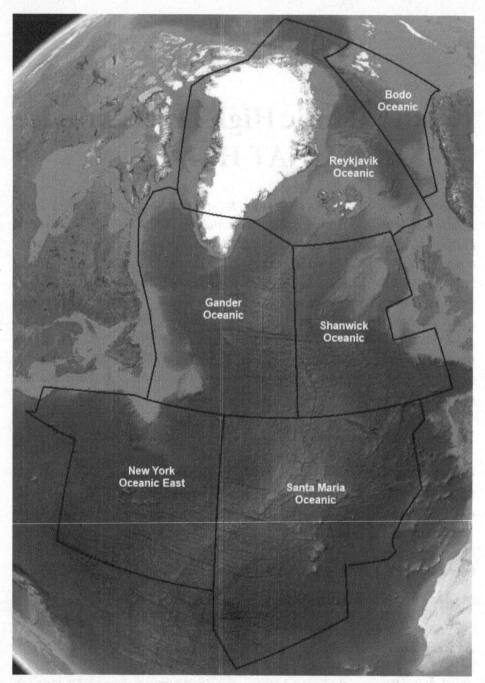

Figure: North Atlantic HLA from ICAO NAT Doc 007, figure 1

[NAT Doc 007, ¶1.1.1] NAT HLA is that volume of airspace between flight level (FL) 285 and FL 420 within the oceanic control areas of Bodo Oceanic, Gander Oceanic, New York Oceanic East, Reykjavik, Santa Maria and Shanwick, excluding the Shannon and Brest Ocean Transition Areas.

[NAT Doc 007, ¶1.2.1] All flights within the NAT HLA must have the approval of either the State of Registry of the aircraft, or the State of the operator.

Without RVSM . . .

. . . you cannot cruise at levels between FL290 - FL410 inclusive in the NAT region. You can fly at FL280 westbound, FL270 eastbound, or FL430 in either direction. Additionally:

[NAT Doc 007, ¶1.6]

To Climb/Descend Through RVSM Levels: 1.6.1 NAT HLA approved aircraft that are not approved for RVSM operation will be permitted, subject to traffic, to climb/descend through RVSM levels in order to attain cruising levels above or below RVSM airspace. Flights should climb/descend continuously through the RVSM levels without stopping at any intermediate level and should "Report leaving" current level and "Report reaching" cleared level (N.B. this provision contrasts with the regulations applicable for RVSM airspace operations in Europe, where aircraft not approved for RVSM operations are not permitted to effect such climbs or descents through RVSM levels.). Such aircraft are also permitted to flight plan and operate at FL430 either Eastbound or Westbound above the NAT HLA.

[NAT Doc 007, ¶1.6.2]

To Operate at RVSM Levels: ATC may provide special approval for a NAT HLA approved aircraft that is not approved for RVSM operation to fly in the NAT HLA provided that the aircraft:

a) is on a delivery flight; or

b) was RVSM approved but has suffered an equipment failure and is being returned to its base for repair and/or re-approval; or

c) is on a mercy or humanitarian flight.

Without CPDLC . . .

. . . you can't operate FL 290 - FL 410 anywhere in the NAT HLA. You can cruise at FL 280 or below, or FL 410 or above anywhere in the HLA, including the tracks. There are exempted areas, where you're all good: North of 80N, Surveillance airspace (where ATC can see you on radar or ADS-B), the Tango Routes, and New York Oceanic East. If you have ADS-B and VHF, Gander will accept you on a line RATSU 61N20W 63N30W 62N40W 61N50W SAVRY or north of.

[NAT Doc 007, ¶1.8.1] The NAT Data Link Mandate (DLM) requires aircraft to be equipped with, and operating, CPDLC and ADS-C in the NAT region. Currently, the mandate incorporates FL290 to FL410 inclusive.

[NAT Doc 007, ¶1.8.2] The DLM is not applicable to aircraft operating in:

Airspace north of 80° North;

New York Oceanic East flight information region (FIR);

Airspace where an ATS surveillance service is provided by means of radar, multilateration and/or ADS-B, coupled with VHF voice communications as depicted in State Aeronautical Information Publications (AIP), provided the aircraft is suitably equipped (transponder/ADS-B extended squitter transmitter).

Without ADS-C . . .

. . . you can't operate FL 290 - FL 410 anywhere in the NAT HLA. Where you can go is the same as CPDLC, above.

[NAT Doc 007, ¶1.8.1] The NAT Data Link Mandate (DLM) requires aircraft to be equipped with, and operating, CPDLC and ADS-C in the NAT region. Currently, the mandate incorporates FL290 to FL410 inclusive.

[NAT Doc 007, ¶1.8.2] The DLM is not applicable to aircraft operating in:

- Airspace north of 80° North;
- New York Oceanic East flight information region (FIR);
- Airspace where an ATS surveillance service is provided by means of radar, multilateration and/or ADS-B, coupled with VHF voice commu-

nications as depicted in State Aeronautical Information Publications (AIP), provided the aircraft is suitably equipped (transponder/ADS-B extended squitter transmitter).

Without More Than One LRNS . . .

. . . you cannot fly in most of the airspace, with a few exceptions. For a full crossing, use the Blue Spruce routes. You only need a single LRNS - and HLA approval if using them between FL 285 - FL 420. You need HF for the ones that enter Shanwick OCA. You can use Tango 9 with a single LRNS, but T213, T13 and T16 need two.

[NAT Doc 007, ¶1.4.1] Routes for Aircraft with Only One LRNS. A number of special routes have been developed for aircraft equipped with only one LRNS and carrying normal short-range navigation equipment (VOR, DME, ADF), which require to cross the North Atlantic between Europe and North America (or vice versa). It should be recognised that these routes are within the NAT HLA, and that State approval must be obtained prior to flying along them. These routes are also available for interim use by aircraft normally approved for unrestricted NAT HLA operations that have suffered a partial loss of navigation capability and have only a single remaining functional LRNS. Detailed descriptions of the special routes known as 'Blue Spruce Routes' are included in Chapter 3 of this Document. Other routes also exist within the NAT HLA that may be flown by aircraft equipped with only a single functioning LRNS. These include routings between the Azores and the Portuguese mainland and/or the Madeira Archipelago and also routes between Northern Europe and Spain/Canaries/Lisbon FIR to the east of longitude 009° 01' W (viz.T9). Other routes available for single LRNS use are also established in the NAT HLA, including a route between Iceland and the east coast of Greenland and two routes between Kook Islands on the west coast of Greenland and Canada.

[NAT Doc 007, ¶1.4.2] If this single LRNS is a GPS it must be approved in accordance with FAA TSO-C129 or later standard as Class A1, A2, B1, B2, C1 or C2, or with equivalent EASA documentation ETSO- C129a. Some States may have additional requirements regarding the carriage and use of GPS (e.g. a requirement for FDE RAIM) and flight crews should check with their own State of Registry to ascertain what, if any, they are.

Without a transponder . . .

. . . you cannot fly in the NAT region at all.

[NAT Doc 007, ¶6.8.1] All aircraft operating as IFR flights in the NAT region shall be equipped with a pressure- altitude reporting SSR transponder.

Without TCAS 7.1 . . .

. . . you cannot fly anywhere in the NAT region.

[NAT Doc 007, ¶6.9.1] Turbine-engined aircraft having a maximum certificated take-off mass exceeding 5,700 kg or authorized to carry more than 19 passengers are required to carry ACAS II in the NAT region. The technical specifications for ACAS II are contained in ICAO Annex 10 Volume IV. Compliance with this requirement can be achieved through the implementation of traffic alert and collision avoidance system (TCAS) Version 7.1 as specified in RTCA/DO-185B or EUROCAE/ED-143.

Without ETOPS . . .

. . . you cannot operate further than 180 minutes from adequate airports – unless you're not operating a commercial flight, or have an exemption.

[NAT Doc 007, ¶16.6.22] A large portion of NAT crossings are ETOPS operations. ETOPS rules require that one or more suitable enroute alternate airports are named prior to dispatch and then monitored while aircraft are enroute. Enroute alternate airports in the NAT region are limited to those in the Azores, Bermuda, Greenland and Iceland. In determining ETOPS alternate minima, the dispatcher must consider weather conditions, airport conditions (in addition to simple runway lengths), navigation approach aids, and the availability of ATS and ARFF facilities.

Without RNP 4 . . .

. . . you cannot fly the PBCS tracks.

[NAT Doc 007, ¶1.3.3] The navigation system accuracy requirements for NAT MNPSA/HLA operation should only be based on the PBN specifications, RNP 10 (PBN application of RNAV 10) or RNP 4.

Without RNP 10 . . .

. . . you cannot enter NAT HLA airspace. You can operate at FL 280 or below, FL 430 or above, or outside the HLA area.

[NAT Doc 007, ¶1.3.3] The navigation system accuracy requirements for NAT MNPSA/HLA operation should only be based on the PBN specifications, RNP 10 (PBN application of RNAV 10) or RNP 4.

Without HF . . .

. . . You cannot fly in Shanwick airspace. Other OCA's may approve Satcom for primary comms. If you're making a full NAT crossing, then you're basically going via Iceland. One example route is RATSU-ALDAN-KFV-EPENI-63N30W–61N40WOZN-58N50W-HOIST-LOACH-YYR. Canada publishes two routes that can be flown VHF only, without prior approval: below FL 195, routing Iqaluit (Frobay) – Sondre Stromfjord – Keflavík. FL 250 or above, routing Goose VOR – Prins Christian Sund (or Narsarsuaq) – Keflavik. You still need HLA approval to go above FL285. Gander will probably approve other routes without HF, but ask ATC nicely first. In general, crossing from Greenland-Canada south of 60N, at FL200 or above, should be fine.

[NAT Doc 007, ¶4.2.12] Aircraft with only functioning VHF communications equipment should plan their route according to the information contained in the appropriate State AIPs and ensure that they remain within VHF coverage of appropriate ground stations throughout the flight.

Without SELCAL . . .

. . . you are okay, but you have to maintain a listening watch to HF, even if you have CPDLC.

[NAT Doc 007, ¶6.1.22ß] When using HF, SATVOICE, or CPDLC, flight crews should maintain a listening watch on the assigned frequency, unless SELCAL equipped, in which case they should ensure the following sequence of actions:

a) provide the SELCAL code in the flight plan; (any subsequent change of aircraft for a flight will require refiling of the flight plan or submitting a modification message (CHG) which includes the new registration and SELCAL);

b) check the operation of the SELCAL equipment, at or prior to entry into oceanic airspace, with the appropriate radio station. (This SELCAL check must be completed prior to commencing SELCAL watch); and

c) maintain thereafter a SELCAL watch.

Without PBCS . . .

. . . you cannot fly along the core NAT Tracks between FL 350 - 390.

Note: These core tracks are often suspended during extended periods of low traffic volume, spacing out the tracks for use by non-PBCS aircraft.

PBCS for the NAT means having both RCP240 (4 minute comms loop) and RSP180 (3 minute position reporting). If you're missing approval for either, then you can fly anywhere other than along the core NAT tracks FL 350 - 390.

[NAT Doc 007, ¶1.10.2] Within the OTS the 42.6km (23 NM) lateral separation minimum is implemented by applying 42.6km (23 NM) lateral spacing through whole and half degrees of latitude between PBCS designated NAT OTS Tracks between flight levels FL 350-390 inclusive, except when the OTS occurs in the New York OCA East. In the OTS this PBCS-based separation implementation supersedes and replaces the previous trials of RLatSM. In addition to requiring RNP-4 Approval, Operators must appreciate that unlike the filing criteria for the half degree spaced RLatSM Tracks, the simple equipage and operation of CPDLC and ADS-C will not be a sufficient criteria for planning and flying on the designated PBCS-based OTS Tracks. To utilize these tracks the aircraft must have formal State Authorization for filing RCP 240 and RSP 180.

Documentation / Certification

[ICAO NAT Doc 007 § 1.1.3] Aircraft operating within the NAT HLA are required to meet specified navigation performance in the horizontal plane through the carriage and proper use of navigation equipment that meets identified standards and has been approved as such by the State of Registry or State of the operator for the purpose. Such approvals encompass all aspects affecting the expected navigation performance of the aircraft, including the designation of appropriate cockpit/flight deck operating procedures.

14 CFR 135 Approval

[8900.1, Volume 3, Chapter 18, Paragraph B039.] OpSpec/MSpec/LOA B039 is issued to authorize aircraft operations within the airspace designated by the International Civil Aviation Organization (ICAO) as NAT HLA. FAA authorization is a prerequisite for operations within NAT HLA. B039 applies to operations performed under 14 CFR parts 91, 91K, 121, 125, and 135.

14 CFR 91 Approval

[8900.1, Volume 4, Chapter 12, Paragraph 4-1296.] In the United States, operational approval for part 91 operators to fly in NAT HLA (vertical bounds are flight level (FL) 285 to FL 420) is obtained by the issuance of LOA B039.

Keeping Up-to-Date

Good sources to monitor for changes:

NAT OPS Bulletins — available at www.icao.int/EURNAT/, following "EUR & NAT Documents," then "NAT Documents," in folder "NAT OPS Bulletins."

NBAA Air Mail — https://www.nbaa.org/airmail/), several forums, including one for international operations. (Membership required.)

OpsGroup — ops.group, a platform for pilots, controllers, dispatchers, and managers to ask questions, provide answers, and to learn from peers. (Membership required.)

Chapter 8

Performance Based Communications and Surveillance (PBCS)

*P*BCS is akin to Performance Based Navigation (PBN) when it comes to communications and surveillance. You measure PBCS in terms of Required Communications Performance (RCP) and Required Surveillance Performance (RSP). As is true with Required Navigation Performance (RNP), the objective is to pack more and more airplanes in the same amount of airspace.

Location

[ICAO Doc 9869, ¶1.6.5] RCP and RSP specifications can be applied to communication and surveillance capabilities in an airspace or to support an ATM operation. Examples of such applications include:

- a defined airspace (e.g. North Atlantic or Pacific Regions) for safety or to support application of a 5-minute or 55.5 km (30 NM) longitudinal separation minimum;

- a fixed ATS route (e.g. between Sydney, Australia, and Auckland, New Zealand);

- random track operations (e.g. between Hawaii and Japan); or

- a volume of airspace (e.g. a block altitude on a specified route).

Performance Standards

[AC 90-117, ¶22.15.1] An RCP specification represents operational parameters for the complete communication transaction. It is identified by a designator (e.g., RCP 240 or RCP 400) in order to simplify the designator naming convention and to make the RCP Expiration Time (ET) readily apparent to airspace planners, aircraft manufacturers, and operators. The designator represents the value for the communication ET after which the initiator is required to revert to an alternative procedure. The RCP specifications are applied to achieve the performance required of the communication process and may support aircraft separation minima.

[ICAO Doc 9869, ¶2.2.1.13] RCP 240 may be applied to maintain the performance for normal means of communication, which supports controller intervention capability in procedurally controlled airspace, where the separation minimum applied is predicated on communication performance.

[ICAO Doc 9869, ¶2.2.1.14 RCP 400 may be applied to maintain the performance for emerging technology (e.g. satellite voice) used to provide normal means of communication supporting controller intervention capability in procedurally controlled airspace, where the separation minimum applied is based on position reporting at compulsory reporting points. RCP 400 may also be applied to maintain the performance required for emerging technologies used to provide alternative means of communication, that may be required in combination with the normal means of communication, to which RCP 240 is applied.

You can think of RCP 400 as old school and RCP 240 as full up CPDLC at the highest levels available in 2020.

[AC 90-117, ¶22.16.3] An RSP specification is identified by a designator (e.g., RSP 180) in order to simplify the designator naming convention and to make the RSP Data Operational Overdue Time (OT) readily apparent to airspace planners, aircraft manufacturers and operators. The designator represents the value for the surveillance data delivery time when the surveillance data delivery is considered overdue. RSP specifications are applied to airspace based on specific objectives (e.g., the performance required of the surveillance process used to support particular separation minima). The RSP specification is a set of requirements/operational parameters for ATS provision and associated ground equipment, aircraft capability, and operations needed to support performance-based surveillance. Surveillance performance requirements are included and allocated to system components (Required Surveillance Technical Performance (RSTP)). It includes surveillance data delivery time, continuity, availability, integrity, and safety. A specified RSP specification is intended to define the surveillance performance required of a surveillance process to support a particular ATM function.

RSP specification is applied to the airspace, route, or procedure based on the most stringent RSP specification of the required ATM functions.

[ICAO Doc 9869, ¶2.4.1.1] RSP 180 may be applied to maintain the performance for normal means of surveillance, which supports controller intervention capability in procedurally controlled airspace, where separation minimum applied is predicated on surveillance performance.

[ICAO Doc 9869, ¶2.4.1.11] RSP 400 may be applied to maintain the performance for emerging technology (e.g. satellite voice) used to provide normal means of surveillance supporting controller intervention capability in procedurally controlled airspace, where the separation minimum being applied is based on position reporting at compulsory reporting points. RSP 400 might also be applied to maintain the performance required for emerging technologies used to provide alternative means of surveillance, that may be required in combination with the normal means of surveillance, to which RSP 180 is applied.

You can think of RSP 400 as old school and RSP 180 as full up ADS-C at the highest levels available in 2020.

Documentation / Certification

Aircraft Eligibility

[AC 90-117, ¶3.3] Due to the complexity of the criteria to determine eligibility, the operator must obtain a statement of compliance from the entity that owns the design approval for their data link installation. This may be the aircraft manufacturer, the operator, the manufacturer of the data link system, or another party. The statement of compliance should be provided in the AFM, AFM Supplement, or other acceptable document.

Authorization

You will need A056 to use data link outside the United States and you will have to be authorized specifically to use PBCS airspace at that level.

[FAA Order 8900.1, Volume 3, Chapter 18, §3, A056, ¶B.] This paragraph is for U.S. aircraft and operators conducting data link communications operations under parts 91, 91K, 121, 125 (including part 125 LODA holders), and 135. NOTE: Part 91 operators do not require operational authorization for the use of data link in U.S. domestic airspace. For data link operations in oceanic and remote continental airspace and/or foreign countries requiring specific data link approval, LOA A056 applies.

[FAA Order 8900.1, Volume 3, Chapter 18, §3, A056, ¶C. 1) b)] If applicable, the SOC should reference AC 20-140B or a later revision for any of the following performance specifications:

- RCP 400, RCP 240; or
- RSP 400, RSP 180.

Section III - Navigate

Chapter 9

Precision Area Navigation (P-RNAV)

P-RNAV is giving way to RNAV-1 under Performance Based Navigation but the specification continues. Some procedures allow for either, but even without that, the ICAO rules allow you to fly a RNAV-1 procedure with a P-RNAV authorization.

Location

Europe

[ICAO Doc 7030, §EUR, ¶4.1.1.5.2] Precision RNAV (P-RNAV) and basic RNAV (B-RNAV) The provisions in respect of precision area navigation (P-RNAV) shall be applied whenever RNAV terminal control area (TMA) procedures, excluding the final and missed approach segments, are used.

You used to see these all over Europe and other places, such as Hong Kong. As the world gravitates to RNP-1 for the terminal sector they are becoming a bit more scarce. If applicable, you should see "RNAV-1" or "P-RNAV APPROVAL REQUIRED" annotated on the arrival or departure procedure.

Accuracy / Performance Standards

[AC 90-96A, ¶4.c.] P-RNAV is defined as RNAV that meets a track keeping accuracy equal to or better than ±1 nm for 95 percent of the flight time. This value includes signal source error, airborne receiver error, display system error, and flight technical error. This navigation performance assumes the necessary coverage provided by satellite or ground-based navigation aids is available for the intended operation.

Documentation / Certification

Aircraft P-RNAV System Eligibility

[AC 90-96A, Appendix 2 ¶1.c.(1)] Consider the aircraft eligible for P-RNAV operations, if the AFM or POH shows the appropriate instrument flight rules (IFR) navigation system installation has received airworthiness approval in accordance with this AC or has a statement of compliance to the performance and functional requirements of JAA TGL-10.

Part 91 Aircraft/Operator Approval

LOA B034 (B-RNAV and P-RNAV operations) is no longer required or offered for Part 91 operators. I am told that no action is required for operators who already have an approved B034 but they are encouraged to get LOA C063, if they have not already done so. LOA C063 authorizes RNAV-1 and RNP-1 and serves as a partial replacement for B034 in airspaces where still required.

U.S. Air Carrier Aircraft/Commercial Operator Approval

[AC 90-96A, Appendix 2 ¶1.c.(3)] Part 121, 125, or 135 operators should present the following documentation to their CHDO: sections of the AFM or POH that establish P-RNAV eligibility. Once the operator has satisfied the requirements described in Appendix 2, sections 3, 4, and 5; the CHDO: issues OpSpecs to reflect Basic Area Navigation (B-RNAV) and P-RNAV approval; and, approves changes to the minimum equipment list (MEL) to account for B-RNAV and P-RNAV operations. Appendix 2, paragraph 1d provides guidance if the operator is unable to determine from the AFM or POH whether the aircraft system is approved in accordance with an appropriate FAA AC.

[FAA Order 8900.1, Vol 3, Chapter 18, OPSEC B034, ¶B.] B034 also authorizes an operator to conduct IFR operations in designated European Basic RNAV (B-RNAV) and European Precision RNAV (P-RNAV) airspace.

If your AFM or POH has the necessary statement, you have what you need to apply for OpSpec B034 under 14 CFR 135. Otherwise, there are other means listed in AC 90-96A to get approval.

Chapter 10

Required Navigation Performance-1 (RNP-1)

In the world of Performance Based Navigation, RNP-1 is the new standard for terminal operations, but RNAV 1 and 2 are still in use. In fact, as of late 2020, the only place you really need RNP-1 is Hong Kong. Australia requires it for their own aircraft, but not foreign aircraft. If you are going to Hong Kong, you will need an LOA or commercial specification.

Location

Australia

Australia AIC H13/17, ¶4.2] As of 26 May 2016 and where specifically promulgated, ATS Routes, Terminal Procedures and Instrument Approach Procedures should be flown to the following standard PBN Navigation Specifications:

c. Terminal Procedures (SIDs and STARs) - RNP 1.

Exemptions are allowed for foreign registered aircraft but appears they are not needed. In a statement to the press the same year the requirement came out, the Australia Civil Aviation Safety Authority said an exemption is not needed for foreign-registered aircraft.

Hong Kong

[Hong Kong AIP, GEN 1.5-2, ¶3.5.3 RNP 1 SID / STAR]

3.5.3.1 Operational Approval. Any aircraft arriving or departing HKIA other than those exempted categories of flights as specified in para 3.5.3.5 shall be equipped with appropriate systems and approved by the regulatory authority of the State of Registry/State of the Operator in accordance with ICAO RNP 1 standard for the conduct of RNP 1 SID and STAR. Carriage of a certified GNSS receiver is mandatory. Aircraft or avionics manufacturers shall provide aircraft documentation that shows compliance with the applicable criteria as appropriate. RNP 1 operational approval or compliance documentation shall be readily available for Ramp or Safety Assessment of Foreign Aircraft (SAFA) inspections conducted by the Civil Aviation Department Hong Kong.

3.5.3.2 GNSS RAIM availability prediction service and the associated NOTAM information related to GNSS availability will not be provided by the Hong Kong Civil Aviation Department. In accordance with ICAO Doc 9613, PBN Manual, aircraft operators shall subscribe the necessary information provided by other service providers to verify the RAIM availability for the intended route of flight.

3.5.3.3 RNP 1 navigation specifications are listed in ICAO Doc 9613, 'Performance-based Navigation (PBN) Manual'. The implementation procedures are given in Volume II, Part C, Chapter 3 of this document.

3.5.3.4 An operational approval issued in accordance with the ICAO Doc 9613 assumes that the operator and flight crew take into account all communication and surveillance requirements related to the relevant routes and/ or airspace. Operators must therefore observe the equipment requirements when they file a flight plan. (see ENR 1.10 para. 12.3.1).

3.5.3.5 Exemption Policy. The following categories of flights are granted exemptions from the RNP 1 requirement, and approved to operate in / out of HKIA using contingency procedures stated in AD 2.22 para. 2.2.3 and para. 7.1.3:

a) Humanitarian or SAR flights;

b) State aircraft;

c) Flight Check;

d) Maintenance or delivery flights;

e) Air tests (e.g. post maintenance);

f) When specific prior approval has been given by Director-General of Civil Aviation.

Accuracy / Performance Standards

[ICAO Doc 9613, Volume II, Part A, ¶2.3.13]

- Accuracy: During operations in airspace or on routes designated as RNP 1, the lateral TSE must be within ±1 NM for at least 95 per cent of the total flight time. The along-track error must also be within ±1 NM for at least 95 per cent of the total flight time.

- Integrity: Malfunction of the aircraft navigation equipment is classified as a major failure condition under airworthiness regulations (i.e. 10–5 per hour).

- Continuity: Loss of function is classified as a minor failure condition if the operator can revert to a different navigation system and proceed to a suitable airport.

- On-board performance monitoring and alerting: The RNP system, or the RNP system and pilot in combination, shall provide an alert if the accuracy requirement is not met, or if the probability that the lateral TSE exceeds 2 NM is greater than 10–5.

- SIS: If using GNSS, the aircraft navigation equipment shall provide an alert if the probability of SIS errors causing a lateral position error greater than 2 NM exceeds 10–7 per hour.

Operational Approval

This used to be a mess for Part 91 operators wanting to fly to Hong Kong because the U.S. FAA said no LOA needed, Hong Kong said it was. At first the FAA refused to issue the LOA, and then they would if you could prove you are flying to Hong Kong. I think that is resolved as we've seen operators get the LOA without too much trouble.

Part 91 Operators

[AC 90-105A, ¶7.1] A letter of authorization (LOA) is not required for Title 14 of the Code of Federal Regulations (14 CFR) part 91 operators (other than part 91 subpart K (part 91K)) except for oceanic operations (see Appendices E, F, and G) or if required in foreign airspace. Part 91 operators (other than 91K) should comply with the aircraft eligibility and operational guidance in this advisory circular (AC).

Parts 91K, 121, 125, 129, and 135 Operators

- [AC 90-105A, ¶7.3] Title 14 CFR parts 91K, 121, 125, 129, and 135 operators receive approval to fly RNP operations as described in this AC via operations specifications (OpSpecs), management specifications (MSpecs), or LOAs as follows:

- OpSpec/MSpec/optional LOA, paragraph C063, Area Navigation (RNAV) and Required Navigation Performance (RNP) Terminal Operations;

- OpSpec/MSpec, paragraph B035, Class 1 Navigation in U.S. Class A Airspace Using Area or Long-Range Navigation Systems;

- OpSpec/MSpec/LOA (to include Part 91 operators), paragraph B036, Oceanic and Remote Continental Navigation Using Multiple Long-Range Navigation Systems(M-LRNS); or

- Helicopter Specification (HSpec)/LOA, paragraph H123, Class I Navigation Using Area or Long-Range Navigation Systems with Wide Area Augmentation System(WAAS) for Rotorcraft Required Navigation Performance (RNP) 0.3 En Route and Terminal Operations.

Chapter 11

Required Navigation Performance-4 (RNP-4)

*O*f the current RNP designations, RNP-4 is the specification used for oceanic and remote continental navigation applications. While RNP-10 is also
used, it is not a true Performance Based Navigation standard. As of late 2020,
only a handful of places in the world say RNP-4 is required but they all have
work arounds in place if you are RNP-10 authorized. To get your RNP-4 authorization you will first need CPDLC and ADS. Then, under 14 CFR 91 you
will need an LOA and under 14 CFR 135 you will need OpSpec B036.

Location

Asia

[ICAO Doc 7030, $MID/ASIA, ¶4.1.2.1.2] For flights on designated con-
trolled oceanic routes or areas within the Auckland Oceanic, Brisbane, Fukuoka, Honiara, Melbourne, Nauru, New Zealand and Port Moresby FIRs,
a longitudinal separation minimum of 55.5 km (30 nm) derived by RNAV
may be applied between RNAV-equipped aircraft approved to RNP 4 or better, in accordance with the provisions of the PANS-ATM, 5.4.2.6.

Pacific

[ICAO Doc 7030, $PAC, ¶4.1.2.1.2] For flights on designated controlled oce-
anic routes or areas within the Anchorage Arctic, Anchorage Continental,
Anchorage Oceanic, Auckland Oceanic, Nadi, Oakland Oceanic and Tahiti
FIRs, a longitudinal separation minimum of 55.5 km (30 nm) derived by
RNAV may be applied between RNAV-equipped aircraft approved to RNP 4
or better, in accordance with the provisions of the PANS-ATM, 5.4.2.6.

*In both the Asia and Pacific instances, the 30 nm longitudinal separation "may
be applied." If you do not have RNP-4 authorization the following PANS-ATM
provisions are cited:*

RNAV Provisions

[ICAO Doc 4444, ¶5.4.2.6] LONGITUDINAL SEPARATION MINIMA BASED ON DISTANCE USING RNAV WHERE RNP IS SPECIFIED

5.4.2.6.2.2 Direct controller-pilot communications shall be maintained while applying a distance-based separation minima. Direct controller-pilot communications shall be voice or CPDLC. The communication criteria necessary for CPDLC to satisfy the requirement for direct controller-pilot communications shall be established by an appropriate safety assessment.

5.4.2.6.3 Longitudinal distance-based separation minima in an RNP RNAV environment not using ADS.

5.4.2.6.3.1 For aircraft cruising, climbing or descending on the same track, the following separation minimum may be used:

Separation minimum: 93 km (50 NM)

RNP type: 10

Communication requirement: Direct controller-pilot communications

Surveillance requirement: Procedure position reports

Distance verification: At least every 24 minutes

5.4.2.9.2 The following separation minima may be used for aircraft cruising, climbing or descending on: a) the same track; or b) crossing tracks provided that the relative angle between the tracks is less than 90 degrees.

Separation minima	RNP	RCP	RSP	Maximum ADS-C periodic reporting interval
93 km (50 NM)	10	240	180	27 minutes
	4	240	180	32 minutes
55.5 km (30 NM)	2 or 4	240	180	12 minutes
5 minutes	2 or 4 or 10	240	180	14 minutes

If you do not have ADS and are not RNP-4 authorized, the controllers have the option of accepting you but using increased separation standards provided: you are RNP-10 qualified, you are in direct communications with the controller, and the controller has the capability of intervening within 4 minutes.

Accuracy / Performance Standards

[ICAO Doc 9613, Volume II, Part C,¶1.3.3.5]

1.3.3.5.1 Accuracy: During operations in airspace or on routes designated as RNP 4, the lateral TSE must be within ±4 NM for at least 95 per cent of the total flight time. The along-track error must also be within ±4 NM for at least 95 per cent of the total flight time.

1.3.3.5.2 Integrity: Malfunction of the aircraft navigation equipment is classified as a major failure condition under airworthiness regulations (i.e. 10–5 per hour).

1.3.3.5.3 Continuity: Loss of function is classified as a major failure condition for oceanic and remote navigation. The continuity requirement is satisfied by the carriage of dual independent long-range navigation systems (excluding SIS).

1.3.3.5.4 On-board performance monitoring and alerting: The RNP system, or the RNP system and pilot in combination, shall provide an alert if the accuracy requirement is not met, or if the probability that the lateral TSE exceeds 8 NM is greater than 10–5.

1.3.3.5.5 SIS: If using GNSS, the aircraft navigation equipment shall provide an alert if the probability of SIS errors causing a lateral position error greater than 8 NM exceeds 10–7 per hour.

[ICAO Doc 9613, Volume II, Part C,¶1.3.4.1] It is important to understand that additional requirements will have to be met for operational authorization in RNP 4 airspace or on RNP 4 routes. Controller pilot data link communications (CPDLC) and automatic dependent surveillance — contract (ADS-C) systems will also be required when the separation standard is 30 nm lateral and/or longitudinal. The on-board navigation data must be current and include appropriate procedures.

Documentation / Certification

Operational Approval - 14 CFR 91

[AC 90-105A]

7.1 Part 91 Operators. A letter of authorization (LOA) is not required for Title 14 of the Code of Federal Regulations (14 CFR) part 91 operators (other than part 91 subpart K (part 91K)) except for oceanic operations (see Appendices E, F, and G) or if required in foreign airspace. Part 91 operators (other than 91K) should comply with the aircraft eligibility and operational guidance in this advisory circular (AC).

7.2 Operational Authorization. To obtain operational authorization, aircraft eligibility must be determined in accordance with the applicable appendix of this AC. Operational authorizations issued under a previous version of this AC or other canceled ACs does not need to be reissued or reevaluated.

Note: Previous approvals under FAA Order 8400.12C, Required Navigation Performance 10 (RNP 10) Operational Authorization, and FAA Order 8400.33, Procedures for Obtaining Authorization for Required Navigation Performance 4 (RNP-4) Oceanic and Remote Area Operations, are still valid for these operations. Operators must ensure their operations remain consistent with the performance and functional requirements of this AC.

Operational Approval - 14 CFR 91K, 121, 125, 129, and 135

[AC 90-105A] Parts 91K, 121, 125, 129, and 135 Operators. Title 14 CFR parts 91K, 121, 125, 129, and 135 operators receive approval to fly RNP operations as described in this AC via operations specifications (OpSpecs), management specifications (MSpecs), or LOAs as follows:

- OpSpec/MSpec/optional LOA, paragraph C063, Area Navigation (RNAV) and Required Navigation Performance (RNP) Terminal Operations;

- OpSpec/MSpec, paragraph B035, Class 1 Navigation in U.S. Class A Airspace Using Area or Long-Range Navigation Systems;

- OpSpec/MSpec/LOA (to include Part 91 operators), paragraph B036, Oceanic and Remote Continental Navigation Using Multiple Long-Range Navigation Systems (M-LRNS); or

- Helicopter Specification (HSpec)/LOA, paragraph H123, Class I Navigation Using Area or Long-Range Navigation Systems with Wide Area Augmentation System (WAAS) for Rotorcraft Required Navigation Performance (RNP) 0.3 En Route and Terminal Operations.

Chapter 12

Required Navigation
Performance-10 (RNP-10)

Required Navigation Performance (RNP) standards are almost always performance based, requiring on-board performance monitoring and alerting. This is as opposed to the older RNAV systems which are an equipment-based standard that do not require on-board performance monitoring and alerting. We say almost always because RNP-10 is an exception . . .

Inconsistent RNP Designation

[ICAO Doc 9613, Volume I, Part A, ¶1.2.5.1] The existing RNP 10 designation is inconsistent with PBN RNP and RNAV specifications. RNP 10 does not include requirements for on-board performance monitoring and alerting. For purposes of consistency with the PBN concept, RNP 10 is referred to as RNAV 10 in this manual. Renaming current RNP 10 routes, operational approvals, etc., to an RNAV 10 designation would be an extensive and expensive task, which is not cost-effective. Consequently, any existing or new operational approvals will continue to be designated RNP 10, and any charting annotations will be depicted as RNP 10.

Location

Africa

[ICAO Doc 7030, §AFI, ¶4.1.1] For flights on designated controlled oceanic routes or areas within the Canarias FIR (southern sector), Dakar Oceanic, Recife and Sal Oceanic FIRs, and on designated routes over continental Africa, a lateral separation minimum of 93 km (50 nm) may be applied.

For flights in the EUR/SAM corridor (Canarias (southern sector), Dakar Oceanic, Recife and Sal Oceanic FIRs), a longitudinal separation minimum of 93 km (50 nm) derived by RNAV may be applied between RNAV-equipped aircraft approved to RNP 10 or better, in accordance with the provisions of the PANS-ATM, 5.4.2.6.

Longitudinal distance-based separation minima of 93 km (50 nm) between RNAV aircraft on the same track on RNP 10 routes over continental Africa shall not be used.

Asia

[ICAO Doc 7030, $MID/ASIA, ¶4.1.1] For flights on designated controlled oceanic routes or areas within the Auckland Oceanic, Brisbane, Fukuoka, Honiara, Melbourne, Nauru, New Zealand and Port Moresby FIRs, a lateral separation minimum of 93 km (50 nm) may be applied.

For flights on designated controlled oceanic routes or areas within the Auckland Oceanic, Brisbane, Fukuoka, Honiara, Melbourne, Nauru, New Zealand and Port Moresby FIRs, a longitudinal separation minimum of 93 km (50 nm) derived by RNAV may be applied between RNAV-equipped aircraft approved to RNP 10 or better, in accordance with the provisions of the PANS-ATM, 5.4.2.6.

Pacific

[ICAO Doc 7030, $PAC, ¶4.1.1]

For flights on designated controlled oceanic routes or areas within the Anchorage Arctic, Anchorage Continental, Anchorage Oceanic, Auckland Oceanic, Nadi, Oakland Oceanic and Tahiti FIRs, a lateral separation minimum of 93 km (50 nm) may be applied.

For flights on designated controlled oceanic routes or areas within the Anchorage Arctic, Anchorage Continental, Anchorage Oceanic, Auckland Oceanic, Nadi, Oakland Oceanic and Tahiti FIRs, a longitudinal separation minimum of 93 km (50 nm) derived by RNAV may be applied between RNAV-equipped aircraft approved to RNP 10 or better, in accordance with the provisions of the PANS-ATM, 5.4.2.6.

South America

[ICAO Doc 7030, $SAM, ¶4.1.1] For flights on designated controlled oceanic routes or areas within the Canarias FIR (southern sector), Dakar Oceanic, Recife and Sal Oceanic FIRs a lateral separation minimum of 93 km (50 nm) may be applied.

For flights in the EUR/SAM corridor (Canarias (southern sector), Dakar Oceanic, Recife and Sal Oceanic FIRs), a longitudinal separation minimum of 93 km (50 nm) derived by RNAV may be applied between RNAV-equipped aircraft approved to RNP 10 or better, in accordance with the provisions of the PANS-ATM, 5.4.2.6.

Accuracy / Performance Standards

[ICAO Doc 9613, Volume II, Part C,¶1.3.4.1]

Accuracy: During operations in airspace or on routes designated as RNP 10, the lateral total system error must be within ±10 nm for at least 95 percent of the total flight time. The along-track error must also be within ±10 nm for at least 95 percent of the total flight time.

Note 1.— For RNP 10, operational approval of aircraft capable of coupling the area navigation (RNAV) system to the flight director or autopilot, a navigational positioning error is considered to be the dominant contributor to cross-track and along-track error. Flight technical error, path definition error and display errors are considered to be insignificant for the purposes of RNP 10 approval.

Note 2.— When the data collection method described in Appendix 1 of FAA Order 8400.12A (as amended) is used as the basis for an RNP 10 operational approval, these error types are included in the analysis. However, when the data collection method described in Appendix 6 of FAA Order 8400.12A is used, these errors are not included since that method is more conservative. The Appendix 6 method uses radial error instead of cross-track and along-track error.

- Integrity: Malfunction of the aircraft navigation equipment is classified as a major failure condition under airworthiness regulations (i.e. 10^{-5} per hour).

- Continuity: Loss of function is classified as a major failure condition for oceanic and remote navigation. The continuity requirement is satisfied by the carriage of dual independent LRNSs (excluding signal-in-space).

- Signal-in-space: If using GNSS, the aircraft navigation equipment shall provide an alert if the probability of signal-in- space errors causing a lateral position error greater than 20 nm exceeds 10^{-7} per hour.

Documentation / Certification

Determining Eligibility of Aircraft

[FAA Order 8900.1, Vol 3, Ch 18, §4, ¶B036.E.] Manufacturers should evaluate their systems against these criteria and document the Required Navigation Performance (RNP) capabilities as per guidance in the current editions of AC 90-105, Approval Guidance for RNP Operations and Barometric Vertical Navigation in the U.S. National Airspace System and in Oceanic and Remote Continental Airspace, and AC 20-138, Airworthiness Approval of Positioning and Navigation Systems.

Operational Approval - 14 CFR 91

[AC 90-105A, ¶7.1 and 7.2] A letter of authorization (LOA) is not required for Title 14 of the Code of Federal Regulations (14 CFR) part 91 operators (other than part 91 subpart K (part 91K)) except for oceanic operations (see Appendices E, F, and G) or if required in foreign airspace. Part 91 operators (other than 91K) should comply with the aircraft eligibility and operational guidance in this advisory circular (AC). To obtain operational authorization, aircraft eligibility must be determined in accordance with the applicable appendix of this AC. Operational authorizations issued under a previous version of this AC or other canceled ACs does not need to be reissued or reevaluated.

Operational Approval - 14 CFR 91K, 121, 125, 129, and 135

[AC 90-105A] Parts 91K, 121, 125, 129, and 135 Operators. Title 14 CFR parts 91K, 121, 125, 129, and 135 operators receive approval to fly RNP operations as described in this AC via operations specifications (OpSpecs), management specifications (MSpecs), or LOAs.

Chapter 1

Required Communications Performance (RCP)

*M*ost pilots who have flown internationally in the last decade or so are well acquainted with the concept of Required Navigation Performance (RNP), the idea that where you can fly will be determined on how accurately you can fly and how well the system alerts you when things are less than promised. The same concept holds true for communications and surveillance. In the case of communications, the number attached to your Required Communications Performance (RCP) is the number of seconds it takes for an instruction to travel from the ground to you and your acknowledgement back to the ground. Does it matter? Yes, the lower the number the tighter the airspace you will be allowed to fly. Put another way: the higher the number, the more airspace around the world that will be denied you.

History

[ICAO Doc 9869, ¶1.1.4] The fourth meeting of the Aeronautical Mobile Communications Panel (AMCP/4) (Montreal, April 1996) recognized the absence of objective criteria to evaluate communication performance requirements. This objective criteria was seen as a set of values for parameters, which would be based on the operational requirements for communication systems in the various phases of flight. The meeting agreed that there was an urgent need to assess the various technical options of communication systems against such a set values for these parameters. The term RCP type is used to denote a set of values for these parameters.

This all grew out of the initial efforts to formalize the Future Air Navigation System (FANS) that led to the development of a Required Navigation Performance (RNP) standard. RCP is the underlying principle behind getting rid of HF and moving toward SATCOM. That also spawned the need to differentiate SATVOICE versus SATCOM.

Concept

[ICAO Doc 9869, ¶1.1]

1.1.1 The performance-based communication and surveillance (PBCS) concept provides objective operational criteria to evaluate different and emerging communication and surveillance technologies, intended for evolving air traffic management (ATM) operations. Once these criteria have been established and accepted, implementation of a specific ATM operation including its technical and human performance may be evaluated against these operational criteria to assess their viability.

1.1.2 The PBCS concept is aligned with that of performance-based navigation (PBN). While the PBN concept applies required navigation performance (RNP) and area navigation (RNAV) specifications to the navigation element, the PBCS concept applies required communication performance (RCP) and required surveillance performance (RSP) specifications to communication and surveillance elements, respectively. Each RCP/RSP specification includes allocated criteria among the components of the communication and surveillance systems involved.

1.1.3 Where beneficial, RCP, RNP/RNAV and RSP specifications are applied to communication, navigation and surveillance elements to ensure that the operational system and its components perform in accordance with the specifications.

Note 1.- While RCP and RSP specifications may be applied where beneficial, the PBCS concept is primarily intended for emerging technologies, and not traditional ones, such as HF voice communication or radar.

Note 2. - Similar to the PBN concept, security is beyond the scope of the PBCS concept. However, in some cases, the RCP and RSP specifications may include criteria to support mitigations from security threats. For example, the RCP and RSP specifications that may be applied to SATVOICE contain provisions for satellite service providers (SSPs) to oversee communication services providers (CSPs), in administering accounts to authorized subscribers with personal identification numbers (PIN) and priority level calling. Aircraft SATVOICE systems only route calls to the flight deck from authorized subscribers or alert the flight crew of the appropriate call priority for ATS communication.

RCP Specification

[ICAO Doc 9869, ¶3.2]

[AC 90-117, ¶22.15.1] An RCP specification represents operational parameters for the complete communication transaction. It is identified by a designator (e.g., RCP 240 or RCP 400) in order to simplify the designator naming convention and to make the RCP Expiration Time (ET) readily apparent to airspace planners, aircraft manufacturers, and operators. The designator represents the value for the communication ET after which the initiator is required to revert to an alternative procedure. The RCP specifications are applied to achieve the performance required of the communication process and may support aircraft separation minima.

[ICAO Doc 9869, ¶2.2.1.13] RCP 240 may be applied to maintain the performance for normal means of communication, which supports controller intervention capability in procedurally controlled airspace, where the separation minimum applied is predicated on communication performance.

[ICAO Doc 9869, ¶2.2.1.14 RCP 400 may be applied to maintain the performance for emerging technology (e.g. satellite voice) used to provide normal means of communication supporting controller intervention capability in procedurally controlled airspace, where the separation minimum applied is based on position reporting at compulsory reporting points. RCP 400 may also be applied to maintain the performance required for emerging technologies used to provide alternative means of communication, that may be required in combination with the normal means of communication, to which RCP 240 is applied.

You can think of RCP 400 as old school and RCP 240 as full up CPDLC and ADS-C at the highest levels available in 2020.

Chapter 2

High Frequency (HF) Radio

*T*here is much about HF to be confused about. It is a High Frequency (HF), for example, which turns out to be lower than most of the frequencies we deal with on a daily basis. Younger pilots often hear from the older pilots about just how difficult it was to make a position report "back in the day," but it seems rather easy these days. It is true that technology has made the radios easier to use and the transmitted signals much clearer. But there are still a few things to be gained from learning the technical stuff behind the technology.

Principles of Radio Communications

Amplitude, frequency, and wave lengths

[Radio Communications, Chapter 1]

Radio waves belong to the electromagnetic radiation family, which includes x-ray, ultraviolet, and visible light. Much like the gentle waves that form when a stone is tossed into a still lake, radio signals radiate outward, or propagate, from a transmitting antenna. However, unlike water waves, radio waves propagate at the speed of light.

Radio wave amplitude, or strength, can be visualized as its height being the distance between its peak and its lowest point. Amplitude, which is measured in volts, is usually expressed in terms of an average value called root-mean-square, or RMS.

The frequency of a radio wave is the number of repetitions or cycles it completes in a given period of time. Frequency is measured in Hertz (Hz); one Hertz equals one cycle per second. Thousands of Hertz are expressed as kilohertz (kHz), and millions of Hertz as megahertz (MHz). You would typically see a frequency of 2,345,000 Hertz, for example, written as 2,345 kHz or 2.345 MHz.

Radio wavelength is the distance between crests of a wave. The product of wavelength and frequency is a constant that is equal to the speed of propagation. Thus, as the frequency increases, wavelength decreases, and vice versa. Radio waves propagate at the speed of light (300 million meters per second). To determine the wavelength in meters for any frequency, divide 300 by the frequency in megahertz. So, the wavelength of a 10 MHz wave is 30 meters, determined by dividing 300 by 10.

The HF Spectrum

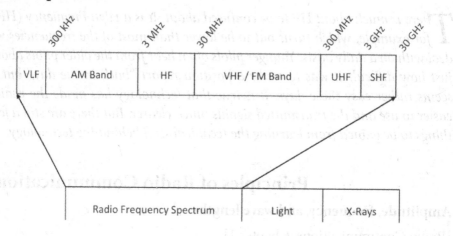

Figure: Radio Frequency Spectrum.[Radio Communications, Chapter 1]

The HF band is defined as the frequency range of 3 to 30 MHz. In practice, most HF radios use the spectrum from 1.6 to 30 MHz.

Sidebands

[Radio Communications, Chapter 1]

Today's common methods for radio communications include amplitude modulation (AM), which varies the strength of the carrier in direct proportion to changes in the intensity of a source such as the human voice. In other words, information is contained in amplitude variations. The AM process creates a carrier and a pair of duplicate sidebands — nearby frequencies above and below the carrier. AM is a relatively inefficient form of modulation, since the carrier must be continually generated. The majority of the power in an AM signal is consumed by the carrier that carries no information, with the rest going to the information-carrying sidebands.

You can think of the data as existing in the fat lobes of the signal where as the center has no space for any data at all.

162

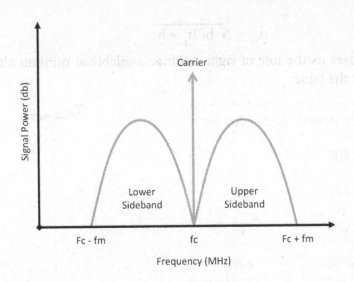

Figure: AM Signal Sidebands.

In a more efficient technique, single sideband (SSB), the carrier and one of the sidebands are suppressed. Only the remaining sideband — upper (USB) or lower (LSB) — is transmitted. An SSB signal needs only half the bandwidth of an AM signal and is produced only when a modulating signal is present. Thus, SSB systems are more efficient both in the use of the spectrum, which must accommodate many users, and of transmitter power. All the transmitted power goes into the information-carrying sideband.

In aviation we used to note our frequency as "Upper" or "Lower" to differentiate between the two. You would say, "transmitting 8060 upper," for example. All aircraft HF communication, outside of the military, seems to have gravitated to the upper sideband so we no longer need to say it. (It is assumed.)

Line of Sight / Minimum Altitude

So, at what point does your VHF lose its air-to-ground capability? A little geometry:

$$(r_p + h)^2 = r_p^2 + d_{los}^2$$

Where r_p is the radius of the earth (20,025,643 feet at the equator), h is the height of the aircraft, and d_{los} is the line of sight distance from the aircraft to the horizon. Solving for d_{los} we get:

$$d_{los} = \sqrt{h(2r_p + h)}$$

Which gives us the line of sight distance available at minium altitudes, as shown in the table:

Altitude (feet)	Distance (nm)
10,000	104
20,000	147
30,000	180
40,000	208
50,000	233

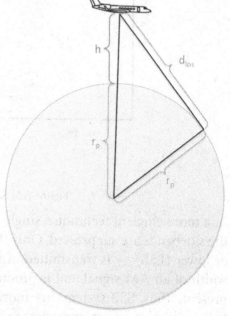

Figure: Line of sight.

You can use your VHF or HF for line of sight communications, but to go beyond the horizon, you will need to bounce an HF signal off the ground, water, or the ionosphere.

Sky Wave Propagation

[Radio Communications, Chapter 2]

The ionosphere is a region of electrically charged particles or gases in the earth's atmosphere, extending from approximately 50 to 600 km above the earth's surface. Ionization, the process in which electrons are stripped from atoms and produces electrically charged particles, results from solar radiation. When the ionosphere becomes heavily ionized, the gases may even glow and be visible. This phenomenon is known as Northern and Southern Lights.

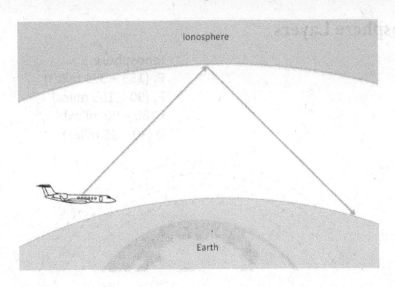

Figure: Sky wave propagation.

Why is the ionosphere important in HF radio? Well, this blanket of gases is like nature's satellite, making HF BLOS radio communications possible. When radio waves strike these ionized layers, depending on frequency, some are completely absorbed, others are refracted so that they return to the earth, and still others pass through the ionosphere into outer space. Absorption tends to be greater at lower frequencies, and increases as the degree of ionization increases.

The angle at which sky waves enter the ionosphere is known as the incident angle. This is determined by wavelength and the type of transmitting antenna. Like a billiard ball bouncing off a rail, a radio wave reflects from the ionosphere at the same angle it hits it. Thus, the incident angle is an important factor in determining communications range. If you need to reach a station that is relatively far from you, you would want the incident angle to be relatively large. To communicate with a nearby station, the incident angle should be relatively small.

Ground station HF radio operators worry about the angle of incidence as a way of aiming their signals to a desired distance. Since aircraft are closer to the ionosphere, the achievable angles are far greater as is the achievable distance. The pilot doesn't need to worry about the angle, other than to know how the angle can be affected by atmospheric conditions.

Ionosphere Layers

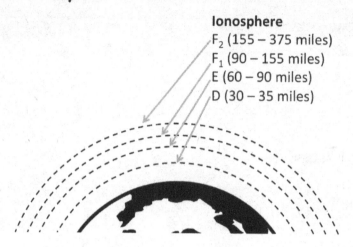

Ionosphere
F_2 (155 – 375 miles)
F_1 (90 – 155 miles)
E (60 – 90 miles)
D (30 – 35 miles)

Figure: Ionosphere Layers

[Radio Communications, Chapter 2]

Within the ionosphere, there are four layers of varying ionization. Since ionization is caused by solar radiation, the higher layers of the ionosphere tend to be more highly ionized, while the lower layers, protected by the outer layers, experience less ionization. Of these layers, the first was designated E for electric waves. Later, D and F were discovered and noted by these letters. Additional ionospheric phenomena were discovered through the 1930s and 1940s, such as sporadic E and aurora.

In the ionosphere, the D layer is the lowest region affecting HF radio waves. Ionized during the day, the D layer reaches maximum ionization when the sun is at its zenith and dissipates quickly toward sunset.

The E layer reaches maximum ionization at noon. It begins dissipating toward sunset and reaches minimum activity at midnight. Irregular cloud-like formations of ionized gases occasionally occur in the E layer. These regions, known as sporadic E, can support propagation of sky waves at the upper end of the HF band and beyond.

The most heavily ionized region of the ionosphere, and therefore the most important for long-haul communications, is the F layer. At this altitude, the air is thin enough that the ions and electrons recombine very slowly, so the layer retains its ionized properties even after sunset.

In the daytime, the F layer consists of two distinct layers, F1 and F2. The F1 layer, which exists only in the daytime and is negligible in winter, is not important to HF communications. The F2 layer reaches maximum ionization at noon and remains charged at night, gradually decreasing to a minimum just before sunrise.

During the day, sky wave reflection from the F2 layer requires wavelengths short enough to penetrate the ionized D and E layers, but not so short as to pass through the F layer. Generally, frequencies from 10 to 20 MHz will accomplish this, but the same frequencies used at night would penetrate the F layer and pass into outer space. The most effective frequencies for long-haul nighttime communications are normally between 3 and 8 MHz.

There are free electrons everywhere and when these electrons attach themselves to molecules in the atmosphere these molecules are said to be ionized. An ionized molecule is good for bouncing radio waves so an ionized layer of atmosphere is good for long distance communications. Where the knowledge shown here comes in handy is when selecting a frequency. During the day the lowest ionosphere is as ionized as it gets and a higher frequency (with the longest wavelength) bounces best. During the night this layer isn't so effective so you want to pass through it. So a lower frequency (with a shorter wavelength) will pass through the D layer on its way to the F layers where a better bounce can be had. That validates the old pilot's rule of thumb: the higher the sun, the higher the frequency.

Atmospheric Ionization Factors

[Radio Communications, Chapter 2]

The intensity of solar radiation, and therefore ionization, varies periodically. Hence, we can predict solar radiation intensity based on time of day and the season, and make adjustments in equipment to limit or optimize ionization effects.

Ionization is higher during spring and summer because the hours of daylight are longer. Sky waves are absorbed or weakened as they pass through the highly charged D and E layers, reducing, in effect, the communication range of most HF bands.

Because there are fewer hours of daylight during autumn and winter, less radiation reaches the D and E layers. Lower frequencies pass easily through these weakly ionized layers. Therefore, signals arriving at the F layer are stronger and are reflected over greater distances.

Another longer term periodic variation results from the 11-year sunspot cycle. Sunspots generate bursts of radiation that cause higher levels of ionization. The more sunspots, the greater the ionization.

During periods of low sunspot activity, frequencies above 20 MHz tend to be unusable because the E and F layers are too weakly ionized to reflect signals back to earth. At the peak of the sunspot cycle, however, it is not unusual to have worldwide propagation on frequencies above 30 MHz.

In addition to these regular variations, there is a class of unpredictable phenomena known as sudden ionospheric disturbances (SID), which can affect HF communications as well. SIDs are random events due to solar flares that can disrupt sky wave communication for hours or days at a time. Solar flares produce intense ionization of the D layer, causing it to absorb most HF signals on the side of the earth facing the sun.

Magnetic storms often follow the eruption of solar flares within 20 to 40 hours. Charged particles from the storms have a scattering effect on the F layer, temporarily neutralizing its reflective properties.

Required for Oceanic?

U.S. Requirement

[AC 91-70B, ¶4.4. Note 2] Equipage with CPDLC does not eliminate the requirement for operable two-way radios. For most oceanic operations this means operable HF radios are required.

ICAO Requirement

[ICAO Annex 2, §3.6.5.1] An aircraft operated as a controlled flight shall maintain continuous air-ground voice communication watch on the appropriate communication channel of, and establish two-way communication as necessary with, the appropriate air traffic control unit, except as may be prescribed by the appropriate ATS authority in respect of aircraft forming part of aerodrome traffic at a controlled aerodrome.

Note 1. SELCAL or similar automatic signalling devices satisfy the requirement to maintain an air-ground voice communication watch.

Note 2. The requirement for an aircraft to maintain an air-ground voice communication watch remains in effect after CPDLC has been established.

[ICAO Annex 2, §5.1.1] Aircraft shall be equipped with suitable instruments and with navigation equipment appropriate to the route to be flown.

North Atlantic Requirement

[ICAO Doc 7030, §NAT, ¶3.4.1] Within the NAT Region, aircraft equipped for SATCOM voice shall restrict the use of such equipment to emergencies and non-routine situations. An unforeseen inability to communicate by voice radio constitutes a non-routine situation. Since oceanic traffic typically communicates through aeradio facilities, a SATCOM call due to an unforeseen inability to communicate by other means should be made to such a facility rather than the ATC centre unless the urgency of the communication dictates otherwise. Dedicated SATCOM telephone numbers (short codes) for aeradio facilities and air traffic control facilities are published in national AIPs.

Yes, you can use your SATCOM for position reporting if you really needed to, and yes, you do make position reports with CPDLC. But the requirement remains: you need the HF when beyond VHF coverage. You need at least one; you might need two if you don't have CPDLC or a qualified satellite voice system.

North Atlantic Track (NAT) Frequency Families

The North Atlantic is probably the busiest oceanic airspace in the world and hunting for the correct frequency can be a challenge if your assigned frequencies become unusable. A system of "frequency families" make it a little easier.

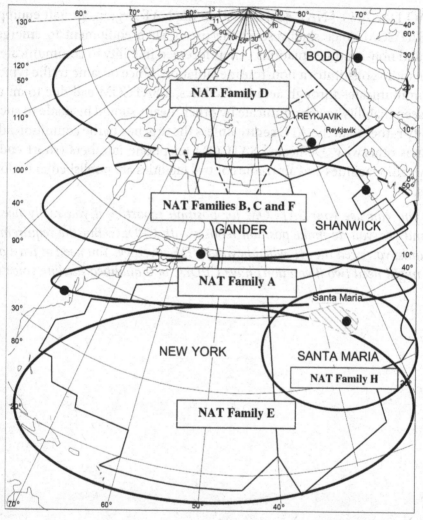

NAT HF Families, ICAO NAT Doc 003, Figure 3.

[ICAO Doc 003, ¶3.1.6] The NAT Families were defined utilising the frequencies allocated for the purpose of providing an AMS [Aeronautical Mobile Service] throughout the coverage area required.

170

NAT Family	Frequencies
A	3016, 5598, 8906, 13306 and 17946 KHz
B	2899, 5616, 8864, 13291 and 17946 kHz
C	2872, 5649, 8879, 11336, 13306 and 17946 kHz
D	2971, 4675, 8891, 11279, 13291 and 17946 kHz
E	2962, 6628, 8825, 11309, 13354 and 17946 kHz
F	3476, 6622, 8831, 13291 and 17946 kHz
H	3491, 6667

[ICAO Doc 003, ¶4.1]

The frequencies assigned to an aircraft should belong to the same sub-network, which includes all the stations that may be affected by the aircraft flight route.

If you are assigned a frequency that becomes unusable, you should attempt contact on a frequency from the same family.

Frequencies should be guarded only during the periods when they are usable, instead of maintaining the current twenty-four hour watch practice.

Do not be surprised if a frequency is completely silent; it may very well be unused.

During off-peak periods, when it is unnecessary to guard all frequencies and families, radio stations should use common families to achieve more efficient use of staff resources.

You may hear other stations on the same frequency.

Chapter 3

Voice Position Reports

A position report will normally be required in oceanic airspace unless instructed to "omit position reports" by the air traffic service (ATS) unit. There is a certain etiquette to be followed, to be sure. You can survive without it, but the radio operator on the other end and the pilots sharing HF time will appreciate your efforts if your transmissions are brief, clear, and follow the correct format.

The radio operator is typing away at a console and is ready to enter the data in a specific order and format. If you deviate from the format, the radio operator has to do a mental translation from poor to proper. If you deviate from the order, the radio operator will have to make liberal use of the TAB and DELETE keys. All of this introduces the possibility of errors.

Figure: ARINC Radio Operator
(Photo by Chris Parker)

HF Issues

- *Most of your position reporting will be made to an ARINC station which is not an ATS entity but a communications relay point. They are passing your position report to ATC and any ATC instructions to you. The radio operator may be monitoring several frequencies so you should always initiate HF radio calls with the frequency. I.e., "Shanwick, Shanwick, November Seven Seven Zero Zero, position on three, zero, one, six."*

- *HF connectivity can be problematic depending on the aircraft, the weather, and solar sun spot activity. A rule of thumb is: "the higher the sun, the higher the frequency." Pick higher frequencies in the day and lower at night.*

- *The best source of frequency information is on the en route chart. Some regions employ "frequency families" that are determined by the aircraft registration, location, and/or route of flight. If the assigned frequency is unusable, selecting another frequency in the same family would be appropriate.*

- *Satellite phones provide another option, though most regions still classify this option as a last resort. (Many international recurrent training vendors say the service providers really don't care; I've not seen evidence to back that up.) The person answering the phone is a radio operator and expects the normal position reporting format.*

Note: if the phone number on the chart is six digits long it is for an INMARSAT satellite phone. Your aircraft might be using INMARSAT satellites (most do) but it may not be an INMARSAT phone (many aren't). If you don't have an INMARSAT phone you might not be able to use that six-digit number. Many of the phone numbers are standard telephone numbers that can be used on any aircraft satellite phones.

Format: Position (Section 1)

[ICAO Doc 4444, Appendix A, §1]

The person on the other end of the radio is sitting in front of a computer terminal with a form laid out in the following format. If you give your position report in this order, the radio operator will have an easier time relaying an accurate position the first time. If you skip around, it will slow things down and introduce the chance of error. So use this format.

Section 1	1	Aircraft identification	*(aircraft identification)*
	2	Position	POSITION *(latitude and longitude)* OVER *(significant point)* ABEAM *(significant point)* *(significant point) (bearing) (distance)*
	3	Time	*(time)*
	4	Flight level or altitude	FLIGHT LEVEL *(number)* or *(number)* METRES or FEET CLIMBING TO FLIGHT LEVEL *(number)* or *(number)* METRES or FEET DESCENDING TO FLIGHT LEVEL *(number)* or *(number)* METRES or FEET
	5	Next position and estimated time over	*(position) (time)*
	6	Ensuing significant point	*(position)* NEXT

Figure: Model AIREP, Section 1, from ICAO Doc 4444, Appendix A, §1.

[ICAO Doc 4444, Appendix A, §1, ¶1.1] Section 1 is obligatory, although Items 5 and 6 thereof may be omitted when prescribed in Regional Supplementary Procedures.

Item 1 — AIRCRAFT IDENTIFICATION. Report the aircraft radiotelephony call sign.

Item 2 — POSITION. Report position in latitude (degrees as 2 numerics or degrees and minutes as 4 numerics, followed by "North" or "South") and longitude (degrees as 3 numerics or degrees and minutes as 5 numerics, followed by "East" or "West"), or as a significant point identified by a coded designator (2 to 5 characters), or as a significant point followed by magnetic bearing (3 numerics) and distance in nautical miles from the point (e.g. "4620 North 07805 West," "4620 North 07800 West," "4600 North 07800 West," LN ("LIMA NOVEMBER"), "MAY," "HADDY" or "DUB 180 DEGREES 40 MILES"). Precede significant point by "ABEAM",,if applicable.

Item 3 — TIME. Report time in hours and minutes UTC (4 numerics) unless reporting time in minutes past the hour (2 numerics) is prescribed on the basis of regional air navigation agreements. The time reported must be the actual time of the aircraft at the position and not the time of origination or transmission of the report. Time shall always be reported in hours and minutes UTC when making a special air-report.

Item 4 — FLIGHT LEVEL OR ALTITUDE. Report flight level by 3 numerics (e.g. "FLIGHT LEVEL 310"), when on standard pressure altimeter setting. Report altitude in metres followed by "METRES" or in feet followed by "FEET," when on QNH. Report "CLIMBING" (followed by the level) when climbing, or "DESCENDING" (followed by the level) when descending, to a new level after passing the significant point.

Item 5 — NEXT POSITION AND ESTIMATED TIME OVER. Report the next reporting point and the estimated time over such reporting point, or report the estimated position that will be reached one hour later, according to the position reporting procedures in force. Use the data conventions specified in Item 2 for position. Report the estimated time over this position. Report time in hours and minutes UTC (4 numerics) unless reporting time in minutes past the hour (2 numerics) as prescribed on the basis of regional air navigation agreements.

Item 6 — ENSUING SIGNIFICANT POINT. Report the ensuing significant point following the "next position and estimated time over."

Format: Company data (Section 2)

Section 2	7	Estimated time of arrival	(aerodrome) (time)
	8	Endurance	ENDURANCE (hours and minutes)

Figure: Model AIREP, Section 2, from ICAO Doc 4444, Appendix A, §1.

[ICAO Doc 4444, Appendix A, §1, ¶1.1] Section 2 shall be added, in whole or in part, only when so requested by the operator or its designated representative, or when deemed necessary by the pilot-in- command.

This will not apply to the vast majority of corporate aviation.

Format: Meteorology data (Section 3)

[ICAO Doc 4444, Appendix A, §1, ¶1.1] Section 3 shall be added in accordance with Annex 3 and the Regional Supplementary Procedures, Part 3 — Meteorology.

The requirement for a position report varies with region and is normally specified in the applicable en route chart or state pages. In the North Atlantic, not too long ago, the report was mandatory for aircraft not on the organized track system or upon request. These days, with so many aircraft giving real time CPDLC weather reports, the only time you will need to do this is if, for some reason, they ask you to.

If required, the Met Report is given immediately following the position report. If a mid-point report is also given, the position is given first in terms of a four-digit latitude and three digit longitude, such as 4124N 030W.

	9	Air temperature	TEMPERATURE PLUS (degrees Celsius) TEMPERATURE MINUS (degrees Celsius)	
	10	Wind direction	WIND (number) DEGREES	or CALM
	11	Wind speed	(number) KILOMETRES PER HOUR or KNOTS	
	12	Turbulence	TURBULENCE LIGHT TURBULENCE MODERATE TURBULENCE SEVERE	
	13	Aircraft icing	ICING LIGHT ICING MODERATE ICING SEVERE	
	14	Humidity (if available)	HUMIDITY (per cent)	
Section 3	15	Phenomenon encountered or observed, prompting a special air-report: • Severe turbulence • Severe icing • Severe mountainwave • Thunderstorms without hail • Thunderstorms with hail • Heavy dust/sandstorm • Volcanic ash cloud • Pre-eruption volcanic activity or volcanic eruption SST: • Moderate turbulence • Hail • Cumulonimbus clouds	TURBULENCE SEVERE ICING SEVERE MOUNTAINWAVE SEVERE THUNDERSTORMS THUNDERSTORMS WITH HAIL DUSTSTORM or SANDSTORM HEAVY VOLCANIC ASH CLOUD PRE-ERUPTION VOLCANIC ACTIVITY or VOLCANIC ERUPTION TURBULENCE MODERATE HAIL CB CLOUDS	

Figure: Model AIREP, Section 3, from ICAO Doc 4444, Appendix A, §1.

Example Position Report

Item	Spoken
Aircraft identification	NOVEMBER SEVEN SEVEN ZERO ZERO
Position	CHECKS FIVE SEVEN NORTH ZERO THREE ZERO WEST
Time (ATA)	AT TWO ONE TWO ZERO ZULU
Altitude	FLIGHT LEVEL FOUR THREE ZERO
Next reporting point	ESTIMATES FIVE SIX NORTH ZERO FOUR ZERO WEST
Time (ETA)	AT TWO TWO ZERO FOUR
Next significant point	FIVE THREE NORTH ZERO FIVE ZERO WEST NEXT
Temperature (at this point)	MINUS FOUR FIVE
Wind (at this point)	TWO FOUR ZERO DIAGONAL TWO ONE

Midpoint position	FIVE SEVEN ZERO FIVE NORTH ZERO TWO FIVE WEST
Temperature (mid-point)	MINUS FOUR EIGHT
Wind (midpoint)	TWO FIVE ZERO DIAGONAL TWO FIVE
	OVER

About the met report: back in the old days you could tell a pro by the seamless transition between each item, right after the word "Next" would come "minus . . .", it was a thing of beauty. These days, however, nobody is giving weather reports and the radio operator is likely to be just as out of practice receiving met reports as you are giving them.

Chapter 4

Satellite Voice Communications

*W*e used to refer to the satellite phones in our cockpit as "SATCOM" be-*cause we were communicating via satellite. But the addition of data transmission has changed all that so it is important to have the new definitions in your head. This from the glossary in ICAO Doc 9869:*

- *SATCOM: Satellite communications (used only when referring generally to both voice and data satellite communication)*
- *SATVOICE: Satellite voice communications*

SATCOM is pretty much behind the scenes with other data communications and is effectively transparent to us as pilots. Your interfaces with CPDLC and ADS-C could be through SATCOM or VHF. It is all some form of data link to you.

SATVOICE is just another form of radio that allows you to talk to someone. Can you use SATVOICE to make a position report? In most parts of the world, yes. Can you use SATVOICE to replace the requirement for an HF? No, you still need at least one HF. Can you plan on using SATVOICE for air traffic services with an HF as backup? If the region you are flying has made such provisions and you have a qualified system, yes. But how do you know your system qualifies? The easiest way to tell is to look at your MEL.

SATVOICE as a Long Range Communications System (LRCS)

Can SATVOICE be used as a LRCS? Yes.

[AC 91-70B, ¶4.3.3] In keeping with ICAO's recognition of SATVOICE as a valid Long-Range Communication System (LRCS), the FAA accommodates SATVOICE through arrangements with the recognized Aeronautical Mobile Satellite (Route) Service (AMS(R)S) providers. Direct SATVOICE contact between the pilot and ATC is currently limited to distress and urgency situations, or other exceptional circumstances only.

[ICAO Doc 9869, ¶3.2.1.1.] The RCP 400/V$_{RO}$ allocations are applicable to the controller intervention capability via a radio operator using SATVOICE.

[ICAO Doc 9869, Table B-3] The SATVOICE system shall be capable of detecting loss of service, equipment failures and/or logon failures and provide indication to the controller/radio operator or flight crew of system status.

You can use SATVOICE to communicate, but the RCP is no better than your HF radio, and not every SATVOICE system qualifies. How do you know your SATVOICE qualifies? The easiest way is to research your MEL.

Does your SATVOICE qualify as a LRCS? Maybe.

[FAA MMEL Policy Letter (PL)106]

The regulations now address long-range communication requirements in terms of LRCS. With that as a basis, an aircraft on extended range segments unable to utilize line-of-sight systems must have at least two operational LRCSs to honor regulatory communication requirements (unless specifically excepted under the operational rules).

While CPDLC enhances ATS communications for normal use, it is not adequate for non-routine and emergency communications and therefore not appropriate as a basis for MMEL relief of HF communication systems (ref. FAA Legal Interpretation dated 06 Dec 2011 regarding 14 CFR § 121.99 data/com in lieu of voice requirements). In addition, some ATS facility may not be capable of providing SATVOICE services as a LRCS. HF-voice is the only LRCS currently available for Air Traffic Control communications in many areas. Therefore, in areas requiring two operational LRCSs, at least one must be HF-voice when the MEL is applied. In areas requiring one LRCS, that system must be HF-voice.

Example Aircraft SATVOICE LRCS

You cannot assume a satellite telephone installed in your aircraft qualifies as a suitable LRCS that can take the place of one HF. The satellite telephone must pass several security and Required Communications Performance (RCP) tests. The easiest way for you, the pilot, to tell if your system qualifies is to check your MMEL. The following example shows an acceptable system:

POLICY:

Aircraft SATVOICE systems accessed from ground operators by direct dial commercial numbers vice the aircraft address will not be considered for HF MEL relief.

The following standard MMEL proviso and repair category is adopted to provide standardization among all MMELs:

ATA 23 COMMUNICATIONS	Repair Interval	Number Installed	Number Required for Dispatch	Remarks or Exceptions
23-XX High Frequency (HF) Communications System	D	-	-	Any in excess of those required by 14 CFR may be inoperative.
	C	-	1	(O) May be inoperative while conducting operations that require two LRCS provided: a) **Aircraft SATVOICE system** operates normally, b) **SATVOICE services are available as a LRCS** over the intended route of flight, c) **The ICAO Flight Plan is updated (as required) to notify ATC of the communications equipment status of the aircraft, and** d) Alternate procedures are established and used.

Each Flight Operations Evaluation Board (FOEB) Chair should apply this Policy to affected MMELs through the normal FOEB process.

Figure: FAA LRCS MMEL Policy, p. 3

If your MMEL does not have this statement, you might not have a qualified system, you will have more research to do. (You should contact your aircraft manufacturer.)

ARINC SATCOM Voice Procedures

[ARINC Handbook, ¶2.6]

ARINC Communications Centers are equipped to receive and originate SATCOM Voice calls from or to suitably equipped aircraft. It is recognized that these systems, due to cost and other requirements, are still not available to a large number of aircraft; however, ARINC has the capability to use SAT-COM Voice as an alternative means of communications for either ATC or AOC communications with those aircraft that have been equipped. The me-

181

dium used for communications is transparent to the end user. All ARINC services using HF/VHF are available, and SATCOM Voice messages either can be relayed by the ARINC Radio Operator or the call-in progress can be connected to other phone lines (conferenced) through the telephone control system at each ARINC Communications Center.

ARINC says the use of SATCOM is "transparent" to the end user, meaning ATC. Many of the ATC sources say you should use SATCOM in lieu of HF or CPDLC only in unusual circumstances.

Note: When using SATCOM voice, continue to use radio discipline procedures. Using the SATCOM phone like a regular telephone can cause misunderstandings and confusion.

The phone call ends up with the HF radio operator who is expecting you to use the same terminology as if on HF.

Satellite Voice-equipped aircraft should direct calls to the appropriate ARINC Communications Center using either INMARSAT-assigned security phone numbers (ICAO short codes) or direct dial using the 10-digit PSTN phone number:

Pacific Flights	Atlantic Flights
SFO 436625	NYC 436623
1-925-371-3920	1-631-244-2492

You will be using INMARSAT satellites but your aircraft may or may not have an INMARSAT phone. To use the short codes you need an INMARSAT phone.

Note: These six-digit numbers are converted by the Ground Earth Station (GES) receiving the aircraft call announcement to the respective PSTN dial number for connection to the appropriate ARINC Center. This only works on the INMARSAT satellite system.

After an answer by the ARINC Radio Operator, the parties should complete the exchange of information using the same procedures as would be used on other voice (HF/VHF) communications mediums.

Chapter 5

Controller-Pilot Data Link Communications (CPDLC)

*Y*ou can think of Controller-Pilot Data Link Communications as a replacement for your HF when oceanic and VHF over some domestic areas. It is
far superior to your HF and has distinct advantages over VHF.

Purpose

*The role CPDLC plays in the Future Air Navigation System is to reduce the
time it takes for air traffic control to issue instructions to a pilot and the pilot
to acknowledge. In a domestic environment this is rarely a problem. When
oceanic, however, it can be a factor. Reducing that time, known as Required
Communications Performance (RCP), allows ATC to reduce aircraft spacing.*

[ICAO Doc 4444, ¶5.4.1.2.1.6] Lateral separation of aircraft on parallel or
non-intersecting tracks or ATS routes. Within designated airspace or on
designated routes, lateral separation between aircraft operating on parallel
or non-intersecting tracks or ATS routes shall be established in accordance
with the following:

- for a minimum spacing between tracks of 93 km (50 NM) a navigational
  performance of RNAV 10 (RNP 10), RNP 4 or RNP 2 shall be prescribed;

- for a minimum spacing between tracks of 42.6 km (23 NM) a navigational performance of RNP 4 or RNP 2 shall be prescribed. The communication system shall satisfy required communication performance
  240 (RCP 240) and the surveillance system shall satisfy required surveillance performance 180 (RSP 180). Conformance monitoring shall
  be ensured by establishing an ADS-C event contract specifying a lateral
  deviation change event with a maximum of 5 NM threshold and a waypoint change event;

- for a minimum spacing between tracks of 27.8 km (15 NM) a navigational performance of RNP 2 or a GNSS equipage shall be prescribed. Direct controller-pilot VHF voice communication shall be maintained while such separation is applied;

- for a minimum spacing between tracks of 13 km (7 NM), applied while one aircraft climbs/descends through the level of another aircraft, a navigational performance of RNP 2 or a GNSS equipage shall be prescribed. Direct controller-pilot VHF voice communication shall be maintained while such separation is applied; and

- for a minimum spacing between tracks of 37 km (20 NM), applied while one aircraft climbs/descends through the level of another aircraft whilst using other types of communication than specified in d) above, a navigational performance of RNP 2 or a GNSS equipage shall be prescribed.

You need CPDLC to begin the process of reducing separation standards. This is in your best interests, since the best routes — best winds, shortest distances — will be reserved for those able to fly with reduced separation.

Operational Differences Between Voice Communications and CPDLC

If you have CPDLC and you are in airspace where CPDLC is being used, you should use CPDLC as primary, voice communications as secondary. The general rule of thumb is: if contacted by CPDLC, respond with CPDLC; if contacted by voice, response with voice. When oceanic you still need to check in with HF, get a good SELCAL check, and maintain a listening watch if SELCAL fails.

[ICAO Doc 10037, ¶4.1.2.]

With voice, the natural ability for each flight crew member to understand incoming and outgoing transmissions for their own aircraft has provided a certain level of situational awareness among the flight crew. With CPDLC, flight crew procedures need to ensure that the flight crew has an equivalent level of situational awareness associated with understanding the content and intent of a message in the same way.

Each flight crew member (e.g. pilot flying and pilot monitoring) should individually review each CPDLC uplink message prior to responding to and/or executing any clearance, and individually review each CPDLC downlink message prior to transmission. Reading a message individually is a key element to ensuring that each flight crew member does not infer any preconceived intent different from what is intended or appropriate.

To minimize errors, when responding to a clearance with RSPD-1 WILCO, each flight crew member should read the uplink message individually (silently) before initiating a discussion about whether and how to act on the message.

In a similar manner, each flight crew member should individually review CPDLC downlink messages before the message is sent. Having one flight crew member (e.g. the pilot monitoring) input the message and having a different flight crew member (pilot flying) review the message before it is sent provides an adequate level of situational awareness comparable to or better than voice communication.

If an operator uses augmented crews, the flight crew carrying out the 'handover' briefing should thoroughly brief the 'changeover' flight crew or flight crew member on the status of ADS-C and CPDLC connections and messages, including a review of any pertinent uplink and downlink CPDLC messages (e.g. conditional clearances).

[ICAO Doc 10037, ¶4.1.2.]

When operating within airspace beyond the range of DCPC VHF voice communication, CPDLC is available and local ATC procedures do not state otherwise, the flight crew should normally choose CPDLC as the means of communication. The flight crew would use voice as an alternative means of communication (e.g. VHF, HF or SATVOICE direct or via a radio operator).

In airspace where both DCPC VHF voice and CPDLC communication services are provided, and local ATC procedures do not state otherwise, the flight crew will determine the communication medium to use at any given time.

Note.— ICAO Doc 4444, paragraph 8.3.2, requires that DCPC be established prior to the provision of ATS surveillance services, unless special circumstances, such as emergencies, dictate otherwise. This does not prevent the use of CPDLC for ATC communications, voice being immediately available for intervention and to address non-routine and time critical situations.

To minimize pilot head down time and potential distractions during critical phases of flight, the flight crew should use voice for ATC communications when operating below 10,000 ft AGL.

During an emergency, the flight crew would normally revert to voice communications. However, the flight crew may use CPDLC for emergency communications if it is either more expedient or if voice contact cannot be established.

Except as provided in paragraph 4.6.1.2, the flight crew should respond to a CPDLC message via CPDLC, and should respond to a voice message via voice (ICAO Doc 4444 14.3.1.3).

Note.— This will lessen the opportunity for messages to get lost, discarded or unanswered between the ATS unit and the flight crew and cause unintended consequences.

If the intent of an uplink message is uncertain, the flight crew should respond to the uplink message with RSPD-2 UNABLE and obtain clarification using voice.

Note.— For FANS 1/A aircraft, some uplink messages do not have a DM 1 UNABLE response. On these aircraft, the flight crew should respond with DM 3 ROGER and then obtain clarification via voice.

Regardless of whether CPDLC is being used, the flight crew should continuously monitor VHF/HF/UHF emergency frequency. In addition, the flight crew should continuously maintain a listening or SELCAL watch on the specified backup or secondary frequency (frequencies).

Domestic CPDLC

It may seem confusing, but you can begin to grasp the problem by understanding not all CPDLC is created equally:

[ICAO Doc 10037, Table 1-1.]

ACARS ATS — ATS applications, departure clearance (DCL), oceanic clearance (OCL) and data link – automatic terminal information service (D-ATIS), supported by aircraft communications addressing and reporting system (ACARS).

FANS 1/A — Initial future air navigation system (FANS 1/A) ATS applications, AFN, CPDLC and ADS-C, supported by FANS 1/A over ACARS. Note.— FANS 1/A typically involve communication (CPDLC), navigation (RNAV/RNP) and surveillance (ADS-C). This document refers to the FANS 1/A for the data link system, which includes the CPDLC and ADS-C applications.

FANS 1/A+ — Same as FANS 1/A, except with additional features, such as the message latency monitor function.

ATN B1 — ATS applications, CM and CPDLC, supported by aeronautical telecommunication network – baseline 1 (ATN B1): a) Context management (CM) application for data link initiation capability (DLIC); b) CPDLC for ATC communications management (ACM), ATC clearance (ACL), and ATC microphone check (AMC), except that: 1) CONFIRM ASSIGNED LEVEL and SYSU-5 USE OF LOGICAL ACKNOWLEDGEMENT PROHIBITED will not be used by the ATSU; and 2) ASSIGNED LEVEL (level) is not required by the aircraft.

VDL M2 — Very high frequency data link – mode 2

[ICAO Doc 10037, ¶1.2.1.2.]

The ATN B1 data link system relies on the aeronautical telecommunication network (ATN), which is provided and maintained by various communication service providers (CSPs) and/or ANSPs.

The ATN relies only on VHF (VDL M2) to meet the performance required for the intended operations.

Most aircraft certified, equipped, maintained, and operated in the United States will have installed an older version of CPDLC called Future Air Navigation System (FANS 1/A) with Air Traffic Services (ATS) applications, ATC Facilities Notification (AFN), CPDLC and ADS-C.

Many aircraft certified, equipped, maintained, and operated outside the United States recently, as well as many recently certified in the United States, will have installed a newer version of CPDLC that adheres to a newer standard called Aeronautical Telecommunications Network Baseline 1 (ATN B1). A part of the newer standard that is probably not installed on FANS 1/A aircraft is Very High Frequency Data Link Mode 2 (VDL M2), sometimes called "protected mode VHF Data Link" (PM CPDLC).

You can operate in most (if not all) oceanic and remote airspace with a FANS 1/A aircraft, even if you do not have VDL M2. This capability carries into at least the first domestic ATSU, since they are responsible for the transition to and from oceanic.

You may find yourself without CPDLC coverage domestically if you do not have ATN B1 and VDL M2. Most European countries specifically say "log-on from FANS 1/A or non-PM CPDLC capable aircraft will not be accepted."

CPDLC in the United States: Departure Clearance (DCL)

[NAS Data Communications Guide, Ch 3] The Controller-Pilot Data Link Communication-Departure Clearance (CPDLC DCL) provides automated assistance for delivering initial and revised departure clearances. CPDLC DCL provides the following: flight plan route, initial and requested altitude, beacon code assignment and departure frequency. CPDLC DCL messages are established message sets in Future Air Navigation System (FANS) equipped aircraft. The CPDLC DCL service is designed for use in surface operations and replaces the existing Pre-Departure Clearance (PDC) at Tower Data Link Services (TDLS) sites for participating aircraft.

[NAS Data Communications Guide, Ch 4]

Flight crews will have a flight plan (paper or electronic) on board to initially load the FMS with the filed route of flight. Crews should load the flight plan that was filed with ATC.

Logon or Notification to ATC may be completed anytime during pre-flight operations. Within 30 minutes of the proposed departure time (P-30), an "ATC Connection Established" message will be received by the aircraft. [. . .] If the initial attempt to logon/notification fails, flight crews should ensure that a flight plan is on file, verify the logon information is correct, then one additional logon attempt should be made. If the second logon attempt fails, the crew should revert to voice and contact clearance delivery for the departure clearance.

Once a successful ATC session has been established and your departure clearance has been approved by the controller, the CPDLC DCL will be automatically sent to the aircraft.

Flight crews should treat any CPDLC DCL sent to the aircraft just like they would any voice or PDC per company approved CPDLC standard operating procedures when reviewing and accepting route clearances. One additional feature of the CPDLC DCL is the ability to send revisions to a previously cleared flight plan. Revisions can be received at any time until the aircraft is ready for takeoff. Amendments can be a simple altitude change or a more complex full re-route clearance. When notified of a revised clearance, flight crews should use good judgment and follow company procedures, especially when the clearance is received just prior to takeoff.

When an initial/revised CPDLC DCL is received, flight crews should, in accordance with company policy or best operational judgment, review the initial or revised clearance and respond with ACCEPT-WILCO / REJECT-UNABLE / STANDBY, as appropriate.

CPDLC in the United States: En Route

As of late 2020, the CPDLC En Route program in the United States is still in a test phase with limited participation. Contact your manufacturer to see if your participation in the program is possible.

[NAS Data Communications Guide, Ch 7]

After departure from an airport with CPDLC DCL services and the aircraft had a CPDLC session while on the ground, the CPDLC session will be maintained by the FAA ground system while climbing through TRACON airspace until the aircraft enters En Route airspace. Once the aircraft has entered En Route ATC airspace and the controller has CPDLC turned on at their workstation the ground system will assign CPDLC eligibility (assuming the flight is approved for en route CPDLC services and is properly equipped) with the appropriate controller and CPDLC services may then be used. The first indication of CPDLC services availability would be an uplinked CPDLC clearance or transfer of communication from the ATC controller.

Takeoff without a CPDLC session or Logging On to KUSA while Airborne. If a flight crew is located at a non-CPDLC equipped airport, and CPDLC network coverage is available, a log on can be performed while the aircraft is on the ground. The flight crew may also log on while airborne within U.S. domestic airspace, or prior to entering U.S. domestic airspace. Assuming the logon is accepted, the connection request will be handled and established via the triggers in the next session.

After successful initiation of a CPDLC session by the En Route automation system, the En Route system will uplink a Current Data Authority (CDA) confirmation message to confirm that the connection is recognized by the aircraft as a CDA connection. A UM169 free text message containing adapted text (e.g., CONFIRM CPDLC CONTACT WITH KUSA. ROGER/ACCEPT THIS MESSAGE) is used for this uplink.

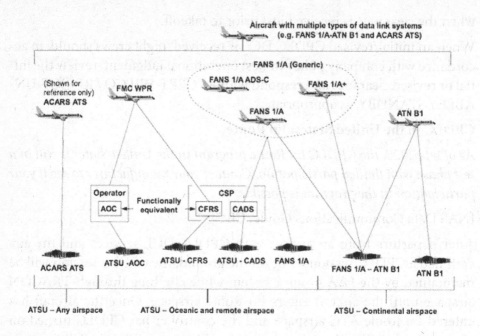

Figure: Different ATSU/Aircraft Connectivity (ICAO Doc 10037, fig. 1-2)

Why Europe is Different

[EU Commission Regulation No 29/2009, Article I, ¶ 3.] This Regulation shall apply to all flights operating as general air traffic in accordance with instrument flight rules within the airspace above FL285 defined in Parts A and B of Annex I.

[EU Commission Regulation No 29/2009, Annex I, Parts A and B] The airspace referred to in [. . .] Article 1(3) shall include the airspace above FL 285 within the following Flight Information Regions (FIR) and Upper Flight Information Regions (UIR): Amsterdam FIR, Wien FIR, Barcelona UIR, Brindisi UIR, Brussels UIR, Canarias UIR, France UIR, Hannover UIR, Lisboa UIR, London UIR, Madrid UIR, Milano UIR, Rhein UIR, Roma UIR, Scottish UIR, Shannon UIR, Bratislava FIR, Bucuresti FIR, Budapest FIR, Kobenhavn FIR, Ljubljana FIR, Nicosia FIR, Praha FIR, Sofia FIR, Warszawa FIR, Zagreb FIR, Finland UIR south of 61°30, Hellas UIR, Malta UIR, Riga UIR, Sweden UIR south of 61°30, Tallinn UIR, Vilnius UIR.

[EU Commission Regulation No 29/2009, Annex IV, Part B] Requirements for air-ground communications based on ATN and VDL Mode 2.

Air-ground communications shall be designed to support end-to-end communications and to ensure seamless provision and use of communications services to air-ground applications defined in the ICAO standards specified in points 2 and 3 of Annex III in the airspace referred to in Article 1(3).

Air-ground communications shall comply with safety and performance requirements of the data link services defined in Annex II.

Air-ground communications shall be based on a common addressing scheme.

The transmission and reception of data units between ground and aircraft systems hosting the air-ground applications defined in the ICAO standards specified in points 2 and 3 of Annex III shall be based on communication protocols which comply with the ICAO standards defining the Aeronautical Telecommunication Network referred to in point 4 of Annex III.

The ground and aircraft communication system characteristics and the transmission and reception of bit frames between ground and aircraft communication systems shall comply with the ICAO standards defining the very high frequency digital link, VDL Mode 2, referred to in point 5 of Annex III.

[EU Commission Regulation No 29/2009, Annex III, Part B, Points 2, 3, 4]

Chapter 3 — Aeronautical Telecommunication Network, Section 3.5.1.1 'Context Management' (CM) application items (a) and (b) of ICAO Annex 10 — Aeronautical Telecommunications — Volume III, Part I (Digital Data Communication Systems) (Second edition, July 2007, incorporating amendments 70-82).

Chapter 3 — Aeronautical Telecommunication Network, Section 3.5.2.2 'Controller-Pilot Data Link Communications' (CPDLC) application items (a) and (b) of ICAO Annex 10 — Aeronautical Telecommunications — Volume III, Part I (Digital Data Communication Systems) (Second edition, July 2007, incorporating amendments 70-82).

Chapter 3 — Aeronautical Telecommunication Network, Sections 3.3, 3.4 and 3.6 of ICAO Annex 10 — Aeronautical Telecommunications — Volume III, Part I (Digital Data Communication Systems) (Second edition, July 2007, incorporating amendments 70-82).

[ICAO Annex 10, Volume III, Part I, ¶3.3, 3.4, and 3.6 extracted]

The ATN shall either use International Organization for Standardization (ISO) communication standards for open systems interconnection (OSI) or use the Internet Society (ISOC) communications standards for the Internet Protocol Suite (IPS).

ATN/IPS implementation is preferred for ground-ground networks. While ATN/OSI continues to be supported in air-ground networks, particularly when using VDL Mode 2, it is expected that future air-ground implementations will use the ATN/IPS.

[ICAO Doc 10037, ¶1.2.1.2] The ATN B1 data link system relies on the aeronautical telecommunication network (ATN), which is provided and maintained by various CSPs and/or ANSPs. The ATN was developed by ICAO to support the need for ATS communications. The ATN relies only on VHF (VDL M2) to meet the performance required for the intended operations.

You will need an ATN B1 system to use your CPDLC over domestic European airspace once you've coasted in. FANS 1/A will not work. As of late 2020, you can fly anywhere in Europe without ATN B1, you just can't use data link. Even if you have it, however, you have to get onto a "white list."

The European Data Link Services Mandate aims to restrict noncompliant and non-exempt aircraft to flight below FL285. Some older aircraft will be exempt. The GI, GII, GIII, GIV, G450, G100, G150, and G200, for example are exempt. EuroControl publishes a "Logon List," known as the "White List" to some, Information about the list, getting on the list, and why it does or does not matter: https://ext.eurocontrol.int/WikiLink/index.php/Logon_List.

This is a moving target. The Gulfstream GVII-G500, for example, has ATN B1 but cannot join the White List for a while longer.

Operational Notes

Confirm Assigned Route Message

This message started as a way of reminding pilots on "half-tracks" in the North Atlantic of that fact, but it has spread to everyone.

[http://flightservicebureau.org/shanwick-new-nat-procedure/]

Short and simple: with the half-tracks, the potential for Nav Errors are now (quite a lot, perhaps) higher than before. Waypoints are that bit more complicated, and 5030N 30W is a little too similar to 50N 30W.

So, to prevent you reading back the clearance correctly and then screwing up the route in the FMS, Shanwick (and Gander from 01DEC16) will ask you via data link "What are you planning to fly?" once you enter the Ocean.

All you have to do is ack the message, scroll through your route and check it looks OK, and send it back down to them. If it's the same as your clearance, then that's that. If not, or you don't reply, you'll get an additional telegram from Shanwick.

Flight Crew Response Times

[ICAO GOLD, ¶4.3.2.]

System performance requirements have been established to support reduced separation standards. Specific latency times have been allocated to the technical performance, and flight crew and controller response times. Regional/ State monitoring agencies analyze actual performance to ensure the technical and operational components of the system meet required standards. For example, to support RCP 240 operations, the flight crew is expected to be able to respond to a CPDLC uplink message within one minute.

For an ATN-B1 aircraft, the flight crew should respond to a CPDLC uplink message within 100 seconds to prevent the CPDLC uplink message from automatically timing out.

Note.— ATN-B1 aircraft use a CPDLC message response timer, which is set at 100 seconds upon receipt of the CPDLC uplink message. If the flight crew has not sent a response within this time:

- the flight crew is no longer provided with any response prompts for the message;
- the aircraft sends an ERROR message for display to the controller; and
- the aircraft and ground systems close the dialogue.

When a CPDLC uplink message automatically times out, the flight crew should contact ATC by voice.

The flight crew should respond to CPDLC messages as soon as practical after they are received. For most messages, the flight crew will have adequate time to read and respond within one minute. However, the flight crew should not be pressured to respond without taking adequate time to fully understand the CPDLC message and to satisfy other higher priority operational demands. If additional time is needed, the flight crew should send a RSPD-3 STANDBY response.

Note.— For ATN B1 aircraft systems, if the flight crew does not send an operational response within 100 seconds after the RSPD-3 STANDBY was sent, the CPDLC uplink message will time out (refer to paragraph 4.3.2.3).

If a RSPD-3 STANDBY response has been sent, the flight crew should provide a subsequent closure response to the CPDLC message.

Note 1.— In the case of a RSPD-3 STANDBY response, the uplink message remains open until the flight crew responds with a RSPD-1 WILCO or RSPD-2 UNABLE. If the closure response is not received within a reasonable period of time, the controller is expected to query the flight crew per paragraph 3.3.1.2.

Note 2.— Transmission times for messages may vary for a number of reasons including the type of transmission media, network loading, or the criteria for transitioning from one media to another (e.g. VHF/Satcom). Operational response times may vary depending on workload and complexity of the instruction or clearance.

It is said that if they don't hear back from you in sixty seconds, they will consider the communication lost and if a clearance was involved, that clearance is cancelled. I've not seen that in writing but the threat is clear: respond within a minute, use "STANDBY" if you must. When dealing with clearances, I usually hit the print button, send the acknowledge, and then read the contents. I figure I can always respond a second time if I have to.

FMS Waypoint Sequencing

You don't have to worry about flying a Strategic Lateral Offset because your FMS will sequence the waypoints even if you are two miles away from the intended course. But if you are further than the tolerance allowed by your FMS, it may not sequence. If that happens, the position report will not be made.

[ICAO Doc 10037, ¶4.5.1.6]

The flight crew should ensure that waypoints are sequenced correctly. If an aircraft passes abeam a waypoint by more than the aircraft FMS waypoint sequencing parameter, the flight crew should sequence the waypoints in the FMS, as appropriate.

Latency Timer

[NAT OPS Bulletin 2018-002, ¶2.1] The intention of the message latency monitor function is to prevent pilots from acting on a CPDLC uplink message that has been delayed in the network. The most serious of such cases would be the pilot executing a clearance that was no longer valid.

There have been instances with airlines and business jets receiving ATC instructions to climb via CPDLC that did not get delivered to the crew until the following flight. In at least one case the crew executed the climb causing a possible loss of separation.

[NAT OPS Bulletin 2018-002, ¶2.1] When the pilot receives the uplink CPDLC message SET MAX UPLINK DELAY VALUE TO [delayed message parameter] SECONDS he/she shall:

a) Send a positive response to ATC as prompted by the avionics (ACCEPT [ROGER]) regardless of whether the aircraft supports the latency monitor.

b) If the aircraft is equipped with a correctly functioning message latency monitor, enter the specified uplink delay into the avionics in accordance with the aircraft procedures. Some avionics will automatically set the delay value in accordance with the uplink message and do not allow for a manual input.

Refer to your aircraft manuals for specific responses. Three particular Gulfstreams provide examples of three possible reponses:

Older G450's without latency timers will respond: "TIMER NOT AVAILABLE"

GVII will respond "ROGER" and enter the requested time in the "Max Uplink Delay" field on the TSC data link page.

G280 will respond and set the value automatically, no pilot action required.

Position Reporting With CPDLC

When do you need to do a CPDLC position report? It depends! ADS-C might have you covered but some ATSU's want them anyway. The only way to know for sure is to check Appendix B of ICAO Doc 10037. For example, position reports with Gander Oceanic are not required because they don't ask for them. Position reports are required with Mauritus because they do ask for them in Appendix B.

[ICAO Doc 10037, ¶4.4.6.1] When using CPDLC to provide position information, the flight crew should report unnamed waypoints (latitudes/longitudes) using the ICAO format of nn[N/S]nnn[E/W] or, if both degrees and minutes are required, nnnn[N/S]nnnnn[E/W].

Note.— The flight crew and flight operations officers/dispatchers should not use the ARINC 424 format. ARINC 424 describes a 5-character latitude/longitude format for aircraft navigation databases (e.g. 10N40 describes a lat/long of 10N140W). The ATS unit may reject or be unable to process any downlink message containing waypoint names in the ARINC 424 format.

[Oakland Center Guidance, ¶3] Oakland OCA/FIR (KZAK) cannot accept position reports containing latitude and longitude (Lat/Long) in the ARINC 424 format, which is limited to five characters (e.g. 40N50). Position reports in the KZAK CPDLC service area containing Lat/Long waypoints will be accepted in complete latitude and longitude format only. Flights unable to send position reports in complete latitude and longitude format must accomplish position reporting via HF voice communications.

This holds true everywhere in the world. Air Traffic Control does not understand what you mean by "40N50" even if your FMS does. In that case, 40N050W would be called for.

Position Reporting in a non-ADS-C environment

[ICAO Doc 10037, ¶4.4.6.2]

When ADS-C is not available, the flight crew should conduct position reporting by voice or CPDLC. When using CPDLC, the flight crew should send RTED-5 POSITION REPORT (position report) whenever an ATC waypoint is sequenced, (or passed abeam when offset flight is in progress).

When using CPDLC for position reporting, the flight crew should send position reports only at compulsory reporting points and ensure that the position and next position information applies to compulsory reporting points, unless requested otherwise by ATC. The ensuing significant point after the next position may be either a compulsory or non-compulsory reporting point (refer AIREP form ICAO Doc 4444, Appendix 1).

Position Reporting in an ADS-C environment

[ICAO Doc 10037, ¶4.4.6.3]

Note.— In an ADS-C environment, the flight crew should not provide position reports or revised waypoint estimates by CPDLC or voice, unless otherwise instructed or under conditions in certain airspace as stipulated in AIP (or other appropriate publication).

If required by regional supplementary procedures or AIP (or other appropriate publication), the flight crew should provide a CPDLC position report when either of the following events occurs:

an initial CPDLC connection is established; or

the CPDLC connection transfer has been completed (i.e. at the associated boundary entry position).

Note.— Some ANSPs require a single CPDLC position report, even when in an ADS-C environment, to provide the controlling ATS unit confirmation that it is the CDA and the only ATS unit able to communicate with the aircraft via CPDLC (refer to Appendix B).

In general you should not provide position reports or revised waypoint estimates by CPDLC or voice unless you see something that tells you to do so. Appendix B can be misleading. The subject is only brought up in the North Atlantic region where you are explicitly told "For ADS-C flights, the flight crew should not submit position reports via voice to reduce frequency congestion, unless requested by aeronautical radio operator." Makes sense, but don't let that talk you into thinking now you need to do so in other regions because the same phrase is missing.

The flight crew should include only ATC waypoints in cleared segments of the aircraft active flight plan. However, when an ATC clearance eliminates a waypoint, it is permissible to retain and report the point abeam of that waypoint since this ensures retention of meteorological data associated with the eliminated waypoint.

Note.— If the flight crew inserts non-ATC waypoints (e.g. mid-points) into the aircraft active flight plan and activates the change, the aircraft system may trigger an ADS-C waypoint change event report at the non-ATC waypoint, or include information about the non-ATC waypoint in the predicted route group, as well as the intermediate and fixed projected intent groups. As a result, the ADS-C report will include information about the non-ATC waypoint, which is not expected by the ATC ground system.

The flight crew should maintain the active route in the aircraft system to be the same as the ATC cleared route of flight.

Note.— If the flight crew activates a non-ATC cleared route into the aircraft system, the ADS-C reports will include information that will indicate the aircraft is flying a route that is deviating from the cleared route.

When reporting by ADS-C only, the flight crew should include ATC waypoints in the aircraft active flight plan even if they are not compulsory reporting points.

Position Reports at FIR Boundaries

[ICAO Doc 10037, ¶4.4.6.3.1 Note] Some ANSPs require a single CPDLC position report, even when in an ADS-C environment, to provide the controlling ATS unit confirmation that it is the CDA and the only ATS unit able to communicate with the aircraft via CPDLC (refer to Appendix B).

Fukuoka	O	O	N	RJJJ	FUKJJYA	IPACG FIT	CPDLC voice transfer: CONTACT TOKYO CENTER [frequency] Confirm CPDLC CDA: One CPDLC position report at FIR boundary. See paragraph E.2.2.
Gander	O	O	O	CZQX	YQXE2YA	NAT CNSG	Report revised ETA: Next waypoint ETA error 3 minutes or more, use free text DM 67k

Figure: Gander vs. Fukuoka Position Reporting Requirements under CPDLC, from ICAO Gold, Appendix B.

This is often taught this way: "Send a position report whenever entering oceanic airspace, except in the North Atlantic," meaning the North Atlantic is the only exception. In fact, the rule seems to be: "Send a position report crossing an FIR boundary if Appendix B tells you to."

Chapter 6

CPDLC Checklist

*L*ike anything else, after you become familiar with the procedures the check-list becomes less necessary. Also like many things in aviation, if you don't do this often, you should consider using the checklist every single time because you might forget an important step. If your manufacturer or operator doesn't provide a CPDLC checklist it will be up to you to devise one. What follows is the one we've designed for a Gulfstream G450, equipped with a Honeywell system. The procedures may not work for your airplane, but they will get you started.

CPDLC Preflight Setup

1. Ensure you have the following documents in paper form, EFB, or iPad:

    a. ICAO Doc 10037, Global Operational Data Link Document (GOLD)

    b. Any aircraft or company specific guidance

2. Review latest ICAO NAT Bulletins

3. Verify the following appears in your ICAO Flight Plan

    a. Block 7 - Aircraft ID agrees with FMS Flight ID

    b. Block 10A - Equipment Code "J3" and "J5" (Data Link System)

    c. Block 10B - Equipment Code "D1" (ADS)

4. Master Document / En Route Charts

    a. Annotate FIR boundaries

    b. Check FIRs versus GOLD Appendix B and make note of:

        i. CPDLC status

        ii.   ADS-C status

        iii.   AFN address

    c.   Any instructions under Remarks

5.   Confirm COM/NAV3 in Data Mode

6.   Verify Data Link works by any of the following methods:

    a.   Downlink the flight plan

    b.   Downlink D-ATIS

    c.   Downlink PDC

    d.   Downlink Terminal Wx

7.   Check VHF Data Link

    a.   DLK > SYSTEM > DATA LINK MGR

        i.   If data link is GND VHF (VDL) test SATCOM (DLK > STATUS > TEST > DATA LINK SEND)

        ii.   If data link is SAT check GND VHF (VDL) when airborne

8.   Confirm FMS Settings for CPDLC

    a.   Confirm Flight ID entered into TCAS details page of FMS agrees with Block 7 of Flight Plan

    b.   Confirm Data Link is Operational:

        i.   DLK > SYSTEM > DATA LINK MGR

        ii.   VHF available

        iii.   SATCOM available

Downlink Oceanic Clearance

Downlink Oceanic Clearance From DSP (Applies to all except NY Center)

1.   DLK > ATS > OCEANIC CLX

2.   Set ENTRY POINT, ENTRY TIME, and adjust Req Mach and Req FL if required

3.   SEND

4.   ACKNOWLEDGE on receipt

Eastbound North Atlantic Notes

Gander ACC sends the clearance to the GDC 10 to 60 min prior to aircraft entry into oceanic airspace. Gander ACC generally sends the clearance by 70° West longitude.

For aircraft departing Gander (CYQX), Goose Bay (CYYR), and St. John's (CYYT) airports, Gander ACC sends the oceanic clearance to the GDC at the same time it sends the departure clearance to the tower. Read back of the oceanic clearance is given to the tower, after which the tower issues the departure clearance.

With automatic position reports enabled, the GDC automatically sends the clearance to the aircraft as a data link message as soon as it is received from Gander ACC.

If automatic position reports are disabled, the flight crew must request the clearance. Begin requesting the clearance approaching 70° West longitude, but if the clearance is not received by 25 min prior to entry into oceanic airspace, contact Gander ACC on the appropriate voice frequency.

If the GDC has received the oceanic clearance from Gander ACC, the clearance is sent to the aircraft as a data link message. If the GDC has not received the oceanic clearance from Gander ACC, a data link message indicating that the oceanic clearance has not been received from Gander ACC and that the oceanic clearance can be requested again in 10 min is sent to the aircraft.

Multiple oceanic clearance requests can be sent until 25 min prior to entry into oceanic airspace. Oceanic clearances are valid for 30 min beyond the issue time and voice read back of oceanic clearances is required.

Westbound North Atlantic Notes

Delivery of oceanic clearances by way of data link for westbound transatlantic flights for the Shanwick Oceanic Control Area (OCA) is known as Oceanic Route Clearance Authorization (ORCA) and requires that the aircraft be registered with the GDC for the service.

ORCA does not support use of variable call signs. The flight crew should request the clearance by way of data link between 30 and 90 min prior to entry into the Shanwick OCA. Shanwick normally responds to the clearance request with a message indicating that the clearance should be received within the next 15 min. Shanwick then sends the clearance to the aircraft, which contains:

- The aircraft registration
- Entry point, ETA at the entry point
- Mach number
- Flight level
- Route
- Destination

The flight crew must promptly acknowledge the clearance by way of data link, by line selecting ACKNOWLEDGE on the message page containing the clearance. Failure to promptly acknowledge the clearance results in cancellation of the clearance transaction and requires that Shanwick be contacted by voice. Upon receipt of the clearance acknowledgement, Shanwick sends a message to the aircraft confirming the clearance. If this message is not received, Shanwick must be contacted by voice. If the flight crew requests a new clearance or if Shanwick requires a change to an existing clearance, one or more reclearances may be received by the flight crew. These reclearances are annotated RECLEARANCE 1, RECLEARANCE 2, etc., although may not necessarily be numbered consecutively.

Downlink Oceanic Clearance from NY Center (via CPDLC)

1. Will get the oceanic from NY Oceanic via ATC UPLINK message
2. ACCEPT within 60 seconds
3. REVIEW
4. ATC CLEARANCE to interpret LLXX waypoints
5. ACTIVATE to insert into FMS flight plan
6. Remove extraneous waypoints at end of flight plan

CPDLC Log On

When to Log On

[ICAO Doc 10037, ¶4.2.2]

When operating outside data link airspace, the flight crew should initiate a logon 10 to 25 minutes prior to entry into airspace where data link services are provided.

Note.— When departing an aerodrome close to or within such airspace, this may require the logon to be initiated prior to departure.

Where a data link service is only provided in upper airspace and where local procedures do not dictate otherwise, the flight crew should log on to that ATS unit in whose airspace a data link service will first be used.

When failure of a data link connection is detected, the flight crew should terminate the connection and then initiate a new logon with the current ATS unit.

1. Log On Procedure

    a. NAV > ATC > LOGON STATUS

    b. Ensure FLT ID and TAIL NO are correct

    c. Ensure ADS ARMED

    d. Ensure ADS EMERGENCY mode is OFF

    e. On second page, ensure ATC COMM is ARMED

    f. On first page, enter LOGIN ID of FIR (From GOLD Appendix B, En Route Chart, or GAC-OMS-4)

    g. SEND

2. You should see ACCEPTED on LOGON field

3. Once handed over to an ATSU with CPDLC you should see:

    a. ATC COMM ESTABLISHED

    b. LOGON TO field should go blank

    c. The FIR's ID should be in the ACT CTR field

    d. ATC COMM should now be ACTIVE

4. If you are also in an ADS location, you will see ADS ESTABLISHED and the ADS will go from ARMED to ACTIVE.

CPDLC Coast Out

1. Establish log on NET 45 minutes, NLT 15 minutes prior to oceanic FIR

2.   Verify ATC COMM ESTABLISHED and ATSU in ACT CTR

3.   When sent to HF, for example:

_____ Radio, November _____, CPDLC, _____ Next,

"Shanwick Radio, November one two three alpha, CPDLC, Gander Next,

flight level _____, request SELCAL check _____

flight level four one zero, request SELCAL check alpha bravo charlie delta"

4.   If you also have ADS-C, you should hear: "November one two three alpha bravo, Shanwick Radio, SELCAL check OK, voice reports not required in Shanwick OCA, at 30 West contact Gander on three zero one six primary or five five niner eight secondary."

5.   For most ATSU's around the world, you will also send a position report. (This is not required in the North Atlantic.) Check GOLD Appendix B Remarks for the ATSU's requirements.

CPDLC Crossing an FIR Boundary

1.   Before crossing an FIR boundary, you should get a conditional clearance to contact the next ATSU.

2.   Accept the clearance, send, but do not contact the next ATSU yet.

3.   On the LOGON/STATUS page you will see the NEXT CTR field has the next ATSU listed.

4.   When the next ATSU takes control, you will see ATC COMM ESTABLISHED

5.   A check-in with the departing controller is not necessary.

6.   At the waypoint listed, contact the new controller.

[ICAO Doc 10037, ¶4.2.3]

Under normal circumstances, the current and next ATS units automatically transfer CPDLC and ADS-C services. The transfer is seamless to the flight crew.

Note.— The flight crew should not need to reinitiate a logon.

The flight crew should promptly respond to CPDLC uplink messages to minimize the risk of an open CPDLC uplink message when transferring to the next ATS unit.

Note.— If a flight is transferred to a new ATS unit with an open CPDLC message, the message status will change to ABORTED. If the flight crew has not yet received a response from the controller, the downlink request will also display the ABORTED status.

Prior to the point at which the current ATS unit will transfer CPDLC and/ or ADS-C services, the flight crew may receive an instruction to close any open CPDLC messages.

When entering the next ATS unit's airspace, the flight crew should confirm the successful transfer from the current ATS unit to the next ATS unit by observing the change in the active ATS unit indication provided by the aircraft system.

When required by local procedures, the flight crew should send RTED-5 POSITION REPORT (position report). Alternatively, the flight crew may be required to respond to a CPDLC message exchange initiated by the ATS unit.

Note.— Since FANS 1/A aircraft do not report that the downstream ATS unit has become the CDA, the only way to confirm that it has taken place is for the ATS unit to receive a CPDLC message from the aircraft (refer to Appendix B).

Crossing an Oceanic Boundary

1. You should get new ADS contracts at least 15 minutes prior to the boundary.

2. At the boundary you should get ATC COMM ESTABLISHED.

3. If you will be leaving oceanic airspace after this OCA, include the last two fixes on the cleared route, for example:

_____ Radio, November _____, CPDLC, _____, _____,

"Gander Radio, November one two three alpha, CPDLC, CARPE, REDBY,

flight level _____ request SELCAL check _____

flight level four one zero request SELCAL check alpha bravo charlie delta."

[ICAO Gold, Appendix B, ¶B.4.3.1.1.3]

If the flight enters an oceanic CTA followed by another oceanic CTA, the flight crew should, on initial contact:

not include a position report;

after the radio operator responds, request a SELCAL check and state the next CTA;

The radio operator will assign primary and secondary frequencies, perform the SELCAL check and designate the position and frequencies to contact the aeronautical radio station serving the next oceanic CTA. If the communications instructions are not issued at this stage, the crew should assume that the frequencies to use prior or upon entering the next CTA will be delivered at a later time by CPDLC or voice.

Example (Initial contact from an eastbound flight entering GANDER Oceanic)

GANDER RADIO, AIRLINE 123, SELCAL CHECK, SHANWICK NEXT

AIRLINE 123, GANDER RADIO, HF PRIMARY 5616 SECONDARY 2899, AT 30 WEST CONTACT SHANWICK RADIO HF PRIMARY 8891 SECONDARY 4675, (SELCAL TRANSMITTED)

GANDER RADIO, AIRLINE 123, SELCAL OKAY, HF PRIMARY 5616 SECONDARY 2899. AT 30 WEST CONTACT SHANWICK RADIO, HF PRIMARY 8891 SECONDARY 4675

It has been my experience that most Arinc radio operators accept this method routinely for airline traffic but not so for corporate aviation. For non-airline traffic, I recommend keeping the old practice of adding the term "CPDLC" in this transmission. I've witnessed radio operators getting "testy" with corporate pilots when assuming non-CPDLC operations. So, for example:

GANDER RADIO, NOVEMBER 7700, CPDLC, SHANWICK NEXT, REQUEST SELCAL CHECK ALPHA BRAVO CHARLIE DELTA

Note also that current guidance no longer requires you state your flight level for this initial call up.

If the flight will exit an oceanic CTA into continental airspace or surveillance airspace, on initial contact with the oceanic CTA, the flight crew should:

• not include a position report;

- after the radio operator responds, request a SELCAL check.

Example (Initial contact from an eastbound flight about to enter SHAN-WICK Oceanic)

SHANWICK RADIO, AIRLINE 123, SELCAL CHECK

AIRLINE 123, HF PRIMARY 2899 SECONDARY 5616 (SELCAL TRANS-MITTED)

SHANWICK RADIO, AIRLINE 123, SELCAL OKAY, HF PRIMARY 2899 SECONDARY 5616.

It has been my experience that most Arinc radio operators accept this method routinely for airline traffic but not so for corporate aviation. For non-airline traffic, I recommend keeping the old practice of adding the term "CPDLC" in this transmission. I've witnessed radio operators getting "testy" with corporate pilots when assuming non-CPDLC operations. So, for example:

GANDER RADIO, NOVEMBER 7700, CPDLC, REQUEST SELCAL CHECK ALPHA BRAVO CHARLIE DELTA

Note also that current guidance no longer requires you state your flight level and the two points following oceanic exit for this initial call up.

Depending on which data link services are offered in the oceanic CTA and the operational status of those services, the aeronautical radio operator will provide appropriate information and instructions to the flight crew (see paragraph B.4.2.1.1 for information regarding associated aeronautical radio operator procedures).

If a data link connection cannot be established, maintain normal voice communication procedures. In the event of data link connection failure in a NAT CTA after a successful logon revert to voice and notify the appropriate radio station. Inform AOC in accordance with established problem reporting procedures.

For ADS-C flights, the flight crew should not submit position reports via voice to reduce frequency congestion, unless requested by aeronautical radio operator.

ADS-C flights are exempt from all routine voice meteorological reporting, however the flight crew should use voice to report unusual meteorological conditions such as severe turbulence to the aeronautical radio station.

For any enquiries regarding the status of ADS-C connections, flight crew should use CPDLC. Should the ATS unit fail to receive an expected position report, the controller will follow guidelines in paragraph 3.5.1.7 for late or missing ADS-C reports.

When leaving CPDLC/ADS-C or ADS-C-only airspace, the flight crew should comply with all communication requirements applicable to the airspace being entered.

If the flight crew does not receive its domestic frequency assignment by 10 minutes prior to the flight's entry into the next oceanic CTA, the flight crew should contact the aeronautical radio station and request the frequency, stating the current CTA exit fix or coordinates.

Exiting CPDLC and ADS-C Airspace

1. The CPDLC connection and the ADS contract should terminate automatically.

2. If not, switch both off .

[ICAO Doc 10037, ¶4.2.5]

Approximately 15 minutes after exiting CPDLC and/or ADS-C areas, the flight crew should ensure there are no active CPDLC or ADS-C connections. Ensuring that connections are not active eliminates the possibility of inadvertent or inappropriate use of the connections.

The flight crew should consult the current ATS unit prior to the manual termination of any ADS contract, even if it is suspected to be unnecessary or that its termination has failed.

In the event that the connection termination has failed, the flight crew should contact the ATS unit via voice or any other appropriate means.

Note.— ADS contracts are normally managed (e.g. established and terminated) by ATS units.

Chapter 7

Emergency Locator Transmitter (ELT)

The emergency locator transmitter is one of those things you hardly notice, almost never interact with, and may never use. In fact, unless you are responsible for certification or maintenance of your airplane, you may not think about it at all. But you really should know a few basic facts because there may come a time when your life depends on that knowledge.

History

[US AIM, ¶6-2-4.a.2.] ELTs of various types were developed as a means of locating downed aircraft. These electronic, battery operated transmitters operate on one of three frequencies. These operating frequencies are 121.5 MHz, 243.0 MHz, and the newer 406 MHz. ELTs operating on 121.5 MHz and 243.0 MHz are analog devices. The newer 406 MHz ELT is a digital transmitter that can be encoded with the owner's contact information or aircraft data. The latest 406 MHz ELT models can also be encoded with the aircraft's position data which can help SAR forces locate the aircraft much more quickly after a crash. The 406 MHz ELTs also transmits a stronger signal when activated than the older 121.5 MHz ELTs.

Regulagtory

[14 CFR 91 §91.207]

(a) Except as provided in paragraphs (e) and (f) of this section, no person may operate a U.S.-registered civil airplane unless—

(1) There is attached to the airplane an approved automatic type emergency locator transmitter that is in operable condition for the following operations, except that after June 21, 1995, an emergency locator transmitter that

meets the requirements of TSO-C91 may not be used for new installations:

(i) Those operations governed by the supplemental air carrier and commercial operator rules of parts 121 and 125;

(ii) Charter flights governed by the domestic and flag air carrier rules of part 121 of this chapter; and

(iii) Operations governed by part 135 of this chapter; or

(2) For operations other than those specified in paragraph (a)(1) of this section, there must be attached to the airplane an approved personal type or an approved automatic type emergency locator transmitter that is in operable condition, except that after June 21, 1995, an emergency locator transmitter that meets the requirements of TSO-C91 may not be used for new installations.

(b) Each emergency locator transmitter required by paragraph (a) of this section must be attached to the airplane in such a manner that the probability of damage to the transmitter in the event of crash impact is minimized. Fixed and deployable automatic type transmitters must be attached to the airplane as far aft as practicable.

Registration

[US AIM, ¶6-2-4.a.2.(a)] The Federal Communications Commission (FCC) requires 406 MHz ELTs be registered with the National Oceanic and Atmospheric Administration (NOAA) as outlined in the ELT's documentation. The FAA's 406 MHz ELT Technical Standard Order (TSO) TSO–C126 also requires that each 406 MHz ELT be registered with NOAA. The reason is NOAA maintains the owner registration database for U.S. registered 406 MHz alerting devices, which includes ELTs. NOAA also operates the United States' portion of the Cospas–Sarsat satellite distress alerting system designed to detect activated ELTs and other distress alerting devices.

Activation

[AIM, ¶6-2-4.a.2.]

(b) In the event that a properly registered 406 MHz ELT activates, the Cospas–Sarsat satellite system can decode the owner's information and provide that data to the appropriate search and rescue (SAR) center. In the United

States, NOAA provides the alert data to the appropriate U.S. Air Force Rescue Coordination Center (RCC) or U.S. Coast Guard Rescue Coordination Center. That RCC can then telephone or contact the owner to verify the status of the aircraft. If the aircraft is safely secured in a hangar, a costly ground or airborne search is avoided. In the case of an inadvertent 406 MHz ELT activation, the owner can deactivate the 406 MHz ELT. If the 406 MHz ELT equipped aircraft is being flown, the RCC can quickly activate a search. 406 MHz ELTs permit the Cospas–Sarsat satellite system to narrow the search area to a more confined area compared to that of a 121.5 MHz or 243.0 MHz ELT. 406 MHz ELTs also include a low–power 121.5 MHz homing transmitter to aid searchers in finding the aircraft in the terminal search phase.

(c) Each analog ELT emits a distinctive downward swept audio tone on 121.5 MHz and 243.0 MHz.

(d) If "armed" and when subject to crash–generated forces, ELTs are designed to automatically activate and continuously emit their respective signals, analog or digital. The transmitters will operate continuously for at least 48 hours over a wide temperature range. A properly installed, maintained, and functioning ELT can expedite search and rescue operations and save lives if it survives the crash and is activated.

"Legacy" Systems

[AIM, ¶6-2-4.a.2.]

(f) Because of the large number of 121.5 MHz ELT false alerts and the lack of a quick means of verifying the actual status of an activated 121.5 MHz or 243.0 MHz analog ELT through an owner registration database, U.S. SAR forces do not respond as quickly to initial 121.5/243.0 MHz ELT alerts as the SAR forces do to 406 MHz ELT alerts. Compared to the almost instantaneous detection of a 406 MHz ELT, SAR forces' normal practice is to wait for either a confirmation of a 121.5/243.0 MHz alert by additional satellite passes or through confirmation of an overdue aircraft or similar notification. In some cases, this confirmation process can take hours. SAR forces can initiate a response to 406 MHz alerts in minutes compared to the potential delay of hours for a 121.5/243.0 MHz ELT.

[AIM, ¶6-2-4.a.3.] The Cospas–Sarsat system has announced the termination of satellite monitoring and reception of the 121.5 MHz and 243.0 MHz frequencies in 2009. The Cospas–Sarsat system will continue to monitor the 406 MHz frequency. What this means for pilots is that after the termination date, those aircraft with only 121.5 MHz or 243.0 MHz ELT's onboard will have to depend upon either a nearby Air Traffic Control facility receiving the alert signal or an overflying aircraft monitoring 121.5 MHz or 243.0 MHz detecting the alert. To ensure adequate monitoring of these frequencies and timely alerts after 2009, all airborne pilots should periodically monitor these frequencies to try and detect an activated 121.5/243.0 MHz ELT.

Testing

[AIM, ¶6-2-4.a.3.b.]

1. ELTs should be tested in accordance with the manufacturer's instructions, preferably in a shielded or screened room or specially designed test container to prevent the broadcast of signals which could trigger a false alert.

2. When this cannot be done, aircraft operational testing is authorized as follows:

(a) Analog 121.5 / 243 MHz ELTs should only be tested during the first 5 minutes after any hour. If operational tests must be made outside of this period, they should be coordinated with the nearest FAA Control Tower or FSS. Tests should be no longer than three audible sweeps. If the antenna is removable, a dummy load should be substituted during test procedures.

(b) Digital 406 MHz ELTs should only be tested in accordance with the unit's manufacturer's instructions.

(c) Airborne tests are not authorized.

Inflight Monitoring and Reporting

[AIM, ¶6-2-4.a.3.d.1.] Pilots are encouraged to monitor 121.5 MHz and/or 243.0 MHz while inflight to assist in identifying possible emergency ELT transmissions. On receiving a signal, report the following information to the nearest air traffic facility:

(a) Your position at the time the signal was first heard.

(b) Your position at the time the signal was last heard.

(c) Your position at maximum signal strength.

(d) Your flight altitudes and frequency on which the emergency signal was heard: 121.5 MHz or 243.0 MHz. If possible, positions should be given relative to a navigation aid. If the aircraft has homing equipment, provide the bearing to the emergency signal with each reported position.

Cospas-Sarsat System

[http://www.cospas-sarsat.int/en/system-overview/cospas-sarsat-system]
The basic Cospas-Sarsat System is composed of:

- distress radio beacons (ELTs for aviation use, EPIRBs for maritime use, and PLBs for personal use) which transmit signals during distress situations;

- instruments on board satellites in geostationary and low-altitude Earth orbits which detect the signals transmitted by distress radio beacons;

- ground receiving stations, referred to as Local Users Terminals (LUTs), which receive and process the satellite downlink signal to generate distress alerts; and

- Mission Control Centers (MCCs) which receive alerts produced by LUTs and forward them to Rescue Coordination Centers (RCCs), Search and Rescue Points Of Contacts (SPOCs) or other MCCs.

The Cospas-Sarsat System includes two types of satellites:

- satellites in low-altitude Earth orbit (LEO) which form the LEOSAR System.

- satellites in geostationary Earth orbit (GEO) which form the GEOSAR System. The future Cospas-Sarsat System will include a new type of satellite in the medium-altitude Earth orbit (MEO) which will form the MEOSAR System.

LEOSAR System.

The Cospas-Sarsat LEOSAR system uses polar-orbiting satellites and, therefore, operates with basic constraints which result from non-continuous coverage provided by LEOSAR satellites. The use of low-altitude orbiting satellites provides for a strong Doppler effect in the up-link signal thereby enabling the use of Doppler positioning techniques. The LEOSAR system operates in two coverage modes, namely local and global coverage.

GEOSAR System.

Cospas-Sarsat has demonstrated that the current generation of Cospas-Sarsat beacons could be detected using search and rescue instruments on board geostationary satellites. The GEOSAR system consists of repeaters carried on board various geostationary satellites and the associated ground facilities called GEOLUTs which process the satellite signal. Geostationary satellites orbit the Earth at an altitude of 36,000 km, with an orbit period of 24 hours, thus appearing fixed relative to the Earth at approximately 0 degrees latitude (i.e. over the equator). A single geostationary satellite provides GEOSAR uplink coverage of about one third of the globe, except for polar regions. Therefore, three geostationary satellites equally spaced in longitude can provide continuous coverage of all areas of the globe between approximately 70 degrees North and 70 degrees South latitude.

Chapter 1

Required Surveillance Performance (RSP)

*M*ost pilots who have flown internationally in the last decade or so are well acquainted with the concept of Required Navigation Performance (RNP), the idea that where you can fly will be determined on how accurately you can fly and how well the system alerts you when things are less than promised. While it isn't a perfect statement, you can think that the XX in your RNP-XX relates to that accuracy. The same concept holds true for communications and surveillance. In the case of communications, the number attached to your Required Surveillance Performance (RSP) is the number of seconds it takes for surveillance data from the CSP interface to arrive at the ATSU flight data processing system. You won't find a lot about RSP because it is so closely related to Required Communications Performance (RCP). Does it matter? Yes, the lower the number the tighter the airspace you will be allowed to fly. Put another way: the higher the number, the more airspace around the world that will be denied you.

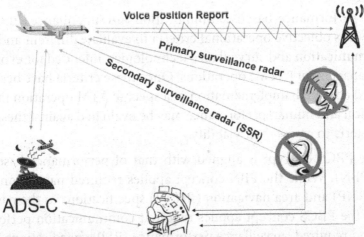

Figure: Evolution of Surveillance (FAA Presentation, 8 February 2012).

History

Surveillance before ADS-C

Surveillance, when you are in radar contact, is achieved with a transponder. if you are in oceanic or remote airspace, without radar coverage, how does air traffic control achieve surveillance? Before the advent of ADS-C surveillance was achieved by voice position reports. You told ATC where you are and ATC assumed that was true.

Surveillance after ADS-C

[ICAO Doc 9869, p. v] The fourth meeting of the Aeronautical Mobile Communications Panel (AMCP/4) (Montreal, April 1996) recognized the absence of objective criteria to evaluate communication performance requirements. This objective criteria was seen as a set of values for parameters, which would be based on the operational requirements for communication systems in the various phases of flight. The meeting agreed that there was an urgent need to assess the various technical options of communication systems against such a set values for these parameters. The term RCP type is used to denote a set of values for these parameters.

In addition, the second edition of Doc 9869 includes required surveillance performance (RSP) specifications to provide the operational, functional, safety and performance criteria for surveillance capability.

Concept

1.1.1 The performance-based communication and surveillance (PBCS) concept provides objective operational criteria to evaluate different and emerging communication and surveillance technologies, intended for evolving air traffic management (ATM) operations. Once these criteria have been established and accepted, implementation of a specific ATM operation including its technical and human performance may be evaluated against these operational criteria to assess their viability.

1.1.2 The PBCS concept is aligned with that of performance-based navigation (PBN). While the PBN concept applies required navigation performance (RNP) and area navigation (RNAV) specifications to the navigation element, the PBCS concept applies required communication performance (RCP) and required surveillance performance (RSP) specifications to communication and surveillance elements, respectively. Each RCP/RSP specification includes allocated criteria among the components of the communication and surveillance systems involved.

1.1.3 Where beneficial, RCP, RNP/RNAV and RSP specifications are applied to communication, navigation and surveillance elements to ensure that the operational system and its components perform in accordance with the specifications.

Note 1.- While RCP and RSP specifications may be applied where beneficial, the PBCS concept is primarily intended for emerging technologies, and not traditional ones, such as HF voice communication or radar. As such, this edition has considered controller-pilot data link communications (CPDLC), automatic dependent surveillance - contract (ADS-C) and SATVOICE technologies, and may be revised to apply to other technologies, such as automatic dependent surveillance - broadcast (ADS-8), as experience is gained.

Note 2. - Similar to the PBN concept, security is beyond the scope of the PBCS concept. However, in some cases, the RCP and RSP specifications may include criteria to support mitigations from security threats. For example, the RCP and RSP specifications that may be applied to SATVOICE contain provisions for satellite service providers (SSPs) to oversee communication services providers (CSPs), in administering accounts to authorized subscribers with personal identification numbers (PIN) and priority level calling. Aircraft SATVOICE systems only route calls to the flight deck from authorized subscribers or alert the flight crew of the appropriate call priority for ATS communication.

RSP Specification

[AC 90-117, ¶22.16.3] An RSP specification is identified by a designator (e.g., RSP 180) in order to simplify the designator naming convention and to make the RSP Data Operational Overdue Time (OT) readily apparent to airspace planners, aircraft manufacturers and operators. The designator represents the value for the surveillance data delivery time when the surveillance data delivery is considered overdue. RSP specifications are applied to airspace based on specific objectives (e.g., the performance required of the surveillance process used to support particular separation minima). The RSP specification is a set of requirements/operational parameters for ATS provision and associated ground equipment, aircraft capability, and operations needed to support performance-based surveillance. Surveillance performance requirements are included and allocated to system components (Required Surveillance Technical Performance (RSTP)). It includes surveillance data delivery time, continuity, availability, integrity, and safety. A specified RSP specification is intended to define the surveillance performance required of a surveillance process to support a particular ATM function. RSP specification is applied to the airspace, route, or procedure based on the most stringent RSP specification of the required ATM functions.

[ICAO Doc 9869, ¶2.4.1.1] RSP 180 may be applied to maintain the performance for normal means of surveillance, which supports controller intervention capability in procedurally controlled airspace, where separation minimum applied is predicated on surveillance performance.

[ICAO Doc 9869, ¶2.4.1.11] RSP 400 may be applied to maintain the performance for emerging technology (e.g. satellite voice) used to provide normal means of surveillance supporting controller intervention capability in procedurally controlled airspace, where the separation minimum being applied is based on position reporting at compulsory reporting points. RSP 400 might also be applied to maintain the performance required for emerging technologies used to provide alternative means of surveillance, that may be required in combination with the normal means of surveillance, to which RSP 180 is applied.

You can think of RSP 400 as old school and RSP 180 as full up CPDLC and ADS-C at the highest levels available in 2020.

Chapter 2

Automatic Dependent Surveillance – Broadcast (ADS-B)

Unlike ADS-C and CPDLC, there is no login procedure with ADS-B and much of its workings are transparent to the crew. ADS-B Out is becoming mandatory throughout much of the world. OpSpec/MSpec/LOA approval used to be required but no longer. ADS-B In is a nice to have feature but isn't, as yet, mandated by any regulatory agency.

Regulatory

[14 CFR 91, §91.225] Automatic Dependent Surveillance-Broadcast (ADS-B) Out equipment and use.

(a) After January 1, 2020, and unless otherwise authorized by ATC, no person may operate an aircraft in Class A airspace unless the aircraft has equipment installed that—

(1) Meets the performance requirements in TSO-C166b, Extended Squitter Automatic Dependent Surveillance-Broadcast (ADS-B) and Traffic Information Service-Broadcast (TIS-B) Equipment Operating on the Radio Frequency of 1090 Megahertz (MHz); and

(2) Meets the requirements of §91.227.

(b) After January 1, 2020, and unless otherwise authorized by ATC, no person may operate an aircraft below 18,000 feet MSL and in airspace described in paragraph (d) of this section unless the aircraft has equipment installed that—

(1) Meets the performance requirements in—

(i) TSO-C166b; or

(ii) TSO-C154c, Universal Access Transceiver (UAT) Automatic Dependent Surveillance-Broadcast (ADS-B) Equipment Operating on the Frequency of

978 MHz;

(2) Meets the requirements of §91.227.

(c) Operators with equipment installed with an approved deviation under §21.618 of this chapter also are in compliance with this section.

(d) After January 1, 2020, and unless otherwise authorized by ATC, no person may operate an aircraft in the following airspace unless the aircraft has equipment installed that meets the requirements in paragraph (b) of this section:

(1) Class B and Class C airspace areas;

(2) Except as provided for in paragraph (e) of this section, within 30 nautical miles of an airport listed in appendix D, section 1 to this part from the surface upward to 10,000 feet MSL;

(3) Above the ceiling and within the lateral boundaries of a Class B or Class C airspace area designated for an airport upward to 10,000 feet MSL;

(4) Except as provided in paragraph (e) of this section, Class E airspace within the 48 contiguous states and the District of Columbia at and above 10,000 feet MSL, excluding the airspace at and below 2,500 feet above the surface; and

(5) Class E airspace at and above 3,000 feet MSL over the Gulf of Mexico from the coastline of the United States out to 12 nautical miles.

(e) The requirements of paragraph (b) of this section do not apply to any aircraft that was not originally certificated with an electrical system, or that has not subsequently been certified with such a system installed, including balloons and gliders. These aircraft may conduct operations without ADS-B Out in the airspace specified in paragraphs (d)(2) and (d)(4) of this section. Operations authorized by this section must be conducted—

(1) Outside any Class B or Class C airspace area; and

(2) Below the altitude of the ceiling of a Class B or Class C airspace area designated for an airport, or 10,000 feet MSL, whichever is lower.

(f) Each person operating an aircraft equipped with ADS-B Out must operate this equipment in the transmit mode at all times unless—

(1) Otherwise authorized by the FAA when the aircraft is performing a sensitive government mission for national defense, homeland security, intelli-

gence or law enforcement purposes and transmitting would compromise the operations security of the mission or pose a safety risk to the aircraft, crew, or people and property in the air or on the ground; or

(2) Otherwise directed by ATC when transmitting would jeopardize the safe execution of air traffic control functions.

(g) Requests for ATC authorized deviations from the requirements of this section must be made to the ATC facility having jurisdiction over the concerned airspace within the time periods specified as follows:

(1) For operation of an aircraft with an inoperative ADS-B Out, to the airport of ultimate destination, including any intermediate stops, or to proceed to a place where suitable repairs can be made or both, the request may be made at any time.

(2) For operation of an aircraft that is not equipped with ADS-B Out, the request must be made at least 1 hour before the proposed operation.

(h) The standards required in this section are incorporated by reference with the approval of the Director of the Office of the Federal Register under 5 U.S.C. 552(a) and 1 CFR part 51. All approved materials are available for inspection at the FAA's Office of Rulemaking (ARM-1), 800 Independence Avenue, SW., Washington, DC 20590 (telephone 202-267-9677), or at the National Archives and Records Administration (NARA). For information on the availability of this material at NARA, call 202-741-6030, or go to http://www.archives.gov/federal__register/code__of__federal__regulations/ibr__locations.html. This material is also available from the sources indicated in paragraphs (h)(1) and (h)(2) of this section.

(1) Copies of Technical Standard Order (TSO)-C166b, Extended Squitter Automatic Dependent Surveillance-Broadcast (ADS-B) and Traffic Information Service-Broadcast (TIS-B) Equipment Operating on the Radio Frequency of 1090 Megahertz (MHz) (December 2, 2009) and TSO-C154c, Universal Access Transceiver (UAT) Automatic Dependent Surveillance-Broadcast (ADS-B) Equipment Operating on the Frequency of 978 MHz (December 2, 2009) may be obtained from the U.S. Department of Transportation, Subsequent Distribution Office, DOT Warehouse M30, Ardmore East Business Center, 3341 Q 75th Avenue, Landover, MD 20785; telephone (301) 322-5377. Copies of TSO -C166B and TSO-C154c are also available on the FAA's Web site, at http://www.faa.gov/aircraft/air__cert/design__approvals/tso/. Select the link "Search Technical Standard Orders."

(2) Copies of Section 2, Equipment Performance Requirements and Test Procedures, of RTCA DO-260B, Minimum Operational Performance Standards for 1090 MHz Extended Squitter Automatic Dependent Surveillance-Broadcast (ADS-B) and Traffic Information Services-Broadcast (TIS-B), December 2, 2009 (referenced in TSO-C166b) and Section 2, Equipment Performance Requirements and Test Procedures, of RTCA DO-282B, Minimum Operational Performance Standards for Universal Access Transceiver (UAT) Automatic Dependent Surveillance-Broadcast (ADS-B), December 2, 2009 (referenced in TSO C-154c) may be obtained from RTCA, Inc., 1828 L Street, NW., Suite 805, Washington, DC 20036-5133, telephone 202-833-9339. Copies of RTCA DO-260B and RTCA DO-282B are also available on RTCA Inc.'s Web site, at http://www.rtca.org/onlinecart/allproducts.cfm.

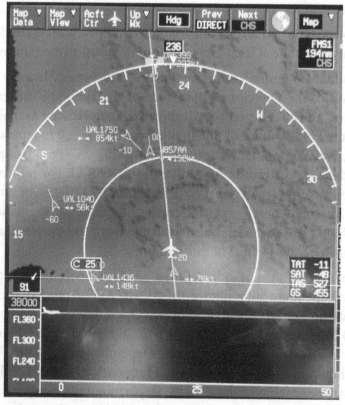

ADS-B In Display (GVII Example)

ADS-B System Description

[AC 90-114B, ¶2.2]

2.2.1 ADS-B System Architecture. The ADS-B system architecture is composed of aircraft avionics and an Air Traffic Service Provider (ATSP) infrastructure. Onboard "position source" avionics determine the position of the aircraft, typically by using the Global Navigation Satellite Systems (GNSS) and transmitting this and additional information about the aircraft to receiver stations for use by ATC, to ADS-B In-equipped aircraft, and to other aviation service providers.

2.2.2 ADS-B Operating Frequencies. In the United States, the ADS-B system operates on two frequencies: 1090 or 978 megahertz (MHz). See Chapter 3, Figure 3-1, Automatic Dependent Surveillance-Broadcast Airspace Rule (§ 91.225) Diagram, for airspace and frequency requirements.

2.2.2.1 The 1090 MHz Frequency. The 1090 MHz frequency is associated with current Mode A, C, and S transponder operations. ADS-B information is included in Mode S transponders' Extended Squitter (ES) transmit messages, and referred to as 1090ES in this AC.

2.2.2.2 The 978 MHz Frequency. ADS-B equipment operating on 978 MHz are referred to as Universal Access Transceivers (UAT) in this AC.

2.2.3 ADS-B Avionics Operating Modes. ADS-B avionics can have the ability to both transmit and receive information.

2.2.3.1 ADS-B Out. The transmission of ADS-B information from aircraft is known as ADS-B Out.

2.2.3.2 ADS-B In. The receipt of ADS-B information by an aircraft is known as ADS-B In.

[AIM, ¶4-5-7.a.4.] In general, operators flying at 18,000 feet and above (Class A airspace) are required to have 1090ES equipment. Those that do not fly above 18,000 may use either UAT or 1090ES equipment. (Refer to 14 CFR §§ 91.225 and 91.227.)

ADS-B Out is what has been mandated in the U.S. and other parts of the world. It is simply a way to broadcast your position and other information to other ADS-B users, normally Air Traffic Control. You can be one of those users if you have ADS-B In, which allows your avionics to display that information. There is no requirement, as of late 2020, mandating you have ADS-B In.

Operating Procedures

[AC 90-114B, ¶4.3.1] Transmit Requirements. In accordance with §
91.225(f), each person operating an aircraft equipped with ADS-B Out must
operate this equipment in the transmit mode at all times, unless authorized
by the FAA or directed by air traffic control (ATC). This equipment operation requirement pertains to all phases of flight operation, including airport surface movement area operations. Pilots should select the transponder
mode that enables the altitude reporting and ADS-B Out transmissions any
time their aircraft is positioned on any portion of an airport movement area.

[AC 90-114B, ¶4.3.3] Operation of Aircraft with Inoperative ADS-B. Section 91.225(g) permits ATC to authorize the operation of aircraft with inoperative ADS-B or that do not have ADS-B installed into airspace where it
is required. Under § 91.225(g), operators must make requests for ATC-au-
thorized deviations from the requirements in § 91.225 to the ATC facility
that has jurisdiction over the concerned airspace or airport movement area
within the time periods specified below:

For operation of an aircraft with inoperative ADS-B equipment to the airport of ultimate destination (including any intermediate stops) or to proceed to a place where suitable repairs can be made, or both, the request may
be made at any time.

For operation of an aircraft that is not equipped with ADS-B, operators must
make the request at least 1 hour before the proposed operation.

[AIM, ¶4-5-7.e.] The ADS–B cockpit display of traffic is NOT intended to be
used as a collision avoidance system and does not relieve the pilot's responsibility to "see and avoid" other aircraft. ADS–B must not be used for avoidance maneuvers during IMC or other times when there is no visual contact
with the intruder aircraft. ADS–B is intended only to assist in visual acquisition of other aircraft. No avoidance maneuvers are provided or authorized,
as a direct result of an ADS–B target being displayed in the cockpit.

International Requirements

*f you do not have ADS-B, you will be well advised to research the Aeronautical
Information Publicaitons (AIPs) of the area you will be visiting and transiting.
The following two examples are offered as representative samples where some
requirements do exist.*

Australia

[Australia AIP, ¶6.1.3] The following table summarises the transponder or ADS-B transmitting equipment (ADS-B OUT) requirements for IFR or VFR operations in various classes of airspace or at specified aerodromes:

IFR, Classes A, B, C, D, E, and G: ADS-B OUT equipment specified for IFR aircraft

VFR, Class A FL 290 and above: IFR ADS-B OUT

IFR or VFR operation at YBBN, YMML, YSSY, YPPH, Class B or C: IFR ADS-B OUT or Mode S transponder

VFR, Class A (below FL 290), B or C: IFR ADS-B OUT, or Mode S trasnponder, or Mode A/C transponder

Hong Kong

I've included Hong Kong because they used to require operational approval, which the U.S. FAA would not provide. The Hong Kong requirement, shown here, no longer requires such approval and the controversy no longer exists.

[Hong Kong AIP, ¶3.7] All aircraft flying within Hong Kong FIR at or above F290 shall be installed with ADS-B equipages complying with the requirements stipulated in paragraph 3.7.6.

3.7.2 For all aircraft flying within Hong Kong FIR equipped with ADS-B equipages not complying with paragraph 3.7.6 the ADS-B equipages shall be: a) deactivated; or b) set to transmit only a value of zero for the Navigation Uncertainty Category (NUCp) or Navigation Integrity Category (NIC) or Navigation Accuracy Category (NAC) or Source Integrity Level (SIL).

3.7.3 Aircraft not complying with paragraph 3.7.6 will not be accorded priority to operate in the designated airspace and flight level assignments would be subjected to air traffic conditions.

3.7.4 When an aircraft is ADS-B equipped but the equipment has become unserviceable during flight, the pilot in command or aircraft operator must inform ATC as soon as possible.

3.7.5 Operational approval from the State of Registry for ADS-B Out operation is no longer required.

Chapter 3

Automatic Dependent Surveillance – Contract (ADS-C)

You can think of ADS-C as a replacement for Air Traffic Control's radar contact. When you have logged on to an Air Traffic Service Unit with ADS-C, you have agreed to contracts which send information to the ATSU, such as your position, on a regular basis. It is a part of the data link system that keeps you on the same page as Air Traffic Control.

Functional Description

[ICAO Doc 10037, ¶1.2.5]

ADS-C uses various systems on board the aircraft to automatically provide aircraft position, altitude, speed, intent and meteorological data, which can be sent in a report to an ATS unit or AOC facility ground system for surveillance and route conformance monitoring.

One or more reports are generated in response to an ADS contract, which is requested by the ground system. An ADS contract identifies the types of information and the conditions under which reports are to be sent by the aircraft. Some types of information are included in every report, while other types are provided only if specified in the ADS contract request. The aircraft can also send unsolicited ADS-C emergency reports to any ATS unit that has an ADS connection with the aircraft.

An ATS unit system may request multiple simultaneous ADS contracts to a single aircraft, including one periodic and one event contract, which may be supplemented by any number of demand contracts. Up to five separate ground systems may request ADS contracts with a single aircraft.

Note.— Although the terms are similar, ADS-C and ADS-B are two different applications. In comparison, ADS-B (PSR, SSR or any comparable ground-based system that enables the identification of aircraft) is an ATS

227

surveillance system. An ADS-B-capable aircraft supports ATS surveillance services and broadcasts information at a relatively high rate, and any appropriate receiver on the ground or in another aircraft within range can receive the information.

ADS-C gives you a better Required Surveillance Performance (RSP) and CP-DLC gives you better Required Communication Performance (RCP). Combined, they allow you to fly in airspace with tighter separation minima which means you have a greater selection of airspace available to you.

Contracts

An ADS Contract is an agreement from you, the pilot, to the Air Traffic Service (ATS), to provide information. You can provide information through various types of contracts and you can do this with up to four different ATS providers. The data is extracted automatically from various electronics in your aircraft. In exchange they grant you access to the airspace you are in, or coordinate with nearby airspace. ADS-C will take the place of voice position reports in many regions of the world. You need special equipment and authorization to use ADS-C.

[AC 91-70B, ¶A.2.16.2] Automatic Dependent Surveillance—Contract (ADS-C) (ICAO). A means by which the terms of an ADS-C agreement will be exchanged between the ground system and the aircraft, via a data link, specifying under what conditions ADS-C reports would be initiated and what data would be contained in the reports. The abbreviated term "ADS contract" is commonly used to refer to ADS event contract, ADS demand contract, ADS periodic contract, or an emergency mode.

[ICAO Doc 10037, ¶1.2.5.3]

After receiving a logon request, the ATS unit will need to establish ADS contract(s) with the aircraft before it can receive any ADS-C reports. There are three types of ADS contracts:

- periodic contract;
- demand contract; and
- event contract.

The ground system can establish ADS contracts without flight crew action provided that ADS-C in the aircraft system is not selected off. The flight crew has the ability to cancel all contracts by selecting ADS-C off and some aircraft systems allow the flight crew to cancel an ADS contract with a specific ATS unit.

Periodic Contracts

[ICAO Doc 10037, ¶1.2.5.3]

A periodic contract allows an ATS unit to specify:

- the time interval at which the aircraft system sends an ADS-C report; and

- the optional ADS-C groups that are to be included in the periodic report. Each optional group

Photo: G450 MCDU, ADS Periodic Contract

may have a unique modulus which defines how often the optional group is included with the periodic report (e.g. a modulus of five indicates that the optional group would be included with every fifth periodic report sent).

Note.— ADS-C groups are referred to as data blocks in ICAO Doc 4444.

The range and resolution of the time interval parameter in the periodic contract allows for an interval to be specified between 1 second and 4,096 seconds (approximately 68 minutes). However, RTCA DO-258A/EUROCAE ED-100A limits the minimum interval to 64 seconds. If the ground system specifies a time interval less than 64 seconds, the aircraft system will respond with a non-compliance notification and establish a periodic contract with a 64-second reporting interval. If the ground system does not specify a time interval, the aircraft will establish a periodic contract of 64 seconds for emergency periodic reporting and 304 seconds for normal periodic reporting.

The ground system may permit the controller to alter the periodic reporting interval to allow for situations where the controller desires a longer or shorter reporting interval. The controller may select a shorter reporting interval to obtain more frequent surveillance information, for example, during an off-route deviation or an emergency.

Note.— The ANSP ensures that separation minima are applied in accordance with appropriate standards. The ground system may prevent the controller from selecting a periodic reporting interval that is longer than the maximum interval specified in the standard for the separation minima being applied.

An ATS unit can establish only one periodic contract with an aircraft at any one time. A number of ATS units can each establish their own periodic contract and specify their own conditions for the report with the same aircraft at the same time.

A periodic contract remains in place until it is either cancelled or modified. Whenever an ATS unit establishes a new periodic contract, the aircraft system automatically replaces the previous periodic contract with the new one.

Demand Contracts

[ICAO Doc 10037, ¶1.2.5.3.4] A demand contract allows an ATS unit to request a single ADS-C periodic report. A demand contract does not cancel or modify any other ADS contracts that may be in effect with the aircraft.

Event Contracts

[ICAO Doc 10037, ¶1.2.5.3.6.] An event contract allows an ATS unit to request an ADS-C report whenever a specific event occurs. An ATS unit can establish only one event contract with an aircraft at any one time. However, the event contract can contain multiple event types as follows:

Photo: G450 MCDU, Event Contract

- waypoint change event (WCE);
- level range deviation event (LRDE);
- lateral deviation event (LDE); and
- vertical rate change event (VRE).

Note.— In accordance with ICAO Doc 4444, paragraph 13.4.3.4.3.2, in airspace where procedural separation is being applied, as a minimum, WCE, LRDE, and LDE shall be contained in ADS-C agreements.

In the example photo, the ATS will be notified automatically if the aircraft's vertical velocity exceeds 5,056 fpm, lateral deviation exceeds 5 nm, the altitude goes below 40,700 or above 41,300 feet, and at every waypoint change. The waypoint change is determined by the FMS so anything you do to the FMS that affects the next waypoint and the waypoint one after that will be reported. For example, if you were to insert your ETP before the next waypoint, that gets reported.

Log On

The log on procedure varies with aircraft. In the case of a Gulfstream G550, the ADS-C log on takes places as a consequence of the CPDLC log on. The CPDLC FIR region code is entered into the ATC LOGON STATUS page of the MCDU after ensuring all other items are correct. The information is sent and once accepted the MCDU scratch pad will show "ADS ESTABLISHED" and the ADS ARMED entry will change to ADS ACTIVE.

Position Reporting

[ICAO Doc 10037, ¶4.4.6.1.1] When using CPDLC to provide position information, the flight crew should report unnamed waypoints (latitudes/longitudes) using the ICAO format of nn[N/S]nnn[E/W] or, if both degrees and minutes are required, nnnn[N/S]nnnnn[E/W].

Note.— The flight crew and flight operations officers/dispatchers should not use the ARINC 424 format. ARINC 424 describes a 5-character latitude/longitude format for aircraft navigation databases (e.g. 10N40 describes a lat/long of 10N140W). The ATS unit may reject or be unable to process any downlink message containing waypoint names in the ARINC 424 format.

Position Reporting in an ADS-C Environment

[ICAO Doc 10037, ¶4.4.6.3]

Note.— In an ADS-C environment, the flight crew should not provide position reports or revised waypoint estimates by CPDLC or voice, unless otherwise instructed or under conditions in certain airspace as stipulated in AIP (or other appropriate publication).

If required by regional supplementary procedures or AIP (or other appropriate publication), the flight crew should provide a CPDLC position report when either of the following events occurs:

- an initial CPDLC connection is established; or

- the CPDLC connection transfer has been completed (i.e. at the associated boundary entry position).

Note.— Some ANSPs require a single CPDLC position report, even when in an ADS-C environment, to provide the controlling ATS unit confirmation that it is the CDA and the only ATS unit able to communicate with the aircraft via CPDLC (refer to Appendix B).

In general you should not provide position reports or revised waypoint estimates by CPDLC or voice unless you see something that tells you to do so. Appendix B can be misleading. The subject is only brought up in the North Atlantic region where you are explicitly told "For ADS-C flights, the flight crew should not submit position reports via voice to reduce frequency congestion, unless requested by aeronautical radio operator." Makes sense, but don't let that talk you into thinking now you need to do so in other regions because the same phrase is missing.

The flight crew should include only ATC waypoints in cleared segments of the aircraft active flight plan. However, when an ATC clearance eliminates a waypoint, it is permissible to retain and report the point abeam of that waypoint since this ensures retention of meteorological data associated with the eliminated waypoint.

Note.— If the flight crew inserts non-ATC waypoints (e.g. mid-points) into the aircraft active flight plan and activates the change, the aircraft system may trigger an ADS-C waypoint change event report at the non-ATC waypoint, or include information about the non-ATC waypoint in the predicted route group, as well as the intermediate and fixed projected intent groups. As a result, the ADS-C report will include information about the non-ATC waypoint, which is not expected by the ATC ground system.

The flight crew should maintain the active route in the aircraft system to be the same as the ATC cleared route of flight.

Note.— If the flight crew activates a non-ATC cleared route into the aircraft system, the ADS-C reports will include information that will indicate the aircraft is flying a route that is deviating from the cleared route.

When reporting by ADS-C only, the flight crew should include ATC waypoints in the aircraft active flight plan even if they are not compulsory reporting points.

Position Reporting in a non-ADS-C Environment

[ICAO Doc 10037, ¶4.4.6.1]

When ADS-C is not available, the flight crew should conduct position reporting by voice or CPDLC. When using CPDLC, the flight crew should send RTED-5 POSITION REPORT (position report) whenever an ATC waypoint is sequenced, (or passed abeam when offset flight is in progress).

When using CPDLC for position reporting, the flight crew should send position reports only at compulsory reporting points and ensure that the position and next position information applies to compulsory reporting points, unless requested otherwise by ATC. The ensuing significant point after the next position may be either a compulsory or non-compulsory reporting point (refer AIREP form ICAO Doc 4444, Appendix 1).

The Importance of FMS Waypoint Sequencing

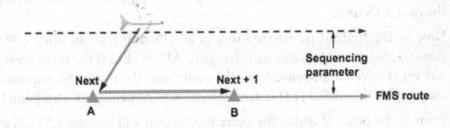

Figure: Waypoint sequencing anomaly, from ICAO Gold, figure 5-2.

You don't have to worry about flying a Strategic Lateral Offset because your FMS will sequence the waypoints even if you are two miles away from the intended course. But if you are further than the tolerance allowed by your FMS, it may not sequence. If that happens, the position report will not be made.

[ICAO Doc 10037, ¶4.5.1.6]

The flight crew should ensure that waypoints are sequenced correctly. If an aircraft passes abeam a waypoint by more than the aircraft FMS waypoint sequencing parameter, the flight crew should sequence the waypoints in the FMS, as appropriate.

As shown in [the figure], when an aircraft passes abeam a waypoint in excess of the defined sequencing parameter (refer to , paragraph F.7) for specific aircraft types), the FMS will not sequence the active waypoint. If the flight crew does not sequence the waypoint, incorrect information will be contained in ADS-C reports, CPDLC position reports and FMC waypoint position reports – the next waypoint in these reports will actually be the waypoint that the aircraft has already passed.

Automatic Transfer of CPDLC and ADS-C Services Between ATS Units

[ICAO Doc 10037, ¶4.2.3.]

Under normal circumstances, the current and next ATS units automatically transfer CPDLC and ADS-C services. The transfer is seamless to the flight crew.

Note.— The flight crew should not need to reinitiate a logon.

The flight crew should promptly respond to CPDLC uplink messages to minimize the risk of an open CPDLC uplink message when transferring to the next ATS unit.

Note.— If a flight is transferred to a new ATS unit with an open CPDLC message, the message status will change to ABORTED. If the flight crew has not yet received a response from the controller, the downlink request will also display the ABORTED status. Refer also to Appendix C, paragraph C.8.

Prior to the point at which the current ATS unit will transfer CPDLC and/ or ADS-C services, the flight crew may receive an instruction to close any open CPDLC messages.

When entering the next ATS unit's airspace, the flight crew should confirm the successful transfer from the current ATS unit to the next ATS unit by observing the change in the active ATS unit indication provided by the aircraft system.

When required by local procedures, the flight crew should send RTED-5 POSITION REPORT (position report). Alternatively, the flight crew may be required to respond to a CPDLC message exchange initiated by the ATS unit.

Exiting CPDLC and ADS-C Service Areas

[ICAO Doc 10037, ¶4.2.5]

Approximately 15 minutes after exiting CPDLC and/or ADS-C areas, the flight crew should ensure there are no active CPDLC or ADS-C connections. Ensuring that connections are not active eliminates the possibility of inadvertent or inappropriate use of the connections.

The flight crew should consult the current ATS unit prior to the manual termination of any ADS contract, even if it is suspected to be unnecessary or that its termination has failed.

In the event that the connection termination has failed, the flight crew should contact the ATS unit via voice or any other appropriate means.

ADS-C Reports

[ICAO Doc 10037, ¶1.2.5.4.1] The aircraft system sends specific aircraft data in different groups of an ADS-C report. Each group contains different types of data. An ADS-C event report contains only some of the groups, which are fixed. The ADS-C periodic report can contain any of the ADS-C groups, which the ATSU specifies in the contract request.

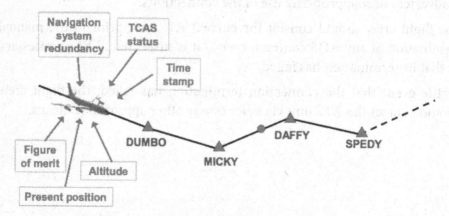

Figure: ADS-C Basic Group, from ICAO Gold, figure 2-38.

Figure: ADS-C Flight Identification Group, from ICAO Gold, figure 2-39.

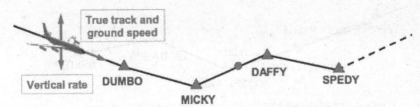

Figure: ADS-C Earth Reference Group, from ICAO Gold, figure 2-40.

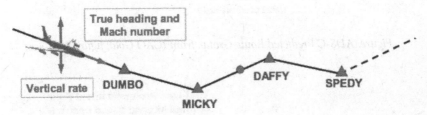

Figure: ADS-C Air Reference Group, from ICAO Gold, figure 2-41.

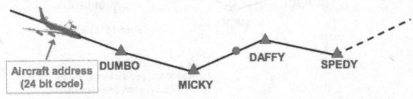

Figure: ADS-C Airframe Identification Group, from ICAO Gold, figure 2-42.

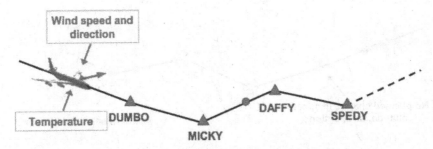

Figure: ADS-C Meteorological Group, from ICAO Gold, figure 2-43.

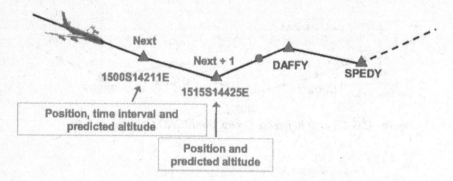

Figure: *ADS-C Predicted Route Group, from ICAO Gold, figure 2-44.*

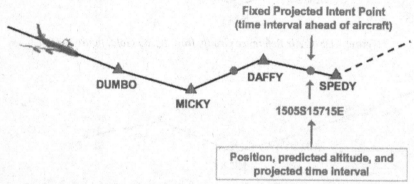

Figure: *ADS-C Fixed Projected Intent Group, from ICAO Gold, figure 2-45.*

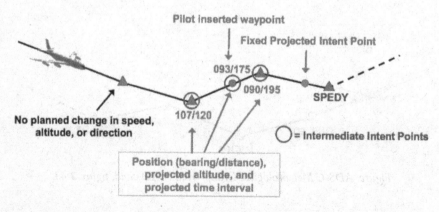

Figure: *ADS-C Intermediate Projected Intent Group, from ICAO Gold, figure 2-46.*

Chapter 4

Transponder Modes and Codes

*M*ost of this stuff is common knowledge, perhaps we miss a few things here *and* there. When exactly do you squawk 2000? What does that former Air Force guy mean when he says IFF? What is a secondary target? More recently: where do you find your Mode S squawk?

History

IFF

[DoD Dictionary of Military and Associated Terms, pg. 123] Identification, friend or foe — A device that emits a signal positively identifying it as a

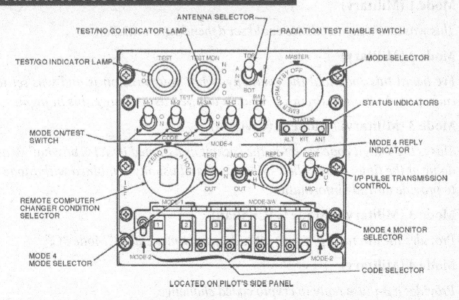

Figure: AN/APX-100 IFF Transponder, from an old Air Force flight manual.

friendly.

You will often hear "IFF" from ex-military types when what they mean to say is "transponder." While the IFF found in many military aircraft are much more than just transponders, for our purposes the terms can be considered synonymous.

ATC: Primary versus Secondary Radar

[Air Traffic Organization Policy Order JO 7110.65Y, pg. PCG P-4] PRIMARY RADAR TARGET– An analog or digital target, exclusive of a secondary radar target, presented on a radar display.

[Air Traffic Organization Policy Order JO 7110.65Y, pg. PCG S-2] SECONDARY RADAR TARGET– A target derived from a transponder return presented on a radar display.

The primary target is the "blip" on the controllers radar screen that is nothing more than the aircraft's radar return, while the secondary target is the signal and information beamed from the aircraft's transponder to the radar.

Modes

Mode 1 (Military)

This was a two digit code we could set depending on mission.

Mode 2 (Military)

I've heard this code told the good guys what your mission is and was set for each aircraft, though aircraft I've flown allowed us to change this in flight.

Mode 3 (Military) / Mode A (Civilian)

This is the 4-digit code we set in the cockpit as assigned by ATC or what we are doing at the time, often called "Mode 3/A" and usually combined with Mode C to provide altitude information.

Mode 3 (Military) / Mode C (Civilian)

Provides the aircraft's pressure altitude, sometimes called "Mode 3C."

Mode 4 (Military)

Provides a 3-pulse reply to crypto coded challenge.

Mode 5 (Military)

Provides a cryptographically secured version of Mode S and ADS-B GPS position.

Mode S (Military and Civilian)

Provides multiple information formats to a selective interrogation. Each aircraft is assigned a fixed 24-bit address.

The code is simply a hexadecimal conversion from your registration. You can check this at: http://www.avionictools.com/.

Codes

1200 — VFR

[Aeronautical Information Manual, ¶4-1-17.g.] Transponder Operation Under Visual Flight Rules (VFR): Unless otherwise instructed by an ATC facility, adjust transponder to reply on Mode 3/A Code 1200 regardless of altitude.

There may be other examples, but for at least in the U.S., squawk 1200 when VFR.

2000 — Oceanic

[ICAO Doc 8168, Vol III, §III-3-1-1, ¶1.1.2] Except in case of emergency, communication failure or unlawful interference (see 1.4, 1.5 and 1.6), the pilot shall:

a) operate the transponder and select Mode A codes as directed by the ATC unit with which contact is being made; or

b) operate the transponder on Mode A codes as prescribed on the basis of regional air navigation agreements; or

c) in the absence of any ATC directions or regional air navigation agreements, operate the transponder on Mode A Code 2000.

[ICAO Doc 7030, §AFI, ¶5.1.1.2.] Africa-Indian Ocean Regional Supplementary Procedures. Unless otherwise directed by air traffic control, the last assigned SSR (Mode A) code shall be retained. If no SSR code has been assigned, Mode A code 2000 shall be selected and retained.

[NAT Doc 007, ¶10.2.1] All aircraft operating as IFR flights in the NAT region shall be equipped with a pressure- altitude reporting SSR transponder. Where radar services are provided in the NAT region, transponder codes issued by the control unit must be retained while operating in radar airspace and for a period of 30 minutes after entry into NAT airspace or after exiting a radar service area. After the 30 minute time frame, transponders must be operated continuously in Mode A/C code 2000.

Note 1: Because of the limited time spent in NAT HLA when flying on Route Tango 9, change to code 2000 should be made 10 minutes after passing BEGAS northbound and 10 minutes after passing LASNO southbound.

Note 2: Tango 290, the change from the last assigned domestic code to Code 2000 Northbound 10 minutes after passing ADVAT, and Southbound 10 minutes after passing GELPO.

Note 3: All eastbound flights routing Reykjavik – Shanwick – Scottish shall squawk Mode A Code 2000 ten minutes after entering EGGX airspace.

10.2.2 This procedure does not affect the use of the special purpose codes (7500, 7600 and 7700) in cases of unlawful interference, radio failure or emergency.

Note: Flight crews should exercise caution when selecting codes so as not to inadvertently cycle through any of the special purpose codes.

[AC 91-70B ¶6.4.3.1] Change your transponder code to 2000 in accordance with regional requirements. This requirement varies with the oceanic airspace. You should confirm these procedures, through applicable AIP or other regional documents during flight planning. In the North Atlantic, for example, the transponder code should be changed 30 minutes after entering oceanic airspace.

[AC 91-70B ¶E.5.4] You must ensure that you comply with transponder procedures as contained in ICAO Procedures for Air Navigation Services— Aircraft Operations (PANS-OPS) Document 8168 and, in the absence of other directions from air traffic control (ATC), operate your transponder on Mode A and C code 2000.

In general you are going to squawk 2000 when oceanic, waiting 30 minutes after the entry waypoint is required over the North Atlantic and doesn't hurt elsewhere. There are exceptions so make sure you view the regional pages before entry.

7500 — Hijacking

[ICAO Doc 4444, ¶15.1.3.2] Note. An aircraft equipped with an SSR transponder is expected to operate the transponder on Mode A Code 7500 to indicate specifically that it is the subject of unlawful interference.

[ICAO Doc 8168, Vol III, §4-1-2, ¶1.6]

If there is unlawful interference with an aircraft in flight, the pilot-in-command shall attempt to set the transponder to Mode A Code 7500 in order to indicate the situation. If circumstances so warrant, Code 7700 should be used instead.

If a pilot has selected Mode A Code 7500 and has been requested to confirm this code by ATC (in accordance with 1.1.5), the pilot shall, according to circumstances, either confirm this or not reply at all.

Note.— If the pilot does not reply, ATC will take this as confirmation that the use of Code 7500 is not an inadvertent false code selection.

[ICAO Doc 8168, Vol III, §4-1-1, ¶1.1.5] When requested by ATC to CONFIRM SQUAWK (code), the pilot shall:

a) verify the Mode A code setting on the transponder;

b) reselect the assigned code if necessary; and

c) confirm to ATC the setting displayed on the controls of the transponder.

7600 — Lost Comm

[ICAO Doc 4444, ¶8.5.2.1] An aircraft equipped with an SSR transponder is expected to operate the transponder on Mode A Code 7600 to indicate that it has experienced air-ground communication failure.

[ICAO Doc 8168, Vol III, §4-1-2, ¶1.5] The pilot of an aircraft losing two-way communications shall set the transponder to Mode A Code 7600. Note.— A controller who observes an SSR response indicating selection of the communications failure code will determine the extent of the failure by instructing the pilot to SQUAWK IDENT or to change code. If it is determined that the aircraft receiver is functioning, further control of the aircraft will be continued using code changes or IDENT transmission to acknowledge receipt of clearances. Different procedures may be applied to Mode S equipped aircraft in areas of Mode S coverage.

7700 — Emergency

[ICAO Doc 8168, Vol III, §4-1-2, ¶1.4] The pilot of an aircraft in a state of emergency shall set the transponder to Mode A Code 7700 unless ATC has previously directed the pilot to operate the transponder on a specified code. In the latter case, the pilot shall continue to use the specified code unless otherwise advised by ATC. However, a pilot may select Mode A Code 7700 whenever there is a specific reason to believe that this would be the best course of action.

Chapter 1

Inflight Contingencies in Oceanic Airspace

The ICAO cleaned up the disparate procedures for oceanic contingencies nicely over the years. The old "Quad Four" maneuver to turn 45° away from track, offset 15 NM, etc. is gone. With the exception of lost communications timing in the Pacific, almost all of the world is on a single oceanic contingency procedure. Now you diverge from the route by 30°, offset by 5 NM, and then descend below FL290 or climb above FL410. Of course there may be regional differences that supersede these procedures and you should use your judgment to ensure safety. If you can communicate with ATC via voice or CP-DLC, your options might expand.

Introduction

[ICAO Doc 4444, ¶15.2.1.1] Although all possible contingencies cannot be covered, the procedures in 15.2.2, 15.2.3, and 15.2.4 provide the more frequent cases such as:

a.   the inability to comply with assigned clearance due to meteorological conditions;

b.   en route diversion across the prevailing traffic flow (for example, due to medical emergencies); and

c.   the loss of, or significant reduction in, the required navigation capability when operating in an airspace where the navigation performance accuracy is a prerequisite to the safe conduct of flight operations, or pressurization failure.

ICAO Doc 4444, ¶15.2.1.2] The pilot shall take action as necessary to ensure the safety of the aircraft, and the pilot's judgment shall determine the sequence of actions to be taken, having regard to the prevailing circumstances. Air traffic control shall render all possible assistance.

General Procedures

Declaring an emergency is a game changer just about anywhere in the world and using "Mayday" or "Pan Pan" is the only way to change the rules of the game in some parts of the world. You shouldn't be shy about using it if you need traffic priority.

[ICAO Doc 4444, ¶15.2.2.1] If an aircraft is unable to continue the flight in accordance with its ATC clearance, a revised clearance shall be obtained, whenever possible, prior to initiating any action.

[ICAO Doc 4444, ¶15.2.2.2] If prior clearance cannot be obtained, the following contingency procedures should be employed until a revised clearance is received. In general terms, the aircraft should be flown at an offset level and on an offset track where other aircraft are less likely to be encountered. Specifically, the pilot shall:

a. leave the cleared track OR ATS route by initially turning at least 30 degrees to the right or to the left, in order to establish and maintain a parallel, same direction track or ATS route offset 5 NM (9.3 km). The direction of the turn should be based on one or more of the following factors:

- aircraft position relative to any organized track or ATS route system;
- the direction of flights and flight levels allocated on adjacent tracks;
- the direction to an alternate airport;
- any strategic lateral offset being flown; and
- terrain clearance;

b. maintain a watch for conflicting traffic both visually and by reference to ACAS (if equipped) leaving ACAS in RA mode at all times, unless aircraft operating limitations dictate otherwise;

c. turn on all aircraft exterior lights (commensurate with appropriate operating limitations);

d. keep the SSR transponder on at all times and, when able, squawk 7700, as appropriate and, if equipped with ADS-B or ADS-C, select the appropriate emergency functionality;

e. as soon as practicable, advise air traffic control of any deviation from their assigned clearance;

f.   use means as appropriate (i.e. voice and/or CPDLC) to communicate during a contingency or emergency;

g.   if voice communication is used, the radiotelephony distress signal (MAYDAY) or urgency signal (PAN PAN) preferably spoken three times, shall be used, as appropriate;

h.   when emergency situations are communicated via CPDLC, the controller may respond via CPDLC. However, the controller may also attempt to make voice contact with the aircraft;

Note.— Guidance on emergency procedures for controllers, radio operators, and flight crew in data link operations can be found in the Global Operational Data Link (GOLD) Manual (Doc 10037).

i.   establish communications with and alert nearby aircraft by broadcasting on the frequencies in use and at suitable intervals on 121.5 MHz (or, as a backup, on the inter-pilot air-to-air frequency 123.45 MHz): aircraft identification, the nature of the distress condition, intention of the pilot, position (including the ATS route designator or the track code, as appropriate) and flight level; and

j.   the controller should attempt to determine the nature of the emergency and ascertain any assistance that may be required. Subsequent ATC action with respect to that aircraft shall be based on the intentions of the pilot and overall traffic situation.

[ICAO Doc 4444, ¶15.2.3] Actions to be taken once offset from track

Note. — The pilot's judgment of the situation and the need to ensure the safety of the aircraft will determine the actions outlined to be taken. Factors for the pilot to consider when deviating from the cleared track or ATS route or level without an ATC clearance include, but are not limited to:

a) operation within a parallel track system;

b) the potential for user preferred routes (UPRs) parallel to the aircraft's track or ATS route;

c) the nature of the contingency (e.g. aircraft system malfunction); and

d) weather factors (e.g. convective weather at lower flight levels).

15.2.3.1. If possible, maintain the assigned flight level until established on the 9.3 km (5.0 NM) parallel, same direction track or ATS route offset. If unable, initially minimize the rate of descent to the extent that is operationally feasible.

15.2.3.2 Once established on a parallel, same direction track or ATS route offset by 9.3 km (5.0 NM), either:

a) descend below FL 290, and establish a 150 m (500 ft) vertical offset from those flight levels normally used, and proceed as required by the operational situation or if an ATC clearance has been obtained, in accordance with the clearance; or

Note 1. — Flight levels normally used are those contained in Annex 2 — Rules of the Air, Appendix 3.

Note 2. — Descent below FL 290 is considered particularly applicable to operations where there is a predominant traffic flow (e.g. east-west) or parallel track system where the aircraft's diversion path will likely cross adjacent tracks or ATS routes. A descent below FL 290 can decrease the likelihood of conflict with other aircraft, ACAS RA events and delays in obtaining a revised ATC clearance.

b) establish a 150 m (500 ft) vertical offset (or 300 m (1000 ft) vertical offset if above FL 410) from those flight levels normally used, and proceed as required by the operational situation, or if an ATC clearance has been obtained, in accordance with the clearance.

Note. — Altimetry system errors (ASE) may result in less than 150 m (500 ft) vertical spacing (less than 300 m (1000 ft) above FL410) when the above contingency procedure is applied.

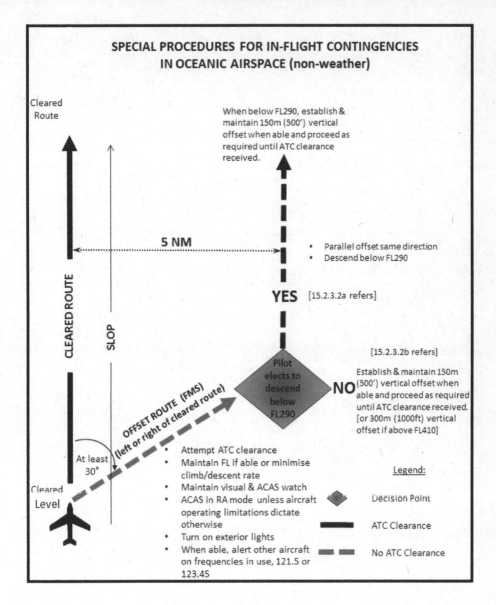

Visual aid for contingency procedures guidance, ICAO Doc 4444, figure 15-1.

Drift Down

*T*he prime directive when it comes to drift down has changed over the years.

A decade or more ago, the idea was you've just lost an engine, you have to descend, fuel will be critical, so maximize your forward distance. Set the maximum continuous thrust available on the operating engines, allow the speed to decrease to a magic value that helps you descend as slowly as possible, and then descend as slowly as possible while heading to an alternate. You are an emergency aircraft, everyone else can get out of your way.

Current thinking realizes that it does you no good, or anybody else for that matter, to descend slowly into another airplane. This is especially (and morally) true for us flying business aircraft. I often cross the North Atlantic with a crew of two and one passenger. Is it right to endanger the lives on an airliner with hundreds of passengers for the sake of us three? So now the idea codified into international regulations is to offset from any known tracks, descend below those tracks, and then turn to an alternate. This is going to cost you fuel and perhaps the ability to make it to your alternate if you didn't plan for this.

So you may be wondering why we need drift down procedures at all. Well, you do need them. We often consider these possible emergencies in a worst case scenario. But let's say you are at 30 West when that critical engine stops and you need to head downstairs. If CPDLC is working, or if you have good connectivity on the HF, why not explain the situation to Gander or Shanwick and see what they can do for you? Chances are you will still have to dive below the tracks, but it doesn't hurt to ask. Or let's say you are stretching your airplane's legs from London to Tokyo over the most barren parts of Canada. You aren't on or above any known tracks but are rightfully worried about other aicraft doing the same thing you are. If air traffic control says you have that part of Canada to yourself, perhaps a proper drift down will get you to your alternate with a little extra gas in case you need to make more than one instrument approach.

Aircraft Theory

The aircraft manufacturer should have evaluated your aircraft's performance and figured out the best way to squeeze the most distance for the least amount of gas in the event of an engine failure. They will have made similar computations for a depressurization scenario and for a simple diversion while remaining at altitude.

At the very least you should have made computations to figure at what point along your route of flight you can make the decision to continue or return to a set of alternate airports in front or behind you. This point is the Equal Time Point (ETP) and is a staple of international operations. Your flight planning service very likely makes these computations for you. But what are the assumptions behind the numbers?

AFM Drift Down Procedure

Your ETP is probably designed for you to do the following:

1. Set your operating engine(s) to a maximum thrust setting, while turning directly to your alternate

2. Allow your speed to decay to drift down speed while maintaining altitude (this may happen almost immediately or in a minute or so for most two-engine aircraft)

3. As drift down speed is reached, descend at that speed until at drift down altitude

This gets you to your ETP alternate at the predicted fuel level, provided the winds, temperature, and other considerations cooperate. In other words, it is a best case scenario. But what is the route of flight for this diversion?

Routing

$$\frac{\text{Total Distance}}{\text{GS}_R + \text{GS}_C} = \frac{\text{ETP (in nm from GS}_R)}{\text{GS}_R}$$

Many pilots assume that when they approach an Equal Time Point (ETP), they will have smooth sailing getting to either ETP airport. It is a safety factor, after all. But they may be surprised to hear that most ETP calculations assume a straight line route of flight and do not provide for approach fuel or any additional fuel needed for the approach or APU.

For more about ETP calculations, see the Appendices, Chapter 19.

Regulatory Theory

[ICAO Doc 4444, ¶15.2.2.2] If prior clearance cannot be obtained, the following contingency procedures should be employed until a revised clearance is received. In general terms, the aircraft should be flown at an offset level and on an offset track where other aircraft are less likely to be encountered. Specifically, the pilot shall [. . .] leave the cleared track OR ATS route by initially turning at least 30 degrees to the right or to the left, in order to establish and maintain a parallel, same direction track or ATS route offset 5 NM (9.3 km).

Theories Meet Realities

There is no doubt you should plan on not being able to drift down when the time comes; it is the safe and legal thing to do. But if you are in airspace devoid of other traffic or you have good communications with air traffic control and they can assure you the sky belongs to you, then doing an AFM drift down can improve your odds of making it to your destination or alternate.

Waypoint Briefing

Depending on your aircraft, the time between an engine failure and needing to start down can be only seconds. Many twin-engine aircraft cruise right at their drift down speeds (such as a Gulfstream G450). Others give you more time (like a Challenger 605). Aircraft with three or more engines can give you 20 or 30 minutes (such as a Falcon 900). But no matter the amount of time you have, you should know what to do before it happens. A good time to think about this is at each waypoint. As your geography (distance along the route), performance (reduce weight), and endurance (reduced fuel) change, your situation changes. You need to brief a new escape plan at every waypoint.

Photo: G450 Single Engine Range page

At each waypoint you should:

- *Brief the aircraft's current weight*
- *Look up and brief the current drift down speed and altitude*
- *Update the weather at any applicable alternates*
- *Brief the proximity of any organized tracks relative to the next leg*
- *Brief the planned direction of turn as well as the route and altitude needed to avoid any organized tracks (your escape plan)*

Chapter 3

Lost Communications

If you are a U.S. pilot who never leaves the confines of the United States and Canada, lost communications are pretty easy to remember and you should have no problem. See United States Exceptions for the specific procedures.

"Exceptions?" you say? Yes, what you grew up with are an exception to International Civil Aviation Organization (ICAO) procedures and if you venture outside our shores, you have some studying to do. Keep in mind that the other countries you visit may have their own exceptions to these rules. So you have to know the ICAO rules as well as the rules for each country you visit or even fly over. Each country is required to post their differences from the ICAO standard in their individual Aeronautical Information Publication (AIP). ICAO Doc 7030 - Regional Supplementary Procedures was supposed to have fixed all this, but it did not. Be careful out there.

When it comes to lost communications when in oceanic airspace, things are standard except for an exception in the Pacific.

If you have a copy of Jeppesen Airways Manual you should have all you need to learn about individual country lost communications procedures, but you need to understand International Standard Procedures first.

Remember that these are as of early 2021. If you are leaving your home country tomorrow, you need to make sure your knowledge is up to date.

International Standard Procedures

These procedures are what most of the world use and you should either have them memorized or easily accessible anytime you fly outside your home country. For us brought up in the United States, the key points are these: (1) timing depends on whether or not you are in radar contact, and (2) your altitude depends on your filed flight plan.

[ICAO Annex 2]

3.6.5.1 An aircraft operated as a controlled flight shall maintain continuous air-ground voice communication watch on the appropriate communication channel of, and establish two-way communication as necessary with, the appropriate air traffic control unit, except as may be prescribed by the appropriate ATS authority in respect of aircraft forming part of aerodrome traffic at a controlled aerodrome.

Note 1.— SELCAL or similar automatic signaling devices satisfy the requirement to maintain an air-ground voice communication watch.

Note 2.— The requirement for an aircraft to maintain an air-ground voice communication watch remains in effect after CPDLC has been established.

3.6.5.2 Communication failure. If a communication failure precludes compliance with 3.6.5.1, the aircraft shall comply with the voice communication failure procedures of Annex 10, Volume II, and with such of the following procedures as are appropriate. The aircraft shall attempt to establish communications with the appropriate air traffic control unit using all other available means. In addition, the aircraft, when forming part of the aerodrome traffic at a controlled aerodrome, shall keep a watch for such instructions as may be issued by visual signals.

3.6.5.2.1 If in visual meteorological conditions, the aircraft shall:

a) continue to fly in visual meteorological conditions; land at the nearest suitable aerodrome; and report its arrival by the most expeditious means to the appropriate air traffic services unit;

b) if considered advisable, complete an IFR flight in accordance with 3.6.5.2.2.

3.6.5.2.2 If in instrument meteorological conditions or when the pilot of an IFR flight considers it inadvisable to complete the flight in accordance with 3.6.5.2.1 a), the aircraft shall:

a) unless otherwise prescribed on the basis of regional air navigation agreement, in airspace where radar is not used in the provision of air traffic control, maintain the last assigned speed and level, or minimum flight altitude if higher, for a period of 20 minutes following the aircraft's failure to report its position over a compulsory reporting point and thereafter adjust level and speed in accordance with the filed flight plan;

b) in airspace where radar is used in the provision of air traffic control, maintain the last assigned speed and level, or minimum flight altitude if higher, for a period of 7 minutes following:

1) the time the last assigned level or minimum flight altitude is reached; or

2) the time the transponder is set to Code 7600; or

3) the aircraft's failure to report its position over a compulsory reporting point;

whichever is later, and thereafter adjust level and speed in accordance with the filed flight plan;

c) when being radar vectored or having been directed by ATC to proceed offset using area navigation (RNAV) without a specified limit, rejoin the current flight plan route no later than the next significant point, taking into consideration the applicable minimum flight altitude;

d) proceed according to the current flight plan route to the appropriate designated navigation aid or fix serving the destination aerodrome and, when required to ensure compliance with e) below, hold over this aid or fix until commencement of descent;

e) commence descent from the navigation aid or fix specified in d) at, or as close as possible to, the expected approach time last received and acknowledged; or, if no expected approach time has been received and acknowledged, at, or as close as possible to, the estimated time of arrival resulting from the current flight plan;

f) complete a normal instrument approach procedure as specified for the designated navigation aid or fix; and

g) land, if possible, within 30 minutes after the estimated time of arrival specified in e) or the last acknowledged expected approach time, whichever is later.

Note 1.— The provision of air traffic control service to other flights operating in the airspace concerned will be based on the premise that an aircraft experiencing communication failure will comply with the rules in 3.6.5.2.2.

Note 2. — See also 5.1.2.

[ICAO Annex 2, ¶5.1.2]

Except when necessary for takeoff or landing, or except when specifically authorized by the appropriate authority, an IFR flight shall be flown at a level which is not below the minimum flight altitude established by the State whose territory is overflown, or, where no such minimum flight altitude has been established:

a) over high terrain or in mountainous areas, at a level which is at least 600 m (2,000 ft) above the highest obstacle located within 8 km of the estimated position of the aircraft;

b) elsewhere than as specified in a), at a level which is at least 300 m (1,000 ft) above the highest obstacle located within 8 km of the estimated position of the aircraft.

Note 1.— The estimated position of the aircraft will take account of the navigational accuracy which can be achieved on the relevant route segment, having regard to the navigational facilities available on the ground and in the aircraft.

Note 2.— See also 3.1.2.

[ICAO Annex 2, ¶3.1.2] Minimum heights

Except when necessary for takeoff or landing, or except by permission from the appropriate authority, aircraft shall not be flown over the congested areas of cities, towns or settlements or over an open-air assembly of persons, unless at such a height as will permit, in the event of an emergency arising, a landing to be made without undue hazard to persons or property on the surface.

[ICAO Annex 10]

5.2.2.7. Communications Failure

5.2.2.7.1 Air-ground

5.2.2.7.1.1 When an aircraft station fails to establish contact with the aeronautical station on the designated frequency, it shall attempt to establish contact on another frequency appropriate to the route. If this attempt fails, the aircraft station shall attempt to establish communication with other aircraft or other aeronautical stations on frequencies appropriate to the route. In addition, an aircraft operating within a network shall monitor the appropriate VHF frequency for calls from nearby aircraft.

5.2.2.7.1.2 If the attempts specified under 5.2.2.7.1.1 fail, the aircraft station shall transmit its message twice on the designated frequency(ies), preceded by the phrase "TRANSMITTING BLIND" and, if necessary, include the addressee(s) for which the message is intended.

5.2.2.7.1.2.1 PANS.— In network operation, a message which is transmitted blind should be transmitted twice on both primary and secondary frequencies. Before changing frequency, the aircraft station should announce the frequency to which it is changing.

North Atlantic Notes

The rules in the North Atlantic are pretty much in accordance with ICAO procedures, but they are complicated by the density of air traffic. It helps to understand a few of the finer points of operating in this airspace.

[ICAO NAT Doc 007, ¶6.6.1] Rules and procedures for the operation of an aircraft following a radio communications failure (RCF) are established to allow ATC to anticipate that aircraft's subsequent actions and thus for ATC to be able to provide a service to all other flights within the same vicinity, so as to ensure the continued safe separation of all traffic. The general principles of such rules and procedures are set out in Annexes 2 and 10 to the ICAO Convention. States publish in their AIPs specific RCF rules and regulations to be followed within their particular sovereign airspace.

[ICAO NAT Doc 007, ¶6.6.2] It must be recognised that there is in general an underlying premise in "normal" radio communications failure procedures that they are for use when a single aircraft suffers an on-board communications equipment failure. Within the NAT Region and some adjacent domestic airspace (e.g. Northern Canada), where HF Voice is used for air-ground ATC communications, ionospheric disturbances resulting in poor radio propagation conditions can also interrupt these communications. While it is impossible to provide guidance for all situations associated with an HF communications failure, it is, however, extremely important to differentiate between two distinct circumstances: - firstly, an on-board communications equipment failure, resulting in an individual aircraft losing HF communications with ATC and; secondly, the occurrence of poor HF propagation conditions (commonly referred to as "HF Blackouts"), which can simultaneously interrupt HF air-ground communications for many aircraft over a wide area.

[ICAO NAT Doc 007, ¶6.6.3] In the case of an on-board communications equipment failure, even though ATC loses contact with that aircraft, it can anticipate that aircraft's actions and, if necessary, modify the profiles of other aircraft in the same vicinity in order to maintain safe separations.

[ICAO NAT Doc 007, ¶6.6.4] However, the occurrence of poor HF propagation conditions can simultaneously interrupt HF air-ground communications for many aircraft over a wide area and ATC may then be unable to make any interventions to assure safe traffic separations using HF. Notwithstanding the growing use of Data link and SATCOM Voice for regular airground ATS communications in the NAT Region, all pilots must recognise that, pending the mandatory carriage and use of such means, an HF blackout will impact the ability of ATC to ensure the safe separation of all traffic. Hence, even if using other than HF for regular communications with ATC, pilots should still exercise appropriate caution when HF blackout conditions are encountered.

[ICAO NAT Doc 007, ¶6.6.5] The following procedures are intended to provide general guidance for aircraft which experience a communications failure while operating in, or proposing to operate in, the NAT Region. These procedures are intended to complement and not supersede State procedures/regulations.

General Provisions

The flight crew of an aircraft experiencing a two-way ATS communications failure should operate the SSR Transponder on identity Mode A Code 7600 and Mode C.

When so equipped, an aircraft should use SATVOICE to contact the responsible radio station via special telephone numbers/short codes published in State AIPs (see also NAT Doc 003, "High Frequency Management Guidance Material for the NAT Region" which can be downloaded from the www. icao.int/EURNAT/, following "EUR & NAT Documents," then "NAT Documents"). However, it must be appreciated that pending further system developments and facility implementations the capability for Ground (ATC)-initiated calls varies between different NAT OACCs.

If the aircraft is not equipped with SATVOICE then the flight crew should attempt to use VHF to contact any (other) ATC facility or another aircraft, inform them of the difficulty, and request that they relay information to the ATC facility with which communications are intended.

The inter-pilot air-to-air VHF frequency, 123.45 MHz, may be used to relay position reports via another aircraft. (N.B. The emergency frequency 121.5

MHz should not be used to relay regular communications, but since all NAT traffic is required to monitor the emergency frequency, it may be used, in these circumstances, to establish initial contact with another aircraft and then request transfer to the inter-pilot frequency for further contacts).

In view of the traffic density in the NAT Region, pilots of aircraft experiencing a two-way ATS communications failure should broadcast regular position reports on the inter-pilot frequency (123.45 MHz) until such time as communications are re-established.

Communications Procedures for Use in the Event of an On-board HF Equipment Failure

[ICAO NAT Doc 007, ¶6.6.6] Use SATVOICE communications, if so equipped.

[ICAO NAT Doc 007, ¶6.6.7] If not SATVOICE equipped try VHF relay via another aircraft.

Communications Procedures for Use during Poor HF Propagation Conditions

[ICAO NAT Doc 007, ¶6.6.8] Poor HF propagation conditions are the result of ionospheric disturbances. These are usually caused by sun-spot or solar flare activity creating bursts of charged particles in the solar wind which can spiral down around the Earth's magnetic lines of force and distort or disturb the ionised layers in the stratosphere which are utilised to refract HF radio waves. As with the Aurora Borealis, which is of similar origin, these ionospheric disturbances most commonly occur in regions adjacent to the Magnetic Poles. Since the Earth's North Magnetic Pole is currently located at approximately 87N 150W, flights through the North Atlantic and Northern Canada regions can, on occasion, experience resulting HF communications difficulties.

[ICAO NAT Doc 007, ¶6.6.9] SATVOICE communications are unaffected by most ionospheric disturbances. Therefore, when so equipped, an aircraft may use SATVOICE for ATC communications.

[ICAO NAT Doc 007, ¶6.6.10] If not SATVOICE equipped, in some circumstances it may be feasible to seek the assistance, via VHF, of a nearby SATVOICE equipped aircraft to relay communications with ATC.

[ICAO NAT Doc 007, ¶6.6.11] Whenever aircraft encounter poor HF propagation conditions that would appear to adversely affect air-ground communications generally, it is recommended that all pilots then broadcast their position reports on the air-to-air VHF frequency 123.45 MHz. Given the density of traffic in the NAT Region and the fact that in such poor propagation conditions ATC will be unable to maintain contact with all aircraft, it is important that even those aircraft that have been able to establish SATCOM Voice contact also broadcast their position reports.

[ICAO NAT Doc 007, ¶6.6.12] If for whatever reason SATCOM Voice communications (direct or relayed) are not possible, then the following procedures may help to re-establish HF communications. Sometimes these ionospheric disturbances are very wide-spread and HF air-ground communications at all frequencies can be severely disrupted throughout very large areas (e.g. simultaneously affecting the whole of the NAT Region and the Arctic.). However, at other times the disturbances may be more localised and/or may only affect a specific range of frequencies.

[ICAO NAT Doc 007, ¶6.6.13] In this latter circumstance, HF air-ground communications with the intended aeradio station may sometimes continue to be possible but on a frequency other than either the primary or secondary frequencies previously allocated to an aircraft. Hence, in the event of encountering poor HF propagation conditions pilots should first try using alternative HF frequencies to contact the intended aeradio station.

[ICAO NAT Doc 007, ¶6.6.14] However, while the ionospheric disturbances may be severe, they may nevertheless only be localized between the aircraft's position and the intended aeradio station, thus rendering communications with that station impossible on any HF frequency. But the aeradio stations providing air-ground services in the NAT Region do co-operate as a network and it may, even then, still be possible to communicate with another aeradio station in the NAT network on HF and request that they relay communications. Efforts should therefore be made to contact other NAT aeradio stations via appropriate HF frequencies.

[ICAO NAT Doc 007, ¶6.6.15] Nevertheless, as previously indicated, there are occasions when the ionospheric disturbance is so severe and so widespread that HF air-ground communications with any aeradio station within the NAT Region network are rendered impossible.

Rationale for Lost Communications Operational Procedures

[ICAO NAT Doc 007, ¶6.6.16] Because of the density of oceanic traffic in the NAT region, unique operational procedures have been established to be followed by flight crews whenever communications are lost with ATC. If communications with the relevant OACC are lost at any time after receiving and acknowledging a clearance then the aircraft must adhere strictly to the routing and profile of the last acknowledged clearance until exiting the NAT region. Flight crews must not revert to their filed flight plan.

Operational Procedures following Loss of HF Communications Prior to Entry into the NAT

[ICAO NAT Doc 007, ¶6.6.17] Due to the potential length of time in oceanic airspace, it is strongly recommended that a flight crew, experiencing an HF communications equipment failure:

Prior to departure

• Coordinate with the initial NAT OAC according to flight planned route to determine if eligible for HF relief waiver as outlined in 6.1.1

• Include any coordinated HF waiver relief details in section 18 of the flight plan

After departure and prior to entering the NAT

• Coordinate with the initial NAT OAC according to flight planned route to determine if eligible for HF relief waiver as outlined in 6.1.1

[ICAO NAT Doc 007, ¶6.6.18] If, however, an oceanic clearance cannot be obtained, the individual aircraft suffering radio communications equipment failure should enter oceanic airspace at the first oceanic entry point, level and speed contained in the filed flight plan and proceed via the filed flight plan route to landfall. The initial oceanic level and speed included in the filed flight plan must be maintained until landfall. Any subsequent climbs included in the filed flight plan must not be executed.

HF Blackout

[ICAO NAT Doc 007, ¶6.6.19] In the case of aircraft that lose ATC communications as a result of poor propagation conditions (HF Blackouts) when approaching NAT airspace through domestic airspace where ATC communications are also conducted via HF (e.g. entering the NAT through Northern Canadian airspace into the Reykjavik OCA), it is probably less advisable to execute unscheduled landings. These poor propagation conditions are very likely to affect many aircraft simultaneously and multiple diversions of "lost comms" aircraft might create further difficulties and risks.

[ICAO NAT Doc 007, ¶6.6.20] As with the equipment failure situation, aircraft approaching the NAT and losing ATC communications as a result of poor HF radio propagation conditions should, if already in receipt of an oceanic clearance, follow the routing specified in that clearance and maintain the initial cleared level and speed throughout the oceanic segment i.e. through to landfall.

[ICAO NAT Doc 007, ¶6.6.21] However, in these HF Blackout circumstances, if no oceanic clearance has been received, the aircraft must remain at the last cleared domestic flight level, not only to the ocean entry point but also throughout the whole subsequent oceanic segment (i.e. until final landfall). This is in stark contrast to the equipment failure case. In such HF Blackouts, pilots must not effect level changes to comply with filed flight plans. Such aircraft should, maintain the last cleared level and, enter oceanic airspace at the first oceanic entry point and speed contained in the filed flight plan, then proceed via the filed flight plan route to landfall.

[ICAO NAT Doc 007, ¶6.6.22] The rationale here must be appreciated. In such circumstances it is likely that ATC will have simultaneously lost HF communications with multiple aircraft in the same vicinity. Should flight crews then wrongly apply the "normal" radio failure procedures and "fly the flight plan," there is a possibility that two such aircraft may have filed conflicting flight paths/levels through the subsequent oceanic airspace, and without communications with either aircraft, ATC would then be unable to intervene to resolve the conflict. Since safe aircraft level separation assurance has already been incorporated into the current domestic clearances, it is consequently imperative that under such (domestic and oceanic) HF-blackout circumstances, all aircraft electing to continue flight into NAT oceanic airspace without a received and acknowledged oceanic clearance, should adhere to the flight level in the last received domestic clearance. No level changes should be made to comply with a filed oceanic level that is different from that of the domestic clearance in effect at the time that ATC air-ground communications were lost.

Operational Procedures following Loss of HF Communications after En-

tering the NAT

[ICAO NAT Doc 007, ¶6.6.23] If the HF communications equipment failure occurs or HF Blackout conditions are encountered after entering the NAT then:

The flight crew must proceed in accordance with the last received and acknowledged oceanic clearance, including level and speed, to the last specified oceanic route point (normally landfall). After passing this point, the flight crew should conform with the relevant AIP specified State procedures/regulations and if necessary rejoin the filed flight plan route by proceeding, via the published ATS route structure where possible, to the next significant point contained in the filed flight plan. Note: the relevant State procedures/regulations to be followed by an aircraft in order to rejoin its filed flight plan route are specified in detail in the appropriate State AIP.

[ICAO NAT Doc 007, ¶6.6.24] Aircraft with a destination within the NAT region should proceed to their clearance limit and follow the ICAO standard procedure to commence descent from the appropriate designated navigation aid serving the destination aerodrome at, or as close as possible to, the expected approach time. Detailed procedures are promulgated in relevant State AIPs.

Summary of Operational Procedures Required following Loss of Air/Ground ATS Communications in the NAT Region

[ICAO NAT Doc 007, ¶6.6.25] The foregoing detailed operational procedures can be simply summarised as follows:

- Equipment Failure before receiving an oceanic clearance:- Divert or fly the flight plan route, speed and initial planned oceanic level to landfall.

- Blackout encountered (in an HF comms Domestic ATC environment) before receiving an oceanic clearance:- Continue at Domestic cleared level and follow flight planned route and speed to landfall.

- Equipment Failure or Blackout after receiving an oceanic clearance:- Fly that clearance to landfall.

In all cases, after landfall rejoin, or continue on, the flight planned route, using appropriate State AIP specified procedures for the domestic airspace entered.

Pacific Exceptions

[ICAO Doc 7030, PAC 9.3)

In the event of total loss of communication, an aircraft shall:

a) try to re-establish communication by all other means;

b) if all attempts to re-establish communication with ATC are unsuccessful:

1) squawk 7600;

2) if able, broadcast in the blind at suitable intervals: flight identification, flight level, aircraft position (including the ATS route designator or the track code) and intentions on the frequency in use, as well as on frequency 121.5 MHz (or, as a back-up, the VHF inter-pilot air-to-air frequency 123.45 MHz);

3) watch for conflicting traffic both visually and by reference to airborne collision avoidance systems or traffic displays (if equipped);

4) turn on all aircraft exterior lights (commensurate with appropriate operating limitations);

5) maintain the last assigned speed and level for a period of 60 minutes following the aircraft's failure to report its position over a compulsory reporting point (including ADS-C flights), and thereafter adjust speed and altitude in accordance with the filed flight plan;

Note.— In airspace where the strategic lateral offset procedure (SLOP) has been authorized, aircraft experiencing communication failure may also elect to initiate SLOP in accordance with State AIP, including an offset of 1.8 or 3.7 km (1 nm or 2 nm) right of track.

6) Upon exiting oceanic airspace, conform to the relevant State procedures and regulations.

United States Exceptions

[14 CFR 91, §91.185]

(a) General. Unless otherwise authorized by ATC, each pilot who has two-way radio communications failure when operating under IFR shall comply with the rules of this section.

(b) VFR conditions. If the failure occurs in VFR conditions, or if VFR conditions are encountered after the failure, each pilot shall continue the flight under VFR and land as soon as practicable.

(c) IFR conditions. If the failure occurs in IFR conditions, or if paragraph (b) of this section cannot be complied with, each pilot shall continue the flight according to the following:

(1) Route.

(i) By the route assigned in the last ATC clearance received;

(ii) If being radar vectored, by the direct route from the point of radio failure to the fix, route, or airway specified in the vector clearance;

(iii) In the absence of an assigned route, by the route that ATC has advised may be expected in a further clearance; or

(iv) In the absence of an assigned route or a route that ATC has advised may be expected in a further clearance, by the route filed in the flight plan.

(2) Altitude. At the highest of the following altitudes or flight levels for the route segment being flown:

(i) The altitude or flight level assigned in the last ATC clearance received;

(ii) The minimum altitude (converted, if appropriate, to minimum flight level as prescribed in §91.121(c)) for IFR operations; or

(iii) The altitude or flight level ATC has advised may be expected in a further clearance.

(3) Leave clearance limit.

(i) When the clearance limit is a fix from which an approach begins, commence descent or descent and approach as close as possible to the expect-further-clearance time if one has been received, or if one has not been received, as close as possible to the estimated time of arrival as calculated from the filed or amended (with ATC) estimated time en route.

(ii) If the clearance limit is not a fix from which an approach begins, leave the clearance limit at the expect-further-clearance time if one has been received, or if none has been received, upon arrival over the clearance limit, and proceed to a fix from which an approach begins and commence descent or descent and approach as close as possible to the estimated time of arrival as calculated from the filed or amended (with ATC) estimated time en route.

Country and Airport Exceptions

Individual countries and even airports within the country may have their own peculiar routings and procedures to be used in the event of lost communications. Your Jeppesen manuals are your best source for this information but the location of the lost communications information is not consistent. You may find it on the individual airport briefing pages, the arrival/departure pages, the approach charts, or in the text pages. Among the text pages, you need to look at the ATC and Emergency pages.

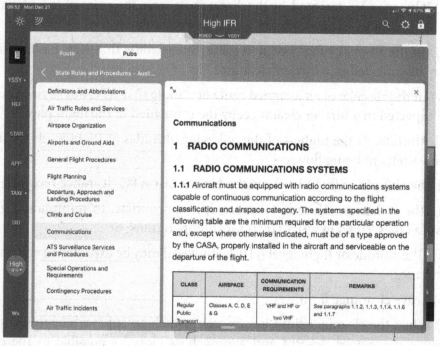

Photo: JeppFD Australia Radio Communications Failure Page Extract

The example shown on the photo comes from the Australia "State Rules and Procedures" pages of the Jeppesen JeppFD application. On an iPad you get there by having an Australian airport in the route, selecting a map, such as the "High IFR" chart selecting the manuals icon, selecting the "Pubs" button, selecting "Route Notes" arrow if it isn't already in view, selecting the Pacific region, selecting Pacific Airway Manual, and then selecting "State Rules and Procedures - Australia" under the "Air Traffic Control" section.

Chapter 4

Loss of Long Range Navigation

The ICAO rules for what you need to navigate are given in ICAO Annex 6 - Operation of Aircraft and are summarized below. The ICAO procedures for "loss of, or significant reduction in, the required navigation capability when operating in an airspace where the navigation performance accuracy is prerequisite to the safe conduct of flight operations" are contained in ICAO Document 4444, Amendment 2 § 15.2.1 and summarized in Chapter 1 of this Section.

Exceptions to these procedures are contained in ICAO Document 7030 for various regions and in each state's Aeronautical Information Publication. The ICAO NAT Doc 007, North Atlantic Operations and Airspace Manual gives greater detail about these procedures that can be helpful anywhere in the world.

ICAO Operation of Aircraft Rules

Before we can consider what to do when you lose long range navigation, we should consider what is required. I've cited ICAO Annex 6, Volume I, which applies to commercial operations, but the exact same language exists in ICAO Annex 6, Volume II, ¶2.5.2, which applies to general aviation.

[ICAO Annex 6, Volume I, §7.2]

7.2.1 An aeroplane shall be provided with navigation equipment which will enable it to proceed:

a) in accordance with its operational flight plan; and

b) in accordance with the requirements of air traffic services; except when, if not so precluded by the appropriate authority, navigation for flights under VFR is accomplished by visual reference to landmarks.

7.2.2 For operations where a navigation specification for performance-based navigation (PBN) has been prescribed, an aeroplane shall, in addition to the requirements specified in 7.2.1:

a) be provided with navigation equipment which will enable it to operate in accordance with the prescribed navigation specification(s);

b) have information relevant to the aeroplane navigation specification capabilities listed in the flight manual or other aeroplane documentation approved by the State of the Design or State of Registry; and

c) have information relevant to the aeroplane navigation specification capabilities included in the MEL.

Note.— Guidance on aeroplane documentation is contained in the Performance-based Navigation (PBN) Manual (Doc 9613).

7.2.3 The State of the Operator shall, for operations where a navigation specification for PBN has been prescribed, ensure that the operator has established and documented:

a) normal and abnormal procedures including contingency procedures;

b) flight crew qualification and proficiency requirements in accordance with the appropriate navigation specifications;

c) a training programme for relevant personnel consistent with the intended operations; and

d) appropriate maintenance procedures to ensure continued airworthiness in accordance with the appropriate navigation specifications.

Note 1.— Guidance on safety risks and mitigations for PBN operations, in accordance with Annex 19, are contained in the Performance-based Navigation (PBN) Operational Approval Manual (Doc 9997).

Note 2.— Electronic navigation data management is an integral part of normal and abnormal procedures. 7.2.4 The State of the Operator shall issue a specific approval for operations based on PBN authorization required (AR) navigation specifications.

Note.— Guidance on specific approvals for PBN authorization required (AR) navigation specifications is contained in the Performance-based Navigation (PBN) Operational Approval Manual (Doc 9997).

7.2.5 For flights in defined portions of airspace where, based on Regional Air Navigation Agreement, minimum navigation performance specifications (MNPS) are prescribed, an aeroplane shall be provided with navigation equipment which:

a) continuously provides indications to the flight crew of adherence to or departure from track to the required degree of accuracy at any point along that track; and

b) has been authorized by the State of the Operator for the MNPS operations concerned.

Note.— The prescribed minimum navigation performance specifications and the procedures governing their application are published in the Regional Supplementary Procedures (Doc 7030).

Loss of Long Range Navigation Capability

General

[ICAO NAT Doc 007, ¶12.1.2] For unrestricted operation in the NAT HLA an approved aircraft must be equipped with a minimum of two fully serviceable LRNSs. Aircraft may be approved for NAT HLA operations when equipped with only a single LRNS. However, such aircraft are only permitted to plan and fly routes specified for this purpose (see paragraph 12.2) and on other particular routings serving individual traffic axes e.g. the Tango routes, routings between the Iberian Peninsula and the Azores/Madeira and routes between Iceland and Greenland (See Chapter 3).

See Chapter 3 of ICAO NAT Doc 007 for more about this.

[ICAO NAT Doc 007, ¶12.1.3] If abnormal navigation indications relating to INS or IRS systems occur after take-off, they should be analysed to discover their cause. Under no circumstances should a flight continue into oceanic airspace with unresolved navigation system errors, or with errors caused by inertial platform misalignment or initial position insertion.

Methods of Determining which System is Faulty

[ICAO NAT Doc 007, ¶12.1.6] With only two systems on board, identifying the defective unit can be difficult. If such a situation does arise in oceanic airspace any or all of the following actions should be considered:

a.　　checking malfunction codes for indication of unserviceability.

b.　　obtaining a fix. It may be possible to use the following:

　　　1.　　the weather radar (range marks and relative bearing lines) to determine the position relative to an identifiable landmark such as an island; or

2. the ADF to obtain bearings from a suitable long-range NDB, in which case magnetic variation at the position of the aircraft should be used to convert the RMI bearings to true; or

3. if within range, a VOR, in which case the magnetic variation at the VOR location should be used to convert the radial to a true bearing (except when flying in the Canadian Northern Domestic Airspace where VOR bearings may be oriented with reference to true as opposed to magnetic north).

c. contacting a nearby aircraft on VHF, and comparing information on spot wind, or ground speed and drift.

d. if such assistance is not available, and as a last resort, the flight plan wind speed and direction for the current DR position of the aircraft, can be compared with that from navigation system outputs.

Action if the Faulty System Cannot be Identified

[ICAO NAT Doc 007, ¶12.1.7] Occasions may still arise when distance or cross track differences develop between systems, but the flight crew cannot determine which system is at fault. The majority of operators feel that the procedure most likely to limit gross tracking errors under such circumstances is to fly the aircraft half way between the cross track differences as long as the uncertainty exists.

Guidance on What Constitutes a Failed System

[ICAO NAT Doc 007, ¶12.1.8] Operations or navigation manuals should include guidelines on how to decide when a navigation system should be considered to have failed, e.g. failures may be indicated by a red warning light, or by self-diagnosis indications, or by an error over a known position exceeding the value agreed between an operator and its certifying authority.

Loss of Navigation/FMS Capability

[ICAO NAT Doc 007, ¶12.2.1] Some aircraft carry triplex equipment (3 LRNSs) and hence if one system fails, even before take-off, the two basic requirements for NAT HLA operations may still be met and the flight can proceed normally. The following guidance is offered for aircraft having state approval for unrestricted operations in the NAT HLA and which are equipped with only two operational LRNSs:

One System Fails Before Take-Off

[ICAO NAT Doc 007, ¶12.2.2] The flight crew must consider:

- delaying departure until repair is possible;

- obtaining a clearance above or below MNPS Airspace;

- planning on the special routes known as the 'Blue Spruce' Routes, which have been established for use by aircraft suffering partial loss of navigation capability (Note: As indicated in Chapter 1, these routes may also be flown by aircraft approved for NAT MNPSA operations but equipped with only a single LRNS).

These Blue Spruce Routes are listed in ICAO NAT Doc 007 and your Jeppesen Airway Manual Atlantic Planning Charts.

One System Fails Before the OCA Boundary is Reached [With only one system remaining]

[ICAO NAT Doc 007, ¶12.2.4] The flight crew must consider:

- landing at a suitable aerodrome before the boundary or returning to the aerodrome of departure;

- diverting via one of the special routes described previously;

- obtaining a [reclearance] above or below the NAT HLA.

One System Fails After the OCA Boundary is Crossed

[ICAO NAT Doc 007, ¶12.2.5] Once the aircraft has entered oceanic airspace, the flight crew should normally continue to operate the aircraft in accordance with the oceanic clearance already received, appreciating that the reliability of the total navigation system has been significantly reduced.

[ICAO NAT Doc 007, ¶12.2.6] The flight crew should however,

- assess the prevailing circumstances (e.g. performance of the remaining system, remaining portion of the flight in the NAT HLA, etc.);

- prepare a proposal to ATC with respect to the prevailing circumstances (e.g. request clearance above or below the NAT HLA, turn-back, obtain clearance to fly along one of the special routes, etc.);

- advise and consult with ATC as to the most suitable action;

- obtain appropriate [reclearance] prior to any deviation from the last acknowledged oceanic clearance.

[ICAO NAT Doc 007, ¶12.2.7] When the flight continues in accordance with its original clearance (especially if the distance ahead within the NAT HLA is significant), the flight crew should begin a careful monitoring programme:

- to take special care in the operation of the remaining system bearing in mind that routine methods of error checking are no longer available;

- to check the main and standby compass systems frequently against the information which is still available;

- to check the performance record of the remaining equipment and if doubt arises regarding its performance and/or reliability, the following procedures should be considered:

1.   attempting visual sighting of other aircraft or their contrails, which may provide a track indication;

2.   calling the appropriate OACC for information on other aircraft adjacent to the aircraft's estimated position and/or calling on VHF to establish contact with such aircraft (preferably same track/level) to obtain from them information which could be useful. (e.g. drift, groundspeed, wind details).

The Remaining System Fails After Entering the NAT HLA

[ICAO NAT Doc 007, ¶12.2.8] The flight crew should:

a.   immediately notify ATC;

b.   make best use of procedures specified above relating to attempting visual sightings and establishing contact on VHF with adjacent aircraft for useful information;

c.   keep a special look-out for possible conflicting aircraft, and make maximum use of exterior lights;

d.   if no instructions are received from ATC within a reasonable period consider climbing or descending 500 feet, broadcasting action on 121.5 MHz and advising ATC as soon as possible.

Note: This procedure also applies when a single remaining system gives an indication of degradation of performance, or neither system fails completely but the system indications diverge widely and the defective system cannot be determined.

Complete Failure of Navigation Systems Computers

[ICAO NAT Doc 007, ¶12.2.9] A characteristic of the navigation computer system is that the computer element might fail, and thus deprive the aircraft of steering guidance and the indication of position relative to cleared track, but the basic outputs of the IRS (LAT/LONG, Drift and Groundspeed) are left unimpaired. A typical drill to minimise the effects of a total navigation computer system failure is suggested below. It requires comprehensive use of the plotting chart.

a.   use the basic IRS/GPS outputs to adjust heading to maintain mean track and to calculate ETAs.

b.   draw the cleared route on a chart and extract mean true tracks between waypoints.

c.   at intervals of not more than 15 minutes plot position (LAT/LONG) on the chart and adjust heading to regain track.

Chapter 5

Loss of RVSM Capability in Oceanic Airspace

L osing your ability to keep the airplane precisely on altitude is becoming a bigger deal every day, as the skies are becoming more tightly packed. Because each situation is likely to be unique, there are no cut and dried rules that always apply. ICAO Contingency Procedures are given in ICAO Doc 9574 and provide a foundation for handling a loss of RVSM ability anywhere in the world. North Atlantic Procedures are given in ICAO Nat Doc 007 and require a few extra steps because of the crowded nature of the airspace. Other Regional Differences are given in ICAO Doc 7030.

ICAO Contingency Procedures

[ICAO Doc 9574, ¶5.1.1 h)] The following contingency procedures should be adhered to after entering RVSM airspace:

1.   the pilot should notify ATC of contingencies (equipment failures, weather conditions) in which the ability to maintain CFL is affected and coordinate a plan of action;

2.   equipment failures should be notified to ATC. Some examples are:

    a.   failure of all automatic altitude-keeping devices on board the aircraft;

    b.   loss of redundancy of altimetry systems, or any part of these, on board the aircraft;

    c.   failure of all altitude-reporting transponders;

    d.   loss of thrust on an engine necessitating descent; and

    e.   any other equipment failure affecting the ability to maintain CFL;

3.   the pilot should notify ATC when encountering severe turbulence; and

4.   if unable to notify ATC and obtain an ATC clearance prior to deviating from the assigned CFL, the pilot should follow established contingency procedures as defined by the region of operation and obtain ATC clearance as soon as possible.

These procedures are given in ICAO Doc 4444 and are provided in Chapter 1 of this Section.

North Atlantic Procedures

North Atlantic loss of RVSM procedures are in compliance with ICAO procedures, given above. ICAO NAT Doc 007 provides a few additional procedures.

In-Flight – Before Operating in the NAT HLA.

[ICAO NAT Doc 007, ¶9.1.7] Most flights will approach the NAT HLA through European or North American RVSM airspaces. It is therefore expected that continuous monitoring of the serviceability of the aircraft's height keeping systems will have been undertaken. Nevertheless, in view of the significant change of operating environment (i.e. to indirect surveillance and communications) it is recommended that a final confirmation of the aircraft systems serviceability is performed immediately prior to entering the NAT HLA. Check to ensure the two primary altimeters are reading within 200 feet of each other (or lesser value if specified in your aircraft's flight manual). Conduct this check while at level flight. You should also note the stand-by altimeter reading. The readings of the primary and standby altimeters should be recorded to be available for use in any possible contingency situations.

Equipment Failures

[ICAO NAT Doc 007, ¶9.2.1] The following equipment failures must be reported to ATC as soon as practicable following their identification:

a.   loss of one or more primary altimetry systems; or

b.   failure of all automatic altitude-control systems

Other Regional Differences

The basic general procedures are outlined below. Consult AIPs, Jeppesen State Pages, and ICAO Document 7030.

[AC 91-85, Appendix 5]

- Africa / Indian Ocean: standard contingency procedures [ICAO Document 7030, AFI, Paragraph 9.5]

- Caribbean: standard contingency procedures [ICAO Document 7030, CAR, Paragraph 9.5]

- Europe: If vertical navigation performance requirements cannot be maintained, pilots must obtain a revised ATC clearance prior to initiating and deviation from the cleared route and/or flight level, whenever possible. Pilots will inform ATC if severe turbulence impacts an aircraft's ability to maintain its cleared flight level, ATC will either establish horizontal separation or an increased vertical separation. [ICAO Document 7030, EUR, Paragraph 9.5]

- Middle East / Asia: Pilots will inform ATC if severe turbulence impacts an aircraft's ability to maintain its cleared flight level, ATC will either establish horizontal separation or an increased vertical separation. [ICAO Document 7030, MID/ASIA, Paragraph 9.5]

- North America: standard contingency procedures [ICAO Document 7030, NAM, Paragraph 9.5]

- North Atlantic: standard contingency procedures [ICAO Document 7030, NAT, Paragraph 9.5] as well as the specific instructions given in ICAO Nat Doc 007, and summarized above.

- Pacific: standard contingency procedures [ICAO Document 7030, PAC, Paragraph 9.5]

- South America: standard contingency procedures [ICAO Document 7030, SAM, Paragraph 9.5]

Chapter 6

Weather Deviation in Oceanic Airspace

I once had an international operations instructor get upset when I asked "where are we?" in response to her question about weather deviation procedures. Lost on many is that if you are in radar contact and talking to an air traffic controller, you should state your intentions and start from there. If you are not in radar contact and your only means of communication is via an ARINC radio operator or CPDLC, well then things change. Most of these procedures are given in ICAO Doc 4444 §15.2, and are repeated below. The basic concepts for contingencies are described in Chapter 1 of this Section.

General

[ICAO Doc 4444 §15.2.4.1]

Note.— The following procedures are intended for deviations around adverse meteorological conditions.

15.2.4.1.1 When weather deviation is required, the pilot should initiate communications with ATC via voice or CPDLC; rapid response may be obtained by either:

a) stating "WEATHER DEVIATION REQUIRED" to indicate that priority is desired on the frequency and for ATC response; or

b) requesting a weather deviation using a CPDLC lateral downlink message.

15.2.4.1.2 When necessary, the pilot should initiate the communications using the urgency call "PAN PAN" (preferably spoken three times) or by using a CPDLC urgency downlink message.

15.2.4.1.2 The pilot shall inform ATC when weather deviation is no longer required, or when a weather deviation has been completed and the aircraft has returned to its cleared route.

Actions to be taken when controller-pilot communications are established

[ICAO Doc 4444 §15.2.4.2]

15.2.4.2.1 The pilot should notify ATC and request clearance to deviate from track or ATS route, advising, when possible, the extent of the deviation requested. The flight crew will use whatever means are appropriate (i.e. voice and/or CPDLC) to communicate during a weather deviation.

Note.— Pilots are advised to contact ATC as soon as possible with requests for clearance in order to provide adequate time for the request to be assessed and acted upon.

15.2.4.2.2 ATC should take one of the following actions:

a.   when appropriate separation can be applied, issue clearance to deviate from track; or

b.   if there is conflicting traffic and ATC is unable to establish appropriate separation, ATC shall:

    1.   advise the pilot of inability to issue clearance for the requested deviation;

    2.   advise the pilot of the conflicting traffic; and

    3.   request the pilot's intentions.

15.2.4.2.3 The pilot should take the following actions:

a.   comply with the ATC clearance issued; or

b.   advise ATC of intentions and execute the procedures listed in 15.2.4.3.

Actions to be taken if a revised ATC clearance cannot be obtained

[ICAO Doc 4444 §15.2.4.3]

Note.— The provisions of this section apply to situations where a pilot needs to exercise the authority of a pilot-in-command under the provisions of Annex 2, 2.3.1.

If the aircraft is required to deviate from track or ATS route to avoid adverse meteorological conditions and prior clearance cannot be obtained, an ATC clearance shall be obtained at the earliest possible time. Until an ATC clearance is received, the pilot shall take the following actions:

a. if possible, deviate away from an organized track or ATS route system;

b. establish communications with and alert nearby aircraft by broadcasting, at suitable intervals: aircraft identification, flight level, position (including the ATS route designator or the track code, as appropriate) and intentions, on the frequency in use and on 121.5 MHz (or, as a backup, on the inter-pilot air-to-air frequency 123.45 MHz);

c. watch for conflicting traffic both visually and by reference to ACAS (if equipped);

d. turn on all aircraft exterior lights (commensurate with appropriate operating limitations);

e. for deviations of less than 9.3 km (5 NM) from the originally cleared track or ATS route, remain at a level assigned by ATC;

f. for deviations greater than or equal to 9.3 km (5 NM) from the originally cleared track or ATS route,, when the aircraft is approximately 9.3 km (5 NM) from track, initiate a level change in accordance with Table 15-1;

g. if the pilot receives clearance to deviate from cleared track or ATS route for a specified distance and, subsequently, requests, but cannot obtain a clearance to deviate beyond that distance, the pilot should apply an altitude offset in accordance with Table 15-1 before deviating beyond the cleared distance;

h. when returning to track or ATS route, be at its assigned flight level when the aircraft is within approximately 9.3 km (5 NM) of the centre line; and

i. if contact was not established prior to deviating, continue to attempt to contact ATC to obtain a clearance. If contact was established, continue to keep ATC advised of intentions and obtain essential traffic information.

Note.— If, as a result of actions taken under the provisions of 15.2.4.3.1, the pilot determines that there is another aircraft at or near the same flight level with which a conflict may occur, then the pilot is expected to adjust the path of the aircraft, as necessary, to avoid conflict.

Table 15-1

Route centerline / track	Deviations ≥ 9.3 km (5.0 nm)	Level Change
East 000 - 179 magnetic	Left of course Right of course	Descend 90 m (300 ft.) Climb 90 m (300 ft.)
West 180 - 359 magnetic	Left of course Right of course	Climb 90 m (300 ft.) Descend 90 m (300 ft.)

Turning north descend, turning south climb.

Volcanic Ash

In 1982, when British Airways 9 flew through a volcanic ash cloud and flamed out all four engines, the dangers of volcanic ash were undocumented. Seven years later, when KLM 867 repeated the incident, it was clear more work was needed to detect and avoid volcanic ash. The ash is dry so does not show up on radar. It is also fine, so when it comes in contact with the airplane the static electricity makes radio communications difficult. It is abrasive and can damage windshields to the point visibility is impaired. Once the particles go through the hot section of the engine they become molten and finally they recool and collect on engine turbine blades, solidifying to the point where air flow is fouled and the engines shut down. Fortunately, in every recorded case once the aircraft descends and the engines cool, the solidified ash tends to break away and the engines can be relit.

I like the Alaska Airlines Procedures for Operating in Volcanic Ash Conditions:

- *When in doubt, don't fly.*
- *Use facts and data.*
- *Identify the location of both the ash and clear areas.*
- *Stay focused.*

Gulfstream adds this cheerful note: "Has significant financial implications, may not be known until major inspection, usually considered an Act of God and is not covered by insurance."

An Overview of the Threat

[Aeronautical Information Manual, ¶7-6-9]

a. Severe volcanic eruptions which send ash and sulphur dioxide (SO2) gas into the upper atmosphere occur somewhere around the world several times each year. Flying into a volcanic ash cloud can be exceedingly dangerous. A B747–200 lost all four engines after such an encounter and a B747–400 had the same nearly catastrophic experience. Piston–powered aircraft are less likely to lose power but severe damage is almost certain to ensue after an encounter with a volcanic ash cloud which is only a few hours old.

b.   Most important is to avoid any encounter with volcanic ash. The ash plume may not be visible, especially in instrument conditions or at night; and even if visible, it is difficult to distinguish visually between an ash cloud and an ordinary weather cloud. Volcanic ash clouds are not displayed on airborne or ATC radar. The pilot must rely on reports from air traffic controllers and other pilots to determine the location of the ash cloud and use that information to remain well clear of the area. Additionally, the presence of a sulphur-like odor throughout the cabin may indicate the presence of SO2 emitted by volcanic activity, but may or may not indicate the presence of volcanic ash. Every attempt should be made to remain on the upwind side of the volcano.

History of Mishaps

There have been nine encounters with Volcanic Ash of transport category aircraft between 1953 and 2009, according to the USGS:

1980 May 25 — L-100, 2 of 4 engines shut down, Mount St. Helens, USA

1982 Jun 24 — B-747 (British Airways 9), 4 of 4 engines failed, Galunggung, Indonesia

1982 Jul 13 — B-747, 3 of 4 engines failed, Galunggung, Indonesia

1989 Dec 15 — B-747, 4 of 4 engines failed, Redoubt, USA

1991 Jun 17 — B-747, 2 of 4 engines failed, Pinatubo, Philippines

1991 Jun 17 — DC-10, 1 of 3 engines failed, Pinatubo, Philippines

1991 Jun 27 — DC-10, 2 of 3 engines failed, Unzen, Japan

2001 Jul 29 — B-767, 1 of 2 engines failed, Soufriere Hilles, Lesser Antilles

2006 Jul 17 — Gulfstream II, 2 of 2 engines failed, Papua New Guinea

The USGS report acknowledges that this list comprises a minimum number, since these reports are not made consistently.

Engine Failures

[USGS, pg. 3] Melting and resolidification of ash within jet turbine engines has been identified as the primary mechanism responsible for engine failure in an ash encounter. The melting temperature of the magmatic silicate glass in ash is lower than the operating temperatures of modern turbine engines; consequently, ingested ash particles can melt in hot sections and then accumulate as re-solidified deposits in cooler parts of the engine, causing ignition flame-out and engine shutdown. In two encounters, climb out from the cloud at maximum thrust was identified as a key operational condition for engine shutdown. When engine power increased, more ash-laden air was ingested by the jet turbines and combustion temperatures were raised; thus, conditions favorable for substantial melting of ash particles were met. This lesson has been incorporated into guidance to pilots about recommended actions to take during an encounter.

[USGS, pg. 5] [The 17 June 1991 incident] is notable in that prolonged exposure to dilute ash may have contributed to significant damage. That incident involved the same aircraft (a B747–200B) as incident 1991–14; both flights were operating between South Africa and Southeast Asia in the aftermath of the June 1991 eruption of Mount Pinatubo. In both encounters, the aircraft was operating in airspace at distances in excess of 500 km from the volcano. In [the 15 June 1991 incident], the crew noted static discharge lasting approximately an hour, but all engine parameters were normal during flight, and no problems were experienced with any of the aircraft systems. Two days later, the aircraft flew for several hours through an area coincident with remote-sensing evidence of an ash cloud before one engine lost power and a second engine was shut down by the crew. During descent, the engine that had been shut down was restarted, and the aircraft made a successful landing. These events raise the possibility of significant damage from cumulative exposure to dilute ash.

[USGS, pg. 5] The 2006 Gulfstream II incident is notable for involving a different mechanism for engine shutdown than melted ash. The aircraft was flying over Papua New Guinea at 11.9 km (39,000 ft) in apparently clear air with no ash or sulfurous odors noted by the cockpit crew. Between 39,000 ft and descent to 24,000, both engines failed and then were restarted; the aircraft landed safely. The operator and engine manufacturer conducted a thorough investigation, including borescope analysis of the engine and fuel analysis. The manufacturer concluded that a cylindrical filter in each fuel-flow regulator may have become blocked by volcanic ash, which at that altitude could have caused loss of fuel flow and thus engine shutdown; on descent, the increasing pressure would have substantially cleared the filter and allowed the engine to restart. The likely source of the ash was an eruption of Manam Volcano in Papua New Guinea.

Threat Areas

[ICAO Doc 9691, pg. I-i_1] The highest concentration of active volcanoes lies around the rim of the Pacific Ocean, the so-called "ring of fire," which stretches northwards, more or less continuously, along the western edge of South and North America, across the Aleutian and Kurile Island chains, down through Kamchatka, Japan and the Philippines and across Indonesia, Papua New Guinea and New Zealand to the islands of the South Pacific. Other active regions are to be found in Iceland, along the great rift valley in Central and East Africa, and in countries around the Mediterranean.

Volcanic Ash Characteristics

The Clouds

[ICAO Doc 9691, ¶2.2.1

The eruption column which results is usually divided into three dynamic regimes: "gas thrust," "convective thrust" and "umbrella region" (or "mushroom").

The gas thrust region is produced by the sudden decompression of super-heated volatile constituents dissolved in the ascending magma. This produces a jet of fluids and pulverized rock material of extremely high kinetic energy at the mouth of the volcano vent, the speed of which in extreme cases could exceed 500 kt. Such exit vent speeds may reach supersonic speed depending on the ambient conditions at the time.

If insufficient air is entrained in the gas thrust region, the column remains denser than the surrounding atmosphere and, as the initial kinetic energy dissipates, the column collapses due to gravitation without forming a convective thrust region. The convective thrust region largely controls the ultimate height of the column and hence is critical to the eruption's potential concern to aviation. It is clear from the foregoing that the hotter the original jet of fluidized material at its release form the vent, the higher the thermal energy which can be carried through to the convective thrust region and the higher the column top.

The third dynamic region of the volcanic ash column is the "umbrella region," to top of the mushroom-like ash cloud as its ascent begins to slow in response to gravity and the temperature inversions at the tropopause, with the top spreading radially to begin and then predominantly in one or more particular directions in response to the upper winds at different levels of the atmosphere. This region of most concern to aviation because vast volumes of airspace at normal jet aircraft cruising level of 10 to 14 km (30,000 to 45,000 ft) become contaminated with high concentrations of volcanic ash.

The Ash

[ICAO Doc 9691, ¶4.1] Volcanic ash is mostly glass shards and pulverized rock, very abrasive and, being largely composed of siliceous materials, with a melting temperature below the operating temperature of jet engines at cruise thrust. The ash is accompanied by gaseous solutions of sulphur dioxide (sulphuric acid) and chlorine (hydrochloric acid). Given these stark facts, it is easy to imagine the serious hazard that volcanic ash poses to an aircraft which encounters it in the atmosphere. Volcanic ash damages the jet turbine engines, abrades cockpit windows, airframe and flight surfaces, clogs the pitot-static system, penetrates into air conditioning and equipment cooling systems and contaminates electrical and avionics units, fuel and hydraulic systems and cargo-hold smoke-detection systems. Moreover, the first two or three days following an explosive eruption are especially critical because high concentrations of ash comprising particles up to ~10 μm diameter could be encountered at cruise levels some considerable distance from the volcano. Beyond three days, it is assumed that if the ash is still visible by eye or from satellite

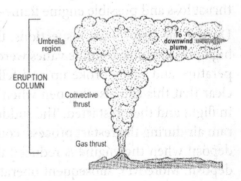

Figure: Three parts or regions from an eruption column, from ICAO Doc 9691, Figure 2-4.

data, it still presents a hazard to aircraft.

Electrical Phenomena

[ICAO Doc 9691, ¶2.3.1] The occurrence of lightning in volcanic ash columns has been reported since antiquity. Moreover, one of the prime means of recognizing that an aircraft has encountered volcanic ash is the static electricity discharge exhibited by St. Elmo's fire at point on the airframe and the glow inside the jet engines. The static electric charge on the aircraft also creates a "cocoon" effect which may cause a temporary deterioration, or even complete loss, of VHF or HF communications.

Effect on Jet Engines

[ICAO Doc 9691, ¶4.2]

There are basically three effects which contribute to the overall engine damage. The first, and most critical, is the fact that volcanic ash has a melting point below jet engine operating temperatures with thrust settings above idle. The ash is made up predominantly of silicates with a melting temperature of 1,100°C, while at normal thrust the operating temperature of jet engines is 1,400°C. The ash melts in the hot section of the engine and fuses on the high pressure nozzle guide vanes and turbine blades. This drastically reduces the high pressure turbine inlet guide-vane throat area causing the static burner pressure and compressor discharge pressure to increase rapidly which, in turn, causes engine surge. This effect alone can cause immediate thrust loss and possible engine flame-out.

During the strip-down inspections, the fused volcanic ash deposits on the high pressure nozzle guide vanes were found to be very brittle at room temperature and easily broke up and fell off the nozzle guide vanes. It seems clear that this can also happen when contaminated engines are shut down in flight and then restarted. The sudden thermal and pressure shocks of the ram air during the restart process, coupled with the cooling of the fused ash deposit when the engine is reduced to idle, seem to break off much of the deposit. Moreover, subsequent operation of the engines after restart, in the clearer air outside the ash cloud, also seems to further dislodge and evacuate some of the fused ash deposits.

The volcanic ash being abrasive also erodes compressor rotor paths and rotor blade tips (mostly high pressure section), causing loss of high pressure turbine efficiency and engine thrust. The erosion also results in a decrease in the engine stall margin. The main factors that affect the extent of the erosion of the compressor blades are the hardness of the volcanic ash, particle size and concentration, the ash particle impact velocity, and thrust setting and core protection. Although this abrasion effect takes longer than the melting fusion of volcanic ash to shut down an engine, the abrasion damage is permanent and irreversible. Reduction of engine thrust to idle slows the rate of erosion of the compressor blades but cannot eliminate it entirely while the engine is still ingesting air contaminated by volcanic ash.

In addition to the melting/fusing of the volcanic ash and the blade erosion problems referred to above, the ash can clog flow holes in the fuel and cooling systems, although these particular effects appear to be rather variable. In ground tests of jet engines subjected to forced volcanic ash ingestion, a deposition of black carbon-like material was found on the fuel nozzles. Analysis confirmed that the contaminating material was predominantly carbon, and although the main fuel nozzle appeared to remain clear, the swirl vanes which atomize the fuel were clogged. Such a condition would render engine restart very difficult if not impossible, because there seems to be no tendency for the material to break off during restart attempts.

Aviation Color Codes

GREEN	Volcano is in typical background, noneruptive state.
	Or, after a change from a higher level:
	Volcanic activity has ceased and volcano has returned to noneruptive background state
YELLOW	Volcano is exhibiting signs of elevated unrest above known background level.
	Or, after a change from a higher level:
	Volcanic activity has decreased significantly but continues to be closely monitored for possible renewed increase.
ORANGE	Volcano is exhibiting heightened or escalating unrest with increased potential of eruption, timeframe uncertain.
	Or:
	Eruption is underway with no or minor ash emissions [ash-plume height specified, if possible].
RED	Eruption is imminent with significant emission of volcanic ash into the atmosphere likely.
	Or:
	Eruption is underway or suspected with significant emission of volcanic ash into the atmosphere [ash-plume height specified, if possible].

Figure: Aviation color codes, from Alaska Volcano Plan, pg. 15.

Ash Encounter Indicators

[ICAO Doc 9974, ¶1.3 and 1.4]

In day visual meteorological conditions (VMC) a precursor to a volcanic ash encounter will likely be a visual indication of a volcanic ash cloud or haze. If a flight crew observes a cloud or haze suspected of containing volcanic ash they should be aware that a volcanic ash encounter is imminent and they should take action to avoid the contaminated airspace.

Indicators that an aircraft is encountering volcanic ash are related principally to the following:

- Odour. When encountering volcanic ash, flight crews usually notice a smoky or acrid odour that can smell like electrical smoke, burnt dust or sulphur.

- Haze. Most flight crews, as well as cabin crew or passengers, see a haze develop within the aircraft cockpit and/or cabin. Dust can settle on surfaces.

- Changing engine conditions. Surging, torching from the tailpipe, and flameouts can occur. Engine temperatures can change unexpectedly, and a white glow can appear at the engine inlet.

- Airspeed. If volcanic ash fouls the pitot tube, the indicated airspeed can decrease or fluctuate erratically.

- Pressurization. Cabin pressure can change, including possible loss of cabin pressurization.

- Static discharges. A phenomenon similar to St. Elmo's fire or glow can occur. In these instances, blue-coloured sparks can appear to flow up the outside of the windshield or a white glow can appear at the leading edges of the wings or at the front of the engine inlets.

Any of these indicators should suffice to alert the flight crew of an ash encounter, and appropriate action should be taken to vacate the contaminated airspace as safely and expeditiously as possible.

Pilot Procedures

[ICAO Doc 9691, ¶4.4]

1. The foregoing analysis of the effect of volcanic ash on aircraft forms the basis for the procedures recommended for use by pilots whose aircraft inadvertently encounter a volcanic ash cloud.

    a. In such circumstance, the following general procedures have been recommended:

        i.   immediately reduce thrust to idle. This will lower the exhaust-gas temperature (EGT), which in turn will reduce the fused ash build-up on the turbine blades and hot-section components. Volcanic ash can also cause rapid erosion and damage to the internal components of the engines;

        ii. turn autothrottles off (if engaged). The autothrottles should be turned off to prevent the system from increasing thrust above idle. Due to the reduced surge margins, limit the number of thrust adjustments and make changes with slow and smooth thrust-lever movements;

        iii. exit volcanic ash cloud as quickly as possible. Volcanic ash may extend for several hundred miles. The shortest distance/time out of the ash may require an immediate, descending 180-degree turn, terrain permitting. Setting climb thrust and attempting to climb above the volcanic ash cloud is not recommended due to accelerated engine damage/flame-out at high thrust settings;

iv. turn engine and wing anti-ice on. All air conditioning packs on. Turn on the engine and wing anti-ice systems and place all air conditioning packs to "on," in order to further improve the engine stall margin by increasing the bleed-air flow. It may be possible to stabilize one or more engines at the idle thrust setting where the EGT will remain within limits. An attempt should be made to keep at least one engine operating at idle and within limits to provide electrical power and bleed air for cabin pressurization until clear of the volcanic ash;

v. start the auxiliary power unit (APU), if available. The APU can be used to power the electrical system in the event of a multiple-engine power loss. The APU may also provide a pneumatic air source for improved engine starting, depending on the aircraft model; and

vi. put oxygen mask on at 100 percent, if required. If a significant amount of volcanic ash fills the cockpit or if there is a strong smell of sulphur, don an oxygen mask and select 100 percent. Manual deployment of passenger oxygen masks is not recommended if cabin pressure is normal because the passenger oxygen supply will be diluted with volcanic ash-filled cabin air. If the cabin altitude exceeds 4,250 m (14,000 ft), the passenger oxygen masks will deploy automatically.

b. In the event of engine flame-out:

i. turn ignition on. Place ignition switches to "on" as appropriate for the engine model (position normally used for in-flight engine start). Cycling of fuel levers (switches) is not required. For aircraft equipped with autostart systems, the autostart selector should be in the "on" position. The autostart system was designed and certified with a "hands-off" philosophy for emergency air starts in recognition of crew workload during this type of event;

ii.   monitor EGT. If necessary, shut down and then restart engines to keep from exceeding EGT limits;

iii.   close the outflow valves, if not already closed;

iv.   do not pull the fire switches;

v.   leave fuel boost pump switches "on" and open cross-feed valves;

vi.   do not use fuel heat — this would be undesirable if on suction fuel feed;

vii.   restart engine. If an engine fails to start, try again immediately. Successful engine start may not be possible until airspeed and altitude are within the air-start envelope. Monitor EGT carefully. If a hung start occurs, the EGT will increase rapidly. If the engine is just slow in accelerating, the EGT will increase slowly. Engines are very slow to accelerate to idle at high altitude, especially in volcanic ash — this may be interpreted as a failure to start or as a failure of the engine to accelerate to idle or as an engine malfunction;

viii.   monitor airspeed and pitch attitude. If unreliable, or if a complete loss of airspeed indication occurs (volcanic ash may block the pitot system), establish the appropriate pitch attitude dictated by the operations manual for "flight with unreliable airspeed." If airspeed indicators are unreliable, or if loss of airspeed indication occurs simultaneously with an all-engine thrust loss, shutdown or flame-out, use the attitude indicator to establish a minus-one degree pitch attitude. Inertial ground speed may be used for reference if the indicated airspeed is unreliable or lost. Ground speed may also be available from approach control during landing;

ix.   land at the nearest suitable airport. A precautionary landing should be made at the nearest suitable airport if aircraft damage or abnormal engine operation occurs due to volcanic ash penetration; and

x.   because of the abrasive effects of volcanic ash on windshields and landing lights, visibility for approach and landing may be markedly reduced. Forward visibility may be limited to that which is available through the side windows. Should this condition occur, and if the autopilot system is operating satisfactorily, a diversion to an airport where an autolanding can be accomplished should be considered. After landing, if forward visibility is restricted, consider having the aircraft towed to the parking gate.

2.   The foregoing general procedures should be supplemented by specific procedures in the aircraft operations manual — developed by aircraft operators for each aircraft type in their fleet — dealing with the particular aircraft engine combination concerned.

3.   Given that the most serious threat to an aircraft from volcanic ash is the risk of multiple-engine flame-out, it is extremely important to consider the ways and means of improving the success of engine restarts in air contaminated by volcanic ash. In the United States in 1991, the Aerospace Industries Association of America (AIA) ad hoc Propulsion Committee was formed comprising AIA members and representatives from international aircraft and engine manufacturers and the U.S. Geological Survey (USGS). The mandate of the Committee was to evaluate the threat of multiple-engine flameout due to volcanic ash and to make appropriate recommendations to the aviation industry and responsible government agencies. The Committee made a number of recommendations but, in particular, the following bear directly on the problem of engine restart, after flame-out:

a.   "Aircraft manufacturers, with assistance from the engine manufacturers, should define maximum engine power levels (expressed in engine pressure ratio (EPR), fan speed (N1), and (or) exhaust-gas temperature (EGT) levels) that will minimize buildup of melted and resolidified ash on HPT nozzle guide vanes. These values should be added to flight-manual procedures and should be used only when the recommended flight idle power will not assure adequate terrain clearance.

b.   Aircraft manufacturers, with assistance from engine manufacturers, should consider addition of a time-delay circuit to allow an air-started engine to reach stabilized idle speed before the electrical or generator load is applied. This would facilitate engine restarts under less-than-ideal conditions.

c.   FAA and other equivalent government agencies should require that air crews practice engine air-restart procedures in a simulator on recurring basis. Normal and deteriorated engine start characteristics should be simulated."

The prime importance of the last recommendation cannot be overestimated. Engine shut-downs or flame-outs in flight are rare events which many pilots will never be called upon to deal with in their whole careers. This is further complicated by the different procedures used for air-start as compared to normal ground-start. The only solution is for pilots to be provided with a set of air-start procedures which also cover procedures in volcanic ash contaminated air and for simulator air-starts to be part of basic and recurrent pilot training.

Resources to Avoid Ash Encounters

- Volcanic Ash Advisory Centers. There are nine volcanic ash advisory centers established by the ICAO to forecast volcanic activity and to inform aviators of potential hazards.

http://www.ssd.noaa.gov/VAAC/vaac.html

- UK Met Office provides volcanic activity forecasts when applicable.

http://www.metoffice.gov.uk/public/weather

- Smithsonian / USGC Weekly Volcanic Activity Report is updated at 2300 UTC every Wednesday with recently volcanic activity.

http://volcano.si.edu/reports_weekly.cfm

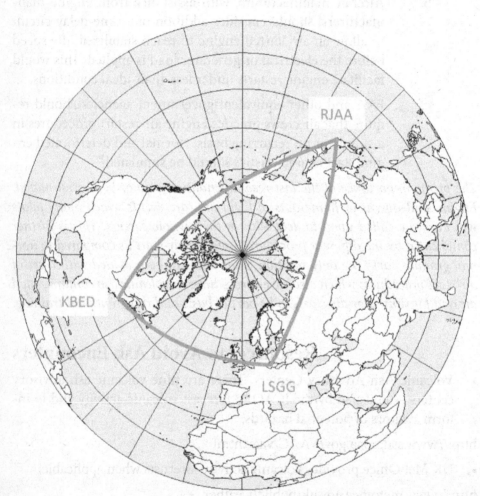

Figure: Example routing as requested.

Chapter 1

Trip Preparation

*P*reparation is the key to a successful international trip. With experience the process becomes easier, but preparation is still necessary. Much of the "leg work" is taken care of by handling agents and flight planning services, but the pilot remains responsible for their completion.

It really pays to be diligent about this, even if you are a seasoned pro. I once flew into China with a veteran international ops pilot that hadn't been in a few years. He was stunned to find the Flight Level Allocation Scheme in China was unique to the world. I thought he was an idiot. Years later I flew into London, Luton for the one-hundredth time and was stunned to find every single approach into EGGW was deleted from the database. I felt like an idiot. Just because you've been doesn't make you an expert; if you haven't been recently, you need to study up.

Example: Trip Set Up

From	To	Distance
KBED	LSGG	3203 nm
LSGG	RJAA	5312 nm
RJAA	KBED	5812 nm
	Total	14328 nm

This section looks at an example trip in a G650 from Bedford, Massachusetts (KBED) to Geneva, Switzerland (LSGG), to Tokyo, Japan (RJAA), back to Bedford. The first four chapters deal with the North Atlantic oceanic flight in detail. Subsequent chapters will cover the remaining flights with an eye to covering some of the differences involved for those parts of the world.

The trip was originally designed for the ultra long-range G650 which could have made all three legs without a doubt, but the G650 dropped out because of a maintenance issue and the trip has come to you, in a shorter range G450.

Aircraft Range / Crew Duty Limits

While aircraft range changes with passenger / cargo load, temperature, winds, and other factors, it helps to know what your airplane can do in generic conditions. In the case of the G450: a 4,000 nm trip at Mach 0.80, ISA conditions, no wind, and about a 43,000 lbs. operating weight will leave the airplane with 5,000 lbs. of fuel remaining at the destination. Based on this we know the last two destinations will require a fuel stop and possibly a crew change:

KBED LSGG – non-stop okay, single crew okay

LSGG RJAA – fuel stop required, augmented crew or crew swap needed

RJAA KBED – fuel stop required, augmented crew or crew swap needed

Crew duty limits will vary by operation and that will determine the need for crew augmentation or replacement. We will save that decision after looking for two refueling stops, what many call "technical stops."

Adding Technical Stops

It appears the second and third legs will require fuel stops.

We can take a chart and draw 4,000 nm circles around the two airports involved in the search for the first technical stop. We need to be careful about the projection of the chart, a circle isn't a circle on most charts because the chart is usually distorted near the poles, the chart ends before the projected distance, or a combination of both factors. Automatic software, such as the excellent free resource available at http://gc.kls2.com/, can simplify this chore and identify the areas that are within 4,000 nm of both LSGG and RJAA. In the example chart, we see LSGG surrounded by one arc and RJAA by another. The area between the two arcs north of India identifies those points within 4,000 miles of both airports.

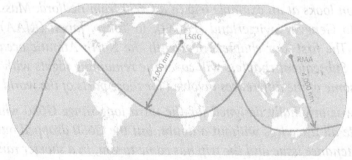

We offer Moscow (UUEE) to our passengers as somewhat along the great circle route, an easy location for a crew swap, and a bit more reliable than many of the other options. Our passengers express an interest in spending a day in Mumbai, India (VABB) which is within the 4,000 nm range of both LSGG and RJAA. So we add VABB to our itinerary.

We run a similar exercise with the RJAA to KBED leg and determine that adding Anchorage, Alaska (PANC) could easily get the trip home in a day with a simple crew swap. Once again the passengers have a better idea and ask about spending a few days in Hawaii. From the standpoint of aircraft range and crew duty days, our itinerary becomes:

From	To	Distance
KBED	LSGG	3203 nm
LSGG	VABB	3630 nm
VABB	RJAA	3669 nm
RJAA	PHNL	3318 nm
PHNL	KSFO	2084 nm
KSFO	KBED	2336 nm
	Total	18241 nm

Since each of these legs are well within the airplane's range and the passengers have asked to spend the night in each location, we will not need an augmented crew or crew swaps.

Aircraft Performance

Aircraft performance should be considered for each airport and each en route leg.

Aircraft takeoff performance for the expected conditions

Can the aircraft make it off the ground?

When considering maximizing the range of your aircraft, it helps to have a general idea about how much runway is needed under most conditions at maximum weight. A G450, for example, can takeoff fully loaded up to 105°F at sea level in less than 7,000 feet of pavement.

Our example trip will take place in late March and there may be weather to consider when departing and arriving at KBED. We let our passengers know that if the runway is likely to be contaminated, we may need to reposition the airplane to KBOS to take advantage of the longer runways and the greater number of runways which will minimize the impact of crosswinds on contaminated surfaces. The other airports do not appear to have takeoff and landing performance issues.

Airport obstacle analysis

Can the aircraft out climb the obstacles near the airport?

Obstacles between the airport and your en route altitude can be a factor and should be considered. Simply ensuring your AFM performance numbers are satisfied by meeting SID requirements might be good enough, but it could needlessly reduce your payload (and therefore your range).

Of the selected airports, Geneva can pose problems. In fact, the common practice of using AFM engine-out climb data when assessing all-engine Standard Instrument Departure (SID) procedures will make the LSGG - VABB leg impossible because the G450 cannot make SID climb requirements engine-out. Using only the data available in the cockpit, a knowledgeable pilot can plan a safe takeoff at maximum gross weight by planning to shuttle between two VORs away from mountainous terrain in the event of an engine failure during takeoff or the initial climb. Alternatively, the crew can use commercially available obstacle analysis software to determine the highest possible grossweight from each runway under the expected conditions following an engine loss.

Aircraft en route performance

Can the aircraft make it to a divert airport if an engine is lost at any point along the way?

You have minimum en route altitude restrictions to meet in the event of an engine failure which could be a factor, especially in mountainous terrain. Unfortunately many aircraft manufacturers do not provide easily understood data to make this determination. Nevertheless, you need to consider this.

Since we plan on performance to beat close-in obstacles, keeping minimum

302

safe en route altitudes is rarely an issue. So too with this trip, only the obstacles in Switzerland pose a risk and we have ensured these are beaten early in the flight.

Aircraft landing performance for the expected conditions

Can the aircraft stop in the available runway distance?

You should know the absolute minimum amount of pavement your airplane needs to safely stop, the minimum your company requires, and the minimum you require. In the case of the G450, the book says the aircraft must have at least 2,500' to stop in absolutely ideal conditions. In my opinion you would be crazy to try anything less than 4,000' and I rarely venture to a runway less than 5,000'.

Only the runways at Bedford pose a risk at this time of year, so we make a note to include an alternate for our return home.

Airspace Considerations

Theoretically, ICAO Doc 7030, Regional Supplementary Procedures, is your best source of airspace requirements throughout the world. Unfortunately, it is rarely updated. Airspace rules are changing every year and it pays to have a good international trip planning service to keep on top of this.

You should consider any special airspace requirements for each leg of the trip:

Automatic Dependent Surveillance-Broadcast (ADS-B) Out

ADS-B Out is becoming required in parts of the world, but workarounds are readily available. You can expect delays and reroutes if you are not equipped and authorized. See Section V, Chapter 2.

Extended Operations of Multi-engine Airplanes (ETOPS)

ETOPS does not apply to 14 CFR 91 operators and only constrains 14 CFR 135 operators from flying in the most remote regions of the world. It only applies when flying beyond 3 hours of a suitable airport with an engine failed. See the Appendices, Chapter 20.

Note: ETOPS is now EDTO, Extended Diversion Time Operations.

High Latitude and Northern Domestic Airspace

Operating in what many simply call "polar ops" requires special certification under 14 CFR 135 and special procedures for anyone venturing the high latitude regions. High latitude operations occur in areas above 78°N, below 60°S, the northern and southern poles, and the Canadian Northern Domestic Area (NDA). The NDA includes the Northern Control Area (NCA), the Arctic Control Area (ACA) and the Area of Magnetic Unreliability (AMU). The NDA, NCA and ACA are depicted on Canadian HI en route charts and encompass the northernmost Canadian airspace. See the Appendices, Chapter 24.

North Atlantic High Level Airspace (NAT HLA)

NAT HLA applies to most of the North Atlantic and the Canadian Arctic Control Area. See Section III, Chapter 7.

Overflight Permits

You may need permission to overfly some countries, some countries may have rules that permit specific nations, restrict some, and ban still others. You need to check every country you overfly and in some cases you need to be wary of who has claim to the airspace you are using. The Jeppesen State pages are a great place to start. Having an international trip planner who knows the area is an even better way to go.

Reduced Vertical Separation Minimum (RVSM)

While RVSM is now the standard just about everywhere, there are country-specific rules for flight level selection and contingency procedures. See Section II, Chapter 6.

Required Navigation Performance-4 (RNP-4)

The Required Navigation Performance-4 (RNP-4) applies to parts of Australia, New Zealand, and Japan, but all of these still allow RNP-10 as a substitute. In theory, ATS can monitor aircraft with RNP-4 more closely and will have traffic priority. See Section III, Chapter 9.

Required Navigation Performance-10 (RNP-10)

RNP-10 is required in the Central East Pacific (CEP) between Hawaii and the west coast of the United States, and portions of the North Pacific (NOPAC) require RNP-10. There are other areas of the world that have adopted RNP-10, such as parts of Africa, the Indian Ocean, Australia, New Zealand, Tahiti, and some parts of South America near Recife. See Section III, Chapter 10.

Our trip takes us through the NAM, NAT, EUR, MID/ASIA, and PAC regions.

A review of ICAO Doc 7030 reveals:

- *Europe: our routes of flight will take us over regions where RVSM, and 8.33 kHz spacing are termed "mandatory," though some exceptions are allowed. If you don't have any of these capabilities, you may be restricted to non-optimal altitudes or routes, or you may not be able to fly the routes at all. See ICAO Doc 7030, $EUR, for more details.*

- *Middle East / Asia: our routes of flight will take us over regions where RNP-4, RNP-5, RNP-10, and RVSM are either "mandatory" or recommended. You may be restricted to non-optimal altitudes or routes, or you may not be able to fly the routes at all. See ICAO Doc 7030, $MID/ASIA, for more details.*

- *North America: the only airspace requirement listed for us here is RVSM. See ICAO Doc 7030, $NAM, for more details.*

- *North Atlantic: our route of flight will take us over regions where MNPS, RVSM, as well as ACAS II are mandatory, though exceptions are allowed. See ICAO Doc 7030, $NAT, for more details.*

- *Pacific: our routes of flight will take us over regions where RNP-4, RNP-10, and RVSM are either "mandatory" or recommended. You may be restricted to non-optimal altitudes or routes, or you may not be able to fly the routes at all. See ICAO Doc 7030, $PAC, for more details.*

Note that some of these requirements are changing back and forth rapidly. RNP-4, for example, was supposed to be mandatory over much of the ASIA region by December 2013, but many countries are showing increasing flexibility as their air traffic has been slow to equip. You need to ask yourself (or your flight planning service provider) prior to every trip if you are lacking a requirement they classify as mandatory.

Note also that ICAO Doc 7030 is quiet on the subject of ADS-B Out, which is becoming required in parts of the world.

Airport Suitability

Each ICAO member is free to make exceptions to ICAO rules but they must post these exceptions in their individual Aeronautical Information Publications, which many countries offer online.

A good source: https://gis.icao.int/gallery/ONLINE_AIPs.html

The Jeppesen State pages attempt to compile the notable differences and are your best "go to" source of these individual country differences. The Airport Directory for each destination airport and likely alternates are good places to start when researching airport suitability. A legend and explanation appears in the Jeppesen Airway Manual text pages under Airport Directory, Airport Data General, Legend and Explanation. Note: these pages often have errors and you should double check on anything critical or anything that just doesn't make sense. For example, I've found they don't do a good job of keeping up with WGS-84 status on these pages, though their web site on the issue is excellent.

Airport of Entry

The first and last airports visited in a foreign country must normally be designated as "Apt of Entry" in the Jeppesen Airport Directory and AIP. In some countries, any declared alternates must also be airports of entry. You need to check each country's pages to be sure.

Airport Hours of Operation

Will the airport be open at the necessary times for arrival and departure? The Airport Directory provides UTC-to-local time conversions, the airport hours of operation, and other items of interest.

Having a trip handler with a presence at the airport will be helpful, as the times in the JeppView pages may not be up-to-date. If you do not have anyone with local knowledge, the page does provide phone numbers you can call.

Runway Suitability

Are the runways long and strong enough? Are the ramps adequately stressed? The Airport Directory Pages are a good source of the following information:

- Runway Data. This is more than just the length of the runway: the Airport Directory provides runway length, TORA, LDA, TODA, and ASDA when available. It could be that you have far less than the published distances available to you.

- Runway Load Bearing. Runway strength is given in a variety of systems. Common methods, such as LCN/PCN may be explained in individual AFM or POH, as well as the Jeppesen Airport Directory, Legend. The airport directory does not always list runway load bearing information and it never lists data for associated taxiways and parking areas. If you are taking a large aircraft into an airport you aren't familiar with, it may be worth the phone call to find out if they've had aircraft of your type land and park where you intend to put your airplane.

- Lighting. Given in a variety of systems, each explained in the Jeppesen Airport Directory, Legend.

- Don't forget to consider fuel loading when computing ACNs. I was once scheduled into Maun, Botswana as the last stop in Africa and then on to Paris. A fully loaded GV exceeded the only suitable runway's PCN so we had to reorder the trip so Maun wasn't our last stop in the area.

Fuel

Does the airport offer the required grade of fuel, if refueling is necessary? If you are planning on a full load of fuel, remember fuel densities often preclude that in some parts of the world. A G450's fuel capacity, for example, can vary over 2,000 lbs from the highest allowed fuel density to the lowest. The best place to put on a full load of fuel is the west coast of the United States. The worst? Southeast Asia. See the Appendices, Chapter 23.

Rescue and Fire Fighting System

When given a choice of airports in a city, it may be advantageous to select the airport with appropriate airport rescue and fire fighting capability. See the Appendices, Chapter 2.

Other Considerations

You should also consider the following:

- Landing Permit. Is a landing permit needed? The country's Airport Information Publication and the Jeppesen Entry Requirements pages may be consulted to determine if a landing permit is required. Your flight handling services should be consulted to ensure you have the best, up-to-date, information about landing permits. [Jeppesen Entry Requirements]

- Aircraft and Crew Support. Can the airport and the handling agent adequately support the aircraft and crew? Your familiarity with each airport will determine your need for a ground-handling agent. In many cases language difficulties and coordination between stops will make a ground-handling agent a necessity.

- Ramp space. Can the airport provide space for the aircraft for the duration? You might need a parking reservation.

- Hangar space. If needed, is hangar space available? You should consider the possibility of needing aircraft hangar facilities, battery and freezable liquids removal, and other overnight issues.

- Fueling, oxygen, potable water, de-icing, lavatory service, catering needs. Do the handler or other agents on the airport provide these necessary services?

- Aircraft security. State Department notices and the Jeppesen Airway Manual State pages may suggest the level of security needed for the aircraft during its stay at each location.

- Hours of operation. You should insure the airport, FBO, and handlers will be open for business during planned arrival and departure times.

- Payment methods. You should know what forms of payment are accepted by each agency you will be dealing with at each airport.

- Maintenance availability. It may be beneficial to identify authorized repair facilities near your routing as well as know what services are available at each airport.

- Ground transportation. The handler may be able to provide adequate transportation to and from the hotel or recommend rental car and taxi options.

- Hotel Reservations. Overnight accommodations should be secured.

- Special Airport Qualification. Does the applicable State require special airport qualification? These may be found in the country's Airport Information Publication and the Airport Briefing page in the Jeppesen Airway Manual terminal chart series. For example, Innsbruck, Austria considers previous experience in VMC essential prior to IMC approaches at LOWI. The Airport Briefing details training requirements and simulator options. [Jeppesen Airway Manual, Terminal Charts, Innsbruck, Austria, Page 10-1P]

Example: Airport Suitability

Airports of Entry (AOE) — The JeppView pages do not list PHNL or KSFO as airports of entry, but they are. Each of the other destinations are listed as AOE's. When we flight plan, we should ensure that any declared weather and ETP alternates are also AOE's. While this isn't always a requirement, it simpli-

fies trip planning in case a particular country does mandate it.

Hours of Operation — Each of our airports is listed as H24 but LSGG is PPR, so that merits a phone call by you or your handler.

Runways — Each airport on our itinerary has runways of adequate length, load bearing strength, and lighting.

Fuel — Each airport has the correct type of fuel but Japanese fuel is notoriously weak in terms of fuel density. We know from a Gulfstream study that a G450's total fuel capacity can be reduced from 29,500 lbs to just 28,230 lbs at the lowest available densities. Contrary to popular belief, jet engines derive thrust from the fuel in terms of weight, not volume. So warned, we run flight plans for the RJAA to PHNL range and find our worst case winds requires only 23,000 lbs of fuel, including reserves.

Rescue and Fire Fighting System — Each airport has good rescue and fire fighting capability. Note that this is rarely a show stopper for most operators.

Other Considerations — On our example trip we could run into problems with getting adequate ramp space for the aircraft, hotels for the crew, and we may want to consider hiring aircraft security at one of the locations. I recommend having a good trip planner who has recent experience with each airport. Failing that, call upon your network of pilot associates to get up-to-date intel.

Country-Specific Concerns

There are a lot of things to consider here and if you don't spend a lot of time in the areas you will be visiting, you may miss something. It helps to have someone with local and recent knowledge, a good trip planner can be invaluable. But you should be aware of at least the following issues.

Routing

Are there any US State Department Warning regarding the routing?

Available at: https://travel.state.gov/content/travel/en/traveladvisories/traveladvisories.html/

Flight path Notice To Airmen (NOTAMs) can provide advance warning of problems.

Available at: https://notams.aim.faa.gov/notamSearch/

Agriculture

There are quite often restrictions on what food, plants, and animal products you can bring into a country, including the United States. Within the United States, there are also restrictions into and out of the State of Hawaii.

- Entry into Other Countries. Check the Jeppesen Airway Manual Entry Requirements pages for a primer on any restrictions.

- Entry into the United States. The best source of information is available in the United States Department of Agriculture's Traveler's Page: https://www.aphis.usda.gov/aphis/resources/travelers-int

- Insecticide. Some countries, Australia for example, may require the aircraft interior be sprayed with a suitable insecticide and a suitable time interval allowed prior to allowing anyone to deplane. If you have the spray before already, some countries will allow you to spray prior to landing, getting you and your passengers off the airplane earlier.

- Entry into the State of Hawaii. In general, foods that are cooked, canned, frozen, or commercially processed and/or packaged can be brought into the state as long as the product originates from the U.S. There are strict importing regulations for all animals. Refer to the State of Hawaii Department of Agriculture web site for more details, at http://www.hawaii.gov/hdoa/.

- Export from the State of Hawaii. The best source of information is available in the United States Department of Agriculture's Traveler's Page, http://www.hawaii.gov/hdoa/.

Cabotage

The definition of cabotage, adopted by ICAO at the Chicago Convention, is: "Each state shall have the right to refuse permission to the aircraft of other contracting states to take on its territory passengers, mail, and cargo destined for another point within its territory." Although cabotage rules are different in various countries and usually incorporate the term "for hire," some countries do not allow foreign aircraft within their boundaries to carry even non-revenue passengers. The restrictions range from no restrictions to not allowed. The fines for cabotage can be extremely high; therefore, pilots and flight departments should be absolutely sure of a country's cabotage rules before carrying passengers.

Generally speaking, you cannot fly to some foreign countries, pick up local cit-

izens and transport them within that country. Not all countries have cabotage restrictions and many that do will allow exceptions if the citizens are employees of a company associated with the airplane. The rules vary by country and you are left to ask your flight planning service provider or looking for the country's AIP.

Refer to the Appendices, Chapter 10.

Customs and Immigration Requirements

Customs requirements vary by country of departure and arrival. You should check with your handler, and the Jeppesen Airway Manual Entry Requirements pages. It may be helpful to have customs and immigration phone numbers available. See the Appendices, Chapter 16.

Passport & Visa. Is a passport and entry Visa required? Rules can vary between passengers and crewmembers, can depend on the duration of stay, and in some cases can be waived. The Jeppesen Entry Requirements pages will summarize the rules. If you need a quick passport or visa, your best resource may be http://www.g3visas.com.

Entry Airports. Do the first landing and final departure airports have to be from airports of entry, international airports, or certain gateway airports? The Jeppesen Airway Manual Entry Requirements pages will summarize the rules and the Airport Directory will list which airports qualify.

Forms for Entry and Exit. Are special forms required upon arrival and departure? Your handler may have an up-to-date list of what is needed at each country.

eAPIS. The U.S. requires eAPIS for all trips leaving and returning to the U.S. Refer to the Appendices, Chapter 18.

Emissions Standards

The so-called European Union Emissions Trading System (ETS), formally known as the Emission Trading Scheme, is an on-again, off-again effort to tax aviation. The system, as of 2020, is on-again. While compliance is mandatory, enforcement is less than clear. Most business aviation qualifies for "small emitter" status and may not have to pay for "cap and trade" credits. But payment is required for registration. If you fly to Europe, even infrequently, you should keep up with the news on this topic or pay an international trip planner to do that for you.

(There are also plans from other countries, including the United States, to initiate their own emissions schemes. Once again, you need to keep up with the news on this.)

Immunizations and Vaccinations

Some countries will not allow you off the airplane unless you have proof of immunizations and/or vaccinations against specific conditions. The Jeppesen State pages contain some immunization and vaccination information. An even better resource is www.medaire.com.

Return to the U.S. From Areas South of the U.S.

All private aircraft arriving in the Continental U.S. via the U.S./Mexican border or the Pacific Coast from a foreign place in the Western Hemisphere south of 33°N latitude, or from the Gulf of Mexico and Atlantic Coasts from a place in the Western Hemisphere south of 30°N latitude, from any place in Mexico, from the U.S. Virgin Islands, and from Puerto Rico (in some cases) may be required to land only at certain specially designated airports. Exemptions are given, depending on crew and passengers.

Special restrictions cover flights to and from Cuba.

If the trip does return from one of these locations, check the requirements covered in the "US Customs and Border Protection Guide for Private Flyers," [19 CFR 122.23 - 122.27] You may be eligible for overflight exemptions, see the Appendices, Chapter 16.

Import Concerns

Are there aircraft import or other taxation issues? Refer to the country's AIP. Aircraft flying into European Union countries will need temporary admission or full importation. Ask your international planner about this prior to every trip. See also: https://www.opmas.dk/theme-page-for-temporary-admission/

Destination Security

Does a State Department warning exist for health, security, or other precautions? This information could prevent travel to the country or limit access to the airport only.

Available at: https://travel.state.gov/content/travel/en/traveladvisories/traveladvisories.html/

Aircraft Security

You may wish to invest in aircraft security tape seals that you can apply to all doors, hatches, or other access points that will allow you to detect unauthorized access. Make sure you have all necessary locks and pins to secure doors and hatches.

Cash

Some countries restrict the amount of cash you can bring in or leave with. Generally speaking, transporting more than $10,000 in U.S. currency may require a Currency Transaction Report, such as the FinCen Form 104. Information is available under 31 CFR 1010.311.

Our example trip will be concerned with multiple country-specific concerns:

Local support will depend on a handler who speaks the language and can negotiate on our behalf with agriculture, immigration, customs, air traffic control officials in Switzerland, India, and Japan.

Agriculture concerns are expressed in the States pages for India and Japan, as well as unique issues in Hawaii.

Cabotage will not be an issue, since all crew and passengers are U.S. citizens. It would not be a concern even if we had foreign nationals on board, since we are not making flights within any one particular foreign country's borders.

Customs and Immigration requirements apply to all our foreign stops. A good handler will either have the paperwork completed for us when we arrive, or will forward the necessary forms ahead of time to speed our arrivals.

Import issues are problematic in Europe, though Switzerland hasn't been a problem area. Our handler assures us that they have not been pressing the issues.

Security concerns exist in India so we have our handler contract a local security company to provide guards for the aircraft during our stay.

Chapter 2

Oceanic Departure

*W*hen departing from a domestic to an oceanic area, pilots will have a few extra steps prior to and during the oceanic crossing. While procedures worldwide have become much more standardized, there are differences in various regions. The basic procedures are covered here, with regional differences noted. Of course these procedures are changing every day and you should check prior to every trip.

This section continues an example G450 trip from Bedford, Massachusetts (KBED) to Geneva, Switzerland (LSGG), to Tokyo, Japan (RJAA), back to Bedford, with additional legs planned as "technical" stops. For the purpose of covering an oceanic departure, this section will focus on the KBED to LSGG leg.

Preflight

A clear delineation of preflight tasks can ensure all duties are accomplished and a good level of crosscheck exists between pilots. A possible technique is to have the PIC accomplish all plotting and master document work while the SIC completes the aircraft exterior inspection. Once the interior inspection begins, the PF programs the FMS while the PM accomplishes the aircraft interior inspection checklist. Once that is done, the PM checks the FMS entries while the PF turns his or her attention to other airplane related matters.

Master Document

[AC 91-70B, ¶6.3.1.1.] Maintain only one copy of the master document in the cockpit..

The flight deck can have multiple copies of the electronic flight plan but only one of these can be used as a "master document." Our example master document includes a cover page, pages on equal time point information, NOTAMS, weather, airport information, and a track message. For the sake of organization, we staple these together and label the cover page "Master Document."

While some crews like to have a copy for each pilot, I discourage the practice to avoid recording required items on the wrong copy. If we have an extra copy, I store it outside the cockpit.

The same discipline should hold when using an electronic master document. It may be possible to link iPads so both pilots can make entries onto the same document in different colors. Otherwise, it should be agreed upon which device has the actual master document and that copy should be labeled accordingly.

Master Document

```
FLIGHTPLAN N7700    KBED TO LSGG  GLF4  M80 /F  IFR   29DEC13   ~~ AB
COMPUTED 2024Z FOR ETD 1700Z   PROGS 281200Z              WGT IN LBS

              FUEL   TIME   DIST ARRIVE TAKEOFF  LAND   AV PLD  OPNLWT
DEST LSGG  019340 06:22  3261  2322Z  073508  054168 000500  043908
RESV       001931 00:45
ALTN       000000 00:00  0000  0000Z
HOLD       000000 00:00
REQD       029100 10:10                        ES ZFW   MX ZFW
TAXI       000400                                44408    49000
XTRA       007829 03:03                         ES LNDG  MX LNDG
TOTL       29500  10:10                          54168   058500

KBED DCT LBSTA ENE J581 YJT CYMON DENDU 5150N 5240N 5230N 5220N
DINIM ELSOX GAPLI UL739 LIZAD UN160 PIGOP UN491 RESMI UM975 LUSAR
DCT LSGG

WIND P062   MXSH 10/LUSAR   AVG WIND 268/071
TAS 451     FL 410 YJT 390 5240N 410

 CLIMB SCHED:300/M80     CRUISE SCHED:M80     DESCENT SCHED:M80/300
```

Flight Plan Entry

You have several options for getting the flight plan from the master document to the FMS, each with its own set of challenges. Among the options:

- Manual entry — If you are diligent, you can get every single point in the flight plan into the FMS. Make sure you don't input any extra points not on the filed flight plan, such as the TOC (Top of Climb), TOD (Top of Descent), FIR boundaries, and ETPs (Equal Time Points). This method risks entry errors due to reading and typing mistakes.

- Disk or Memory Stick — Some FMS allow for saving a flight plan to a memory device which can be read by the FMS. While this method eliminates the chance of reading or typing errors, it risks the use of the wrong memory device and uploading a similar, but wrong flight plan.

- Satellite Downlink — If your FMS provides for an electronic downlink of the flight plan you can eliminate most potential pilot induced errors, except one notable error from which all three methods suffer. (See the next paragraph.)

FMS Limitations — No matter which method you use, it is imperative you check every leg of the master document's flight plan against that in the FMS. Some aircraft have their own peculiarities that require cross checking.

The G450 offers a reliable satellite downlink and we have our flight plan in its entirety on all three FMS.

Flight Plan Winds

Some FMS will not automatically include downlinked winds and you will have to ensure the winds are included in the FMS flight plan. A few cautions:

- A downlinked wind may be tied to the flight plan itself and could be hours out of date. You should either update each leg with current winds or downlink current winds if available.

- Entering an average wind might work for some areas of the world but not others. Between Hawaii and California you normally have steady winds, but not always. Between the U.S. and Europe the winds often change dramatically half way across, but not always.

- You should get to know how your FMS adapts to changes in the flight plan with previously downlinked, averaged, or manually entered winds. Some FMS will zero the winds for some types of changes.

FMS Flight Plan Versus Filed Flight Plan

You should check the flight plan that was actually filed versus what is in your FMS, just in case. Even a downlinked flight plan could have differences that are important. At some locations the local airport is required to enter the flight plan manually and may give you a copy of what they filed. Use that against your FMS.

Our example trip was filed through ARINCDirect and the last page of the master document includes the filed flight plan. We check that against our primary FMS and are satisfied they are the same.

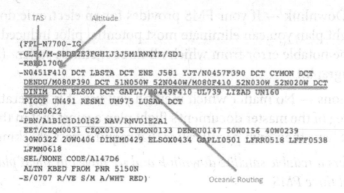

```
(FPL-N7700-IG
-GLF4/M-SBDE2E3FGHIJ3J5M1RWXYZ/SD1
-KBED1700Q
-N0451F410 DCT LBSTA DCT ENE J581 YJT/N0457F390 DCT CYMON DCT
 DENDU/M080F390 DCT 51N050W 52N040W/M080F410 52N030W 52N020W DCT
 DINIM DCT ELSOX DCT GAPLI/M0449F410 UL739 LIZAD UN160
 PIGOP UN491 RESMI UM975 LUSAN DCT
-LSGG0622
-PBN/A1B1C1D1O1S2 NAV/RNVD1E2A1
 EET/CZQM0031 CZQX0105 CYMON0133 DENDU0147 50W0156 40W0239
 30W0322 20W0406 DINIM0429 ELSOX0434 GAPLI0501 LFRR0518 LFFF0538
 LFMM0618
 SEL/NONE CODE/A147D6
 ALTN KBED FROM PNR 5150N
-E/0707 R/VE S/M A/WHT RED)
```
TAS   Altitude   Oceanic Routing

Filed Flight Plan Verification

[AC 91-70B, ¶6.3.2.]

Two pilots should independently coordinate the loading and verification of all flight plan entries. One pilot should load the entire route into the LRNS, to include all waypoints, using the master document as source. He or she should then verify the routing has been loaded correctly.

Prior to loading the flight plan, carefully cross-check the waypoint routing on your master document against your filed flight plan to verify both documents show the same routing.

For systems with pilot-defined waypoint designators or numbers, we recommend you use a consistent procedure from the outset of the flight. Enter this designator on the master document and also use it to store waypoints in the navigational computer.

You must verify all navigational information contained in the master document against the navigation data information in the FMS.

Your procedures should provide for a means of verification of the data you loaded. You should check the expanded coordinates and course/distance between waypoints against the same information on your master document. You may also check the route presentation on your navigation display. Most intercontinental-capable aircraft have a modern FMS that is capable of automatically downloading flight plans that have been sent from ATC or from a dispatch service. These flight plan transmission mechanisms are very reliable, but there are occasional glitches that can lead to downloading partial routes, requiring you to make changes to complete the route load. Regardless of whether you have an automatic or manual download of your flight plan into your FMS, you should have procedures to verify your flight plan route against your FMS entries.

There is no agreed upon standard for marking up waypoints to denote pre-checks, passage, or post checks. See the Appendices, Chapter 42, for my technique.

CPT FREQ LAT	FLT T TRO TDV LONG	WIND COMP	S	TAS GRS	AWY	MH MCRS	DST DSTR	ETE ATE	ETR ATR	FU AFU	FR AFR	FF/E
CYMON	390 −55 36 M02	287123 P084	3	457 542	DCT	080 088	0160 2438	018	0449	896	22874	1518
N49430 W054599												
DENDU	390 −52 36 P04	288105 P075	7	463 538	DCT	083 090	0123 2315	014	0435	698	22176	1531
N50302 W052041												
51⊘0N	390 −50 36 P06	288090 P067	4	465 531	DCT	095 097	0084 2231	009	0426	485	21690	1531
N51000 W050000												
52⊘0N	390 −50 52 P07	276063 P060	2	466 527	DCT	106 104	0379 1851	043	0343	2204	19487	1516
N52000 W040000												
52⊘0N	410 −51 52 P06	252054 P051	1	465 516	DCT	103 100	0371 1481	043	0300	2076	17411	1445
N52000 W030000												
52⊘0N	410 −53 31 P05	241060 P051		464 515	DCT	124 117	0371 1110	043	0217	2026	15385	1407
N52000 W020000												
DINIM	410 −55 36 P03	236069 P040	1	462 502	DCT	102 097	0197 0913	024	0153	1081	14305	1377
N51000 W015000												
ELSOX	410 −56 36 P01	236075 P060	3	460 520	DCT	116 109	0038 0876	004	0149	198	14106	1359
N51000 W014000												

After the first pilot has loaded and verified the FMS entries against the flight plan, a second pilot should recall and confirm the waypoint data against source information.

It is not sufficient for one crewmember to simply observe another crewmember entering the data. Exercise an independent cross-check method with each other so no FMS entry goes unverified. An attitude of "healthy suspicion" can facilitate good cross-checks.

Cross-checks should include comparing the expanded coordinates of the waypoints loaded in the FMS to the filed flight plan, track message (if applicable), and the master document.

Plotting

The FAA's Advisory Circular leads you to believe plotting is optional:

[AC 91-70B, ¶6.4.8.2.] Up to now the only recommended method of cross-checking aircraft position in the oceanic airspace environment was manual plotting on a chart. However, a panel of aviation industry and FAA personnel completed an Operational Safety Assessment of methods for cross-checking oceanic flight navigation. The panel determined that an alternative to manual plotting, by which aircraft position could be checked through use of aircraft FMS-driven navigation displays and indications, would provide for an equivalent level of safety.

But principle inspectors are asked the following to make sure crews are plotting:

[AC 91-70B, ¶6.4.8.4.] Do they require use of a plotting or orientation chart, of adequate scale, for reference/situational awareness purposes?

Plotting procedures are fairly straightforward but require a level of precision and perhaps some practice. See Section II, Chapter 5.

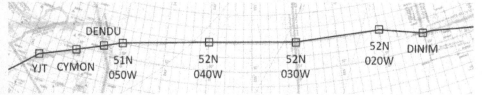

Plot Relevant Tracks

If your route or any potential diversionary routes cross any relevant track systems, the tracks should be plotted. Tracks should be considered relevant if the route of flight is within or over the track system and an aircraft drift down or diversion will conflict any of the tracks. This is especially true over the North Atlantic (NAT) Organized Track System (OTS).

[ICAO NAT Doc 007, Paragraph 4.1.8] Flight crews of all NAT flights at or above FL290, even those that will transit the NAT either above the NAT HLA, or laterally

```
ORGANIZED TRACK SYSTEM//
------------------------
NAT TRACKS FLS 310/390 INCLUSIVE
DEC 29/1130Z TO DEC 29/1900Z
A MALOT 54/20 55/30 55/40 55/50 OYSTR
EAST LVLS NIL
WEST LVLS 310 320 330 340 350 360 370 380 390
EUR RTS WEST NIL
NAR -
B LIMRI 53/20 54/30 54/40 54/50 CARPE
EAST LVLS NIL
WEST LVLS 310 320 330 340 350 360 370 380 390
EUR RTS WEST NIL
NAR -
C DINIM 52/20 53/30 53/40 53/50 HECKK
EAST LVLS NIL
WEST LVLS 310 320 330 340 350 360 370 380 390
EUR RTS WEST NIL
NAR -
D SOMAX 48/20 48/20 48/40 48/50 RONPO
EAST LVLS NIL
WEST LVLS 310 320 330 340 350 360 370 380 390
EUR RTS WEST NIL
NAR -
E BEDRA 47/20 47/30 47/40 47/50 URTAK
EAST LVLS NIL
WEST LVLS 310 320 330 340 350 360 370 380 390
EUR RTS WEST NIL
NAR -
F 47/40 44/50 41/60 JOBOC
EAST LVLS NIL
WEST LVLS 320 340 360 380
EUR RTS WEST
NAR -
REMARKS.
1. TMI IS 363 AND OPERATORS ARE REMINDED TO INCLUDE THE
TMI NUMBER AS PART OF THE OCEANIC CLEARANCE READ BACK. 2
CPDLC MANDATED OTS ARE AS FOLLOWS
   TRACK A 350 360 370 380 390
   TRACK B 350 360 370 380 390
```

clear of the OTS, must carry a copy of the NAT track message, including any amendments.

The eastbound and westbound tracks will not be active when we cross 30W but there could be leftover westbound traffic, so we've plotted the westbound tracks. We plotted all the tracks north of our route of flight, since we will have to cross them if we need to divert to Iceland. We've also plotted one track to our south, as a reminder about how far we can maneuver if turning right of track.

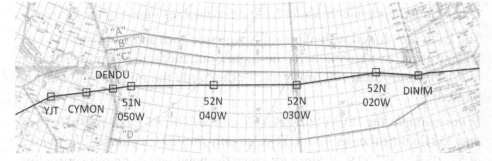

Compute and Plot Equal Time Points (ETPs)

```
                         CRITICAL FUEL SUMMARIES

        1E INOP
        LAT/LONG      N52 05.0/W037 17.3       CYQX           EINN
        TIME TO ETP DIVRSN PT        02.51
        DIST TO ETP DIVRSN PT        01510
        FUEL TO ETP DIVRSN PT/RMNG   010177 /18923
        FL/BURN/TIME TO ETP AP       300/05553/02.36    310/05557/02.37
        TAS/ETA/DIST TO ETP AP       340/2227/000686    340/2228/001036
        MAG CRS/AVG WIND COMP TO ETP AP   271/M076         105/P052
        ISA TEMP DEV TO ETP AP                M000             M003
        TOTAL FUEL TO ETP AP /RMNG   15730/13366        15734/13366

        DEPRESS - FL PROFILE: OXYGEN ALTITUDE FOR 120 MIN THEN FL150

        LAT/LONG      N52 05.8/W036 28.0       CYQX           EINN
        TIME TO ETP DIVRSN PT        02.55
        DIST TO ETP DIVRSN PT        01541
        FUEL TO ETP DIVRSN PT/RMNG   010347 /18753
        FL/BURN/TIME TO ETP AP       150/11951/03.00    150/11974/02.57
        TAS/ETA/DIST TO ETP AP       278/2254/000717    281/2252/001007
        MAG CRS/AVG WIND COMP TO ETP AP   271/M046         105/P051
        ISA TEMP DEV TO ETP AP                M016             M010
        TOTAL FUEL TO ETP AP /RMNG   22298/06779        22321/06779


        MEDICAL
        LAT/LONG      N52 05.3/W037 00.9       CYQX           EINN
        TIME TO ETP DIVRSN PT        02.52
        DIST TO ETP DIVRSN PT        01521
        FUEL TO ETP DIVRSN PT/RMNG   010234 /18866
        FL/BURN/TIME TO ETP AP       200/11482/02.49    200/11505/02.48
        TAS/ETA/DIST TO ETP AP       302/2241/000697    304/2240/001027
        MAG CRS/AVG WIND COMP TO ETP AP   271/M060         105/P057
        ISA TEMP DEV TO ETP AP                M012             M010
        TOTAL FUEL TO ETP AP /RMNG   21716/07361        21739/07361
```

Besides telling you they are needed, there is very little regulatory guidance on Equal Time Points (ETPs). Having an ETP plotted gives you a decision making tool if you find yourself between suitable airports with an engine failure requiring an altitude drift down, a medical emergency requiring a divert with-

321

out requiring an altitude change, or a loss of cabin pressurization requiring an immediate descent.

You can calculate your ETPs with pencil and paper, have your flight plan provider automatically compute them, or your aircraft FMS may have an appropriate function. I recommend using the flight plan provider's, at least as a start, since they would be using the same winds as used in the flight plan. See the Appendices, Chapter 19, Equal Time Points.

Our flight plan provider includes ETPs on request, as shown in the figure.

The ETPs are plotted with a line off to one side with arrows pointing to the ETP airports. As a technique, if the engine-out, medical, and pressurization loss ETPs are within 100 nm of each other, only the middle ETP need be plotted.

In our example, the 1E INOP, DEPRESS, and MEDICAL ETPs are 1510, 1541, and 1521 nautical miles from CYQX, so only the 1521 is plotted. The point is at 52° 05.8'N 37° 00.9'W. Since we know the point will be on our course line, we just need to put our tick mark along the course at 37° 00.9'W. The line is drawn away from the course for clarity and arrows are drawn in the direction of CYQX and EINN.

If we have any reason to divert prior to this ETP, we will choose to reverse course to CYQX. Beyond that point, we press forward to EINN.

Compute and Plot PSRs, if required

```
PNR
LAT/LONG        N51 26.5/W046 36.0              KBED
TIME TO ETP DIVRSN PT            02.11
DIST TO ETP DIVRSN PT            01161
FUEL TO ETP DIVRSN PT/RMNG  008170 /20930
FL/BURN/TIME TO ETP AP          200/20928/04.46
TAS/ETA/DIST TO ETP AP          308/2357/001141
MAG CRS/AVG WIND COMP TO ETP AP    262/M072
ISA TEMP DEV TO ETP AP                  M003
TOTAL FUEL TO ETP AP /RMNG      29098/00001
```

The Point of Safe Return (PSR) provides the pilot with the farthest point to which the aircraft can go and be able to return safely to the departure point with adequate holding, approach, landing, and alternate fuel. It is normally used when flying to remote island destinations with no diversion possibilities en route but can be useful even when alternates are available. See the Appendices, Chapter 31.

ARINCDirect provides a "PNR," as shown. The "Point of No Return" is the same thing as the "Point of Safe Return," with a more dramatic name.

If any of our passengers decide they need to go back to our departure airport (KBED), the last moment you can do this without having to make a fuel stop is shown with the red bracket on the chart. Keep in mind that if you return at this point, you will need to fly direct to the airport, the PSR does not use normal routings that anyone less than an emergency aircraft will be offered.

Add CPDLC Addresses, if desired

You can add the applicable FIR boundaries and CPDLC addresses, if you are so equipped and would like the information available on the chart. For more about this see: Section IV, Chapter 5.

For our example we'll highlight the FIR boundary between Gander and Shanwick, and enter the CPDLC addresses. Our plotting chart is now ready for the flight.

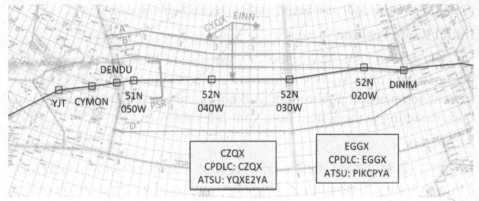

Ramp

UTC Time Check

[AC 91-70B, Appendix D, ¶D.2.2.1] You must have an identified master clock on board synchronized to Coordinated Universal Time (UTC) (generally via GPS). You must use this single time source, typically the FMS, for all ETAs and ATAs.

Fuel Check

Record fuel onboard on the master document; this quantity will become the basis for subsequent fuel checks.

Domestic Clearance

You will typically have a domestic clearance that will include your destination but not the oceanic portion of the trip. Your clearance at this stage does not normally give you clearance into oceanic airspace.

Our domestic clearance is: "Gulfstream seven seven zero zero is cleared to Geneva via radar vector Lobstah then as filed. After takeoff maintain runway heading and climb to two thousand feet, expect flight level four three zero ten minutes after takeoff. Contact departure control on one two four point four, squawk four three two one." We are cleared to our destination but we do not have clearance into oceanic airspace.

SELCAL Configuration

Some aircraft encode their SELCAL codes in software and may lose the code on occasion. In the G450, for example, the code can be entered from any cockpit audio control panel but only when on the ground. It is a good idea to make sure the code is entered and correct when you can.

Initial Ramp Position

[AC 91-70B, ¶6.2.3.4] Regardless of your type of LRNS or the method of insertion, you must verify your current ramp position in the LRNS against current aeronautical publications and not solely based on the present position remaining in the system from your last shutdown.

Altimeters

[AC 91-70B, ¶6.3.2.10] Before taxi, set your altimeters to the airport local altimeter setting. Both primary altimeters must read within ± 75 feet of field elevation. The two primary altimeters must also agree with each other within the limits noted in the aircraft operating manual.

Groundspeed Check

[AC 91-70B, ¶6.3.2.9] Check your ground speed in the blocks and on taxi out. If you are still in the blocks and your ground speed reads other than zero (0), you may have a developing error in your LRNS. Similarly, if your groundspeed on taxi out appears unreasonable, this may also indicate a problem with your LRNS.

An inertial ground speed while stationary is an indication there is significant drift in the unit. Some aircraft offer a "quick align" to reset the inertial's ground speed to zero. In older Gulfstreams, for example, switching from NAV to ALIGN to NAV in less than six seconds caused such a quick align. Other aircraft with Hybrid IRS, such as the G450, automatically perform a quick realign any time the aircraft is motionless for more than 7.5 minutes.

RVSM/NAV Performance Log

You should have a log to record your altimeter and navigation system performance so that you remember to check all that needs to be checked, and so that you have a written record of it. A blank log is available in the Appendices, Chapter 30.

Oceanic Checklist and RVSM/NAV Performance Log

Preflight

☑ Label one copy of the computer flight plan "Master Document"
☑ Plot route over Class II airspace and any relevant tracks
☑ Add ETPs (loss of pressurization, all-engine cruise, loss of engine) if required
☑ Position Check: Ramp (GPS) N/S   42°27.6   E/W   71°17.4

IRS #1	IRS #2	IRS #3	GPS #1	GPS#2
Diff 0.0	Diff 0.0	Diff 0.0	Diff 0.0	Diff 0.0

☑ Altimeter Check: QNH 2992 Pilot's 120 Stby 130 Copilot's 120
☑ Time Check: Source (circle) WWV/GPS/ATC +/- 10 sec ✓
☑ Compare Master Document course/distance with plotting or en route chart, circle waypoint
☑ Compare Master Document course/distance with FMS, draw diagonal over waypoint
☑ Record fuel onboard on the Master Document

CPDLC Checklist

If you are CPDLC-equipped and departing into an area with CPDLC coverage, you have several steps to accomplish while still sitting on the ramp. It may be helpful to add a printed copy of your CPDLC checklist to the RVSM/NAV Performance Log and Master Document. See Section IV, Chapter 6.

Local Procedures Review

The Jeppesen Airway Manual approach charts for the airport may have several pages of local procedures that should be reviewed prior to request for clearance or engine start. These procedures can include specific instructions that are critical to successfully operating at the airport, such as:

- Engine start procedures
- Clearance delivery procedures
- Start-up, push-back and taxi procedures
- Noise abatement procedures
- Speed restrictions on departure and arrival
- Runway entry and exit procedures

If you are at an unfamiliar airport it always pays to listen to the ground control or tower frequencies for a while to get the "lay of the land" and a heads up as to your immediate future. A few things to listen for:

- Is ground control giving ATC clearances before taxi? (That is not the normal procedure for most of the world.) If they are giving ATC clearance that is what you ask for, "Request ATC clearance."

- Which departure procedures are in use? At locations where advance ATC clearance is not given, you will be listening to your ATC clearance while you are taxiing, just minutes away from takeoff. You will often have a difficult time understanding what the departure procedure is and it will be to your benefit to have an idea early on. Some airports group departures based on the runway in use, for example.

- Taxi routings can include instructions you've never heard before. You may hear other aircraft instructed to "Holding Point Whiskey" but not see that immediately on any charts. Hearing this given to another airplane gives you some time to look it up.

Oceanic Clearance Prior to Departure

You normally request your oceanic clearance while airborne but there are exceptions for some airports that are close to oceanic airspace. For example:

[Jeppesen Airway Manual / State Rules and Procedures - Ireland] NAT flights departing Irish aerodromes excluding Dublin, Weston and Casement (Baldonnel) airports, planned to enter NAT airspace between GOMUP and BEDRA (inclusive) should request Oceanic Clearance from Shanwick Oceanic via ORCA Data Link prior to departure. Shannon ACC will on request obtain Oceanic Clearance from Shanwick Oceanic and pass the clearance to the flight prior to departure.

If you are departing from an airport that is near the oceanic airspace you will be transitting, you should check the applicable Jeppesen Airway Manual page for a requirement to obtain oceanic clearance prior to departure.

Prior to Oceanic Boundary/Oceanic Clearance

Departure Timing

- Time to Taxi. If assigned a wheels up time or a time crossing your first oceanic point, you may need to carefully plan when you plan leaving the chocks. You can estimate your taxi time using the airfield diagram.

- Scale: The longitude scale should include the degree minutes in the format degree - minutes. 46-14, for example, means 46°14'. Each minute of longitude equals one nautical mile.

- Distance to Taxi: Using that scale, you can estimate the distance from your parking stand to the runway holding point.

- Time to Taxi: If you taxi at twenty knots, you will cover each nautical mile in 3 minutes. Remember to add a few seconds for each turn as you will probably slow a bit.

Time to climb - FMS Capable

A modern FMS should give you an accurate ETA to your first oceanic waypoint if you input the estimated takeoff time.

If in EINN, for example, expecting the ERAB2B departure to ERABI, DOGAL, and then oceanic routing, you can enter expected takeoff times and see the ETA for each point update. If your oceanic clearance stipulates a 0837Z time overhead DOGAL, you can subtract the FMS time at DOGAL from the planned departure time to come up with an ETE, then use that to adjust the departure time. For our G450, we see it takes 37 minutes, so we enter /0800Z at LSK 1L on the first page of the flight plan. The FMS computes we will reach DOGAL at 0837Z. Now we know we must takeoff at 0800Z to make that happen.

Time to climb - FMS Not Capable

Some older FMS will not correctly compute ETAs during or following a climb to altitude. In the older G-IIIs, for example, the FMS assumed 250 knots ground speed until level off, which was way too slow. We found adding 5 minutes to the ETA for any point between FL 300 and FL 350 plus an additional 1 minute per every additional 5,000 feet worked well. Of course that was for the G-III, you will have to experiment to find a rule for your FMS.

Transition Altitude

[ICAO Document 4444, Ch 1]

- Transition Altitude: The altitude at or below which the vertical position of an aircraft is controlled by reference to altitudes.

- Transition Layer: The airspace between the transition altitude and the transition level.

- Transition Level: The lowest flight level available for use above the transition altitude.

Crews should brief the transition altitude based on information from approach plates, ATIS, or the applicable State pages. After climbing through the transition altitude, the altimeters should be reset to 29.92 inches or 1013.2 hPa. See the Appendices, Chapter 6.

Climb Level-off Procedure

[ICAO NAT Doc 007, ¶9.1.10] To prevent unwanted TCAS/ACAS warnings or alerts, when first approaching any cleared flight level in NAT RVSM airspace, flight crews should ensure that the vertical closure speed is not excessive. It is considered that, with about 1500 ft to go to a cleared flight level, vertical speed should be reduced to a maximum of 1500 ft per minute and ideally, to between 1000 ft per minute and 500 ft per minute. Additionally, it is important to ensure, by manually overriding if necessary, that the aircraft neither undershoots nor overshoots the cleared level by more than 150 ft.

En Route Timing (Prior to Oceanic Airspace)

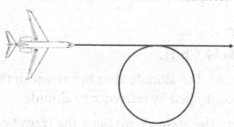

If en route to the oceanic entry waypoint with a timing restriction, you can make minor adjustments with speed, larger adjustments with routing changes. If late more than a few minutes you may need to get a reclearance.

Adjusting speed — If flying at typical en route speeds, it will take about 100 nm to impact your ETA by 1 minute if adjusting by 30 knots.

360° Turn — A half-standard rate turn takes 4 minutes.

Timing Triangle — A turn 60° off course, followed t-seconds by a turn 60° back towards course, followed t-seconds later by a turn back onto course costs a total of t-seconds.

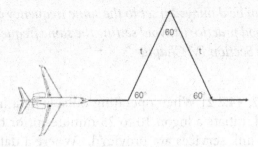

Note: These adjustments are only for making adjustment aimed at making your oceanic entry point good. Once you are in oceanic airspace, these techniques are expressly forbidden. See Section VIII, Chapter 26, Mach Number Technique.

HF Radio

[AC 91-70B, Appendix D, ¶D.2.2.8] You should conduct an HF check on the primary and secondary HF radios in areas where dual HF radios are required. (Two long-range communications systems are typically required for oceanic and remote continental airspace operations.)

If possible, you should accomplish the HF checks on the ground or before entering oceanic airspace.

Even if you are data link equipped, you should accomplish a SELCAL check at each oceanic control area boundary.

[ICAO NAT Doc 007, ¶6.1.22] When using HF, SATVOICE, or CPDLC, flight crews should maintain a listening watch on the assigned frequency, unless SELCAL equipped, in which case they should ensure the following sequence of actions:

- provide the SELCAL code in the flight plan; (any subsequent change of aircraft for a flight will require refiling of the flight plan or submitting a modification message (CHG) which includes the new registration and SELCAL);

- check the operation of the SELCAL equipment, at or prior to entry into oceanic airspace, with the appropriate aeradio station. (This SELCAL check must be completed prior to commencing SELCAL watch); and

- maintain thereafter a SELCAL watch.

Proper HF frequency selection can be a challenge in some regions and is not always facilitated by VHF center controllers when leaving domestic airspace.

Some HF radios can be damaged if set to the same frequency as another radio's transmitter, it is good practice to avoid setting the same frequency in more than one HF radio. See Section IV, Chapter 2.

CPDLC or ADS

[ICAO Doc 10037, ¶4.2.2] When operating outside data link airspace, the flight crew should initiate a logon 10 to 25 minutes prior to entry into airspace where data link services are provided. Where a data link service is only provided in upper airspace and where local procedures do not dictate otherwise, the flight crew should log on to that ATS unit in whose airspace a data link service will first be used.

Oceanic Clearance

[AC 91-70B, ¶6.4.1]

- Oceanic clearances are unique clearances that frequently require coordination between two or more air traffic agencies. The clearance you receive from an ATC facility on the ground before departure may not constitute a clearance into or through your filed oceanic and remote continental airspace. Depending on the first oceanic FIR you enter, you may need to obtain this clearance separately and specifically as you approach the oceanic and remote continental airspace boundary. Check the Aeronautical Information Publication (AIP) or source document to determine if such separate oceanic clearance is required.

```
OCEANIC CLX

1939 120313 LSGG
CLRNCE 599
N7700 CLRD TO LSGG VIA
DENDU
RANDOM ROUTE
51N050W 52N040W 52N030W
52N020W DINIM
FM DENDU/1850 MNTN F390
M080
END OF MESSAGE
```

- In cases when your departure airport is close to the oceanic and remote continental airspace boundary you may, and at some airports must, obtain your oceanic clearance prior to departure. Check the AIP or source documents to determine clearance requirements unique to your departure airport. Note: Some airspace authorities have begun issuing the route portion of the oceanic clearance before the aircraft departs, even when the departure airport is not close to the oceanic boundary. In this case, the altitude and airspeed portion will be assigned prior to entering oceanic airspace. New York Oceanic and Oakland Oceanic both operate in this manner.

Master Document

```
FLIGHTPLAN N7700    KBED TO LSGG  GLF4  M80 /F  IFR  29DEC13   -- AB
COMPUTED 2024Z FOR ETD 1700Z   PROGS 281200Z              WGT IN LBS

               FUEL    TIME   DIST ARRIVE TAKEOFF  LAND  AV PLD  OPNLWT
DEST LSGG   019340  06:22   3261 2322Z 073508 054168 000500  043908
RESV        001931  00:45
ALTN        000000  00:00   0000  0000Z
HOLD        000000  00:00
REQD        029100  10:10                         ES ZFW   MX ZFW
TAXI        000400                                 44408    49000
XTRA        007829  03:03                         ES LNDG  MX LNDG
TOTL         29500  10:10                          54168   058500

KBED DCT LBSTA ENE J581 YJT CYMON DENDU 5150N 5240N 5230N 5220N
DINIM ELSOX GAPLI UL739 LIZAD UN160 PIGOP UN491 RESMI UM975 LUSAR
DCT LSGG

WIND P062   MXSH 10/LUSAR   AVG WIND 268/071
TAS 451    FL 410 YJT 390 5240N 410

CLIMB SCHED:300/M80      CRUISE SCHED:M80     DESCENT SCHED:M80/300
```

LSGG RV LBSTA TAF RH 2000'
CLEARANCE *X430/10MIN D124.4 / 4321*
Oceanic: DENDU 51N050W, 52N040W, 52N030W, 52N020W, DINIM, X DENDU @ M.80 FL390 1850Z

```
CPT    FLT T   WIND  S TAS AWY   MH   DST  ETE ETR  FU   FR   FF/E
FREQ   TRO TDV COMP    GRS        MCRS DSTR ATE ATR  AFU  AFR
LAT    LONG                       ATD 1705Z   Fuel: 29,200

LBSTA  CLB            DCT    005  0036 006 0616 1103 27997
N42480 W070368              016  3225

ENE    CLB            J581   048  0037 005 0611 518  27479
117.1                       058  3188
N42255 W070368
```

- In most cases, obtain your oceanic clearance via voice at least 40 minutes prior to entry, or 30 to 90 minutes prior if using the Aircraft Communications Addressing and Reporting System (ACARS) data link Oceanic Clearance Delivery (OCD) to receive the clearance. As discussed above, if your departure point is close to the oceanic and remote continental airspace boundary, you may be able to obtain your clearance prior to departure.

- At least two pilots should be involved in the clearance receipt and read back process, one actively obtaining the clearance and the other monitoring. We recommend both pilots be on a headset during this process.

- Both pilots should independently copy the clearance. Each pilot cross-checks and verifies both the routing, altitudes, and Mach number assigned (if applicable) for the crossing.

- Read all waypoint coordinates back to the ATS provider in detail. Sometimes, approved local procedures make full read back optional. Always cross-check each detail of the clearance with your master document.

- Ensure the ATS provider acknowledges your correct read back.

A few notes about oceanic clearances:

- CPDLC (Everywhere except NYC) — If you are CPDLC- or ACARS-equipped in any region other than the NYC FIR you can downlink your oceanic through a data link service provider. See: International Operations / CPDLC - Oceanic Clearance (DSP).

- CPDLC (NYC FIR) — If you are CPDLC in the NYC FIR, you can downlink your oceanic clearance directly through CPDLC. See: International Operations / CPDLC - Oceanic Clearance (NYC).

- Voice Procedures (Gander) — Panel 1 of the Jeppesen Atlantic Orientation Chart includes Gander OCA procedures and frequencies needed to obtain an eastbound oceanic clearance.

- Voice Procedures (Shanwick) — Panel 11 of the Jeppesen Atlantic Orientation Chart includes Shanwick OCA procedures and frequencies needed to obtain oceanic westbound clearance.

We receive our clearance via data link and notice that we have been cleared at FL390, which is a bit unusual for us. A quick glance at the flight plan reveals that we are too heavy to cross any higher but there is a plan to climb to FL410 passing 030W. Of course the flight plan accounts for this but what if, for some reason, we don't get clearance to climb? A quick look at the fuel burns tells us we are okay even if the entire crossing is made at the lower altitude, but just the same we made a note on the plotting chart to remind ourselves to climb.

SELCAL Check

[AC 91-70B, ¶6.4.2.2] Accomplish a Selective Calling (SELCAL) check prior to oceanic and remote continental airspace entry and then again at each control area boundary. Check your SELCAL even when your CPDLC is working properly

The SELCAL check is more than a test of your radio equipment, it is a test of the complete connection from your airplane to the radio station. You need to check it every time you change frequencies or FIR. If you are unable to get a good SELCAL check, you must maintain a listening watch on the frequency, even if you are CPDLC equipped.

Coast-Out Navigation Accuracy Check

[AC 91-70B, Appendix D, ¶D.2.5.1] Before oceanic entry, you should check the accuracy of your LRNS against a suitable ground-based NAVAID, as applicable. A latitude/longitude radar fix from ATC can also support a navigation accuracy check in lieu of a NAVAID. You should record the results of the accuracy check on the master document, with the time and position. A large difference between the ground-based NAVAID and your LRNS, such that the ability to navigate with the accuracy required by ATC is questionable, requires immediate action, to include notification of ATC prior to entry into oceanic airspace. Note: Crews should not attempt to correct an error by performing an air alignment or by manually updating the position of the LRNS, because this has often resulted in worsening the problem. You should establish a navigation accuracy check tolerance based on your type of LRNS. Rank each navigation system by accuracy if applicable. Record aircraft compass/inertial/radio magnetic indicator (RMI) headings and note differences and deviations. A compass deviation check is particularly important if your aircraft is not equipped with an FMS.

Before you stray out of ground-based NAVAID range — sooner actually, before you leave the service volume of an appropriate NAVAID — you need to compare what it is telling you versus what your FMS is telling you. The procedure can be checking a VOR Radial/DME plot versus your FMS latitude/longitude on your plotting chart, or using an FMS "Cross Points" function versus the VOR Radial/DME. See the Appendices, Chapter 28.

Prior to Oceanic Boundary Altimeter Check

[AC 91-70B, Appendix D, ¶D.2.5.8] Prior to oceanic entry, you must check the two primary altimeters are reading within 200 feet of each other (or lesser value if specified in your aircraft operating manual). Conduct this check while at level flight. You should also note the stand-by altimeter reading. Record the altimeter readings along with the time on the master document.

See Section VI, Chapter 5, Loss of RVSM Capability in Oceanic Airspace.

Oceanic Checklist and RVSM/NAV Performance Log

Preflight

☑ Label one copy of the computer flight plan "Master Document"
☑ Plot route over Class II airspace and any relevant tracks
☑ Add ETPs (loss of pressurization, all-engine cruise, loss of engine) if required
☑ Position Check: Ramp (GPS) N/S   42°27.6   E/W   71°17.4

IRS #1	IRS #2	IRS #3	GPS #1	GPS#2
Diff 0.0	Diff 0.0	Diff 0.0	Diff 0.0	Diff 0.0

☑ Altimeter Check: QNH 2992 Pilot's 120 Stby 130 Copilot's 120
☑ Time Check: Source (circle) WWV GPS ATC +/- 10 sec ✓
☑ Compare Master Document course/distance with plotting or en route chart, circle waypoint
☑ Compare Master Document course/distance with FMS, draw diagonal over waypoint
☑ Record fuel onboard on the Master Document

Coast Out

☑ Check both HFs, check SELCAL prior to entering oceanic airspace
☑ Nav Accuracy Check:

RAW: Fix YQX   Radial 270   Distance 113
FMS: Fix YQX   Radial 270   Distance 112

☑ Altimeter Check: QNH 2992 Pilot's 41000 Stby 40900 Copilot's 41020
☑ Record oceanic clearances on the Master Document

At Each Waypoint

☐ Record ATA, fuel remaining, winds/temperature (if required), next ETA, HF frequencies, three altimeters on Master Document
☐ Make the position report, draw a second diagonal over waypoint on Master Document
☐ Check distance, time, heading, and fuel remaining to the next waypoint against the Master Document
☐ Plot aircraft position approximately 10 minutes after waypoint passage

Coast In

☐ Nav Accuracy Check:

RAW: Fix _____ Radial _____ Distance _____
FMS: Fix _____ Radial _____ Distance _____

Post-flight

☐ Position Check: Ramp (GPS) N/S _____ E/W _____

IRS #1	IRS #2	IRS #3	GPS #1	GPS#2
Diff _____	Diff _____	Diff _____	Diff _____	Diff _____

☐ Altimeter Check: QNH _____ Pilot's _____ Stby _____ Copilot's _____

Oceanic En Route

*F*lying in oceanic airspace requires pilots take on some of the burden that domestically belongs to air traffic control with radar contact. There are a few extra steps prior to and during the oceanic crossing. While procedures worldwide have become much more standardized, there are differences in various regions. The basic procedures are covered here, with regional differences noted. Of course these procedures are changing every day and you should check prior to every trip.

This section continues an example G450 trip from Bedford, Massachusetts (KBED) to Geneva, Switzerland (LSGG), to Tokyo, Japan (RJAA), back to Bedford, with additional legs planned as "technical" stops. For the purpose of covering an oceanic departure, this section will focus on the KBED to LSGG leg. To view the steps required prior to oceanic airspace entry, see the previous chapter.

Entering Oceanic Airspace

There are two sets of rules when it comes to making these ETAs.

- Prior to entering oceanic airspace, it is usually worth your while to adjust speed or use other techniques to make the ETA plus or minus 2 minutes. See Section VII, Chapter 2, En Route Timing, for techniques.

- After entering oceanic airspace you are expressly forbidden from adjusting speed in an attempt to make an ETA good. See the next section for the rationale behind this restriction.

Mach Number Technique

The primary method of maintaining proper longitudinal separation between aircraft throughout almost all of the world's oceanic airspace is for each aircraft to maintain a constant Mach Number. See the Appendices, Chapter 27, Mach Number Technique.

Do not chase the Mach indicator to make your ETAs good. Fly your cleared Mach Number and monitor your ETA progress. If you are off by three minutes or more, inform ATC. If you adjust your speed and the aircraft ahead or behind you do not, there could be a loss of longitudinal separation.

We were assigned Mach 0.80 for our example flight's oceanic clearance and our G450 cockpit indication gives us a True Mach. So we set 0.80 and allow the auto throttles to manage the speed control. We keep an eye on each ETA and if they vary by three minutes or more, we inform ATC. Since we are in the North Atlantic, we'll wait 30 minutes after DENDU before switching the transponder to Code 2000.

CPT FREQ LAT	FLT T TRO TDV LONG	WIND COMP	S	TAS GRS	AWY	MH MCRS	DST DSTR	ETE ATE	ETR ATR	FU AFU	FR AFR	FF/E
							ATD 1705	Fuel 29,200 (-300)				
CYMON 36 N49430	390 -55 M02 W054599	287123 P084	3	457 542	DCT	080 088	0160 2438	018	0449	896	22874	1518
DENDU 36 N50302	390 -52 P04 W052041	288105 P075	7	463 538	DCT	083 090	0123 2315	014 *ETA 1705* *Direct*	0435	698	22176	1531
5?50N 36 W050000	390 -50 P06	288090 P067	4	465 531	DCT	095 097	0084 2231	009 *ETA 1713*	0426	485	21690	1531
5?40N 52 W040000	390 -50 P07	276063 P060	2	466 527	DCT	106 104	0379 1851	043	0343	2204	19487	1516
5?30N 52 W030000	410 -51 P06	252054 P051	1	465 516	DCT	103 100	0371 1481	043	0300	2076	17411	1445
5?20N 31 W020000	410 -53 P05	241060 P051		464 515	DCT	124 117	0371 1110	043	0217	2026	15385	1407
DINIM 36 W015000	410 -55 P03	236069 P040	1	462 502	DCT	102 097	0197 0913	024	0153	1081	14305	1377
ELSOX 36 N51000	410 -56 P01 W014000	236075 P060	3	460 520	DCT	116 109	0038 0876	004	0149	198	14106	1359

VHF Switch from ATC to Guard / Interplane

[AC 91-70B, ¶6.4.3] Once you have departed very high frequency (VHF) radio range, set your radios to air-to-air (generally 123.45) and guard (121.5) frequencies. ATC and air defense authorities will generally attempt contact with aircraft on guard (121.5 or 243.0 megahertz (MHz)) before ordering an intercept.

[ICAO Annex 10 Vol V, ¶4.1.3.2.1] An air-to-air VHF communications channel on the frequency of 123.45 MHz shall be designated to enable aircraft engaged in flights over remote and oceanic areas out of range of VHF ground stations to exchange necessary operational information and to facilitate the resolution of operational problems.

Hand off procedures are not standard, but HF frequencies are normally given by ATC on VHF or CPDLC, and may also be published on en route charts.

- When checking in on HF, you normally call the station by name, add your call sign and the frequency being called.

- If the domestic controller advised you to contact the radio station with a position report, you add the word "position" to your initial call. For example: "Gander Radio, November Seven Seven Zero Zero, Position on eight eight six four."

- Tune and listen to the frequency for a few moments to make sure you don't block someone's transmission and to get a feel for how good the frequencies are. If the frequencies are clear, you can combine your SELCAL request with the initial call. For example, let's say you are CP-DLC equipped, your call could be: "Gander Radio, November seven seven zero zero, CPDLC, Shanwick Next, request SELCAL check Alpha Bravo Charlie Delta."

- Once ATC with VHF is terminated, you should switch to 123.45 and 121.5, as discussed next.

Gander gives us direct to 51N 050W before we reach DENDU and asks for our "five zero west" estimate. We turn the aircraft direct 51N 050W and see the FMS estimates that point at 1713Z. We pass that on to Gander and record that on the master document, since we will now have to make that time plus or minus 2 minutes or have to revise it.

Since we are CPDLC equipped, Gander Radio tells us "November seven seven zero zero, Gander Radio, voice reports not required in Gander OCA, at thirty west contact Shanwick on three zero one six primary or five five niner eight secondary." We tune 121.5 and 123.45 on our VHF radios, turn the cockpit speakers on to listen to those frequencies and rely on the SELCAL for any HF contact.

Transponder Code

[AC 91-70B, ¶6.4.3.1] Change your transponder code to 2000 in accordance with regional requirements. This requirement varies with the oceanic airspace. You should confirm these procedures, through applicable AIP or other regional documents during flight planning. In the North Atlantic, for example, the transponder code should be changed 30 minutes after entering oceanic airspace.

Thirty minutes after DENDU we switch the transponder to Code 2000.

Traffic Information Broadcasts by Aircraft (TIBA)

In areas where Traffic Information Broadcasts by Aircraft (TIBA) or the IATA In-Flight Broadcast Procedure is mandated by the country specific AIP, Jeppesen Airway ATC pages, or en route charts, cockpit radios should be set up and procedures for these broadcasts. See the Appendices, Chapter 38, Traffic Information Broadcast by Aircraft (TIBA).

For our example flight, there are no TIBA requirements in the North Atlantic, so we do not bother with this.

Strategic Lateral Offset (SLOP)

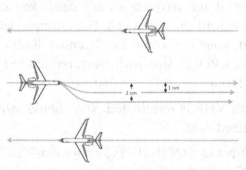

Aircraft with an automatic FMS offset capability should routinely fly 1 nm or 2 nm right of course centerline while in oceanic airspace in most of the world, and in increments of 0.1 nm for much of the world. The selection of how much right of course can be made based on wake turbulence consider-ations. Where authorized, there is no ATC clearance required and it is not necessary to advise ATC. Position reports are based on the waypoints of the current ATC clearance and not offset positions. Aircraft without an auto-matic FMS offset capability should fly the centerline only.

SLOP is not universal, you cannot use it everywhere, but where it is autho-rized you should use it. See the Appendices, Chapter 37, Strategic Lateral Offset Procedure (SLOP).

SLOP is recommended in the North Atlantic, so we initiate a 2 NM SLOP to the right.

Waypoint Passage

Approaching Each Waypoint

```
CPT    FLT T  WIND   S TAS AWY    MH   DST  ETE ETR FU   FR    FF/E
FREQ   TRO TDV COMP    GRS       MCRS DSTR ATE ATR AFU  AFR
LAT    LONG                    A/D 1705 Fuel 29,200 (-300)

CYMON  390 -55 287123 3 457 DCT  0?0  0160 018 0449 896  22874 1518
       36 M02 P084     542       ?88  2438
N49430 W054599

DENDU  390 -52 288105 7 463 DCT  083  0123 014 0435 698  22176 1531
       36 P04 P075     538       090  2315 ETA 1705
N50302 W052041                        Direct

51 50N 390 -50 288090 4 465 DCT  095  0084 009 0426 485  21690 1531
       36 P06 P067     531       097  2231 ETA 1713
N510?  W050000

52 40N 390 -50 276063 2 466 DCT  106  0379 043 0343 2204 19487 1516
       52 P07 P060     527       10?  185?
N52 0? W040000

53 30N 410 -51 252054 1 465 DCT  103  0371 043 0300 2076 17411 1445
```

[AC 91-70B, ¶6.4.4.2] Two minutes before reaching each oceanic waypoint, verify the next and subsequent ("next + 1") waypoints. Using your currently effective route clearance, we recommend this verification include (1) a check of the expanded FMC coordinates for the next and subsequent waypoints and (2) a check that the expected outbound magnetic course and distance to the next waypoint presented in the FMC agrees with that clearance.

[ICAO NAT Doc 007, ¶8.4.14.(b)] at the waypoint, check the distance to the next waypoint, confirm that the aircraft turns in the correct direction and takes up a new heading and track appropriate to the leg to the next waypoint.

You will be fairly busy during waypoint passage and with most FMSs the distance between waypoints starts to decrease once the waypoint is crossed. A good technique to get around all this is to place the pilot's heading bug on the next expected magnetic heading listed on the flight plan a minute or so prior to the waypoint and at that point make sure the distance to the next waypoint checks. At waypoint passage, if a turn is needed, the aircraft should turn to the heading bug.

We are heading direct to 51N 050W and our next waypoint will be 52N 040W. Our example flight plan shows the heading to 52N 040W should be 106° and the distance will be 379 nm. We set the heading bug to 106 and verify the distance shown on the FMS is correct.

Master Document Update

The first thing we do passing the waypoint is make note of the fuel, since that number is constantly changing. The annotation "21,300 (-400)" tells us how much we had at that point and that the amount is 400 lbs short of the flight plan estimate. Since we started at "(-300)" on takeoff, we know the trend is against us and make note of the fact we need to keep an eye on this.

We also make note of the ATA, the frequencies, all three altimeters, and the next ETA.

CPT FREQ LAT	FLT T TRO TDV LONG	WIND COMP	S	TAS GRS	AWY	MH MCRS	DST DSTR	ETE ATE	ETR ATR	FU AFU	FR AFR	FF/E
						ATD 1705 Fuel 29,200 (-300)						
CYMON 36 N49430	390 -55 M02 W054599	287123 P084	3	457 542	DCT	080 088	0160 2438	018	0449	896	22874	1518
DENDU 36 N50302	390 -52 P04 W052041	288105 P075	7	463 538	DCT	083 090	0123 2315	014 ETA 1705 Direct	0435	698	22176	1531
⊗5?50N 36 W050000	390 -50 P06	288090 P067	4	465 531	DCT	095 097	0084 2231	009 ETA 1713	0426 21,300 (-400)	485	21690	1531
		3016/5598 - 39000/38700/39020 - ATA 1713										
⊗5?40N 52 W040000	390 -50 P07	276063 P060	2	466 527	DCT	106 104	0379 1851	043 ETA 1756	0343	2204	19487	1516
⊗5?30N 52 W030000	410 -51 P06	252054 P051	1	465 516	DCT	103 100	0371 1481	043	0300	2076	17411	1445
⊗5?20N 31 W020000	410 -53 P05	241060 P051		464 515	DCT	124 117	0371 1110	043	0217	2026	15385	1407
⊗D?NIM 36 W015000	410 -55 P03	236069 P040	1	462 502	DCT	102 097	0197 0913	024	0153	1081	14305	1377

Position Report

[AC 91-70B, ¶D.1.8.3] Make position report.

[AC 91-70B, ¶6.1.2.4.3)] When position reports are made by voice, ICAO requires you to report to ATS authorities any change to your ETA in excess of 2 minutes, both for your initial oceanic entry point as well as all required reporting points along your route of flight through oceanic and remote continental airspace.

Position reports can be made via voice or CPDLC. See Part IV, Chapter 3, Voice Position Reports; and Part IV, Chapter 5, CPDLC.

Since we are CPDLC-equipped, our HF radio conversation goes like this:

Us: "Gander Radio, November seven seven zero zero, on three zero one six."

Them: "November seven seven zero zero, Gander Radio, go ahead."

Us: "November seven seven zero zero, CPDLC, Shanwick next, request SELCAL check alpha bravo charlie delta."

Them: "November seven seven zero zero, Gander Radio, voice reports not required in Gander OCA, at thirty west contact Shanwick on five five niner eight primary, three zero one six secondary, SELCAL check alpha bravo charlie delta."

At this point we get the SELCAL, acknowledge that, and get ready for our next chores.

After Waypoint Passage

Heading Check

If you preset the heading bug during the Approaching Each Waypoint step, you need only verify that the aircraft turned to the correct heading. Otherwise you should now crosscheck the aircraft's heading against the master document.

We make a second diagonal on the 050W waypoint, signifying the waypoint duties have been completed. At this point you should set a timer to make the post-position plot, about ten minutes after waypoint passage. Flying east-to-west or west-to-east at a mid-latitude, two degrees on longitude will make this chore easier. More on that next. . .

Post-Position Plot

[AC 91-70B, ¶D.2.9] Cross-check navigational performance and course compliance by one of the following methods:

D.2.9.1 The "plotting" method is appropriate for all aircraft navigation configurations.

1.   Verify your plotting/orientation chart reflects the currently effective route clearance.

2.   Plot your present latitude/longitude and record the time on your chart.

3.   You should plot your position using coordinates from the nonsteering LRNS.

4.   Investigate/take corrective action if your plotted position does not agree with your currently effective route clearance.

5.   Using the steering LRNS, verify the next waypoint is consistent with the currently effective route clearance.

6.　　Verify your autopilot steering mode is in LNAV/VNAV or other appropriate mode to ensure steering to the next intended waypoint.

D.2.9.2 The "navigation display" method is appropriate for and available for use in aircraft equipped with an operable FMS:

1.　　Confirm the aircraft symbol is on the programmed route on the navigation display (at smallest scale).

2.　　Check system-generated cross-track deviation or similar indication of any deviation from the programmed route of flight.

3.　　Using the steering LRNS verify the "TO" waypoint is consistent with your currently effective route clearance.

4.　　Investigate/take correction action to address any anomalies or unexpected deviations.

5.　　Verify your autopilot steering mode is LNAV/VNAV or other appropriate mode to ensure steering to the next intended waypoint.

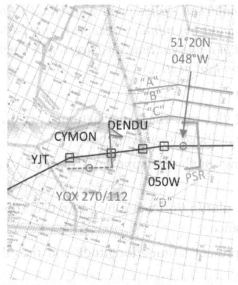

Plotting procedures are fairly straight forward but require a level of precision and perhaps some practice. Need a refresher? See Section II, Chapter 5.

Next Waypoint Preparation / Revised Estimates

If changes in winds and/or temperature change your next ETA by 3 minutes or more, you need to forward a new estimate. What about aircraft with data link? It depends on whom you believe. The ICAO says:

[ICAO Doc 10037, ¶ B.4.1.4] In the NAT Region, if the estimated time for the next position last provided to ATC is found to be in error by three minutes or more, the flight crew should provide a revised estimated time. The flight crew may assume that the estimate for the next waypoint, shown on the FMS at the time a waypoint is crossed, is the estimate transmitted to ATC. The flight crew should provide the revised estimate to the controlling ATS unit as soon as possible via voice or CPDLC using free text DM 67 REVISED ETA (position) (time).

The NAT SPG says:

[ICAO Nat Doc 007, ¶5.1.7] The flight crew should monitor the forward estimate for oceanic entry, and if this changes by 3 minutes or more, unless providing position reports via ADS-C, pass a revised estimate to ATC. As planned longitudinal spacing by these OACCs is based on the estimated times over the oceanic entry fix or boundary, failure to adhere to this ETA amendment procedure may jeopardise planned separation between aircraft, thus resulting in a subsequent [reclearance] to a less economical track/flight level for the complete crossing. Any such failure may also penalise following aircraft.

[ICAO Nat Doc 007, ¶6.3.4] Unless providing position reports via ADS-C, if the estimated time for the 'next position', as last reported to ATC, has changed by three minutes or more, a revised estimate must be transmitted to the ATS unit concerned as soon as possible.

Midpoint Weather

[AC 91-70B, ¶D.2.10.1] We recommend you cross-check the winds midway between oceanic waypoints by comparing the master document, LRNS, and winds aloft chart. This cross-check will also assist with situational awareness and in the event your navigation capability is degraded to the point where you need to dead reckon (DR).

[AC 91-70B, ¶D.2.8.2] In 2010, ICAO eliminated the requirement to report weather data via voice reports.

Oceanic Checklist and RVSM/NAV Performance Log

Preflight

☑ Label one copy of the computer flight plan "Master Document"
☑ Plot route over Class II airspace and any relevant tracks
☑ Add ETPs (loss of pressurization, all-engine cruise, loss of engine) if required
☑ Position Check: Ramp (GPS) N/S ___42°27.6___   E/W ___71°17.4___

	IRS #1	IRS #2	IRS #3	GPS #1	GPS#2
Diff	0.0	Diff 0.0	Diff 0.0	Diff 0.0	Diff 0.0

☑ Altimeter Check: QNH 2992 Pilot's 120 Stby 130 Copilot's 120
☑ Time Check: Source (circle) WWV/GPS/ATC +/- 10 sec ✓
☑ Compare Master Document course/distance with plotting or en route chart, circle waypoint
☑ Compare Master Document course/distance with FMS, draw diagonal over waypoint
☑ Record fuel onboard on the Master Document

Coast Out

☑ Check both HFs, check SELCAL prior to entering oceanic airspace
☑ Nav Accuracy Check:

    RAW: Fix __YQX__   Radial __270__   Distance __113__
    FMS: Fix __YQX__   Radial __270__   Distance __112__

☑ Altimeter Check: QNH 2992 Pilot's 41000 Stby 0900 Copilot's 41020
☑ Record oceanic clearances on the Master Document

At Each Waypoint

☑ Record ATA, fuel remaining, winds/temperature (if required), next ETA, HF frequencies, three altimeters on Master Document
☑ Make the position report, draw a second diagonal over waypoint on Master Document
☑ Check distance, time, heading, and fuel remaining to the next waypoint against the Master Document
☐ Plot aircraft position approximately 10 minutes after waypoint passage

Coast In

☐ Nav Accuracy Check:

    RAW: Fix _____ Radial _____ Distance _____
    FMS: Fix _____ Radial _____ Distance _____

Post-flight

☐ Position Check: Ramp (GPS) N/S _____ E/W _____

	IRS #1	IRS #2	IRS #3	GPS #1	GPS#2
Diff	Diff	Diff	Diff	Diff	

☐ Altimeter Check: QNH ____ Pilot's ____ Stby ____ Copilot's ____

From here on each waypoint uses the same procedure, but we'll have to remember to:

- *Note when we pass our ETP that our primary divert location changes from Gander to Shannon.*

- *Look for new ADS-C contracts with Shanwick approaching 030W, followed by a "NEXT CTR" notification with CPDLC, in the case of a Honeywell-equipped Gulfstream.*

- *Contact Shanwick at 030W and request our climb to FL410.*

Chapter 4

Oceanic Arrival

*T*ransforming *your craft from an oceanic vessel back to domestic operations is just a matter of making the right contacts, finishing some paperwork, removing SLOP (if any), and getting the cockpit ready for airways, radar contact, and full time air traffic control. This section continues an example trip from Bedford, Massachusetts (KBED) to Geneva, Switzerland (LSGG), to Tokyo, Japan (RJAA), back to Bedford. For the purpose of covering an oceanic arrival, this section will focus on the KBED to LSGG leg. To view the steps required prior to oceanic airspace entry and the en route portion, see the previous chapters in this section.*

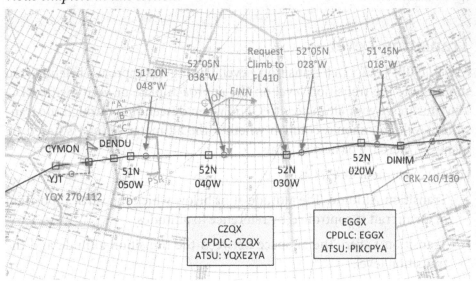

Coast-in Navigation Accuracy Check

[AC 91-70B, ¶D.2.11.3] Compare LRNS to ground-based NAVAID (as applicable depending on your equipage). 1. When departing oceanic airspace and acquiring ground-based NAVAIDs, you should note the accuracy of your LRNS compared to the position information provided by those NAVAIDs. 2. You should note discrepancies in your maintenance log.

See the Appendices, Chapter 28, Navigation Accuracy Check.

Strategic Lateral Offset

[AC 91-70B, ¶D.2.11.1] Remove strategic lateral offset. You must remove the strategic lateral offset prior to exiting oceanic airspace at coast-in. We recommend you include this as a checklist item.

See the Appendices, Chapter 37, Strategic Lateral Offset.

Domestic Routing

[AC 91-70B, ¶D.2.11.2] Confirm routing beyond oceanic airspace. Before entering the domestic route structure, you must confirm your routing and speed assignment.

Transition Level

[AC 91-70B, ¶D.2.12.1] Transition Level. During the approach briefing, you should note the transition level on the approach plate or verify with ATC. You must reset your altimeters to QNH when descending through the transition level. You should confirm whether the altimeter setting is based on inches of mercury or hectopascals.

[ICAO Document 4444, Ch 1]

- Transition Altitude: The altitude at or below which the vertical position of an aircraft is controlled by reference to altitudes.

- Transition Layer: The airspace between the transition altitude and the transition level.

- Transition Level: The lowest flight level available for use above the transition altitude.

See the Appendices, Chapter 6, Altimetery (Transition Level).

Oceanic Checklist and RVSM/NAV Performance Log

Preflight

☑ Label one copy of the computer flight plan "Master Document"
☑ Plot route over Class II airspace and any relevant tracks
☑ Add ETPs (loss of pressurization, all-engine cruise, loss of engine) if required
☑ Position Check: Ramp (GPS) N/S ___42°27.6___ E/W ___71°17.4___

IRS #1	IRS #2	IRS #3	GPS #1	GPS#2
Diff 0.0	Diff 0.0	Diff 0.0	Diff 0.0	Diff 0.0

☑ Altimeter Check: QNH 2992 Pilot's 120 Stby 130 Copilot's 120
☑ Time Check: Source (circle) WWV GPS ATC +/- 10 sec ✓
☑ Compare Master Document course/distance with plotting or en route chart, circle waypoint
☑ Compare Master Document course/distance with FMS, draw diagonal over waypoint
☑ Record fuel onboard on the Master Document

Coast Out

☑ Check both HFs, check SELCAL prior to entering oceanic airspace
☑ Nav Accuracy Check:

RAW: Fix ___YQX___ Radial ___270___ Distance ___113___
FMS: Fix ___YQX___ Radial ___270___ Distance ___112___

☑ Altimeter Check: QNH 2992 Pilot's 41000 Stby 40900 Copilot's 41020
☑ Record oceanic clearances on the Master Document

At Each Waypoint

☑ Record ATA, fuel remaining, winds/temperature (if required), next ETA, HF frequencies, three altimeters on Master Document
☑ Make the position report, draw a second diagonal over waypoint on Master Document
☑ Check distance, time, heading, and fuel remaining to the next waypoint against the Master Document
☑ Plot aircraft position approximately 10 minutes after waypoint passage

Coast In

☑ Nav Accuracy Check:

RAW: Fix ___CRK___ Radial ___240___ Distance ___130___
FMS: Fix ___CRK___ Radial ___240___ Distance ___129___

Post-flight

☑ Position Check: Ramp (GPS) N/S ___46°13.0___ E/W ___06°06.4___

IRS #1	IRS #2	IRS #3	GPS #1	GPS#2
Diff 0.4	Diff 0.2	Diff 1.2	Diff 0.0	Diff 0.0

☑ Altimeter Check. QNH 1010 Pilot's 1410 Stby 1440 Copilot's 1430

Other Coast-in Notes

Position Reporting will be continued until Air Traffic Control instructs: "discontinue position reports," or that "radar contact" is regained.

Mach Number Technique will be continued until returning to domestic airspace or Air Traffic Control approves a change of speed.

Plotting can be discontinued once the aircraft has returned to Class I airspace.

Much of your paperwork will need to retained, see: Record Keeping, below.

At the very least you will need to record altimeter readings after landing and if you do not have a hybrid IRU that records inertial performance, you should record those as well. It would be a good idea to put your RVSM/Nav Performance log near the top of your paperwork so you don't forget it.

Post-Flight

[AC 91-70B, ¶D.2.13.1] When arriving at your destination gate, you should note any drift or circular error in your LRNS. 1. A GPS primary means system normally should not exceed 0.27 NM for the flight. 2. Some inertial systems may drift as much as 2 NM per hour.

[AC 91-70B, ¶D.2.14] You must note problems in the altimetry system, altitude alert, or altitude hold in the maintenance log.

Record Keeping.

There doesn't appear to be any written guidance on keeping records of your oceanic flights any more, now that AC 91-70A has been replaced and the newer AC 91-70B doesn't mention record keeping at all. Here is the old guidance:

1. Record Documentation. Decisions regarding monitoring of an aircraft's navigation performance are largely the prerogative of individual operators. In deciding what records to keep, airlines should consider the stringent requirements associated with special use airspaces such as MNPS. Investigating all errors of 20 nm or greater in MNPS airspace is a requirement for airlines. Whether radar or the flight crew observes these deviations, it is imperative to determine and eliminate the cause of the deviation. Therefore, operators should keep complete flight records so that they can make an analysis. The retention of these documents must include the original and any amended clearances.

2. Documentation Requirements. Operators should review their documentation to ensure that it provides all the information required to reconstruct the flight. These records also satisfy the ICAO standard of keeping a journal. Specific requirements could include, but do not only apply to, the following:

   a. Record of the initial ramp position (latitude/longitude) in the LRNS, original planned flight track, and levels.

b.   Record of the LRNS gross error check, RVSM altimeter comparisons, and heading reference crosschecks before entering oceanic airspace.

c.   Plotting charts to include post waypoint 10-minute plots.

d.   All ATC clearances and revisions.

e.   All position reports made to ATC (e.g., voice, data link).

f.   The master document used in the actual navigation of the flight, including a record of waypoint sequencing allocated to specific points, ETA, and actual times of arrival (ATA).

g.   Comments on any navigation problems relating to the flight, including any discrepancies relating to ATC clearances or information passed to the aircraft following ground radar observations, including weather deviations or wake turbulence areas.

Techniques: Paper Records

It may be useful to carry an envelope for each planned oceanic leg, labeled with the following information:

- *Date*

- *Departure/destination*

- *PIC/SIC/Relief Pilot*

The following items, as applicable, should be retained at the aircraft base:

- *Master Document*

- *RVSM/Nav Performance Log*

- *Navigation Worksheet*

- *Plotting chart*

- *Weather reports*

- *Track Messages*

- *Over-flight/landing permits*

- *NOTAMS*

- *Post-Flight report form*

There is no regulatory guidance on how long these records should be retained, other than "within reasonable limits." (AC 91-70A, ¶3-12.b.) We use six months.

Techniques: Electronic Records

Some online flight planning software provide nearly automatic methods of record keeping. ARINCDirect in combination with their Flight Operations Software (FOS) applications, for example, will archive just about everything done while oceanic. Job Done. But what if your software doesn't offer this capability?

You can take photos — called "screen grabs" — of everything you do on an iPad that is pertinent by pressing the "Home" and "Power" buttons simultaneously. Everything will be saved as a photo to your Photos application. From there it is a matter of sending those photos via an email or text message to whomever does your record keeping.

Chapter 5

A Flight Into the Unknown (using an iPad)

*T*his chapter continues the example trip from Bedford, Massachusetts *(KBED) to Geneva, Switzerland (LSGG), to Tokyo, Japan (RJAA), back to Bedford. We will use the flight to come to illustrate the steps for flying over a region that is unfamiliar to you, and we'll do all of it on an iPad, no paper at all.*

The trip continues to change

Your passengers were full of praise for you and your crew's performance from KBED to LSGG, but expressed unhappiness at having to make several fuel stops because of your G450's limited range. Lucky for them, your company's G650 is available again and will take over the trip. So the trip returns to its original schedule, with the next leg nonstop to Tokyo.

The G650 crew uses paperless procedures, they use their iPad for all cockpit chores normally reserved for pencil and paper. The crew, however, has never made the hop from Europe to Japan over Eastern Europe and Russia. For them, it will be a flight into the unknown.

A quick call to the company's flight planning service confirms the trip is well within the aircraft's range with an augmented crew. Flying a Mach 0.90, the aircraft can make the expected 5,900 nm trip in just over 11 hours using expected routing and forecast winds. That leaves you with a few questions:

1. Is the routing safe?

2. Do we have the necessary communications, navigation, and surveillance capabilities?

3. Will the many countries between departure and destination permit overflight?

4. What are our options if something goes wrong while en route?

The Master Document

A logical first step is to produce a tentative master document to examine the performance requirements and proposed routing.

```
                    LSGG TO RJAA   G650   M90 /F   IFR   24Dec20
COMPUTED 0621Z FOR ETD 1900Z    PROGS 220000Z

            FUEL   TIME   DIST ARRIVE TAKEOFF   LAND    AV PLD  OPNLWT
DEST RJAA   040275 11:04 5896 0604Z  102595   062320  000400  054395
DEST ALT RJTT 000756 00:16 0062 0620Z
CONT        002014 00:33
FINAL RESV  002000 00:51
ADNL        002755 00:45
============================
T/O FUEL    047800 13.30   GCDIST   NAM    AV WIND
                           5310     5362   273/059
TAXI        000400
============================
BLK FUEL    048200 13:30

LSGG MEDAM5B MEDAM UM730 ATMAD M730 TOP Y11 KEGED M730 TORPO ZDA
RUDIK PIXAL VEBAL DUZLA FOGRE ROMKA LONLA KOKUP P26 PNK P727 BUSIN
L999 RATIN N869 INLAL N869 SONAT P865 ADANU N604 PIGUR T580 LITUN
N869 RO A817 NERKA B478 KTN A91 AGINO A810 TELOK A345 HLD B451 NDG
B451 BISUN B451 LURED B451 IGROD Y304 OLKAP Y304 GUGBI Y30 SWAMP RJAA


WIND P048    MXSH  16/FIONA
TAS 490      FL 270 LONLA 390 INLAL 410 TELOK 411 NDG 449 BISUN 450
LURED 410 IGROD 450 OLKAP 470
```

Aircraft Performance

There are obstacle considerations at LSGG but even at the expected departure weight and weather conditions, the G650 will be able to meet required climb gradients.

The aircraft will have adequate fuel reserves flying at Mach 0.90 at the expected weather conditions, routings, and altitudes. If the conditions worsen, the crew can increase their reserves almost two hours by pulling the speed back to Mach 0.85. Aircraft performance does not appear to be a limiting factor.

Crew Limitations

This crew's company requires a three pilot crew if duty times exceed 10 hours, four pilots if it exceeds 12 hours. With a normal show time of 1 hour and post flight time of 30 minutes, the duty day will be 12:34 using the Mach 0.90 schedule. A four pilot crew is called for.

Validating the Flight on an iPad

To answer the remaining questions, the crew will need to know their route of flight. They can get a pretty good idea by cutting and pasting their route from the master document into their JeppFD iPad application.

1. Import the master document to the iPad

Some flight planning companies provide standalone applications that will display the master document for you. Without that, all you need is a PDF copy of the master document that you can email to yourself or use a file transfer program, such as DropBox.

2. Copy the route from the master document

To copy the route from the master document, position and hold your finger or a stylus on a portion of the route and wait for that portion of the route to appear with a colored background. At this point you can lift your finger or stylus and drag the provided handles to start at the first waypoint and to end at the last waypoint. Press the provided "Copy" icon.

```
==============================
T/O FUEL      047800 13.30    GCDIST   NAM    AV WIND
                              5310     5362   273/059
TAXI          000400
==============================
BLK FUEL      048200 13:30         Copy    Speak

LSGG MEDAM5B MEDAM UM730 ATMAD M730 TOP Y11 KEGED M730 TORPO ZDA
RUDIK PIXAL VEBAL DUZLA FOGRE ROMKA LONLA KOKUP P26 PNK P727 BUSIN
L999 RATIN N869 INLAL N869 SONAT P865 ADANU N604 PIGUR T580 LITUN
N869 RO A817 NERKA B478 KTN A91 AGINO A810 TELOK A345 HLD B451 NDG
B451 BISUN B451 LURED B451 IGROD Y304 OLKAP Y304 GUGBI Y30 SWAMP RJAA


WIND P048    MXSH  16/FIONA
TAS 490      FL 270 LONLA 390 INLAL 410 TELOK 411 NDG 449 BISUN 450
LURED 410 IGROD 450 OLKAP 470

N       ED ENROUTE ALTERNATE (ERA):_____  ERA WEATHER:_____
                                                                   Page 1
```

3. Paste the route to JeppFD

To paste the route onto JeppFD, press the arrow that lowers the flight plan window and select "New Flight" to clear any previous information. Double press the route window to allow the "Paste" icon to appear. That will paste the copied route. Enter "LSGG" and "RJAA" in the airport windows.

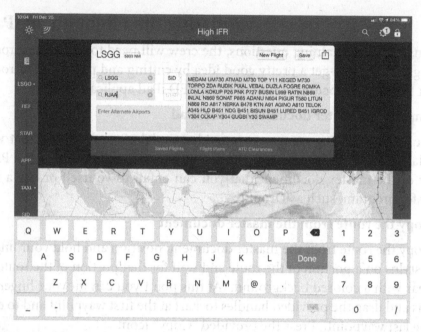

4. Examine the route

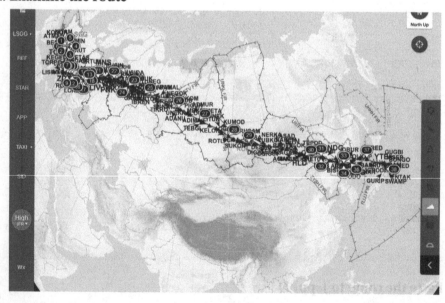

At this point you can zoom in and scroll to examine the route in detail.

From this point we see our route takes us through several FIRs:

LFMM (Marseille, France)

LIMM (Milano, Italy)

LDZO (Zagreb, Croatia)

LQSB (Sarajevo, Serbia)

LHCC (Budapest, Hungary)

UKBU (Ukraine)

UMMV (Belarus)

UUWW (Moscow, Russia)

USSV (Yekaterinburg, Russia)

USTV (Tyumen, Russia)

UNNT (Novosibirsk, Russia)

UNKL (Krasnoyarsk, Russia)

UIII (Irkutsk, Russia)

ZYSH (Shenyang, China)

UHHH (Khabarovsk, Russia)

RJJJ (Fukuoka, Japan)

Is the routing safe?

An airliner was shot down in the Ukraine in 2014, another in 2020, there was a shooting war in Croatia and Serbia about twenty years ago,, and much of Russia was off limits not too long before that. How can we be sure the routing is safe now?

NOTAMS

The "school" answer is to look at International Notices to Airmen (INOTAMS) but those don't exist anymore. You can get NOTAMS that cover the world at: https://www.notams.faa.gov/dinsQueryWeb/

But that doesn't work either because the worldwide NOTAM system is broken. The warnings are seldom timely and there is so much "noise level" information that finding a pertinent warning isn't a sure thing. The 2014 shoot down of Malaysia Airlines Flight 17 happened when the NOTAM system could be argued to have claimed the airspace was safe.

State Departments

You can also visit official government website, such as the U.S. State Department at: https://travel.state.gov/content/travel/en/traveladvisories/traveladvisories.html/.

But these are hit and miss too, since they tend to move slowly and can be said to have a vested interest in calling their airspace safe, even if not.

Ops.group

The most reliable and timely source of safe airspace information can be found at ops.group. Yes, that is a website, type "ops.group" in your Internet browser, no quotation marks.

Ops.group counts in its membership hundreds of airlines and thousands of corporate flight departments who all provide recent and timely information for all parts of the world. Membership is reasonably priced and nothing beats their "Safe Airspace" application.

As of this writing, the Ukraine and Japan have warnings. The level two warning for the Ukraine is in the Simferopol FIR (URFV), Crimea, which is nearly 500 nm to the southeast of our route. The area is disputed between the Ukraine and Russia but the area has been quiet. Japan has a level three warning due to a missile threat warning from 2017. The NOTAM expired in May, 2019 and has not been renewed.

Based on this information, we deem the selected route to be safe.

Do we have the necessary communications, navigation, and surveillance capabilities?

Will the many countries between departure and destination permit overflight?

The answer to both questions can be found with the same sources, but the ease of access or the reliability of those sources bears scrutiny.

Aeronautical Information Publications (AIPs)

If you are taking an exam in international procedures class, the correct answer to "where do you find out about a State's communications, navigation, and surveillance information?" is their AIP. The same holds true of the "where do you find out about a State's overflight and other legal entry requirements?" What they don't tell you is where do you find the AIPs? Here is where you will find most of them:

https://gis.icao.int/gallery/ONLINE_AIPs.html

Most of these come up in English or have a language button that will convert what you see into English. But even if that is the case, finding what you are looking for can be a challenge.

ICAO Doc 7030

Theoretically, you should be able to find everything you need in ICAO Doc 7030, Regional Supplementary Procedures. Problems? Well, yes. It hasn't been updated since 2009.

Jeppesen JeppFD "State" Pages

Most of us pay the Jeppesen-Sanderson Company to provide us with up-to-date charts and part of that subscription should include publications with everything you need. Finding them in the iPad App can be a challenge. With JeppFD, you first load the route, display the route, and then press the book icon.

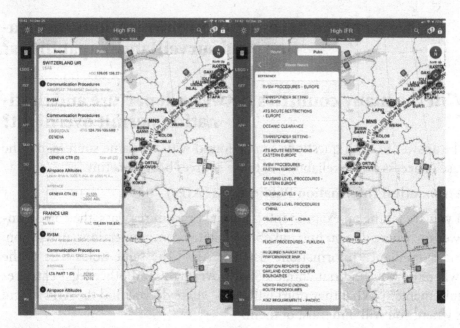

You should get a flyout window that has "Route" and "Pubs." Once you've done that there will be an arrow pointing off screen. Hit the arrow.

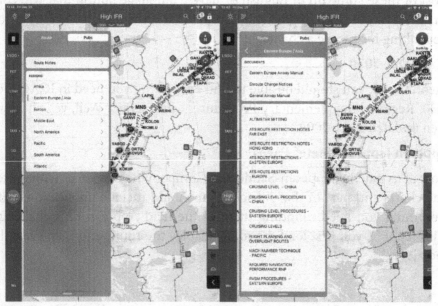

From there select the region you are interested in.

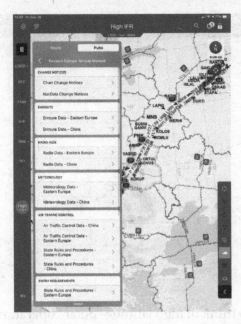

A note about altimetry

I haven't mentioned having to fly metric altitudes or setting QFE instead of QNH because it is no longer necessary in Russia and most of China. If you find yourself wandering into other parts of China or in North Korea, these things will matter to you. See the Appendices, Chapter 4.

What are our options if something goes wrong while en route?

Recall that there are some airspace issues over the Crimea at the time this trip was planned and that we are about 500 nm away from the bad news. Let's say a passenger has a medical episode that demands hospital attention somewhere over the Ukraine. Knowing about the airspace controversy could improve your decision making.

Recall also that one of the FIRs you will be transiting is Irkutsk. Does that mean anything to you? Me neither. But what if I told you Irkutsk is about halfway along your route through Siberia? You can display suitable airports along your route in JeppFD but you will have no idea which airports are nearby hospitals or other facilities that will help you.

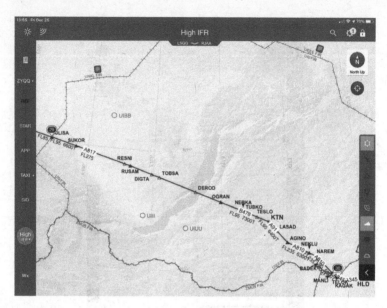

It may be helpful to think of high latitude "polar" operations when considering divert locations. There have been instances where aircraft diverted into airports where the nearest suitable hospital was a day's drive away; the passenger would have been better off had the crew elected to continue to their destination. Other aircraft have diverted for mechanical issues into airports so remote, getting spare parts or mechanical assistance took months, not hours.

This obviously isn't always true, but if you are transiting an area where healthcare and other needed services may be sparse, it would be good to have that information before making a divert decision.

In the case of our example trip, we didn't have any issues and the crew made it in safely to Tokyo, Japan (RJAA).

Section VII – Tutorial

Chapter 6

A Flight Back Home

*T*his chapter continues the example trip from Bedford, Massachusetts
(KBED) to Geneva, Switzerland (LSGG), to Tokyo, Japan (RJAA), back to
Bedford. We will use this flight to illustrate a few common issues when oper-
ating at a foreign airport, a few things to consider when en route over the high
latitudes, and customs and immigration issues when returning to the United
States.

The Master Document

```
                      RJAA TO KBED  G650  M90 /F  IFR  24Dec20
         COMPUTED 0619Z FOR ETD 1900Z   PROGS 220000Z

                      FUEL    TIME  DIST ARRIVE TAKEOFF  LAND   AV PLD  OPNLWT
         DEST KBED    042736 11:03 6121 0602Z  102595  059859 000400  054395
         DEST ALT KBOS 000613 00:10 0044 0612Z
         CONT         002137 00:33
         FINAL RESV   002000 00:52
         ADNL         000314 00:04
         =============================
         T/O FUEL     047800 12.43   GCDIST  NAM   AV WIND
                                     5812    5639  253/048
         TAXI         000400
         =============================
         BLK FUEL     048200 12:43

         RJAA GULBO Y808 PUTER A590 PASRO A590 POWAL A590 PINTT A590 POETT
         J120 BET J501 TED J511 GKN NCA14 GAHAM YQH HUGAR YKJ KEVBO IV YGQ
         CHICA JARRO NOVON PONCT EEGUL ZELKA2 KBED


         WIND P044   MXSH  10/A6R12
         TAS 515    FL 310 PASRO 320 POWAL 380 PINTT 390 POETT 410 YKJ 450
```

*The final leg will be the easiest, repeating many of the oceanic steps of the first
leg from KBED to LSGG. Departing from Tokyo will pose a few language issues and procedures that are a bit different than what many U.S. based pilots
are used to. The flight over Canada can be routine but when the routine is
broken, there are a few things to consider.*

Departure Considerations

Customs / Immigration / Quarantine (CIQ)

Some countries require customs / immigration / quarantine clearance prior to departure that is just as rigorous as that given to arrivals. If you are uncertain of the procedure, it would be prudent to ask upon arrival.

Some airports outside the U.S. offer "preclearance" on departure that will expedite a U.S. arrival. As of 2020, these services are offered in some locations in Canada, Ireland, the United Arab Emirates, and in parts of the Caribbean.

More about this topic in the Appendices, Chapter 16.

For our example RJAA - KBED flight, we will not need CIQ approval prior to departure and there is no preclearance available for our return to the U.S.

Agriculture

Many countries will restrict items you can bring in, even for personal use. In some cases there are health concerns and in others it may just be a matter of collecting the right duties.

More about this topic in the Appendices, Chapter 1.

For our example flight, none of our crew or passengers are carrying any items that will be flagged upon arrival for special duty or prohibition.

Ramp Inspection Program (RIP) aka SAFA

Some countries, especially in the European Union, can subject arriving and departing aircraft to inspections, known as Safety Assesment of Foreign Aircraft (SAFA), which is part of a Ramp Inspection Program (RIP).

More about this topic in the Appendices, Chapter 34.

For our example flight, Japan is not known for RIP or equivalent inspections.

Flight Plan

Some countries require local input of flight plans and what you have filed through a service provider may be changed. At some airports you will be issued what you may think is your flight plan on a form, sometimes handwritten. At other airports you may be given the new flight plan via voice or data link. In any case, you must verify the flight plan they have for you is what you have programmed. Some locations in Mexico, for example, routinely handwrite your flight plan and give you a copy. The flight plan that was actually filed with ATC can vary greatly from the one you filed.

More about this topic in the Appendices, Chapter 22.

For our example flight, Japan is not known for this practice and we receive a flight plan identical to the one we filed.

Fueling

Fuel densities throughout the world tend to be lower than in the United States. You may not be able to load a full load of fuel in some parts of the world if your fuel tanks are volume limited. In other words, 1,000 gallons or liters of fuel from San Francisco will fly you farther than the 1,000 gallons or liters of fuel from Hong Kong. You should not count on a "top off" to result in your desired fuel load in some countries.

More about this topic in the Appendices, Chapter 23.

For our example flight, Japan is known for this problem but the G650 is allowed to takeoff with a greater than published maximum volume so long as the weight limitations are not exceeded.

Slots

Some countries, particularly in Europe, will tightly regulate takeoff times to ensure the en route air traffic structure is not overwhelmed. You may need to negotiate your "off block" time, especially if you encounter delays.

More about this topic in the Appendices, Chapter 35.

For our example flight, Japan does not normally impose slots and we do not experience any delays.

Approach Ban

Under ICAO rules, you may not takeoff unless the weather at your intended destination is above minimums. Many countries, such as the United States, have an exception to this ICAO rule and permit the practice. But you have to abide by the rules of the country you are operating in.

More about this topic in the Appendices, Chapter 7.

For our example flight, Japan does impose approach bans for arrivals but not departures. You cannot continue an approach once it goes below minimums. But it does not prohibit takeoffs.

Engine Start

In some countries you will need ATC approval prior to engine start. The easiest way to find out is to listen to the ground control frequency to see how everyone else is doing it.

For our example flight, Japan does require ATC approval prior to engine start.

ATC Clearance

The U.S. practice of "preclearance" -- getting your IFR clearance prior to engine start -- is becoming more common worldwide but is not yet universal. Some airports will not issue a voice clearance until your are moving. If your clearance is not available via data link, you should listen on ground frequencies to see how it is normally done.

For our example flight, we get our clearance via data link.

"Holding Point"

Some airports will have taxiway holding points designated by signs, painted placards on the pavement, or by runway/taxiway intersections. You can expect taxi clearances to these points.

For our example flight, a prestudy of the airport charts shows various "Apron Hold" lights that we will need to be aware of.

Conditional Clearances

Some countries use conditional clearances to expedite aircraft movement onto runways. These can be unnerving the first time you are cleared onto a runway while another is still on approach.

More about this topic in the Appendices, Chapter 13.

For our example flight, Japan does not appear to use conditional clearances.

Local Procedures Review

For these and many other local procedures, it would be helpful to have a concise summary of everything you need to know. Each country's Aeronautical Information Publication (AIP) is designed for this purpose, but these AIPs tend to be long, organized poorly, and lacking in knowledge the locals consider too mundane to write down. If you are a Jeppesen subscriber, you will find much of the information you need in the "State" pages as well as the informational pages tucked throughout the approach charts. For many countries, there are specific arrival and departure pages presented before the airport taxi charts.

For our example flight, the "State" pages for Japan are rich with content. There are several pages of information alongside the Taxi charts.

En Route Considerations

High Latitude (Polar) Operations

Commercial operators are required to make special preparations and follow specific procedures for flights into high latitudes. In many cases, operations specification approval is required. Non-commercial operators would be wise to study the requirements as well.

More about this topic in the Appendices, Chapter 24.

For our example flight, our flight will be south of the high latitudes but will benefit from a study of the topic in case an en route diversion is needed.

TIBA

In some parts of the world, Traffic Information Broadcast by Aircraft (TIBA) is required practice. In other parts, TIBA is a backup method should air traffic control lose communications.

More about this topic in the Appendices, Chapter 38.

For our example flight, there are no stretches where TIBA is required.

Arrival Considerations

Electronic Advanced Passenger Information System (eAPIS)

An Electronic Advanced Passenger Information System (eAPIS) notification is required by some countries and in some cases this has to be done before you will allowed to takeoff. The United States uses eAPIS. Some other countries use equivalent systems.

More about this topic in the Appendices, Chapter 18.

For our example flight, an eAPIS is required by the United States before we can be permitted to takeoff from Japan. We, as pilots, can complete the eAPIS, but we delegate this to our dispatcher.

Souther Border Overflight Exemption (SBOE)

Arrivals from many areas south of the United States southern border are required to land at the nearest designated airport unless they have a Southern Border Overflight Exemption (SBOE).

More about this topic in the Appendices, Chapter 36.

For our example flight, we are not arriving from an applicable area and an

SBOE is not needed.

Visa Waiver Program (VWP)

Many passengers will need a Visa to be permitted entry into the United States but visitors from some countries may travel on approved carriers under the Visa Waiver Program (VWP). This makes life easier for everyone concerned except when a person enters on the VWP program and then exits on a nonapproved carrier.

More about this topic in the Appendices, Chapter 40.

For our example flight, we do not have any passengers using the VWP.

Disinsection

Disinsection, the fumigation of aircraft before or after arrival, is taken seriously in some parts of the world and may need to be accomplished with your passengers on board.

More about this topic in the Appendices, Chapter 17.

For our example flight, Japan and the United States do not require disensection.

CDFA

While a Continuous Descent Final Approach (CDFA) is always a better choice than a "dive and drive" along a straight-in non-precision approach, it is mandatory in some countries.

More about this topic in the Appendices, Chapter 14.

For our example flight, a CDFA is recommmended in the United States but not mandatory.

Customs / Immigration / Quarantine

Customs, immigration, and possibly quarantine is almost always a concern for entry into a foreign country.

More about this topic in the Appendices, Chapter 16.

For our example flight, the United States does have considerable customs and immigration concerns, as well as occasional quarantines imposed on some countries. Our crew is well versed in these procedures.

Chapter 1

Agriculture Import

The USDA no longer offers a booklet on what you can bring into the United States. Instead, they have website, http://www.aphis.usda.gov/wps/portal/ aphis/home, with guidance on what can and cannot be imported. You don't often get asked by your passengers what is okay and what isn't, but you as the pilot are still the one in jeopardy. You should have an idea of what is okay and where to look if you aren't sure.

The USDA website does not easily link and they often change those links in an effort to make things harder than they should. I will try to point you in the right direction but they seem to change things every six months or so.

Generally Allowed Food Items

[www.aphis.usda.gov] — In the section marked "Popular Topics," select "Imports & Exports."

The following food items are generally allowed entry:

- Condiments such as oil, vinegar, mustard, catsup [ketchup], pickles, syrup, honey without honey combs, jelly, and jam.
- Foodstuffs such as bakery items, candy, and chocolate.
- Hard cured cheeses without meat, such as Parmesan or cheddar.
- Canned goods and goods in vacuum-packed jars (except those containing meat or poultry products) for personal use.
- Fish or fish products for personal use.
- Powdered drinks sealed in original containers with ingredients listed in English.
- Dry mixes containing dairy and egg ingredients (such as baking mixes, cocoa mixes, drink mixes, instant cake mixes, instant pudding mixes, liquid drink mixes containing reconstituted dry milk or dry milk prod-

ucts, potato flakes, and infant formula) that are commercially labeled, presented in final finished packaging, and require no further manipulation of the product are generally allowed.

Remember, you must declare all food and agricultural products, including those listed above, to a CBP agriculture specialist or officer when you arrive in the United States.

Fruits and Vegetables

The United States Department of Agriculture (USDA) Animal and Plant Health Inspection Service (APHIS) maintains a website where you plug in the country or the food item and get a ruling on import. The web site is: epermits.aphis.usda.gov.

If you enter "Papaya," for example, you will find out you can never bring one to Hawaii. You are also restricted from bringing any papaya from Chile, Ecuador, or Malaysia to any port of the United States.

The web site works well but the list is rather large. If you are en route and don't have an Internet connection, the USDA publishes phone numbers for inquiries: 1-301-851-2046 or 1-877-770-5990.

Animal Products and Animal By-Products

[http://www.aphis.usda.gov/wps/portal/aphis/home] — Click "Resources" / "Travelers International" and then "Animal Products and By Products"

- Meat, milk, egg, poultry, and products such as dried soup mix or bouillon, are either prohibited or restricted from entering the United States, depending on the types of animal diseases that occur in the country of origin. Fresh (chilled or frozen), dried, cured, and fully cooked meat is generally prohibited from most countries. Canned meat is allowed entry, except beef, veal, lamb, mutton, venison, elk, bison, etc., from countries affected by bovine spongiform encephalopathy.

- Products containing raw egg ingredients are not allowed from most regions.

- Pork and pork products are not allowed from Mexico, except for cooked pork in small amounts for a meal.

- Effective January 14, 2010, cooked pork skins (also known as pork rinds) entering as commercial cargo or in passenger baggage from some countries must be accompanied by additional documents. For more details, contact USDA's National Center for Import and Export at (301) 734-3277, or email AskNCIE.Products@aphis.usda.gov

Violations

[USDA - APHIS] Individuals who fail to declare non-commercial agricultural items may be subject to penalties ranging from $1,100 to $60,000 per violation. These penalties are based on authorities granted to USDA through the Plant Protection Act and the Animal Health Protection Act.

If you discover a banned item on the aircraft it is best to declare it on inspection. I've done that and had the item confiscated, which was better than the times the item was discovered and the passenger was forced to write a very large check.

Chapter 2

Airport Rescue and Fire Fighting (ARFF) Codes

There is no 14 CFR 91 or 14 CFR 135 requirement for any fire coverage at all at the airports these operators use, but some companies have instituted such requirements. Even if you don't have such a requirement, knowing your aircraft's Airport Rescue and Fire Fighting (ARFF) code may help you decide between two airports of otherwise equal attractiveness. A G450, for example has a US code of A and an ICAO code of 5. A G550 raises these to a US code of B and an ICAO code of 6.

United States ARFF

[14 CFR 139.315] For the purpose of Index determination, air carrier aircraft lengths are grouped as follows:

1. Index A includes aircraft less than 90 feet in length.

2. Index B includes aircraft at least 90 feet but less than 126 feet in length.

3. Index C includes aircraft at least 126 feet but less than 159 feet in length.

4. Index D includes aircraft at least 159 feet but less than 200 feet in length.

5. Index E includes aircraft at least 200 feet in length.

ICAO

[ICAO Annex 14, Table 9-1]

Aerodrome category	Aeroplane overall length	Maximum fuselage width
1	0 m up to but not including 9 m	2 m
2	9 m up to but not including 12 m	2 m
3	12 m up to but not including 18 m	3 m
4	18 m up to but not including 24 m	4 m
5	24 m up to but not including 28 m	4 m
6	28 m up to but not including 39 m	5 m
7	39 m up to but not including 49 m	5 m
8	49 m up to but not including 61 m	7 m
9	61 m up to but not including 76 m	7 m
10	76 m up to but not including 90 m	8 m

Chapter 3

Altimeter Settings

*T*he altimeter is a standard piece of equipment throughout the world but it isn't used in the same way. In the chapters to follow there are concerns about metric setting, QFE/QNH, temperature corrections, and transition layers. But first you will need some basics.

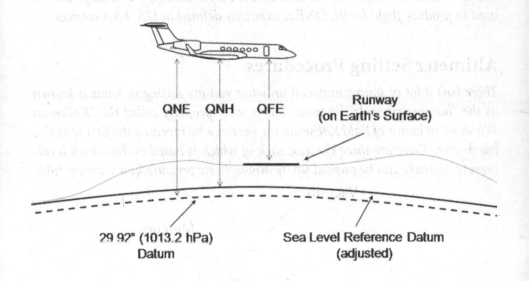

29.92" (1013.2 hPa)
Datum

Sea Level Reference Datum
(adjusted)

QFE / QNH / QNE

[ICAO Document 8168, Vol 1, Ch 2]

QFE: Atmospheric pressure at aerodrome elevation (or at runway threshold)

QNH: Altimeter sub-scale setting to obtain elevation when on the ground

QNE: A pressure type altimeter calibrated in accordance with the Standard Atmosphere . . . when set to a QNE altimeter setting, will indicate height above the QNE reference datum.

QFE ("Field Elevation") is a pressure setting you dial into your altimeter to produce the height above the runway. It reads zero when you are on the runway and gives your height above it when you are airborne. This appears to be consistent between ICAO and U.S. FAA reference material.

QNH ("Height Above Sea Level") is a pressure setting you dial into your altimeter to produce the height above sea level. It reads runway elevation when you are on the runway and is based on an altimeter setting adjusted until the station's correct elevation above sea level is read. This appears to be consistent between ICAO and U.S. FAA reference material.

QNE ("En Route") is a pressure setting of 29.92 inches or 1013 hPa that will produce a standard atmosphere altitude and provides the basis for flight levels. The term does not appear to be used by the ICAO, though the concept itself is used to produce flight levels. QNE is explicitly defined in U.S. FAA sources.

Altimeter Setting Procedures

There isn't a lot of source material on what you are setting in what is known as the "barometric scale" by some, but is more properly called the "Kollsman Window," in honor of Paul Kollsman the person who invented the first sensitive barometer. There are three choices, each of which is based on how high a column of mercury can be pushed up by atmospheric pressure in a vacuum tube.

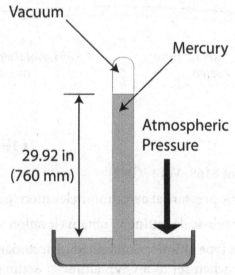

Inches (in) of mercury

Most of us in the United States are accustomed to using inches for that scale. Setting 29.92 means the mercury is pushed 29.92 inches.

Hectopascals (hPa)

The ICAO standard when it comes to setting your altimeter is the hectopascal, abbreviated hPa. A hectopascal is equal to a millibar, which is one-thousandth of a "standard atmosphere" which is equal to 1,000 "dynes" which comes to about 0.0145 pounds per square inch. All that really matters to you is that on a standard day you set 1013 hPa and on less than standard days it varies from there.

Millimeters (mm) of mercury

A competing system that has pretty much died out in all but a few countries is millimeters of mercury, or mm.

Because inches and hPa are so common, most aircraft designed for international travel will have a way of setting either. To set millimeters you may need a table to do the conversion:

MM	+0	+1	+2	+3	+4	+5	+6	+7	+8	+9
	Inches									
700	27.56	27.60	27.64	27.68	27.72	27.76	27.80	27.83	27.87	27.91
710	27.95	27.99	28.03	28.07	28.11	28.15	28.19	28.23	28.27	28.31
720	28.35	28.39	28.43	28.46	28.50	28.54	28.58	28.62	28.66	28.70
730	28.74	28.78	28.82	28.86	28.90	28.94	28.98	29.02	29.06	29.09
740	29.13	29.17	29.21	29.25	29.29	29.33	29.37	29.41	29.45	29.49
750	29.53	29.57	29.61	29.65	29.68	29.72	29.76	29.80	29.84	29.88
760	29.92	29.96	30.00	30.04	30.08	30.12	30.16	30.20	30.24	30.28
770	30.31	30.35	30.39	30.43	30.47	30.51	30.55	30.59	30.63	30.67
780	30.71	30.75	30.79	30.83	30.87	30.91	30.94	30.98	31.02	31.06
790	31.10	31.14	31.18	31.22	31.26	31.30	31.34	31.38	31.42	31.46

Chapter 4

Altimetry (Metric)

*V*ery *few countries fly altitudes in meters and fewer set their altimeters to read zero on the ground. For the latter question, QNH versus QFE, see Chapter 3 of this Section. For the former question, you need to study your approach plates very carefully.*

The ICAO reference documents are remarkably silent on the subject of metric and QFE versus QNH altimeter operations, other than to say they are possible. Even the document devoted to summarizing differences, ICAO Doc 7030, fails to cover either subject. We are left to explore both subjects with hard-earned experience.

Things are getting easier because they are becoming more standard. As of late 2020, 188 out of 193 ICAO member states are using feet and QNH. The only countries still working in meters are China, Mongolia, North Korea, Russia, and Tajikistan. And those last two are only using metric in lower airspace. In Russia you will now get QNH below transition level unless you are a Russian aircraft, which can get mm Hg on request. I think all of those countries except Tajikistan are using QNH at most, if not all, airports.

So let's start by learning how to identify which systems your airport is using.

Chart identification

I will be using Jeppesen approach charts as examples. If you are using charts from another provider, you will have some research to do.

Inches / Hectopascals / Millibars / Millimeters

MISSED APCH: Climb to ~~~ to FDK VOR and hold; ~	(VTK R-023/D13.0) and ~	climbing to FL 100 and
Alt Set: INCHES	Alt Set: hPa Rwy Elev:	Alt Set: MM (hPa on req)
1. DME required. 2. Simul· 3. DME from AML VOR. 4. Rwy 1L, ILS Rwy 1L CAT II 8	1. RADAR required. 2. Simultaneo co-located with glide slope. 4. Ma south of Rwy. 5. Circling not au·...	ALT/HEIGHT CONVERSION QNH _. .--- (QFE) ᴍꜱ ᴀ

Looking just below the "Briefing Strip" and the left you should see "Alt Set:" and the method employed.

- "INCHES" means you will be setting "inches of mercury," such as 29.92 in.

- "hPa" means you will be setting hectopascals, such as 1013. A hectopascal is equal to millibars.

- "MM" means you will be setting "millimeters of mercury," such as 720 mm.

QFE / QNH

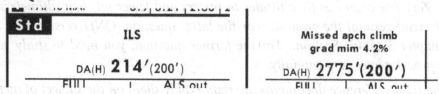

There may be conversion tables on the chart to go from QNH to QFE and back, but the only way to be sure the chart is meant for QFE operations is to look at the minimums section and see which appears in bold.

- The altitude outside the parenthesis is bolded means the minimums are in relation to mean sea level and QNH is in use.

- The altitude inside the parentheses is bolded means the minimums are in relation to the runway and QFE is in use.

Feet / Meters

These approach charts do not give you a sure way to determine if the airport will be issuing altitudes in meters or feet, but there is one clue. The presence of a feet - meters tables indicates that they might be using meters. As of late 2020, only some airports in China, Mongolia, North Korea, Russia, and Tajikistan are using meters. But, importantly, not all the airports in these countries are using meters. The presence of a feet - meters table might be a convenience for those who are equipped for meters but the airport is using feet. If you are flying into these countries, it may be wise to use add "feet" or "meters" to your altitude reports on the radio.

Note: most countries outside the United States express visibility in meters, even though they use feet for altitudes and heights.

ALT/HEIGHT CONVERSION	
QNH	(QFE)
8490'	(5915' - 1800m)
6850'	(4275' - 1300m)
5860'	(3285' - 1000m)
4220'	(1645' - 500m)
3420'	(845' - 255m)
2790'	(215' - 65m)

ICAO Procedures

- Millimeters vs. Hectopascals: hPa
- QFE vs. QNH: QNH
- Metric vs. Feet: Feet

Example ILS DME Rwy 02C, WSSS

The example chart is almost identical to one that may be seen in the U.S. The two key differences are that the altimeter is set using hPa and the visibility minimums are expressed in meters.

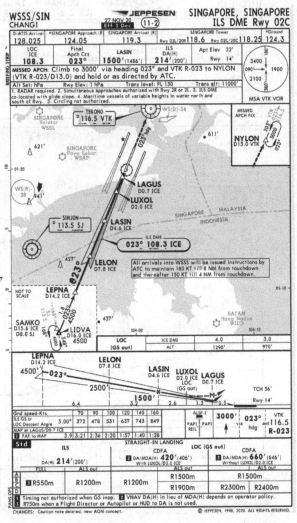

Example ICAO Standard Approach Chart, from Jeppesen Airway Manual, Singapore ILS DME Rwy 02C, WSSS, page 11-2, 27 Nov 20

QFE / Metric Procedures

- Millimeters vs. Hectopascals: mm
- QFE vs. QNH: QFE
- Metric vs. Feet: Meters

Note: Some procedures using QFE may be prohibited by some aircraft manufacturers. In many (if not all) Gulfstreams, for example, VNAV is not allowed using QFE. You could also have limitations with aircraft pressurization, EG-PWS, or other systems.

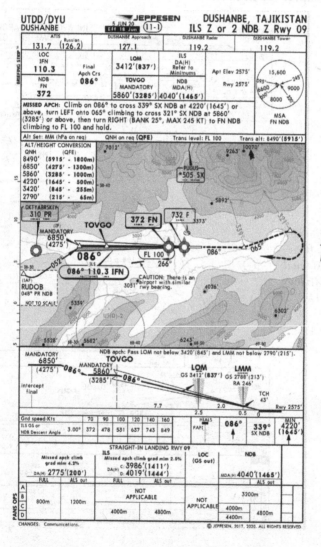

Example QFE / Metric Approach Chart, from Jeppesen Airway Manual, Dushanbe, Tajikistan, ILS Z Rwy 09

Example ILS DME Rwy 09, UTDD

The example chart shows the DA(H) as 2775'(200') with the 200 bolded, telling us this is a QFE airport. We suspect they are using meters instead of feet because there is a conversion table given. This is true for this airport and the controller should give altitudes in meters. You can expect, for example, to be vectored to the TOVGO final approach fix at "one thousand meters." If your avionics can do the conversion for you, you would set 1,000 meters. Otherwise, you would have to look at the table and set 3,285 feet instead.

"Matryoskha"

What is a "matryoshka," you ask? It is a Russian nesting doll, something hiding inside another thing. We ended up with a lot of "matryoshka charts" because formerly QFE/Metric countries are now using QNH/Feet but they have aircraft and pilots still using the older system. So many airports in these countries continue to publish conversion tables as a convenience.

- Millimeters vs. Hectopascals: hPa
- QFE vs. QNH: QNH
- Metric vs. Feet: Feet

Example ILS Rwy 06L, UUEE

(Next page)

It is easy enough to see they will be giving you hPa altimeter settings because it says so right on the chart. You can see that they are using QNH because the DA is bolded, not the (H). This airport also uses feet for altitude but continues to publish the conversion chart. We can surmise they are using feet since those altitudes are given in fairly even numbers and the meters appear to be the conversions. (Notice it is just the opposite for the metric UTDD chart shown earlier.)

I would exercise a great deal of caution and make a point of adding "feet" to every altitude I say on the radio. If the controller says "Descend and maintain three thousand, clear the ILS Runway zero six left approach," I would read back, "Descend and maintain three thousand feet, clear the ILS Runway zero six left approach," just to be sure. The controller might get peeved but you never know when that controller has had a long day and might be reverting to the way things used to be.

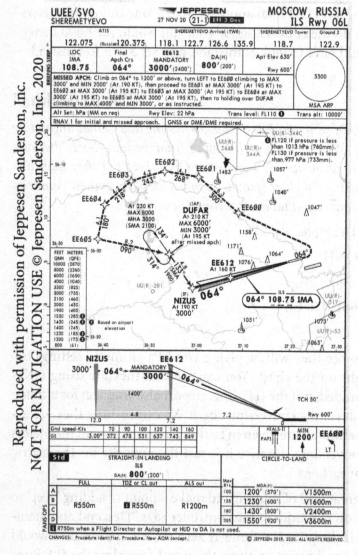

UUEE/SVO SHEREMETYEVO	JEPPESEN 27 NOV 20 (21-1) Eff 3 Dec	MOSCOW, RUSSIA ILS Rwy 06L

Example "Matryoshka" Approach Chart, from Jeppesen Airway Manual, Moscow, Russia, ILS Rwy 06L

Chapter 5

Altimetry (Temperature Correction)

*Y*our altimeter is a marvelous piece of machinery that is highly accurate throughout almost the entire flight envelope of your aircraft. Almost, but not all. When it gets very cold, the error can be enough to lower your actual altitude well below any minimums. You, ATC, or your aircraft will have to make adjustments.

As a pilot, what you need to know is that when it gets cold, your altimeter puts the airplane lower than it should. In most cases the error is insignificant. The colder than 0°C it is, and the higher you are than the airport's elevation, the more significant the error. You can use a set of tables or if your aircraft is allowed to automatically compensate, you can do that. But if you make the corrections, you need to let ATC know. They might be giving you corrected altitudes or your correction could put you in the way of aircraft that are not correcting.

The procedures vary by country and you will have to study individual state procedures to be sure.

Altimeter Temperature Correction

[ICAO Doc 8168 - Aircraft Operations - Vol III, Part II, Ch. 4] Note.— This chapter deals with altimeter corrections for pressure, temperature and, where appropriate, wind and terrain effects. The pilot is responsible for these corrections, except when under radar vectoring. In that case, the radar controller issues clearances such that the prescribed obstacle clearance will exist at all times, taking the cold temperature correction into account.

4.1.1 Pilot's responsibility. The pilot-in-command is responsible for the safety of the operation and the safety of the aeroplane and of all persons on board during flight time (Annex 6, 4.5.1). This includes responsibility for obstacle clearance, except when an IFR flight is being vectored.

4.1.3 State's responsibility. PANS-AIM, Appendix 2 (Contents of Aeronautical Information Publication), indicates that States should publish in Section GEN 3.3.5, "The criteria used to determine minimum flight altitudes." If nothing is published, it should be assumed that no corrections have been applied by the State.

4.1.4 Air traffic control (ATC). If an aircraft is cleared by ATC to an altitude which the pilot-in-command finds unacceptable due to low temperature, then the pilot-in-command should request a higher altitude. If such a request is not received, ATC will consider that the clearance has been accepted and will be complied with. See Annex 2 and the PANS-ATM (Doc 4444), Chapter 6.

4.3.1 Requirement for temperature correction. The calculated minimum safe altitudes/heights must be adjusted when the ambient temperature on the surface is much lower than that predicted by the standard atmosphere. In such conditions, an approximate correction is 4 per cent height increase for every 10°C below standard temperature as measured at the altimeter setting source. This is safe for all altimeter setting source altitudes for temperatures above –15°C.

4.3.2 Tabulated corrections. For colder temperatures, a more accurate correction should be obtained from Tables III-1-4-1 a) and III-1-4-1 b). These tables are calculated for a sea level aerodrome. They are therefore conservative when applied at higher aerodromes. To calculate the corrections for specific aerodromes or altimeter setting sources above sea level, or for values not tabulated, see 4.3.3, "Corrections for specific conditions."

Note 1.— The corrections have been rounded up to the next 5 m or 10 ft increment.

Note 2.— Temperature values from the reporting station (normally the aerodrome) nearest to the position of the aircraft should be used.

Table III-1-4-1 a). Values to be added by the pilot to minimum promulgated
heights/altitudes (m)

Aerodrome temperature (°C)	Height above the elevation of the altimeter setting source (metres)													
	60	90	120	150	180	210	240	270	300	450	600	900	1 200	1 500
0	5	5	10	10	10	15	15	15	20	25	35	50	70	85
−10	10	10	15	15	25	20	25	30	30	45	60	90	120	150
−20	10	15	20	25	25	30	35	40	45	65	85	130	170	215
−30	15	20	25	30	35	40	45	55	60	85	115	170	230	285
−40	15	25	30	40	45	50	60	65	75	110	145	220	290	365
−50	20	30	40	45	55	65	75	80	90	135	180	270	360	450

Table III-1-4-1 b). Values to be added by the pilot to minimum promulgated
heights/altitudes (ft)

Aerodrome temperature (°C)	Height above the elevation of the altimeter setting source (feet)													
	200	300	400	500	600	700	800	900	1 000	1 500	2 000	3 000	4 000	5 000
0	20	20	30	30	40	40	50	50	60	90	120	170	230	280
−10	20	30	40	50	60	70	80	90	100	150	200	290	390	490
−20	30	50	60	70	90	100	120	130	140	210	280	420	570	710
−30	40	60	80	100	120	140	150	170	190	280	380	570	760	950
−40	50	80	100	120	150	170	190	220	240	360	480	720	970	1 210
−50	60	90	120	150	180	210	240	270	300	450	590	890	1 190	1 500

Chapter 6

Altimetry (Transition Altitude, Layer, Level)

*W*here you change your altimeter from QNH to QNE and back is not standard across the world. Fortunately, the way you grew up is pretty much the way most of the world does it and is the ICAO standard. What is different that could trip you up is the location of the transition layer. In the United States it is usually between 18,000 and 19,000 feet. Having an abnormally high altimeter setting could eliminate FL 180; but unless you normally cruise there, you may not notice the change at all. In most of the world the transition layer is significantly lower and you could find yourself significantly off altitude unless you understand when transition altitude or transition level needs to be heeded.

Not everyone in the world obeys these rules and you will find some areas where you need to listen carefully and question the controller when in doubt.

Definitions

Transition altitude

[ICAO Document 4444, Ch 1] The altitude at or below which the vertical position of an aircraft is controlled by reference to altitudes.

Transition Layer

[ICAO Document 4444, Ch 1] The airspace between the transition altitude and the transition level.

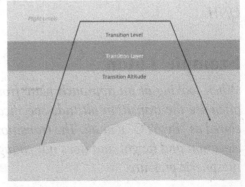

Transition Level

[ICAO Document 4444, Ch 1] The lowest flight level available for use above the transition altitude.

Climbs and Descents

[ICAO Document 4444, ¶4.10.2.1] The appropriate ATS unit shall establish the transition level to be used in the vicinity of the aerodrome(s) concerned and, when relevant, the terminal control area (TMA) concerned, for the appropriate period of time on the basis of QNH (altimeter sub-scale setting to obtain elevation when on the ground) reports and forecast mean sea level pressure, if required.

[ICAO Document 4444, ¶4.10.1.1] For flights in the vicinity of aerodromes and within terminal control areas the vertical position of aircraft shall, except as provided for in 4.10.1.2, be expressed in terms of altitudes at or below the transition altitude and in terms of flight levels at or above the transition level. While passing through the transition layer, vertical position shall be expressed in terms of flight levels when climbing and in terms of altitudes when descending.

[ICAO Document 4444, ¶4.10.1.2] When an aircraft which has been given clearance to land is completing its approach using atmospheric pressure at aerodrome elevation (QFE), the vertical position of the aircraft shall be expressed in terms of height above aerodrome elevation during that portion of its flight for which QFE may be used, except that it shall be expressed in terms of height above runway threshold elevation: for instrument runways, if the threshold is 2 metres (7 feet) or more below the aerodrome elevation, and for precision approach runways.

The key takeaway here is the transition altitude expresses the highest possible altitude, above that they don't exist. So when you are climbing, once you've passed the transition altitude, they no longer exist so you might as well go to 29.92/1013. When you are descending, the lowest possible flight level is at the Transition Level and once you have passed it, you might as well go back to QNH.

Example: Luton

When looking at an approach plate from outside the United States, you will often see the transition altitude specifically listed and the transition level declared as "By ATC" if at all. The transition altitude is in reference to the airport elevation and height and does not change. The transition level varies with atmospheric pressure.

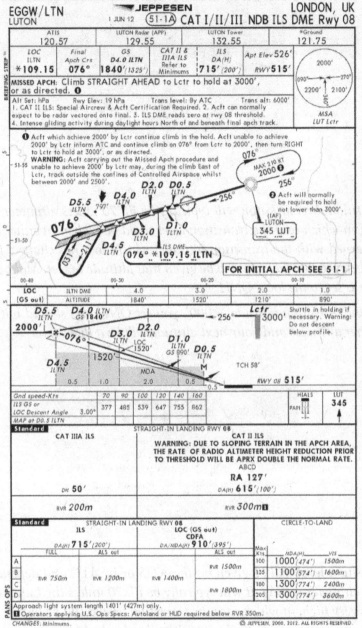

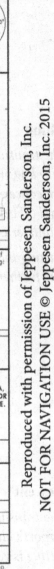

Figure: Luton Cat I/II/III NDB ILS DME Rwy 08, from Jeppesen Airway Manual, EGGW, Page 51-1A, 1 Jun 12

389

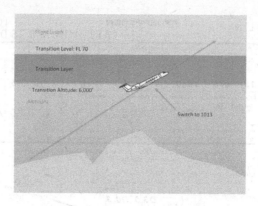

Climb

The transition level at Luton will typically be FL 70 unless altimeter setting is very low, in which case the transition level could be higher. In either case, you are concerned with the transition altitude, which does not change. If given a level off below 6,000 feet you will be given that altitude in feet. Make sure your altimeter is set to the local QNH.

Passing the transition altitude, 6,000', you set QNE. You should not be given any further altitudes and your next altitude will be a flight level.

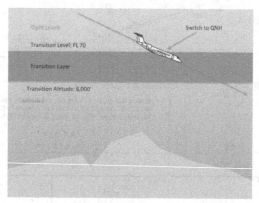

Descent

The transition level will be given on the ATIS or by ATC and depends on the airport's altimeter setting. It will typically be FL 70 unless the Luton altimeter setting is very high, in which case the transition level could be higher. In either case, you are concerned with the transition level, which determines the lowest usable flight level.

Passing the transition level, FL 70, you set QNH.

Chapter 7

Approach Ban

You can think of the term "approach ban" as the U.S. 14 CFR 135 rule that says you can't takeoff unless the weather at your destination is good enough to land. Simple. It is the ICAO Law of the Land, but there are exceptions.

ICAO Standards and Recommended Practices

Commercial Aviation

[ICAO Annex 6, Part I, ¶4.2.8.1 Aerodrome operating minima] The State of the Operator shall require that the operator establish aerodrome operating minima for each aerodrome to be used in operations and shall approve the method of determination of such minima. Such minima shall not be lower than any that may be established for such aerodromes by the State in which the aerodrome is located, except when specifically approved by that State.

Note 1.— This Standard does not require the State in which the aerodrome is located to establish aerodrome operating minima.

Note 2.— The use of head-up displays (HUD) or enhanced vision systems (EVS) may allow operations with lower visibilities than normally associated with the aerodrome operating minima.

[ICAO Annex 6, Part I, ¶4.4.1 Aerodrome operating minima]

4.4.1.1 A flight shall not be continued towards the aerodrome of intended landing, unless the latest available information indicates that at the expected time of arrival, a landing can be effected at that aerodrome or at least one destination alternate aerodrome, in compliance with the operating minima established in accordance with 4.2.8.1.

4.4.1.2 An instrument approach shall not be continued beyond the outer marker fix in case of precision approach, or below 300 m (1,000 ft) above the aerodrome in case of non-precision approach, unless the reported visibility or controlling RVR is above the specified minimum.

4.4.1.3 If, after passing the outer marker fix in case of precision approach, or after descending below 300 m (1,000 ft) above the aerodrome in case of non-precision approach, the reported visibility or controlling RVR falls below the specified minimum, the approach may be continued to DA/H or MDA/H. In any case, an aeroplane shall not continue its approach-to-land at any aerodrome beyond a point at which the limits of the operating minima specified for that aerodrome would be infringed.

Note.— Controlling RVR means the reported values of one or more RVR reporting locations (touchdown, mid-point and stop-end) used to determine whether operating minima are or are not met. Where RVR is used, the controlling RVR is the touchdown RVR, unless otherwise specified by State criteria.

General Aviation

[ICAO Annex 6, Part II, ¶2.2.2.2 Aerodrome operating minima] The pilot-in-command shall not operate to or from an aerodrome using operating minima lower than those which may be established for that aerodrome by the State in which it is located, except with the specific approval of that State. Note.— It is the practice in some States to declare, for flight planning purposes, higher minima for an aerodrome when nominated as an alternate, than for the same aerodrome when planned as that of intended landing.

[ICAO Annex 6, Part II, ¶2.2.4.1] Aerodrome operating minima

2.2.4.1.1 A flight shall not be continued towards the aerodrome of intended landing, unless the latest available information indicates that at the expected time of arrival, a landing can be effected at that aerodrome or at least one destination alternate aerodrome, in compliance with the operating minima established in accordance with 2.2.2.2.

2.2.4.1.2 An instrument approach shall not be continued beyond the outer marker fix in case of precision approach, or below 300 m (1,000 ft) above the aerodrome in case of non-precision approach, unless the reported visibility or controlling RVR is above the specified minimum.

2.2.4.1.3 If, after passing the outer marker fix in case of precision approach, or after descending below 300 m (1,000 ft) above the aerodrome in case of non-precision approach, the reported visibility or controlling RVR falls below the specified minimum, the approach may be continued to DA/H or MDA/H. In any case, an aeroplane shall not continue its approach-to-land beyond a point at which the limits of the aerodrome operating minima would be infringed.

Note.— Controlling RVR means the reported values of one or more RVR reporting locations (touchdown, midpoint and stop-end) used to determine whether operating minima are or are not met. Where RVR is used, the controlling RVR is the touchdown RVR, unless otherwise specified by State criteria.

ICAO Annex 6 Part I is "International Commercial Air Transport - Aeroplanes" and Part II is "International General Aviation - Aeroplanes."

EASA Exception

[EU Regulation No 965/2012, ⸗CAT.OP.MPA.305]

a.   The commander or the pilot to whom conduct of the flight has been delegated may commence an instrument approach regardless of the reported RVR/VIS.

You can start the approach regardless of weather, but there is a limit to how low you can go . . .

b.   If the reported RVR/VIS is less than the applicable minimum the approach shall not be continued:

   1.   below 1,000 ft above the aerodrome; or

   2.   into the final approach segment in the case where the DA/H or MDA/H is more than 1,000 ft above the aerodrome.

c.   Where the RVR is not available, RVR values may be derived by converting the reported visibility.

d.   If, after passing 1,000 ft above the aerodrome, the reported RVR/VIS falls below the applicable minimum, the approach may be continued to DA/H or MDA/H.

If the visibility then goes below, you can continue to the DA/H or MDA/H.

e.   The approach may be continued below DA/H or MDA/H and the landing may be completed provided that the visual reference adequate for the type of approach operation and for the intended runway is established at the DA/H or MDA/H and is maintained.

And if you have the visual references you need to land at that point, you may.

393

U.S. Exception

[14 CFR 135, §135.219] No person may takeoff an aircraft under IFR or begin an IFR or over-the-top operation unless the latest weather reports or forecasts, or any combination of them, indicate that weather conditions at the estimated time of arrival at the next airport of intended landing will be at or above authorized IFR landing minimums.

[14 CFR 135, §135.225]

(a) Except to the extent permitted by paragraph (b) of this section, no pilot may begin an instrument approach procedure to an airport unless—

(1) That airport has a weather reporting facility operated by the U.S. National Weather Service, a source approved by U.S. National Weather Service, or a source approved by the Administrator; and

(2) The latest weather report issued by that weather reporting facility indicates that weather conditions are at or above the authorized IFR landing minimums for that airport.

(b) A pilot conducting an eligible on-demand operation may begin an instrument approach procedure to an airport that does not have a weather reporting facility operated by the U.S. National Weather Service, a source approved by the U.S. National Weather Service, or a source approved by the Administrator if—

(1) The alternate airport has a weather reporting facility operated by the U.S. National Weather Service, a source approved by the U.S. National Weather Service, or a source approved by the Administrator; and

(2) The latest weather report issued by the weather reporting facility includes a current local altimeter setting for the destination airport. If no local altimeter setting for the destination airport is available, the pilot may use the current altimeter setting provided by the facility designated on the approach chart for the destination airport.

(c) If a pilot has begun the final approach segment of an instrument approach to an airport under paragraph (b) of this section, and the pilot receives a later weather report indicating that conditions have worsened to below the minimum requirements, then the pilot may continue the approach only if the requirements of §91.175(l) of this chapter, or both of the following conditions, are met—

(1) The later weather report is received when the aircraft is in one of the following approach phases: (i) The aircraft is on an ILS final approach and has passed the final approach fix;

(ii) The aircraft is on an ASR or PAR final approach and has been turned over to the final approach controller; or

(iii) The aircraft is on a nonprecision final approach and the aircraft—

(A) Has passed the appropriate facility or final approach fix; or

(B) Where a final approach fix is not specified, has completed the procedure turn and is established inbound toward the airport on the final approach course within the distance prescribed in the procedure; and

(2) The pilot in command finds, on reaching the authorized MDA or DA/DH, that the actual weather conditions are at or above the minimums prescribed for the procedure being used.

(d) If a pilot has begun the final approach segment of an instrument approach to an airport under paragraph (c) of this section and a later weather report indicating below minimum conditions is received after the aircraft is—

(1) On an ILS final approach and has passed the final approach fix; or

(2) On an ASR or PAR final approach and has been turned over to the final approach controller; or

(3) On a final approach using a VOR, NDB, or comparable approach procedure; and the aircraft— (i) Has passed the appropriate facility or final approach fix; or

(ii) Where a final approach fix is not specified, has completed the procedure turn and is established inbound toward the airport on the final approach course within the distance prescribed in the procedure; the approach may be continued and a landing made if the pilot finds, upon reaching the authorized MDA or DH, that actual weather conditions are at least equal to the minimums prescribed for the procedure.

(e) The MDA or DA/DH and visibility landing minimums prescribed in part 97 of this chapter or in the operator's operations specifications are increased by 100 feet and 1/2 mile respectively, but not to exceed the ceiling and visibility minimums for that airport when used as an alternate airport, for each pilot in command of a turbine-powered airplane who has not served at least

100 hours as pilot in command in that type of airplane.

(f) Each pilot making an IFR takeoff or approach and landing at a military or foreign airport shall comply with applicable instrument approach procedures and weather minimums prescribed by the authority having jurisdiction over that airport. In addition, no pilot may, at that airport—

(1) Takeoff under IFR when the visibility is less than 1 mile; or

(2) Make an instrument approach when the visibility is less than 1/2 mile.

(g) If takeoff minimums are specified in part 97 of this chapter for the takeoff airport, no pilot may takeoff an aircraft under IFR when the weather conditions reported by the facility described in paragraph (a) (1) of this section are less than the takeoff minimums specified for the takeoff airport in part 97 or in the certificate holder's operations specifications.

(h) Except as provided in paragraph (i) of this section, if takeoff minimums are not prescribed in part 97 of this chapter for the takeoff airport, no pilot may takeoff an aircraft under IFR when the weather conditions reported by the facility described in paragraph (a)(1) of this section are less than that prescribed in part 91 of this chapter or in the certificate holder's operations specifications.

(i) At airports where straight-in instrument approach procedures are authorized, a pilot may takeoff an aircraft under IFR when the weather conditions reported by the facility described in paragraph (a)(1) of this section are equal to or better than the lowest straight-in landing minimums, unless otherwise restricted, if—

(1) The wind direction and velocity at the time of takeoff are such that a straight-in instrument approach can be made to the runway served by the instrument approach;

(2) The associated ground facilities upon which the landing minimums are predicated and the related airborne equipment are in normal operation; and

(3) The certificate holder has been approved for such operations.

The bottom line in the U.S. is this: if you are a commercial operator you cannot takeoff if your destination is below minimums, once you get there you cannot start the approach unless the weather is good enough, and once you've started the approach if the weather goes down you have to abandon the approach. If you are not a commercial operator, this does not apply to you. You can takeoff even if your destination is below minimums. You can begin the approach. If you find yourself at minimums and have the necessary visual references, you can land.

Other Exceptions

You will, of course, find a country's exceptions in their Aeronautical Informa-tion Publication. I find an easier way to do this is to look at their Jeppesen "state pages" under "State Rules and Procedures" and then "Rules and Procedures." You will sometimes find a heading "Approach Ban" with the information you need. You may have to dig deeper into other headings, such as "minimums" to get approach ban exceptions. The following are just a few examples. The dates given are for the update date of the publication on JeppFD.

Japan

[Jeppesen Airway Manual / Air Traffic Control / State Rules and Procedures - Japan, 28 Dec 2020]

An aircraft shall not takeoff or start an approach to land at any airport if the observed RVR is less than the meteorological minimums for that airport.

Prior to commencing an instrument approach, if the weather conditions at the airport are below the published or the pilot's landing minimums, the pilot should notify the ATC facility or Airport Advisory Service Units and request clearance to hold or to proceed to an alternate airport.

After commencing an instrument approach and it is determined that the pilot can continue the approach beyond a prescribed point such as the FAF, OM, 1000 ft above aerodrome elevation or other points accepted by the au-thority and if the reported weather conditions have worsened to below the published or the pilot's landing minimums, the pilot may continue the ap-proach to DA or MDA. An approach to land may be continued if the pilot, upon reaching the DA/H or MDA/H, finds the actual weather conditions are at or above the lowest weather condition for landing.

South Africa

[Jeppesen Airway Manual / Air Traffic Control / State Rules and Procedures - South Africa, 28 Dec 2020] South African Republic State minimums and Approach Ban Information are in accordance with JAR-OPS 1 AOM (EU-OPS 1 Subpart E Appendix 1 to OPS 1.430 old) (ATC Chapter EU-OPS 1

- AERODROME OPERATION MINIMUMS (AOM)).

United Kingdom

[Jeppesen Airway Manual / Air Traffic Control / State Rules and Procedures - United Kingdom, 28 Dec 2020]

An aircraft may commence an instrument approach regardless of the reported RVR/Visibility but the approach shall not be continued below 1000ft above the aerodrome if the relevant RVR/Visibility for that runway is at the time less than the specified minimum for landing.

If, after passing 1000ft in accordance with above paragraph, the reported RVR/Visibility falls below the applicable minimum, the approach may be continued to DA/H or MDA/H.

The approach may be continued below DA/H or MDA/H and the landing may be completed provided that the required visual reference is established at the DA/H or MDA/H and is maintained.

Chapter 8

Approach Categories

*Y*our approach category deals with more than just the circling approach.
*It determines your maximum speeds, maneuvering airspace, and obstacle
clearance on approach as well as missed approach. It is always based on your
maximum certificated landing weight. The speed that is used might be different
between ICAO and U.S. FAA, depending on aircraft.*

Approach Category Determination — United States

[14 CFR 97.3] Aircraft approach category means a grouping of aircraft based
on a speed of V_{REF}, if specified, or if V_{REF} is not specified, $1.3V_{SO}$ at the maximum certificated weight. V_{SO}, and the maximum certificated landing weight
are those values as established for the aircraft by the certification authority
of the country of registry.

These categories are as follows:

Category A: Speed less than 91 knots

Category B: Speed 91 knots or more but less than 121 knots

Category C: Speed 121 knots or more but less than 141 knots

Category D: Speed 141 knots or more but less than 166 knots

Category E: Speed 166 knots or more

Approach Category Determination — International

[ICAO Doc 8168 PANS-OPS Vol 1, §4, ¶1.4]

1.4.1 Aircraft performance has a direct effect on the airspace and visibility
required for the various manoeuvres associated with the conduct of instrument approach procedures. The most significant performance factor is aircraft speed. Accordingly, categories of typical aircraft have been established.

1.4.2 The criterion taken into consideration for the classification of aeroplanes by categories is the indicated airspeed at threshold (Vst).

1.4.3 Aircraft categories will be referred to by their letter designations as follows:

Category A: less than 169 km/h (91 kt) indicated airspeed (IAS)

Category B: 169 km/h (91 kt) or more but less than 224 km/h (121 kt) IAS

Category C: 224 km/h (121 kt) or more but less than 261 km/h (141 kt) IAS

Category D: 261 km/h (141 kt) or more but less than 307 km/h (166 kt) IAS

Category E: 307 km/h (166 kt) or more but less than 391 km/h (211 kt) IAS

Category H: see 1.4.7, "Helicopters."

These speeds are the same as used in the United States but the criteria is slightly different. If you have a VSO and a VS1G for your aircraft, you must use the higher of VSO times 1.3 or VS1G times 1.23. Regardless of the speed used, it must be based on the aircraft's maximum certificated landing mass.

Maximum Speeds During Approach

In the United States

[Aeronautical Information Manual §5-4-7]

Aircraft approach category means a grouping of aircraft based on a speed of VREF at the maximum certified landing weight, if specified, or if VREF is not specified, 1.3VSO at the maximum certified landing weight. VREF, VSO, and the maximum certified landing weight are those values as established for the aircraft by the certification authority of the country of registry. A pilot must maneuver the aircraft within the circling approach protected area to achieve the obstacle and terrain clearances provided by procedure design criteria.

In addition to pilot techniques for maneuvering, one acceptable method to reduce the risk of flying out of the circling approach protected area is to use either the minima corresponding to the category determined during certification or minima associated with a higher category. Helicopters may use Category A minima. If it is necessary to operate at a speed in excess of the upper limit of the speed range for an aircraft's category, the minimums for the higher category should be used. This may occur with certain aircraft types operating in heavy/gusty wind, icing, or non–normal conditions. For example, an airplane which fits into Category B, but is circling to land at a speed of 145 knots, should use the approach Category D minimums. As an additional example, a Category A airplane (or helicopter) which is operating at 130 knots on a straight–in approach should use the approach Category C minimums.

A pilot who chooses an alternative method when it is necessary to maneuver at a speed that exceeds the category speed limit (for example, where higher category minimums are not published) should consider the following factors that can significantly affect the actual ground track flown:

Bank angle. For example, at 165 knots groundspeed, the radius of turn increases from 4,194 feet using 30 degrees of bank to 6,654 feet when using 20 degrees of bank. When using a shallower bank angle, it may be necessary to modify the flightpath or indicated airspeed to remain within the circling approach protected area. Pilots should be aware that excessive bank angle can lead to a loss of aircraft control.

Indicated airspeed. Procedure design criteria typically utilize the highest speed for a particular category. If a pilot chooses to operate at a higher speed, other factors should be modified to ensure that the aircraft remains within the circling approach protected area.

Wind speed and direction. For example, it is not uncommon to maneuver the aircraft to a downwind leg where the groundspeed will be considerably higher than the indicated airspeed. Pilots must carefully plan the initiation of all turns to ensure that the aircraft remains within the circling approach protected area.

Pilot technique. Pilots frequently have many options with regard to flightpath when conducting circling approaches. Sound planning and judgment are vital to proper execution. The lateral and vertical path to be flown should be carefully considered using current weather and terrain information to ensure that the aircraft remains within the circling approach protected area.

It is important to remember that 14 CFR Section 91.175(c) requires that "where a DA/DH or MDA is applicable, no pilot may operate an aircraft below the authorized MDA or continue an approach below the authorized DA/DH unless the aircraft is continuously in a position from which a descent to a landing on the intended runway can be made at a normal rate of descent using normal maneuvers, and for operations conducted under Part

121 or Part 135 unless that descent rate will allow touchdown to occur within the touchdown zone of the runway of intended landing."

See the following category limits:

Category A: Speed less than 91 knots.

Category B: Speed 91 knots or more but less than 121 knots.

Category C: Speed 121 knots or more but less than 141 knots.

Category D: Speed 141 knots or more but less than 166 knots.

Category E: Speed 166 knots or more.

NOTE–VREF in the above definition refers to the speed used in establishing the approved landing distance under the airworthiness regulations constituting the type certification basis of the airplane, regardless of whether that speed for a particular airplane is 1.3 VSO, 1.23 VSR, or some higher speed required for airplane controllability. This speed, at the maximum certificated landing weight, determines the lowest applicable approach category for all approaches regardless of actual landing weight.

In the U.S., the maximum speed for determining an approach category is also the maximum speed for maneuvering. If the pressure altitude, winds, temperature, or any other factor requires you to increase your maneuvering speed, your turn radius goes up and the obstacle clearance is no longer guaranteed. You should increase your approach category.

What the ICAO Says

[ICAO Doc 8168 PANS-OPS Vol 1 §4, Table I-5-1-2]

Aircraft category	Vat	Range of speeds for initial approach (and reversal and racetrack procedures)	Range of final approach speeds	Maximum speeds for circling	Maximum speeds for intermediate missed approach	Maximum speeds for final missed approach
A	<91	90/150 (110)	70/110	100	100	110
B	91/120	120/180 (110)	85/130	135	130	150
C	121/140	160/240	115/160	180	160	240
D	141/165	185/250	130/185	205	185	265
E	166/210	185/250	155/230	240	230	275

While the speed ranges used to determine an aircraft's approach category are identical to 14 CFR 97.3, the maximum permitted speed for visual maneuvering is significantly higher. Additionally, speed ranges are specified for other segments of the approach. While it is true the speeds permitted are higher, the circling approach area is larger too.

Chapter 9

ARINC-424 Shorthand

It is an elegant idea but that isn't the point. Your FMS uses these oceanic codes to represent various points around the globe so you need to know how to decode the code. Once you understand how the points are built, you will be able to crosscheck what is on your screen with reality. Note there has been a change to the specification in the North Atlantic to allow for half-degree latitude spacing.

Oceanic Waypoints

The specification itself comes from Rockwell-Collins who will charge you $504 for a copy. Fortunately you can piece together what you know from a little experience:

These waypoints are named according to ARINC-424 navigation database specification:

1.   Southern hemisphere uses the letters S or W

2.   Northern hemisphere uses the letters N or E

3.   Latitude always proceeds longitude

4.   Only the last two digits of longitude are used

5.   Placement of the letter designator (N, S, E, W) in the string of five characters indicates the value of the longitude one-hundredths digit

    a.   The letter in the last position indicates longitude < 100

    b.   The letter in the third position indicates longitude ≥ 100

    c.   Jeppesen will add Half Degree Grid Waypoints in the Gander and Shanwick Oceanic Control Areas (OCAs): "Hxxyy," where xx = degrees and 30 minutes of NORTH latitude and yy = degrees of WEST longitude (e.g., H5250 = 52°30' NORTH 050°00' WEST).

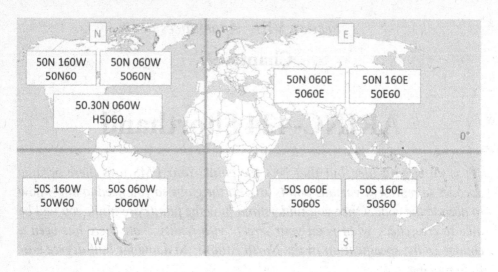

Examples:

N 52 00 / W 075 00	= 5275N
N 75 00 / W 170 00	= 75N70
S 50 00 / E 020 00	= 5020S
N 50 00 / E 020 00	= 5020E
S 52 00 / W 075 00	= 5275W
N 45 30 / W 050 00	= H4550
N 45 00 / W 050 00	= 4550N

CAUTION: Remember this shorthand is for the benefit of your FMS but every possible combination of this shorthand does not work in your FMS. You need to make sure each point translates correctly.

CAUTION: Air traffic control doesn't understand this shorthand. You must format your position reports, voice or CPDLC, with the correct latitude / longitude terminology.

Chapter 10

Cabotage

*C*abotage is simply the legal way of saying transporting people and things within a country. If that country is not your own, you may need permission to do that. The penalty for making a mistake here can be severe, so you need to be smart about the subject if you plan on making multiple stops in a country with people and things you didn't bring with you in the first place.

The Chicago Convention gives each country the right to prohibit cabotage, but not all countries do this. The United States does, I've included the laws to illustrate this. As you travel abroad, if you intend to pick up foreign nationals or cargo and drop them someplace else in the country, you need to make sure cabotage in that country is permitted. There are exemptions in some countries if the people you are carrying are a part of your business. You need to research this to be sure.

Defined

Generally speaking, you cannot fly to some foreign countries, pick up local citizens and transport them within that country. Not all countries have cabotage restrictions and many that do will allow exceptions if the citizens are employees of a company associated with the airplane. The rules vary by country and you need to ensure you follow them.

[ICAO Chicago Convention Article 7]. Each contracting state shall have the right to refuse permission to the aircraft or other contracting States to take on in its territory passengers, mail and cargo carried for remuneration or hire and destined for another point within its territory. Each contracting State undertakes not to enter into any arrangements which specifically grant any such privilege on an exclusive basis to any other State or airline of any other State, and not to obtain any such exclusive privilege from any other State.

You might think your are okay if you are not operating for remuneration or hire. Think again, many countries have expanded the definition to include just about any business purpose. Thankfully, many countries consider an employee of a multinational company a part of a U.S. branch of the same company. You will have to research the country's Aeronautical Information Publication to be sure, or at least check the associated JeppFD "state" pages.

U.S. Law

I've included the pertinent U.S. law to demonstrate how this works.

[19 CFR, §122.165(a)] The air cabotage law (49 U.S.C. 41703) prohibits the transportation of persons, property, or mail for compensation or hire between points of the U.S. in a foreign civil aircraft. The term "foreign civil aircraft" includes all aircraft that are not of U.S. registration except those foreign-registered aircraft leased or chartered to a U.S. air carrier and operated under the authority of regulations issued by the Department of Transportation, as provided for in 14 CFR 121.153, and those aircraft used exclusively in the service of any government.

[Title 49, §41703(b)(c)] (c) Providing Air Commerce.—The Secretary may authorize an aircraft permitted to navigate in the United States under this section to provide air commerce in the United States. However, the aircraft may take on for compensation, at a place in the United States, passengers or cargo destined for another place in the United States only if—

(1) specifically authorized under section 40109(g) of this title; or

(2) under regulations the Secretary prescribes authorizing air carriers to provide otherwise authorized air transportation with foreign registered aircraft under lease or charter to them without crew.

The exemptions provided in Title 49, §40109 are for emegency air transportation.

Chapter 11

Call Signs

*T*he following applies to any "November" registered aircraft flying with the aircraft registration as their call sign. If you have an ICAO registered call sign that is not your aircraft registration, the following does not apply to you. Generally speaking you are better off pronouncing your entire call sign, starting with "November," when overseas. Remember the controller is probably used to dealing with local aircraft and hearing "November" gets his or her attention. Is this required? No, but advisable.

All that being said, by the book, you can indeed use aircraft type as a prefix, but you still need the "November" as part of the call sign. You need to use the entire call sign on initial call up. (The only time you can use an abbreviated call sign is after you have been addressed "in this manner.") The bottom line: you want to get their attention, you want to avoid confusion, you want to make it easy for Air Traffic Control to understand who you are and what you want.

Full Call Signs

[ICAO Annex 10, Vol II, ⁋5.2.1.7.2.] Radiotelephony call signs for aircraft

5.2.1.7.2.1 Full call signs

5.2.1.7.2.1.1 An aircraft radiotelephony call sign shall be one of the following types:

Type a) — the characters corresponding to the registration marking of the aircraft; or

Type b) — the telephony designator of the aircraft operating agency, followed by the last four characters of the registration marking of the aircraft;

Type c) — the telephony designator of the aircraft operating agency, followed by the flight identification.

Note 1.— The name of the aircraft manufacturer or of the aircraft model may be used as a radiotelephony prefix to the Type a) call sign (see Table 5-1).

407

Note 2.— The telephony designators referred to in Types b) and c) are contained in Doc 8585 — Designators for Aircraft Operating Agencies, Aeronautical Authorities and Services.

Note 3.— Any of the foregoing call signs may be inserted in field 7 of the ICAO flight plan as the aircraft identification. Instructions on the completion of the flight plan form are contained in PANS-ATM, Doc 4444.

Generally speaking, if you are operating under a registered call sign as a commercial operator in the United States, your call sign should be okay when operating internationally. If the 3-letter identifier isn't obvious and well known, however, you might expect a few problems. The "Jet Speed" call sign, for example, has a three letter identifier of "EJM" and that is what will be filed in your flight plan. Do not be surprised if air traffic control looks for you as "Echo Juliet Mike" instead.

If your flight plan is filed under your registration you will be better off using that full registration. "November Seven Seven Zero Zero," for example, will be more quickly recognized than "Gulfstream Seven Seven Zero Zero."

Table 5-1. Examples of full call signs and abbreviated call signs
(see 5.2.1.7.2.1 and 5.2.1.7.2.2)

		Type a)		Type b)	Type c)
Full call sign	N 57826	*CESSNA FABCD	*CITATION FABCD	VARIG PVMA	SCANDINAVIAN 937
Abbreviated call sign	N26 or N826	CESSNA CD or CESSNA BCD	CITATION CD or CITATION BCD	VARIG MA or VARIG VMA	(no abbreviated form)

* Examples illustrate the application of Note 1 to 5.2.1.7.2.1.1.

Figure: Examples of full call signs and abbreviated call signs, from ICAO Annex 10, Vol II, Table 5-1.

Abbreviated Call Signs

[ICAO Annex 10, Vol II, ¶5.2.1.7.2.]

5.2.1.7.2.2 Abbreviated call signs

5.2.1.7.2.2.1 The aircraft radiotelephony call signs shown in 5.2.1.7.2.1.1, with the exception of Type c), may be abbreviated in the circumstances prescribed in 5.2.1.7.3.3.1. Abbreviated call signs shall be in the following form:

Type a) — the first character of the registration and at least the last two characters of the call sign;

Type b) — the telephony designator of the aircraft operating agency, followed by at least the last two characters of the call sign;

Type c) - no abbreviated form.

5.2.1.7.3.2 Establishment of radiotelephony communications

5.2.1.7.3.2.1 Full radiotelephony call signs shall always be used when establishing communication. The calling procedure of an aircraft establishing communication shall be in accordance with Table 5-2.

5.2.1.7.3.3 Subsequent radiotelephony communications

5.2.1.7.3.3.1 Abbreviated radiotelephony call signs, as prescribed in 5.2.1.7.2.2, shall be used only after satisfactory communication has been established and provided that no confusion is likely to arise. An aircraft station shall use its abbreviated call sign only after it has been addressed in this manner by the aeronautical station.

5.2.1.7.3.3.2 After contact has been established, continuous two-way communication shall be permitted without further identification or call until termination of the contact.

5.2.1.7.3.3.3 In order to avoid any possible confusion, when issuing ATC clearances and reading back such clearances, controllers and pilots shall always add the call sign of the aircraft to which the clearance applies.

A good rule of thumb is "to respond in kind" when it comes to call signs. If the controller in question abbreviates your call sign, you might be better of using the exact same abbreviation to increase the chances the controller understand it is your readback he or she is hearing.

Table 5-2.   Radiotelephony calling procedure* (*see* 5.2.1.7.3.2.1)

	Type a)	Type b)	Type c)
Designation of the station called	NEW YORK RADIO	NEW YORK RADIO	NEW YORK RADIO
Designation of the station calling	GABCD**	SPEEDBIRD ABCD**	AEROFLOT 321**

* *In certain cases where the call is initiated by the aeronautical station, the call may be effected by transmission of coded tone signals.*

** *With the exception of the telephony designators and the type of aircraft, each character in the call sign shall be spoken separately. When individual letters are spelled out, the radiotelephony spelling alphabet prescribed in 5.2.1.3 shall be used. Numbers are to be spoken in accordance with 5.2.1.4.*

Figure: Radiotelephony calling procedure, from ICAO Annex 10, Vol II, Table 5-2.

Table 5-3.   Radiotelephony reply procedure (*see* 5.2.1.7.3.2.3)

	Type a)	Type b)	Type c)
Designation of the station called	GABCD*	SPEEDBIRD ABCD*	AEROFLOT 321*
Designation of the answering station	NEW YORK RADIO	NEW YORK RADIO	NEW YORK RADIO
Invitation to proceed with transmission	GO AHEAD	GO AHEAD	GO AHEAD

* *With the exception of the telephony designators and the type of aircraft, each character in the call sign shall be spoken separately. When individual letters are spelled out, the radiotelephony spelling alphabet prescribed in 5.2.1.3 shall be used. Numbers are to be spoken in accordance with 5.2.1.4.*

Figure: Radiotelephony reply procedure, from ICAO Annex 10, Vol II, Table 5-3.

Chapter 12

CANPASS / eTA

*V*isiting any foreign country usually requires "border clearance" as well as a Visa or other permit. Canada is no different but coming from the U.S. as a private aircraft might make things easier for you.

Border clearance. *If you are flying a private aircraft with fewer than 15 persons on board and meet a few other requirements, you can enter and depart Canada by calling into a phone number and you may end up not having to see any customs officials at all. This is "CANPASS" and can be done via telephone, but it does require membership.*

Visas. *Some travelers may qualify for an Electronic Travel Authorization (eTA) which is certainly easier than a Visa. In both cases, you need to figure this out before you depart.*

One last thing: *as of 2021 you still need special permission to enter Canada if you've had a Driving Under the Influence conviction on your record. I've heard it takes ten years for them to consider you eligibile, but it isn't something you can assume will be okay.*

CANPASS

CANPASS will take the place of having to report to a customs official following border crossing but there are a number of requirements that must be met first. Not everyone is eligible, but if you are, it greatly simplifies entry and exit.

[CANPASS Website]

The CANPASS – Private Aircraft program makes clearing the border easier for private aircraft carrying no more than 15 people (including the crew) and traveling to Canada from the United States. This program allows members to access more airports and provides expedited clearances for low-risk, pre-screened travelers.

If you are a CANPASS – Private Aircraft member, your private aircraft can have the following privileges:

- It can land at any airport of entry (AOE) in Canada;
- It can land at an AOE any time the airport is open for landing, regardless of the hours of business of the local CBSA office;
- It can land at a CANPASS-only airport, which may be nearer to your destination;
- It receives expedited clearance; and
- It can proceed to the final destination if there is no CBSA officer waiting for the aircraft by the reported time of arrival, without the pilot having to make a second call to the CBSA after landing.

To be eligible for CANPASS – Private Aircraft, you must meet these criteria:

- Be a citizen or permanent resident of Canada or the United States and have lived in Canada and/or the United States continuously for the last three years;
- You are admissible to Canada under applicable immigration laws;
- You have provided true and accurate information on the application;
- You have not been convicted of a criminal offence for which a pardon or rehabilitation has not been granted;
- You have not had a customs seizure within the past six years; and
- You are not in violation of any customs or immigration legislation.

Private aircraft that meet the requirements of the CANPASS – Private Aircraft program can land at any airport of entry any time the site is open, regardless of the hours of operation of the local CBSA office. The aircraft can also land at a designated CANPASS-only airport.

The pilot is in charge of the aircraft and he or she must report all passengers and their goods on behalf of the aircraft. Pilots are responsible for reporting themselves, their crew and passengers to a telephone reporting centre (TRC) by calling 1-888-CANPASS (1-888-226-7277) at least 2 hours before but no more than 48 hours prior to the aircraft's estimated time of arrival in Canada.

The TRC allows individuals who enter Canada by private aircraft, corporate aircraft or private boat to report their arrival and make their declarations to the CBSA by telephone.

Participation in CANPASS is voluntary, but it expands where you can go and when you can go. For more details and the forms needed to apply, see: https://www.cbsa-asfc.gc.ca/prog/canpass/privateair-eng.html

eTA

[eTA Website]

An Electronic Travel Authorization (eTA) is an entry requirement for visa-exempt foreign nationals traveling to Canada by air. An eTA is electronically linked to a traveler's passport. It is valid for up to five years or until the passport expires, whichever comes first. If you get a new passport, you need to get a new eTA.

With a valid eTA, you can travel to Canada as often as you want for short stays (normally for up to six months at a time). You do not need an eTA for travel within Canada.

An eTA doesn't guarantee entry to Canada. When you arrive, a border services officer will ask to see your passport and other documents – for example, a U.S. Green Card. You must convince the officer that you are eligible for entry into Canada.

Travelers who need an eTA: Visa-exempt foreign nationals need an eTA to fly to or transit through a Canadian airport. These travelers do not need an eTA when arriving by car, bus, train or boat (including a cruise ship). Lawful permanent residents of the U.S. need an eTA to fly to or transit through a Canadian airport. They must present a valid Green Card and a valid passport at check-in.

Travelers who may be eligible to apply for an eTA: Citizens from select visa-required countries may be eligible to apply for an eTA, instead of a visa, to travel to Canada by air. However, these travelers need a visitor visa when arriving by car, bus, train, or boat, including a cruise ship. Travelers who cannot apply for an eTA and need to carry other identification: Canadian citizens, including dual citizens, need a valid Canadian passport. American-Canadians can travel with a valid Canadian or U.S. passport.

Canadian permanent residents need a valid permanent resident card or permanent resident travel document. Important – former residents of Canada:

Permanent resident (PR) status does not expire. If you once lived in Canada many years ago, you could still have PR status. Learn more to avoid travel delays. Visa-required including alien's passport holders and stateless individuals.

Travelers who are exempt from the eTA requirement. For example: U.S. citizens are exempt from the eTA requirement and must carry proper identification such as a valid U.S. passport. See the complete list of eTA exceptions.

See the eTA Website for more about visa-exempt foreign nationals and select visa-required countries. If you are a lawful permanent resident of the United States, you are visa-exempt.

Applying for an eTA is a simple online process that takes just a few minutes to complete. Most applicants get their eTA approval (via an email) within minutes. However, some requests can take several days to process if you're asked to submit supporting documents. It is best to get an eTA before you book your flight to Canada.

An eTA costs CAD $7. You can only apply and pay for one person at a time.

To complete the form, you will need your passport, a credit or debit card, and an email address. You must also answer a few questions.

Participation in eTA is mandatory for many arriving by air and needs to be done in advance. There are exceptions. If you have a U.S. passport, for example, no eTA or Via is required. For more details and links to the application process, see: https://www.canada.ca/en/immigration-refugees-citizenship/services/visit-canada/eta.html.

Chapter 13

Conditional Clearances

You are waiting at the end of the runway when tower says "Behind the landing Airbus, line up and wait." In the United States you question the tower's sanity but under ICAO you are expected to acknowledge, repeating the clearance exactly, and as soon as you see the landing aircraft pass in front of you, you line up and wait. It is ICAO, to be sure, but I've only seen this done in Europe.

Phraseologies

[ICAO Doc 4444, ¶12.2.7] Conditional phrases, such as "behind landing aircraft" or "after departing aircraft," shall not be used for movements affecting the active runway(s), except when the aircraft or vehicles concerned are seen by the appropriate controller and pilot. In all cases a conditional clearance shall be given in the following order and consist of:

i. identification;

ii. the condition;

iii. the clearance; and

iv. brief reiteration of the condition,

for example:

"SAS 941, BEHIND DC9 ON SHORT FINAL, LINE UP BEHIND."

Note.— This implies the need for the aircraft receiving the conditional clearance to identify the aircraft or vehicle causing the conditional clearance.

Chapter 14

Continuous Descent Final Approach (CDFA)

Years ago, following a "dive and drive" mishap, a major airline had to remind its pilots that a non-precision approach must be flown with great precision. The U.S. Air Force must have lost a few airplanes to "dive and drive" because, in an obvious overcorrection, our criteria required crews be busted for flying even an inch below the MDA.

Levelling off at the MDA can be problematic if there are distractions or turbulence. Keeping the airplane at the MDA until the runway is sighted is another issue. But the worst problem may be resisting the urge to descend when you spot the runway too far out. So why not bypass all this?

Flying a Continuous Descent Final Approach (CDFA) eliminates the MDA level off, puts the airplane in a position to land when the runway is sighted, and forces you to go around if the runway is not sighted before a normal visual descent point. It is easier to fly than a dive and drive approach and you don't need any special equipment. It makes sense to use a CDFA on most non-precision approaches. About the only exceptions would be a circling approach or an approach where last minute maneuvering is required.

Continuous Descent Final Approach (CDFA)

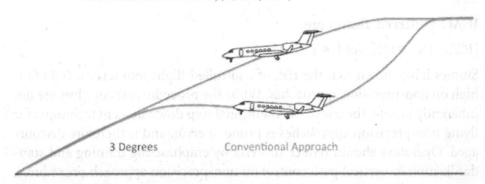

3 Degrees   Conventional Approach

What is it?

A continuous descent final approach is what you do for every straight-in ILS and what you attempt to do for every visual straight-in approach: you hit the glide path and start down on an angle that ends up in the touchdown zone of the runway. You can also do this when in instrument conditions flying a non-precision approach, which we are probably better off calling an "approach without vertical guidance."

[AC 120-108 §4.c] CDFA is a technique for flying the final approach segment of an NPA as a continuous descent. The technique is consistent with stabilized approach procedures and has no level-off. A CDFA starts from an altitude/height at or above the FAF and proceeds to an altitude/height approximately 50 feet (15 meters) above the landing runway threshold or to a point where the flare maneuver should begin for the type of aircraft being flown. This definition harmonizes with the ICAO and the European Aviation Safety Agency (EASA).

[ICAO Doc 8168, Vol I, Ch. 1, Definitions] CDFA: a technique, consistent with stabilized approach procedures, for flying the final approach segment of a non-precision instrument approach procedure as a continuous descent, without level-off, from an altitude/height at or above the final approach fix altitude/height to a point approximately 15 m (50 ft) above the landing runway threshold or the point where the flare manoeuvre should begin for the type of aircraft flown.

Is it Required?

In some countries: yes. In other countries: it is recommended but not mandatory.

ICAO Preferred Technique

[ICAO Doc 8168, Vol I, ¶ 1.8.1.1]

Studies have shown that the risk of controlled flight into terrain (CFIT) is high on non-precision approaches. While the procedures themselves are not inherently unsafe, the use of the traditional step down descent technique for flying non-precision approaches is prone to error, and is therefore discouraged. Operators should reduce this risk by emphasizing training and standardization in vertical path control on non-precision approach procedures.

Operators typically employ one of three techniques for vertical path control on non-precision approaches:

- continuous descent final approach (CDFA);

- constant angle descent; and

- step down approach.

Of these techniques, the CDFA technique is preferred. Operators should use the CDFA technique whenever possible as it adds to the safety of the approach operation by reducing pilot workload and by lessening the possibility of error in flying the approach.

EU Required

[EASA Air Operations, ʃCAT.OP.MPA.115] Approach flight technique — aeroplanes.

All approaches shall be flown as stabilised approaches unless otherwise approved by the competent authority for a particular approach to a particular runway.

Non-precision approaches

(1) The continuous descent final approach (CDFA) technique shall be used for all non-precision approaches.

(2) Notwithstanding (1), another approach flight technique may be used for a particular approach/runway combination if approved by the competent authority. In such cases, the applicable minimum runway visual range (RVR):

(i) shall be increased by 200 m for category A and B aeroplanes and by 400 m for category C and D aeroplanes; or

(ii) for aerodromes where there is a public interest to maintain current operations and the CDFA technique cannot be applied, shall be established and regularly reviewed by the competent authority taking into account the operator's experience, training programme and flight crew qualification.

FAA Recommended

[AC 120-108 §5] The FAA recommends CDFA for all of the following NPAs published with a vertical descent angle (VDA) or glideslope (GS):

- Very high frequency (VHF) Omnidirectional Range (VOR),

- VHF omni-directional range station/distance measuring equipment,
- Non-directional radio beacon (NDB),
- NDB/distance measuring equipment (DME),
- Localizer (LOC), Localizer Back-Course (LOC-BC),
- LOC/DME,
- Localizer-type directional aid (LDA),
- LDA/DME,
- Simplified Directional Facility (SDF),
- SDF/DME,
- Area Navigation (RNAV), and
- Global Positioning System (GPS).

Required by Some Countries

[ICAO Doc 8168, Vol I, ¶ 1.8.2.1] Many Contracting States require the use of the CDFA technique and apply increased visibility or RVR requirements when the technique is not used.

Many countries require CDFA techniques be used but application of the technique is not consistent. Some countries list a CDFA approach with "CDFA" in the minimums section while others use "DA" or "DA/MDA." Even the countries that list "CDFA" are not consistent about the meaning. In India, for example, you are required to add the height loss additive to the CDFA altitude. But in France, you normally do not. The only way to ensure you are following the rules of the host nation is to look it up in the country's Aeronautical Information Publication or the Jeppesen Airways Manual ATC pages.

Vertical Path Angle — Limitations

AC 120-108 does not impose a maximum vertical path angle, per se, but if you have OpSpec, MSpec, or LOA C073 you are already familiar with a VNAV DA(H) in lieu of MDA(H) provision that limits you to 3.77° (Category A, B, and C) or 3.5° (Category D and E). You really should adopt those limits for CDFA as well.

[AC 120-108 §6.d] The VDA or GS is calculated from the FAF/precise final approach fix (PFAF) altitude to the threshold crossing height (TCH). The optimum NPA descent angle (VDA or GS) is 3.0 degrees. Descent angles are found in the following range when the optimum VDA is not possible: 2.75°–3.77° (IAPs w/CAT C minimums), 2.75°–3.50° (IAPs w/CAT D/E minimums). On approaches with stepdown fixes, the goal is to publish a VDA that keeps the Vertical Path (VPATH) above the stepdown fix altitude. However, in some cases, the VDA is calculated from the stepdown fix altitude to the TCH.

Procedures: Determining a Derived Decision Altitude (DDA)

The MDA, under most cases, is still an altitude you cannot go below. The CDFA technique adds an "increment" (an altitude pad) to account for the aircraft's tendency to go below the altitude at which the missed approach is initiated, usually due to autopilot reaction time. In many aircraft a "maximum autotpilot altitude loss" is published and can be used as this increment. The new altitude, that resulting from the addition of this pad to the MDA, is known as the Derived Decision Altitude (DDA).

[ICAO Doc 8168, Vol I, ¶ 1.8.2.4] An increment for the MDA/H may be prescribed by the operator to determine the altitude/height at which the vertical portion of the missed approach shall be initiated in order to prevent descent below the MDA/H. In such cases, there is no need to increase the RVR or visibility requirements for the approach. The RR and/or visibility published for the original MDA/H should be used.

[AC 120-108 §6.F] Pilots must not descend below the MDA when executing a missed approach from a CDFA. Operators should instruct their pilots to initiate the go-around at an altitude above the MDA (sometimes referred to as a DDA) to ensure the aircraft does not descend below the published MDA. Operators conducting approaches authorized by operations specification (OpSpec) C073, IFR Approach Procedures Using Vertical Navigation (VNAV), may use MDA as a DA.

Procedures: Leaving the Final Approach Fix

[ICAO Doc 8168, Vol I, ¶ 1.8.2.2] This technique requires a continuous descent, flown either with VNAV guidance calculated by on-board equipment or based on manual calculation of the required rate of descent, without level-offs. The rate of descent is selected and adjusted to achieve a continuous descent to a point approximately 15m (50 ft) above the landing runway threshold or the point where the flare manoeuvre should begin for the type aircraft flown. The descent shall be calculated and flown to pass at or above the minimum altitude at any step down fix.

The objective of CDFA is to leave the final approach fix fully configured, on speed, and ready to land. You should not have to destabilize the aircraft by making airspeed or trim adjustments when spotting the runway.

Procedures: When to go Missed Approach

The CDFA places the aircraft right on glide path in a position to land in the touchdown zone of the runway. If the runway is sighted before the DDA, you will already be on the correct glide path to take over visually. If you were using conventional "dive and drive" techniques, spotting the runway beyond a proper visual descent point means you will land long. The CDFA eliminates the judgement calls when sighting the runway early or late.

[ICAO Doc 8168, Vol I, Part I, Amdt 3, ¶ 1.7.2.3] If the visual references required to land have not been acquired when the aircraft is approaching the MDA/H, the vertical (climbing) portion of the missed approach is initiated at an altitude above the MDA/H sufficient to prevent the aircraft from descending through the MDA/H. At not time is the aircraft flown in level flight at or near the MDA/H. Any turns on the missed approach shall not begin until the aircraft reaches the Misssed Approach Point. Likewise, if the aircraft reaches the Missed Approach Point before descending to near the MDA/H, the missed approach shall be initiated at the Missed Approach Point.

[ICAO Doc 8168, Vol I, Part I, Amdt 3, ¶ 1.7.2.6] It should be emphasized that upon reaching the MDA/H only two options exist for the crew: continue the descent below MDA/H to land with the required visual references in sight; or, execute a missed approach. There is no level flight segment after reaching the MDA/H.

Chapter 15

Course Reversals

*I*n the United States it is common practice to use holding pattern procedures when flying a procedure turn, what is more properly called a course reversal under ICAO. The U.S. procedures will not always work in other parts of the world. You can use those same procedures in the United States now, just keep in mind you have to limit your entry speeds to 200 knots and you may not be able to fly as fast during some of the maneuvering.

You may have flown internationally for years not knowing the difference between a U.S. procedure turn and an ICAO course reversal. You probably got away with it too, since we hardly ever fly full procedures. And even when you do, chances are you can get away with using U.S. FAA procedures. But not always. An Air Force crew was violated for entering the 45°/180° course reversal shown here just has they had been taught, using U.S. FAA procedures. They were cleared direct to the NDB and for the approach. They hit the NDB and turned right. And they were violated. What would you have done?

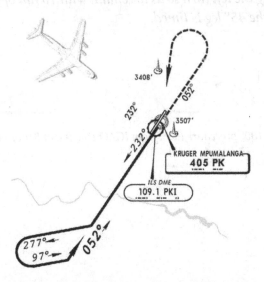

45°/180° Procedure Turn

[ICAO Document 8168, Vol 1 §5, ¶3.2.2.3 a] 45°/180° procedure turn starts at a facility or fix and consists of:

1.   a straight leg with track guidance. This straight leg may be timed or may be limited by a radial or DME distance;

2.   a 45° turn;

3.   a straight leg without track guidance. This straight leg is timed. It is:

    a.   1 minute from the start of the turn for Category A and B aircraft; and

    b.   1 minute 15 seconds from the start of the turn for Category C, D and E aircraft; and

4.   a 180° turn in the opposite direction to intercept the inbound track.

The 45°/180° procedure turn is an alternative to the 80°/260° procedure turn [b) below] unless specifically excluded.

Unlike the U.S. FAA Standard Procedure Turn, also known as the 45°/180° Procedure Turn, the straight leg without track guidance is timed under ICAO procedures. The timing is mandatory unless a DME limit is given.

In the Agana, Guam (PGUM) example, the procedure begins heading 242° and executing the left turn so as to remain with 10 nm of the VOR. Unlike U.S. procedures, the 45° leg is timed.

Figure: 45°/180° procedure turn, from ICAO Document 8168, Vol 1 Figure II-5-3-1.A.

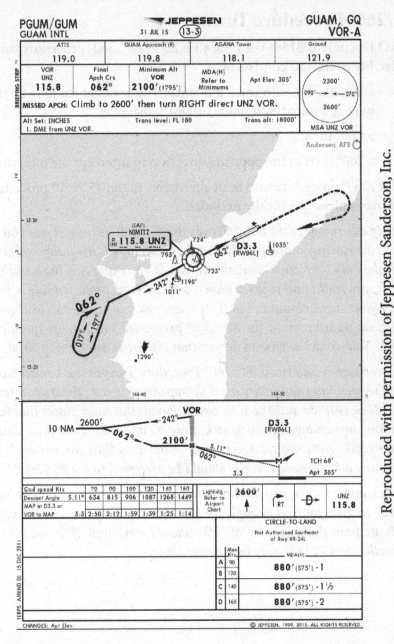

Figure: Agana VOR-A, from Jeppesen Airway Manual, page PGUM 13-3, 31 Jul 2015.

80°/260° Procedure Turn

[ICAO Document 8168, Vol 1 §5, ¶3.2.2.3 b] 80°/260° procedure turn starts at a facility or fix and consists of:

1. a straight leg with track guidance. This straight leg may be timed or may be limited by a radial or DME distance;

2. an 80° turn;

3. a 260° turn in the opposite direction to intercept the inbound track.

The 80°/260° procedure turn is an alternative to the 45°/180° procedure turn [a) above] unless specifically excluded.

The only advantage of the 80°/260° over the 45°/180° is time: it gets you pointed back to the runway more quickly. But there is a big disadvantage: adjusting for wind, the only correction available to you is bank angle. If the wind is strong enough, you could find yourself blown onto the non-protected side before completing your turn inbound. The ICAO says you can use a 45°/180° procedure turn as an alternative to the 80°/260° procedure turn unless specifically excluded. You would be wise to do just that if there is any kind of wind.

I've never seen a published 80°/260° Procedure Turn in the United States and those I've seen internationally are a disappearing breed. There are a few left in Papua New Guinea and I've seen one in Egypt. But most places that have had them long ago changed to racetrack, base turn, or standard procedure turns. The 80°/260° gives the pilot very little room to adjust for winds. If given a choice, any other course reversal should be preferred to the 80°/260°.

In the example shown you should avail yourself of the full 3 minutes outbound allowed to give yourself enough time to intercept the course inbound. If the winds are from the south the 80°/260° should work well. If the winds are from the north, the 45°/180° may be a better choice.

Figure: 80°/260° procedure turn, from ICAO Document 8168, Vol 1 Figure II-5-3-1.B.

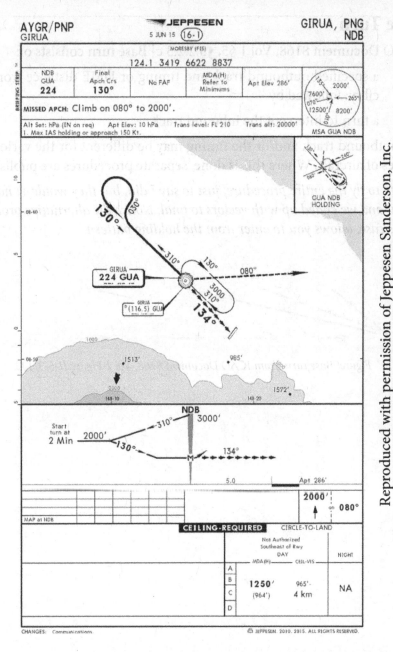

Figure: Girua NDB, from Jeppesen Airway Manual, page AYGR 16-1, 5 Jun 2015.

Base Turn

[ICAO Document 8168, Vol 1 §5, ¶3.2.2.3 c] Base turn consists of:

1.   a specified outbound track and timing or DME distance from a facility; followed by

2.   a turn to intercept the inbound track.

The outbound track and/or the timing may be different for the various categories of aircraft. Where this is done, separate procedures are published.

I asked to fly the entire procedure, just to say I did, but they wouldn't have any of that and we ended up with vectors to final. Notice the alternative procedure, in this case, allows you to enter from the holding pattern.

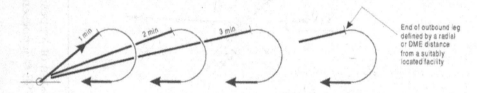

Figure: Base turn, from ICAO Document 8168, Vol 1 Figure II-5-3-1.C.

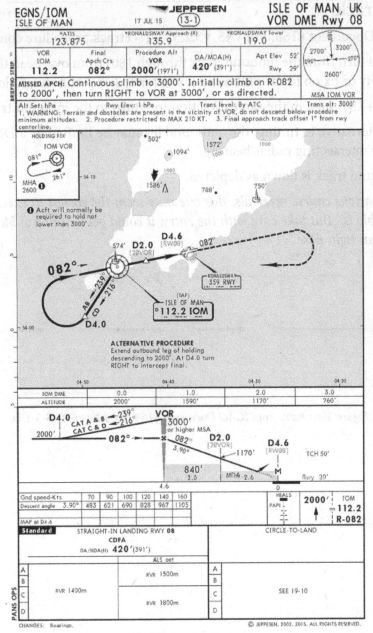

Figure: Isle of Man VOR/DME Rwy 08, from Jeppesen Airway Manual, Page EGNS 13-1, 17 Jul 2015.

Racetrack

[ICAO Document 8168, Vol 1 §5, ¶3.2.3] A racetrack procedure consists of:

1. a turn from the inbound track through 180° from overhead the facility or fix on to the outbound track, for 1, 2 or 3 minutes; followed by

2. a 180° turn in the same direction to return to the inbound track.

As an alternative to timing, the outbound leg may be limited by a DME distance or intersecting radial/bearing.

The ground track is flown as depicted.

Of the various course reversals, this one may seem the easiest to execute and it probably is. But take care with the entry, it could get you in trouble. More about that right now . . .

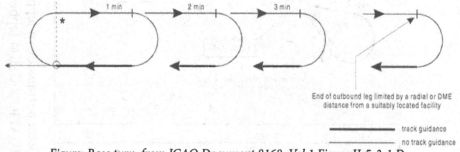

Figure: Base turn, from ICAO Document 8168, Vol 1 Figure II-5-3-1.D.

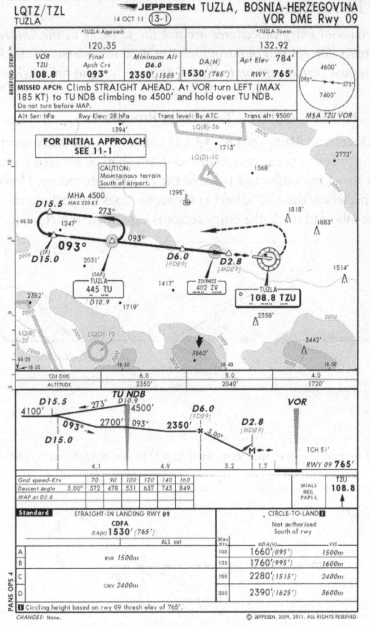

Figure: Tuzla VOR/DME Rwy 09, from Jeppesen Airway Manual,
Page LQTZ 13-1, 14 Oct 2011.

Entry Procedures

Course Reversal entry procedures are not the same as in the United States; the difference can get you into trouble. You need to understand the 30° entry sector, the base turn exception to the 30° entry sector, and racetrack entry procedures.

45°/180°, 80°/260°, and Base Turn Entry Procedures

[ICAO Document 8168, Vol 1 §5, ¶3.3.1] Unless the procedure specifies particular entry restrictions, reversal procedures shall be entered from a track within ±30° of the outbound track of the reversal procedure. However, for base turns, where the ±30° direct entry sector does not include the reciprocal of the inbound track, the entry sector is expanded to include it.

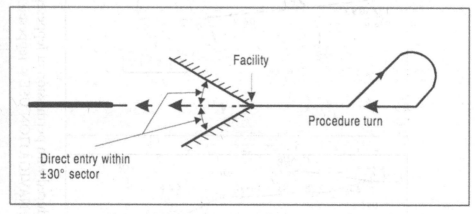

Figure: Direct entry to procedure turn, from ICAO Document 8168, Vol 1, figure I-5-3-2.

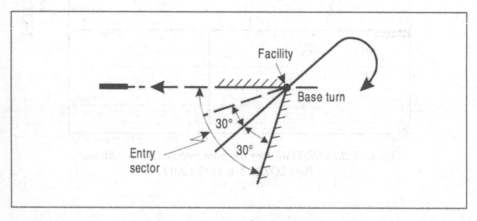

Figure: Direct entry to base turn, from ICAO Document 8168, Vol 1, figure I-5-3-3.

You've got to be within these entry sectors to be permitted to begin the 45°/180°, 80°/260°, or base turn procedure. What if you aren't?

Most of these procedures have a holding pattern nearby and ICAO Document 8168, Vol 1, figure I-4-3-4, states "arrivals from this sector must enter the holding prior to the reversal procedure." What if there isn't a holding pattern depicted? I would request "maneuvering airspace" opposite the course reversal so that I could maneuver the aircraft into the entry sector. That's what the C-141 crew mentioned earlier should have done.

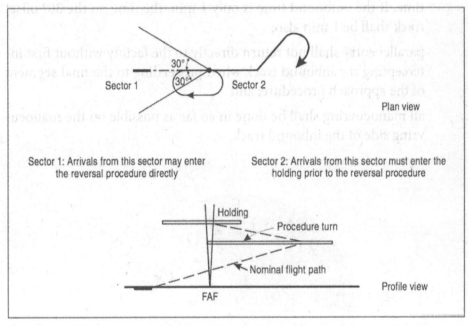

Figure: Omnidirectional arrival holding associated with reversal procedure, from ICAO Document 8168, Vol 1, figure I-5-3-4.

Racetrack Entry Procedures

[ICAO Document 8168, Vol 1 §5, ¶3.2.3.2] Normally a racetrack procedure is used when aircraft arrive overhead the fix from various directions. In these cases, aircraft are expected to enter the procedure in a manner similar to that prescribed for a holding procedure entry with the following considerations:

a.   offset entry from Sector 2 shall limit the time on the 30° offset track to 1 min 30 s, after which the pilot is expected to turn to a heading parallel to the outbound track for the remainder of the outbound time. If the outbound time is only 1 min, the time on the 30° offset track shall be 1 min also;

b.   parallel entry shall not return directly to the facility without first intercepting the inbound track when proceeding to the final segment of the approach procedure; and

c.   all manoeuvring shall be done in so far as possible on the manoeuvring side of the inbound track.

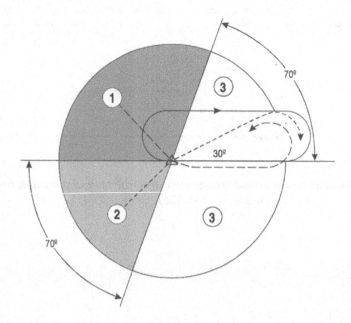

Figure: Entry Sectors, from ICAO Document 8168, Vol 1 Figure I-6-1-2.

Chapter 16

Customs / Immigration / Quarantine

*T*here are three very good rules when it comes to dealing with the customs officials of another country:

- Not all the rules are written and even if they are they are subject to change; it pays to know somebody with first-hand experience with the country.

- Sometimes things don't go well and having an advocate on the ground who speaks the language and actually lives there will work in your favor. If you don't have somebody like that, find a trip planning handler who does.

- Be prepared for delays, don't get upset in public, and make sure your passengers know to do the same. You are playing in someone else's sandbox and they can toss you into the penalty box for no reason at all. Don't give them the excuse to do just that.

In fact, these rules also apply to dealing with the customs officials of your own country too. In the case of the United States, it is often difficult to find the information you need because the rules are always changing and links to their needed spots on their websites seldom stay put for more than a year. The best you can do is to do your best, answer their questions honestly, and don't get upset.

As with many things in international travel, your best source is the host nation's Aeronautical Information Publication (AIP). You might find everything you need in the "State Pages" of your Jeppesen JeppFD application, provided you have the correct subscriptions. Having a handler with "boots on the ground" — local personnel well versed in the country's policies, can be invaluable.

Before Departing the United States

You will probably need a passport to enter another country and then to return to United States. The rules are different for each country and can also change *depending on the other countries on your itinerary. The rules of Visas can also be different for passengers and crewmembers. You may be surprised to hear that many countries even have rules on how many blank pages must be available in your passport or how many months remain before expiration.*

The best way to be certain is to visit: http://travel.state.gov/content/travel/english.html and use the "Learn about your destination" section.

Visa Waiver Program, "Green Cards"

A person who enters the United States under the Visa Waiver Program may not be aware that they cannot depart the country unless the entity providing the transportation is approved under the program. Even as a 14 CFR 91 operator you can be an approved Visa Waiver Program carrier, but even if you aren't and one of your passengers is travelling using the Visa Waiver Program, you need to be smart about it.

For more about this, see the Appendices, Chapter 40.

Minors Traveling Without Their Parents

Some countries required minors traveling without their parents have notarized travel permission from their legal guardians.

Electronic Advanced Passenger Information System (eAPIS)

You have to participate in the Electronic Advanced Passenger Information System (eAPIS). An international flight planning service can make this easy for you, but you can do it yourself. The system the Department of Homeland Security (DHS) gives you through Customs & Border Protection (CBP) is fair, at best, but it does work. It won't remember your passengers or crew, but it remembers you. Several flight planning services that you are probably already using can automate things and make the entire process a bit less painful.

For more about this, see the Appendices, Chapter 18

Entering and Departing Other Countries

Best Source: Aeronautical Information Publication (AIP)

Each nation's AIP should have a similar format. If you are a visitor to the United States, you can find our AIP here: https://www.faa.gov/air_traffic/publications/. What you are looking for should be in PART 1 - General (GEN). GEN 1.3 tells you wihat you need to know for customs requirements, passports, visas, manifests, and public health quarantine rules. This is where you should begin your search in any country's AIP.

You can find AIPs for many other countries here: https://gis.icao.int/gallery/ONLINE_AIPs.html.

Another Good Source: Jeppesen JeppFD

Provided you have the subscriptions required for the region you are interested in, Jeppesen offers most of what you need in their so-called "State Pages." A few pointers for JeppFD:

- You need to download the manuals you are interested in, they don't do this automatically. In JeppFD you will need to selected the gear icon from the main screen, select "Updates" and then the right arrow next to "Manuals." I recommend you always select "General" and your home region, as well as any you expect to travel through.

- Make sure your screen is on a chart by pressing the icon that reads "High IFR," "Low IFR," or "VFR." (You need to do this for the next step.)

- Select the book icon on the top left of the screen.

- If the pull out menu shows "Route" highlighted with route information below it, select "Pubs" instead. You should now see the regions you have access to.

- After you select the desired region, you should get a selection of "Enroute Change Notices," the region-specific manual, such as "Europe Airway Manual," and the "General Airway Manual." Select your desired region.

- The next set of menus should include "Entry Requirements" where you will find your CIQ requirements.

Entry into the United States

Airport of Entry (AOE)

You may have assumed that any airport with the word "international" is designated an Airport of Entry. But that isn't true in the U.S. There are only 58 qualified airports so designated by Title 19 of the Code of Federal Regulations, Section 122.13. Chances are you will be using a "landing rights" airport. The distinction is somewhat minor except that you need permission to land at a landing rights airport. That permission comes from the appropriate customs officer with acknowledgement of the Immigration and Naturalization Service, the Public Health Service, and the Animal and Plant Health Inspection Service of the Agriculture Department. You secure that permission following transmission of an electronic data interchange system known as the Electronic Advance Passenger Information System, or eAPIS.

Electronic Advanced Passenger Information System (eAPIS)

You can't depart for the United States unless you have your eAPIS in order.

For more about this, see the Appendices, Chapter 18.

Southern Border Overflight Exemption (SBOE)

Private aircraft arriving from certain areas south of the U.S. must also furnish a notice of intended arrival to the Customs service at the nearest designated airport to the point of first border or coastline crossing. They must then land at this airport for inspection, unless they have an "SBOE," or Southern Border Overflight Exemption. The arrival areas include:

(a) The U.S./Mexican border or the Pacific Coast from a foreign place in the Western Hemisphere south of 33 deg. north latitude.

(b) The Gulf of Mexico and Atlantic Coasts from a foreign place in the Western Hemisphere south of 30 deg. north latitude, from any place in Mexico, or from the U.S. Virgin Islands.

The requirement to land, the details in the notice to Customs, and the process to obtain an exemption is covered in the U.S. AIP, Section GEN 1.2, Paragraph 4. The list of designated airports is given in Paragraph 5. Further restrictions for flight to and from Cuba are given in Paragraph 7.

For more about this, see the Appendices, Chapter 36.

Immigration

The next step is often called "CIQ," customs, immigration and quarantine. Perhaps ICQ would be better, because you cannot understand the CQ without covering the "I" first.

The "I" of CIQ is immigration and governs the people you attempt to bring into or out of the country. Section GEN 1.3 of the U.S. AIP makes it clear that a valid passport is always required and that a visa is almost always required, but it leaves you guessing about some of the details. Fortunately, the

U.S. Customs and Border Protection (USCBP) website provides an excellent guide, called the "Carrier Information Guide: United States Documentary Requirements for Travel." You can download the guide at: https://www. cbp. gov/document/guides/carrier-information-guide-english.

The guide notes that passports must be valid for the duration of the stay, but for a few countries an additional six months of validity is needed. It also states that a visa is required except for some exempted visitors, including those enrolled in the Visa Waiver Program (VWP).

Visa Waiver Program

The Visa Waiver Program (VWP). This program allows citizens of 38 countries to bypass the need for a visa when travelling on a signatory car- rier after having been approved by the Electronic System for Travel Authorization (ESTA).

For more about this, see the Appendices, Chapter 40.

Non-immigrant Visitors (CBP Form I-94, Arrival/Departure Record)

Foreign visitors to the U.S. arriving via air or sea no longer need to complete paper Customs and Border Protection Form I-94 Arrival/Departure Record or Form I-94W Nonimmigrant Visa Waiver Arrival/Departure Record. Those who need to prove their legal-visitor status—to employers, schools/universities or government agencies—can access their CBP arrival/departure record information online. More about this: http://www.cbp.gov/travel/international-visitors/i-94-instructions.

Customs

Once you've ensured immigration concerns are met (the "I"), you can next turn to Customs (the "C"). While immigration concerns who enters the country, Customs concerns what they bring with them. The U.S. AIP makes it clear that all incoming passengers are required to complete a Customs declaration, but it provides little help on how to do this. The USCBP does provide an example CBP Declaration Form 6059B with instructions online at https://www.cbp.gov/travel/clearing-cbp/traveler-entry-form.

Customs Declaration Form 6059B

[http://www.cbp.gov/travel/clearing-cbp/traveler-entry-form]

Each individual arriving into the United States must complete the CBP Declaration Form 6059B. If you are traveling with other immediate family members who reside in one household, complete one form per family.

A family is considered people who are related by blood, marriage, domestic relationship or adoption. People in a domestic relationship include foster children, stepchildren, half-siblings, legal wards, other dependents or individuals with an in loco parentis or guardianship relationship. It also includes two adults who are in a committed relationship including, but not limited to, long-time companions and couples in civil unions or domestic partnerships, wherein the partners are financially interdependent and are not married to, or a partner of, anyone else. A "domestic relationship" does not extend to roommates or other cohabitants who do not meet this definition.

Quarantine

The question of what you can bring into the country is closely related to what you are prohibited from bringing, which leads us to the "Q" of CIQ. A quick read of the U.S. AIP leads you to believe you cannot bring any meat or meat products, and that you will need permits to bring in most fruits and vegetables. But there are lots of exceptions and there are also lots of additional prohibitions.

For more about this, see the Appendices, Chapter 1.

Disinsection

If you've flown internationally for more than a few years, you probably have some experience with having to spray the aircraft before beginning descent or even having to spray the aircraft after arrival and then having to seal the cabin for ten minutes as the passengers look at you with accusing eyes. "Couldn't you have gotten us out of this, captain?" In my charter GV years we had flight attendants keep a supply of half-spent spray cans so they could spray the entry door into fooling the inspectors that the cabin had been sprayed. I'll leave the ethical questions to you. For me, I don't like having aerosols on the aircraft so I would just assume have the inspectors bring the spray and let them spray.

If you want to buy the spray ahead of time, I've never found a good option in the United States. The vendor of choice is Callington, based in Australia, but they are not allowed to ship to the United States. If you look around you can find vendors in Canada, the United Kingdom, and many places in Asia and the Pacific. Some FBOs keep large quantities on stock and many operators buy cases when overseas. But this isn't very wise, in my opinion. I don't think these cans have been tested under the conditions of a rapid decompression and having a case of the stuff explode at altitude would be bad news.

You might be able to fumigate the aircraft at your home base and have that count for your arrival, a process called "residual disinsection." The unknown is how do you document that so the country you are travelling to will buy off on it? You should first see if the country will allow it and how they want it documented. If they say okay, you should contact your aircraft manufacturer for procedures on how to do this correctly.

Regulatory

[https://www.who.int/ith/mode_of_travel/aircraft_disinsection/en/]

Many countries require disinsection of aircraft (to kill insects) arriving from countries where diseases that are spread by insects, such as malaria and yellow fever, occur. There have been a number of cases of malaria affecting individuals who live or work in the vicinity of airports in countries where malaria is not present, thought to be due to the escape of malaria-carrying mosquitoes transported on aircraft. Some countries, e.g. Australia and New Zealand, routinely carry out disinsection to prevent the inadvertent introduction of species that may harm their agriculture.

Disinsection is a public health measure that is mandated by the International Health Regulations (Annex 2). It involves treatment of the interior of the aircraft with insecticides specified by WHO. The different procedures currently in use are as follows:

- treatment of the interior of the aircraft using a quick-acting insecticide spray immediately before take-off, with the passengers on board;

- treatment of the interior of the aircraft on the ground before passengers come on board, using a residual-insecticide aerosol, plus additional in-flight treatment with a quick-acting spray shortly before landing;

- regular application of a residual insecticide to all internal surfaces of the aircraft, except those in food preparation areas.

Passengers are sometimes concerned about their exposure to insecticide sprays during air travel, and some have reported feeling unwell after spraying of aircraft for disinsection. However, WHO has found no evidence that the specified insecticide sprays are harmful to human health when used as recommended.

Disinsection Procedures

[https://www.who.int/ith/mode_of_travel/aircraft_disinsection/en/]

Pre-flight: A pre-flight aerosol containing an insecticide with rapid action and limited residual action is applied by ground staff to the flight deck, passenger cabin including toilet areas, open overhead and side-wall lockers, coat lockers and crew rest areas. The spray is applied before the passengers board the aircraft but not more than 1 h before the doors are closed. A 2% permethrin cis:trans (25:75) formulation is currently recommended for this application, at a target dose of 0.7 g a.i./100 m3. This requires application at 35 g of formulation per 100 m3 to various types of aircraft, with a droplet size of 10–15 μm. Preflight spraying is followed by a further in-flight spray, i.e. top-of-descent as the aircraft starts its descent to the arrival airport.

Blocks away: Spraying is carried out by crew members when the passengers are on board, after closure of the cabin door and before the flight takes off. An aerosol containing an insecticide for rapid action is used. The air-conditioning system should be switched off during cabin spraying. The flight deck is sprayed before the pilot boards (when no passengers are on board). The doors of overhead luggage racks should be closed only after spraying has been completed. An aerosol containing 2% D-phenothrin is currently recommended by WHO and should be applied at a rate of 35 g of formulation per 100 m3 (i.e. 0.7 g a.i./100 m3). Cargo holds should also be disinsected.

Top-of-descent: Top-of-descent spraying is carried out as the aircraft starts its descent to the arrival airport. An aerosol containing 2% D-phenothrin is currently recommended by WHO for this purpose and is applied with the air recirculation system set at from high to normal flow. The amounts applied are based on a standard spray rate of 1 g/s and 35 g of the formulation per 100 m3 (i.e. 0.7 g a.i./100 m3).

Residual: The internal surfaces of the passenger cabin and cargo hold, excluding food preparation areas, are sprayed with a compression sprayer that has a constant flow valve and flat fan nozzle according to WHO specifications. Permethrin 25:75 (cis:trans) emulsifiable concentrate is currently recommended by WHO at a target dose of 0.2 g/m2 applied at intervals not exceeding 2 months. The emulsion is applied at 10 ml/m2 to avoid run off. Residual sprays are applied by professional pest control operators and are intended for long-term residual activity on aircraft interior surfaces. In electrically sensitive areas, it may be necessary to use an aerosol instead of a compression sprayer. After treatment is completed, air-conditioning packs should be run for at least 1 h before the crew and passengers embark to clear the air of the volatile components of the spray. Areas that undergo substantial cleaning between treatments require supplementary 'touch-up' spraying.

Risks

The World Health Organization says disinsection sprays are not hazardous to your health. You may or may not believe them, there are a number of sources that back them up:

Joint Meeting on Pesticide Residues (JMPR) – Monographs and Evaluations — http://www.inchem.org/pages/jmpr.html

Joint Expert Committee on Food Additives (JECFA) — http://www.inchem.org/pages/jecfa.html

International Programme on Chemical Safety (IPCS) — http://www.inchem.org/pages/cicads.html

Concise International Chemical Assessment Documents — http://www.inchem.org/pages/ehc.html

International Agency for Research on Cancer (IARC) – Monographs on the Evaluation of Carcinogenic Risks to Humans — http://monographs.iarc.fr/

US Environmental Protection Agency (USEPA) – Pesticide evaluations — http://www.epa.gov/pesticides/reregistration/status.htm

Agency for Toxic Substances and Disease Registry (ATSDR) – Toxicological Profiles — http://www.atsdr.cdc.gov/toxpro2.html

European Food Safety Authority (EFSA) – Pesticide Risk Assessments — http://www.efsa.europa.eu/en/pesticides/pesticidesscdocs.htm

European Chemical Substances Information System — http://ihcp.jrc.ec.europa.eu/our_databases/esis

Chapter 18

Electronic Advanced Passenger Information System (eAPIS)

*Y*ou've got no choice in the matter anymore, you have to participate in the *Electronic Advanced Passenger Information System (eAPIS). An international flight planning service can make this easy for you, but you can do it yourself. The system the Department of Homeland Security (DHS) gives you through Customs & Border Protection (CBP) is fair, at best, but it does work. It won't remember your passengers or crew, but it remembers you. Several flight planning services that you are probably already using can automate things and make the entire process a bit less painful.*

Definitions

[19 CFR 122, §122.1]

A "commercial aircraft" is any aircraft transporting passengers and/or cargo for some payment or other consideration, including money or services rendered.

A "private aircraft" is any aircraft engaged in a personal or business flight to or from the U.S. which is not: carrying passengers and/or cargo for commercial purposes; leaving the U.S. carrying neither passengers nor cargo in order to lade passengers and/or cargo in a foreign area for commercial purposes; or returning to the U.S. carrying neither passengers nor cargo in ballast after leaving with passengers and/or cargo for commercial purposes;

Arrival Process

Private Aircraft (Regulatory)

[19 CFR 122, §122.22(b)(1)] The private aircraft pilot is responsible for ensuring the notice of arrival and manifest information regarding each indi-

445

vidual onboard the aircraft are transmitted to CBP. The pilot is responsible for the submission, accuracy, correctness, timeliness, and completeness of the submitted information, but may authorize another party to submit the information on their behalf. Except as provided in paragraph (b)(7) of this section, all data must be transmitted to CBP by means of an electronic data interchange system approved by CBP and must set forth the information specified in this section.

[19 CFR 122, §122.22(b)(2)] The private aircraft pilot is responsible for ensuring that the information [. . .] of this section is transmitted to CBP:

For flights originally destined for the United States, any time prior to departure of the aircraft, but no later than 60 minutes prior to departure of the aircraft from the foreign port or place; or

For flights not originally destined to the United States, but diverted to a U.S. port due to an emergency, no later than 30 minutes prior to arrival; in cases of non-compliance, CBP will take into consideration that the carrier was not equipped to make the transmission and the circumstances of the emergency situation.

[19 CFR 122, §122.22(b)(6)] Prior to departure from the foreign port or place, the pilot of a private aircraft must receive a message from DHS approving landing within the United States, and follow any instructions contained therein prior to departure. Once DHS has approved departure, and the pilot has executed all instructions issued by DHS, the aircraft is free to depart with the intent of landing at the designated U.S. port of entry.

[19 CFR 122, §122.22(b)(7)] The private aircraft pilot is obligated to make necessary changes to the arrival manifest after transmission of the manifest to CBP. If changes to an already transmitted manifest are necessary, an updated and amended manifest must be resubmitted to CBP. Only amendments regarding flight cancellation, expected time of arrival (ETA) or changes in arrival location, to an already transmitted manifest may be submitted telephonically, by radio, or through existing processes and procedures. On a limited case-by-case basis, CBP may permit a pilot to submit or update notice of arrival and arrival/departure manifest information telephonically when unforeseen circumstances preclude submission of the information via eAPIS. Under such circumstances, CBP will manually enter the notice of arrival and arrival/departure manifest information provided by the pilot and the pilot is required to wait for CBP screening and approval to depart.

Changes in ETA and arrival location must be coordinated with CBP at the new arrival location to ensure that resources are available to inspect the arriving aircraft. If a subsequent manifest is submitted less than 60 minutes prior to departure to the United States, the private aircraft pilot must receive approval from CBP for the amended manifest containing added passenger information and/or changes to information that were submitted regarding the aircraft and all individuals onboard the aircraft, before the aircraft is allowed to depart the foreign location, or the aircraft may be, as appropriate, diverted from arriving in the United States, or denied permission to land in the United States. If a subsequent, amended manifest is submitted by the pilot, any approval to depart the foreign port or location previously granted by CBP as a result of the original manifest's submission is invalid.

The process is easier than it seems and is explained in English, below.

Commercial Aircraft (Regulatory)

[19 CFR 122, §122.49a(b)(1)(i)] Basic requirement. Except as provided in paragraph (c) of this section, an appropriate official of each commercial aircraft (carrier) arriving in the United States from any place outside the United States must transmit to the Advance Passenger Information System (APIS; referred to in this section as the Customs and Border Protection (CBP) system), the electronic data interchange system approved by CBP for such transmissions, an electronic passenger arrival manifest covering all passengers checked in for the flight. A passenger manifest must be transmitted separately from a crew member manifest required under §122.49b if transmission is in U.S. EDIFACT format. The passenger manifest must be transmitted to the CBP system at the place and time specified in paragraph (b)(2) of this section, in the manner set forth under paragraph (b)(1)(ii) of this section.

[19 CFR 122, §122.49a(b)(2)] Place and time for submission. The appropriate official [. . .] must transmit the arrival manifest or manifest data [. . .] to the CBP system (CBP Data Center, CBP Headquarters), in accordance with the following:

i. For manifests transmitted under paragraph (b)(1)(ii)(A) or (B) of this section, no later than 30 minutes prior to the securing of the aircraft;

ii. For manifest information transmitted under paragraph (b)(1)(ii)(C) of this section, no later than the securing of the aircraft;

iii. For flights not originally destined to the United States but diverted to a U.S. port due to an emergency, no later than 30 minutes prior to arrival; in cases of non-compliance, CBP will take into consideration whether the carrier was equipped to make the transmission and the circumstances of the emergency situation; and

iv. For an aircraft operating as an air ambulance in service of a medical emergency, no later than 30 minutes prior to arrival; in cases of non-compliance, CBP will take into consideration whether the carrier was equipped to make the transmission and the circumstances of the emergency situation.

The various mysterious paragraphs and bracketed ellipses all refer to minutiae about batch reporting and the like. The bottom line is you have to submit a crew and passenger manifest and CBP has a few extra steps to follow before approving your arrival. Once again this is broken down into English, as follows.

Arrival Process (In English)

Ensure that an eAPIS manifest is submitted to CBP. The pilot is responsible for the submission of an accurate manifest and for validating eAPIS data for travelers arriving in to the United States. eAPIS manifests can be submitted as early as you like, but no later than 60 minutes prior to the flight's departure.

Receive an electronic clearance response from DHS. You should get a confirmation e-mail receipt from APISConfirmNoReply@dhs.gov within a few seconds saying your manifest was successfully processed and cleared, or CBP was unable to systematically clear your manifest.

If your manifest was not processed successfully, you will be given instructions on how to contact a DHS representative to assist with the flight's clearance. It could be a simple entry error or you could have somebody flagged on the "No Fly" list.

Report immediately to CBP for inspection upon arrival in to the United States.

You should keep a copy of the eAPIS e-mail during the flight.

Changes: you must submit another manifest in eAPIS if: additional travelers are added; you can resubmit the previous manifest if the pilot has not changed; the date of travel has changed; the aircraft changes.

Changes: you do not make change in eAPIS if: the travel time on the same day changes; just notify the CBP airport of arrival, the port changes; just notify the original and new CBP, passengers or crew do not fly; you don't need to do anything if the pilot is the same.

Departure Process

Private Aircraft (Regulatory)

[19 CFR 122, §122.22(c)(1)] The private aircraft pilot is responsible for ensuring that information regarding private aircraft departing the United States, and manifest data for all individuals onboard the aircraft is timely transmitted to CBP. The pilot is responsible for the accuracy, correctness, timeliness, and completeness of the submitted information, but may authorize another party to submit the information on their behalf. Data must be transmitted to CBP by means of an electronic data interchange system approved by CBP, and must set forth the information specified [. . .] All data pertaining to the aircraft, and all individuals onboard the aircraft must be transmitted at the same time. On a limited case-by-case basis, CBP may permit a pilot to submit or update notice of arrival and arrival/departure manifest information telephonically to CBP when unforeseen circumstances preclude submission of the information via eAPIS. Under such circumstances, CBP will manually enter the notice of arrival and arrival/departure manifest information provided by the pilot and the pilot is required to wait for CBP screening and approval to depart.

[19 CFR 122, §122.22(c)(2)] The private aircraft pilot must transmit the electronic data required [in this] section to CBP any time prior to departing the United States, but no later than 60 minutes prior to departing the United States.

[19 CFR 122, §122.22(c)(5)] Prior to departure for a foreign port or place, the pilot of a private aircraft must receive a message from DHS approving departure from the United States and follow any instructions contained therein. Once DHS has approved departure, and the pilot has executed all instructions issued by DHS, the aircraft is free to depart.

[19 CFR 122, §122.22(c)(6)] If any of the data elements change after the manifest is transmitted, the private aircraft pilot must update the manifest and resubmit the amended manifest to CBP. Only amendments regarding flight cancellation, expected time of departure or changes in departure location, to an already transmitted manifest may be submitted telephonically, by radio, or through existing processes and procedures. If an amended manifest is submitted less than 60 minutes prior to departure, the private aircraft pilot must receive approval from CBP for the amended manifest containing added passenger information and/or changes to information that were submitted regarding the aircraft before the aircraft is allowed to depart the U.S. location, or the aircraft may be denied clearance to depart from the United States. If a subsequent amended manifest is submitted by the pilot, any clearance previously granted by CBP as a result of the original manifest's submission is invalid.

The process is easier than it seems and is explained in English, below.

Commercial Aircraft (Regulatory)

[19 CFR 122, §122.75a(b)(1)(i)] Basic requirement. Except as provided in paragraph (c) of this section, an appropriate official of each commercial aircraft (carrier) departing from the United States en route to any port or place outside the United States must transmit to the Advance Passenger Information System (APIS; referred to in this section as the Customs and Border Protection (CBP) system), the electronic data interchange system approved by CBP for such transmissions, an electronic passenger departure manifest covering all passengers checked in for the flight. A passenger manifest must be transmitted separately from a crew member manifest required under §122.75b if transmission is in U.S. EDIFACT format. The passenger manifest must be transmitted to the CBP system at the place and time specified in paragraph (b)(2) of this section, in the manner set forth under paragraph (b)(1)(ii) of this section.

[19 CFR 122, §122.75a(b)(2)] The appropriate official specified in paragraph (b)(1)(i) of this section (carrier) must transmit the departure manifest or manifest data as required under paragraphs (b)(1)(i) and (ii) of this section to the CBP system (CBP Data Center, CBP Headquarters), in accordance with the following:

i. For manifests transmitted under paragraph (b)(1)(ii)(A) and (B) of this section, no later than 30 minutes prior to the securing of the aircraft;

ii. For manifest information transmitted under paragraph (b)(1)(ii)(C) of this section, no later than the securing of the aircraft; and

iii. For an aircraft operating as an air ambulance in serice of a medical emergency, no later than 30 minutes after departure.

The various mysterious paragraphs and bracketed ellipses all refer to minutiae about batch reporting and the like. The bottom line is you have to submit a crew and passenger manifest and CBP has a few extra steps to follow before approving your departure. Once again this is broken down into English, as follows.

Departure Process (In English)

Ensure that an eAPIS manifest is submitted to CBP. The pilot is responsible for the submission of an accurate manifest submission and validating eAPIS data for travelers departing the United States. eAPIS manifests must be submitted no later than 60 minutes prior to the flight's departure.

Receive an electronic clearance response from DHS. You should get a confirmation e-mail receipt from APISConfirmNoReply@dhs.gov within a few seconds saying your manifest was successfully processed and cleared as expected, or CBP was unable to systematically clear your manifest.

If your manifest was not processed successfully, you'll be given instructions on how to contact a DHS representative to assist with the flight's clearance.

You are clear to depart without further interaction unless CBP or another DHS agency contacts you and instructs you to report for an outbound inspection. In that case, you must present the aircraft, yourself, and all travelers for inspection just as he would for an inspection upon arrival in to the United States.

You should keep a copy of the eAPIS e-mail during the flight.

Changes: you must submit another manifest in eAPIS if: additional travelers are added; you can resubmit the previous manifest if the pilot has not changed, the date of travel has changed, the aircraft changes

Changes: you do not make change in eAPIS if: the travel time on the same day changes; just notify the CBP airport of arrival, the port changes; just notify the original and new CBP, passengers or crew do not fly; you don't need to do anything if the pilot is the same.

Part 135 Caveat

The process for eAPIS under 14 CFR 135 is similar to 14 CFR 91 but the system goes through extra steps that can create a few problems:

If you are departing and arriving on the same day using the same flight number, the system may only keep the data for the second flight. You may need to change the flight number of one of the flights or delay submitting the eAPIS for the second flight.

If you depart under 14 CFR 91 and return under 14 CFR 135 the steps of the system used to record commercial flights gets bypassed and the return flight could set up a few alarms. If you plan on returning 14 CFR 135 you need to depart 14 CFR 135 as well.

The Actual Mechanics

The eAPIS system is accessed through https://eapis.cbp.dhs.gov.

Chapter 19

Equal Time Points

*A*n Equal Time Point (ETP) is not a "time" at all, it is a position in space *between two remote points. When you get to that point, you will have an equal time between going back or going ahead in various conditions. For example, if you lose an engine over the North Atlantic at your computed ETP, it will take you just as long to turn around and head to your alternate in Canada with the forecast headwind, as it will to continue to Ireland with the forecast tailwind. But there are other ETP situations too, such as what happens if you lose pressurization? Or what if you are able to maintain speed and altitude but have to land as soon as possible for a medical emergency? That's why we need ETPs. Your flight planning service provider can do them for you automatically, but you need to know how to compute one manually to make sure they chose the ETP airports wisely and to compute your own if they didn't. The KBED - LSGG example used in the Tutorial Section is used here as well.*

Equal Time Points for Navigators

Back in the days a navigator was needed to cross oceans, the Air Force used Manual 51-40 for this type of thing. The lessons remain valid today.

[AFM 51-40, page 24-9.] The equal time point is a point along the route from which it takes the same amount of time to return to departure as it would to continue to destination. The ETP is not necessarily the midpoint in time from departure to destination. Its location is somewhere near the midpoint of the route, however, and it dependent upon the wind factor.

A wind factor is a headwind or tailwind component which is computed by comparing the average groundspeed (GS) to the true airspeed (TAS). To do this, algebraically subtract the TAS from the GS. When the wind factor is a minus value (GS less than TAS), it is called a head wind factor; when it is a plus value (GS greater than TAS), it is a tail wind factor. When computing ETP, obtain a wind factor for each half of the route.

Use the following formula to compute a ETP:

$$\frac{\text{Total Distance}}{GS_R + GS_C} = \frac{\text{ETP (in nm from } GS_R)}{GS_R}$$

Total distance is the number of nautical miles from departure to destination. Since ETP is most significant for the overwater portion of a flight, the ETP should be determined from coastal departure points and for alternate landing points. GS_R is the groundspeed to return to departure from the ETP. Compute it for the first half of the route by applying the wind factor with the sign reversed to the TAS. GS_C is the GS to continue from the ETP to destination. Determine it by applying the wind factor for the second half of the route to the TAS.

Equal Time Points for Pilots

The navigator formula is not very useful to a pilot, but we can fix that with a little algebra.

The following formula is used to calculate the ground distance from the departure airport to ETP:

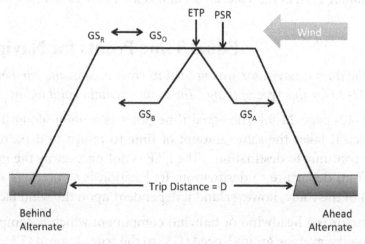

$$\text{Ground distance to ETP} = \frac{(D)\,(GS_B)}{GS_A + GS_B}$$

Where:

D = Total Trip Distance

GS_A = Ground speed to continue to "Ahead" airport at altitude to be flown

GS_B = Ground speed to return to "Behind" airport at altitude to be flown

In most navigator and pilot ETP versions the terms "departure" and "destination" are used when in fact they should refer to the alternate airports "ahead" and "behind." You will seldom opt to return to your departure point or continue to your destination, though it could happen. Regardless, you will often see "GS_R" to denote your groundspeed while returning and "GS_C" to denote your groundspeed while continuing.

The terms GS_O and GS_R are for the Point of Safe Return (PSR), which is sometimes called the "Point of No Return" (PNR). See the Appendices, Chapter 31, Point of Safe Return.

In our example flight from KBED to LSGG we have plotted one equal time point around 37° West:

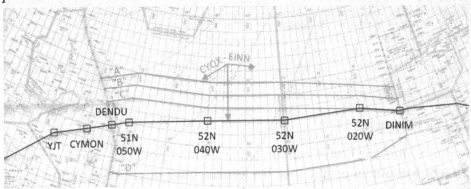

Equal Time Points provide pilots with decision making aids in the event the airplane needs to proceed to a landing airport as soon as possible. An ETP is a geographic location along the route of flight where the time to return to an airport behind the aircraft is equal to the time to proceed to an airport in front of the aircraft.

For some routes, a series of ETP location sets may be called for. In the example problem, ETPs between CYQX and EINN are used. In the event of a problem before the ETP, the airplane would turn back to CYQX. Beyond this point, the airplane would continue eastbound and a diversion to EINN would be called for.

At least three types of ETPs should be considered . . .

Loss of Engine ETP

In the event of an engine loss, driftdown procedures are normally used and the airplane may be required to turn to either Loss of Engine ETP.

This ETP can have other names, "1E INOP" in the example shown, but normally means you have lost an engine and must descend and slow down.

In our example this ETP occurs at N52°05.0' / W037°17.3' which is 1,510 nm along the route of flight from the takeoff point. (This is a useless number when talking ETPs, but four lines later we see the ETP is 686 nm from CYQX.) In the event of an engine loss, the fuel and time are based on descending to FL280 after reversing course to CYQX or FL270 pressing forward to EINN. Both altitudes are lower than optimal, but have been set to descend below the tracks. In either case, it will take 2 hours 36 minutes or 2 hours 37 minutes at the recommended engine out speed.

```
LAT/LONG       N52 05.0/W037 17.3          CYQX                    EINN
TIME TO ETP DIVRSN PT          02.51
DIST TO ETP DIVRSN PT          01510
FUEL TO ETP DIVRSN PT/RMNG   010177 /18923
FL/BURN/TIME TO ETP AP          280/05553/02.36      270/05557/02.37
TAS/ETA/DIST TO ETP AP          340/2227/000686      340/2228/001036
MAG CRS/AVG WIND COMP TO ETP AP    271/M076                 105/P052
ISA TEMP DEV TO ETP AP                  M000                     M003
TOTAL FUEL TO ETP AP /RMNG       15730/13366          15734/13366
```

Loss of Level ETP

In the event of the loss of pressurization or other problem requiring a rapid descent without an engine loss, the airplane may be required to turn to either Loss of Level ETP. Most flight planning programs compute a rapid descent to 10,000 or 15,000 feet, depending on user preferences. A descent to 10,000 feet permits all occupants to breathe without the use of supplemental oxygen. A descent to 15,000 feet permits passengers to breathe without the use of supplemental oxygen, requires the flight crew to remain on supplemental oxygen, but provides greater endurance.

This ETP can also be called "Depressurization" or some variation leading to the idea the airplane must descend.

In our example this ETP occurs just after the Engine-Out ETP, at 1,541 nm along the route of flight from our takeoff point. In the event of loss of pressur-

ization, the aircraft would descend to 15,000' and either turn back or continue east. In either case, it will take around 3 hours at the recommended speed.

```
LAT/LONG        N52 05.8/W036 28.0              CYQX
TIME TO ETP DIVRSN PT           02.55
DIST TO ETP DIVRSN PT           01541
FUEL TO ETP DIVRSN PT/RMNG      010347/18753
FL/BURN/TIME TO ETP AP          150/11951/03.00
TAS/ETA/DIST TO ETP AP          278/2254/000717
MAG CRS/AVG WIND COMP TO ETP AP     271/M046
ISA TEMP DEV TO ETP AP                   M016
TOTAL FUEL TO ETP AP /RMNG      22298/06779
```

Maintain Level ETP

In the event of a need to land as soon as possible without the need to descend, such as a medical emergency, the airplane may be required to turn to either Maintain Level ETP airport.

This ETP can also be called "Medical" or some variation leading to the idea that the airplane must divert but not need to descend or decelerate. But some vendors do select what appears to be an arbitrary descent and you may need to request a change from your vendor or compute your own.

In our example the vendor decided a medical ETP requires a descent to FL200 to make the ETP about the same as what they call the 1E INOP (Loss of Engine) and DEPRESS (Loss of Level) ETPs. This makes flight planning and plotting easier but it is not entirely accurate. Fortunately, with the information they've given us, we can come up with a better answer. See Computing ETPs / Manually, below.

```
MEDICAL
LAT/LONG        N52 05.3/W037 00.9        CYQX              EINN
TIME TO ETP DIVRSN PT           02.52
DIST TO ETP DIVRSN PT           01521
FUEL TO ETP DIVRSN PT/RMNG      010234 /18866
FL/BURN/TIME TO ETP AP          200/11482/02.49    200/11505/02.48
TAS/ETA/DIST TO ETP AP          302/2241/000697    304/2240/001027
MAG CRS/AVG WIND COMP TO ETP AP     271/M060          105/P057
ISA TEMP DEV TO ETP AP                   M012             M010
TOTAL FUEL TO ETP AP /RMNG      21716/07361        21739/07361
```

Selecting ETP Airports

The oceanic or remote area route of flight should be examined and suitable diversion airports identified based on aircraft requirements, airport capability, and weather. The airport must meet the weather requirements for filing as an alternate and if operating under 14 CFR 135, the aircraft must have the performance to fly en route and hold at least 1,500 feet above all obstacles. [14 CFR 135.381]

If using a computerized flight planning service, always look at the selected ETP airports with a eye towards judging its common sense. The flight planner may have made the airport selections prior to a significant change in winds and it may become obvious the selected airports are no longer viable. You may also receive a routing change that negates the previously selected ETP airports.

Multiple ETP location sets may be advantageous when the route of flight is near multiple airport options.

Computing ETPs

Computer Flight Plans

Computer ETP Computations are generally superior to manually calculated ETPs because they consider a greater number of wind points and will yield more accurate ETPs. But, as we've seen with this vendor's "DIST TO ETP DIVRSN PT," you need to carefully consider what the data means before making any assumptions.

$$\text{Ground distance to ETP} = \frac{(D)\,(GS_B)}{GS_A + GS_B}$$

Manually

As shown above, ETPs can be computed manually if the ground speed ahead and behind are known. To manually calculate an ETP:

All you really need is the wind factor, TAS, and distance between the behind and ahead airports. Remember that $GS_B = TAS + Wind$ and $GS_A = TAS + Wind$, and the wind factor is positive for tailwinds and negative for headwinds.

We see from our plotting chart that D = 1722 nm.

Master Document

```
FLIGHTPLAN N7700    KBED TO LSGG  GLF4  M80 /F  IFR  24DEC13  -- AB
COMPUTED 0054Z FOR ETD 1700Z    PROGS 231800Z              WGT IN LBS

            FUEL    TIME    DIST ARRIVE TAKEOFF  LAND   AV PLD  OPNLWT
DEST LSGG  016917  05:56    3295  2256Z  065825  048908  000000  043908
RESV       001921  00:45
ALTN       000000  00:00    0000  0000Z
HOLD       000000  00:00
REQD       018838  06:41                          ES ZFW   MX ZFW
TAXI       000400                                  43908    49000
XTRA       003079  01:12                          ES LNDG  MX LNDG
TOTL        22317  07:53                           48908   058500

KBED DCT PSM ENE J573 EBONY N81B YQX KOBEV 5050N 5040N 4930N 4920N
NERTU ETIKI UN480 REGHI UN482 DEGEX UN490 TERPO UM616 NTS UP860
RUBLO UZ87 BELUS BELU1S LSGG

WIND P105   MXSH  7/KBED   AVG WIND 268/106
TAS 458     FL 410 REGHI 430 DEGEX 410 BEBIX 400 VALKU 390
```

We can also see that our average wind factor during the oceanic portion of the
flight is P062 and our average TAS is 451, as shown on the master document.
The TAS may be different and our winds could be wildly inaccurate for the pertinent portion of the flight so it pays to scan the oceanic portion to make sure.

| CPT | FLT | T | WIND | S | TAS | AWY | | MH | DST | ETE | ETR | FU | FR | FF/E |
| FREQ | TRO | TDV | COMP | | GRS | | | MCRS | DSTR | ATE | ATR | AFU | AFR | |
LAT	LONG													
DENDU	390	-52	288105	7	463	DCT		083	0123	014	0435	698	22176	1531
	36	P04	P075		538			090	2315					
N50302	W052041													
5150N	390	-50	288090	4	465	DCT		095	0084	009	0426	485	21690	1531
	36	P06	P067		531			097	2231					
N51000	W050000													
5240N	390	-50	276063	2	466	DCT		106	0379	043	0343	2204	19487	1516
	52	P07	P060		527			104	1851					
N52000	W040000													
5230N	410	-51	252054	1	465	DCT		103	0371	043	0300	2076	17411	1445
	52	P06	P051		516			100	1481					
N52000	W030000													
5220N	410	-53	241060		464	DCT		124	0371	043	0217	2026	15385	1407
	31	P05	P051		515			117	1110					
N52000	W020000													
DINIM	410	-55	236069	1	462	DCT		102	0197	024	0153	1081	14305	1377
	36	P03	P040		502			097	0913					
N51000	W015000													

The oceanic legs reveal a better average TAS would be 463 and wind factors
of P075, P067, P060, P051, P051, and P040. Rather than use a wind factor of
62 throughout, as the flight plan would suggest, we'll use P067 for our return
scenario and P051 for the continue option:

GSB = TAS + WF = 463 + (-67) = 396

GSA = TAS + WF = 463 + (+51) = 514

459

Therefore:

Ground Distance to ETP = (D)(GSB) / (GSA+GSB) = nm

Ground Distance to ETP = (1722)(396) / (514 + 396) = 749 nm

Our manually computed ETP is 52 nm further east than the computerized version because the vendor selected a descent to lower the TAS in an attempt to make the three provided ETPs about the same. If your decision is based on really staying at flight level, the actual ETP is the one we computed, 52 nm east.

Circular Slide Rule

With a circular slide rule, place the Total Distance (D) on the outer scale opposite the added groundspeeds (GSB + GSA), and place the sliding index over the return groundspeed (GSB) on the inner scale. The ETP will appear on the outer scale under the sliding index:

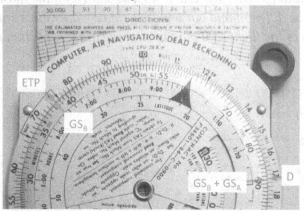

The technique works but it introduces an opportunity for error and has been relegated to the "You can, but why would you?" category.

Three Airport Example

There are times when a third airport may become advantageous. (This occurs frequently in the North Atlantic when the route of flight is near Iceland.) For this example, we will compute only the Maintain Level ETP between EINN-BIKF and BIKF-CYQX to illustrate the positioning of the ETP on the route of flight. (The process of checking the Loss of Level and Loss of Engine ETPs is the same, using the appropriate groundspeeds for those scenarios.)

Maintain Level ETP (EINN-BIKF). Using our FMS or by measuring the dis-

tance on the plotting chart, we see the distance between EINN and BIKF is 798 nm. For the example our True Airspeed is 492 knots but this time our winds will be out of the west at 20 knots.

ETP (EINN-BIKF) = (798 x 512) / (512 + 472) = 415 nm from EINN

Maintain Level ETP (BIKF-CYQX). Using our FMS or by measuring the distance on the plotting chart, we see the distance between BIKF and CYQX is 1367 nm. Once again our True Airspeed is 492 knots but this time our winds will be out of the west at 10 knots.

ETP (BIKF-CYQX) = (1367 x 502) / (502 + 482) = 697 nm from BIKF

Each of these points are plotted on straight lines between airports. A line is then drawn from these points at a right angle towards the actual aircraft route of flight. Where the lines intersect are the appropriate equal time points:

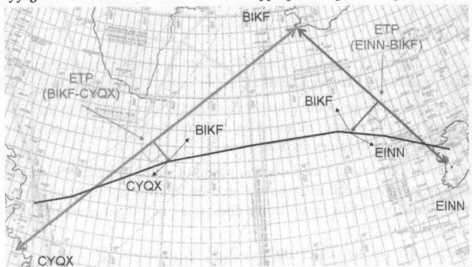

In this example, the emergency options will be to turn back to EINN before the first ETP, to divert north to BIKF between the first and second ETPs, and finally to press on to CYQX after the second ETP.

If the winds were especially strong up north and the route of flight was further south, we could see a case where it is never advantageous to proceed to one of the three ETP choices. In the example shown below, the flight time to either EINN or CYQX is always shorter than BIKF:

461

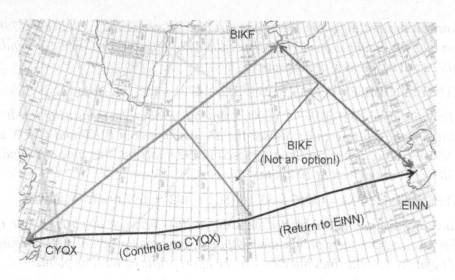

Plot ETPs

If a plotting chart is required the ETPs should be noted along the route of flight. See Part II, Chapter 6, Plotting.

A perpendicular line pointing to the route and arrows pointing to the ETP airports will allow rapid and easy identification of a course of action if a diversion decision becomes necessary.

If a plotting chart is not used, another means of identifying the ETP should be employed. A pencil mark on the en route chart is normally sufficient. Some FMS units allow an electronic display of a non-flight plan point that allows easy reference.

CAUTION: Do not enter the ETP into the FMS as a way-point. The extra waypoint will be reported through data link and can throw off ETAs.

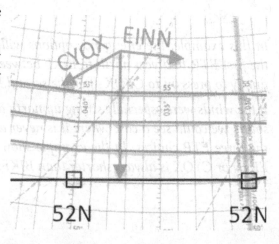

Chapter 20

Extended Diversion Time Operations (EDTO/ETOPS)

*A*s turbine engines have become more and more reliable the definition of what constitutes extended operations has changed. Even the name has changed: ETOPS started out at "Extended Twin Operations" and than became "Extended Operations. ETOPS is now EDTO, "Extended Divertion Time Operations." What remains constant is confusion among many pilots as to what it means, who it impacts, and how to "comply."

- *What it means, for most aircraft, is any operation that is beyond 180 minutes with one engine inopearative from a suitable airport.*

- *Who it impacts are commercial operators, 14 CFR 121 and 135.*

- *How to comply is quite complicated, involves many steps for pilots, mechanics, the airplane and the operator.*

This isn't an article about becoming ETOPS eligible, it is an article on how to fly just about everywhere in the world without having to become ETOPS certified.

Under 14 CFR 135, to fly without ETOPS certification, you need to demonstrate that the aircraft can make it to a suitable airport in under 180 minutes, using engine-out altitudes and airspeeds of your choosing. You do not need to use Equal Time Point (ETP) altitudes and speeds. If you have the fuel and performance to do this, the rule book is satisfied. Under real engine-out situations, the actual altitudes and airspeeds are up to you and you need not do this in under 180 minutes.

None of this make sense to you? If you fly more than 3 hours from the nearest airport under 14 CFR 135, you need to understand ETOPS. If you fly a Challenger or Boeing it may not impact how you fly over water at all, but you need to know why. If you fly a Gulfstream, however, ETOPS may impact your fuel loading.

Location

To find out where your aircraft can operate and remain within the 180-minute ETOPS criteria, you figure your airplane's expected engine-out speed, multiple that by 3, and draw distance rings around all suitable airports. You can also do this manually, for example using 360 KTAS on a GV:

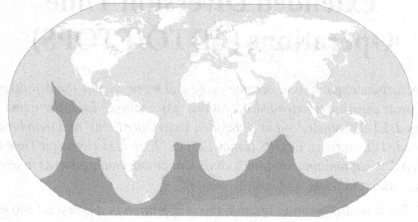

Figure: GV 360 KTAS ETOPS (world map courtesy Gustav Giradeli)

To fly a GV in the shaded area under 14 CFR 135, you would need to be certified for ETOPS. So long as you stay out of these areas, you are good to go without ETOPS certification.

[14 CFR 135, §135.364 Maximum flying time outside the United States.] After August 13, 2008, no certificate holder may operate an airplane, other than an all-cargo airplane with more than two engines, on a planned route that exceeds 180 minutes flying time (at the one-engine-inoperative cruise speed under standard conditions in still air) from an Adequate Airport outside the continental United States unless the operation is approved by the FAA in accordance with Appendix G of this part, Extended Operations.

If you are flying under 14 CFR 135 and your planned range exceeds 14 CFR § 135.364 criteria, you and your airplane have to meet 14 CFR 135 Appendix G requirements. This is an expensive and time-consuming process. Aircraft not under an ETOPS program must be able to return to an acceptable airport within 180 minutes (in still air) in the event of an engine failure.

Obtaining ETOPS Certification

If you want to get ETOPS certified I recommend you contact your aircraft manufacturer and start from there. If you spend considerable time flying routes where your aircraft is impacted, it might be worth your while.

Most aircraft are grand fathered into a 180-minute engine-out capability, which means they may fly as far as 180 minutes from the nearest suitable airport engine-out, no wind, but no further.

Refer to 14 CFR 135 Appendix G to determine your 180-minute engine out qualification:

- 14 CFR 135.98, Operations in the North Polar Area
- 14 CFR 135.364, Maximum Flying Time Outside the United States
- 135.411, Maintenance Requirement Applicability
- 135 Appendix G, ETOPS

A GIV, GV, G450, and G550 are all 180-minute engine-out qualified. They can qualify for ETOPS, which extends that range to either 207 or 240 minutes, but the process is so time consuming and expensive, I've not heard of a single operator who has bothered.

To be ETOPS qualified, 14 CFR 135 operators must have Operations Specification B342 and B344, as detailed under FAA 8900.1, Volume 4, Chapter 6.

If you plan all of your 14 CFR 135 operations to be within 180 minutes, engine-out of a suitable airport, you do not need ETOPS certification.

MMEL / MEL "ER"

In an MEL or MMEL, the abreviation "ER" can lead you to believe ETOPS applies to you, even if you are operating under 14 CFR 91. That is not true.

[FAA MMEL Policy Letter 25] Extended Range Operations (ER). ER refers to extended range operations (ETOPS) of an airplane with operational approval to conduct ETOPS in accordance with the applicable regulations.

In my aircraft, for example, an APU generator can be inoperative "except for ER operations." That does not apply to me operating under Part 91, so I could operate at extended ranges without the APU.

Example: Is a Gulfstream V Impacted by ETOPS?

The Gulfstream V is a good aircraft for a case study because it has incredibly long range and is impacted in two out of the three scenarios presented here.

North Atlantic Example: No Issues

If your Equal Time Points (ETPs) come to less than 180 minutes, you know without further research that the aircraft can lose an engine at the furthest point and make a suitable airport. A GV, for example, can easily make the hop from the east coast of the United States to Europe and never be more than 180 minutes from the nearest suitable airport, even flying at single-engine endurance speeds.

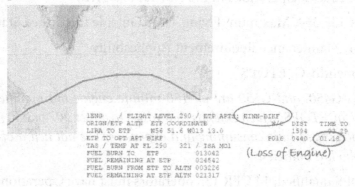

```
1ENG      / FLIGHT LEVEL 290 / ETP APTS: EINN-BIKF
ORIGIN/ETP ALTN  ETP COORDINATE                  W/C   DIST   TIME TO
LIRA TO ETP       N56 51.6 W019 13.0                    1594    03.29
ETP TO OPT APT BIKF                              P018  0440    01.18
TAS / TEMP AT FL 290    321 / ISA M01
FUEL BURN TO   ETP            013042                      (Loss of Engine)
FUEL REMAINING AT ETP         024542
FUEL BURN FROM ETP TO ALTN 003226
FUEL REMAINING AT ETP ALTN 021317
```

East Pacific: Some Thought Required

A Challenger 604 can make the hop from KSFO to PHNL with suitable fuel reserves, but just barely. A Gulfstream GV can make the same trip and fly back all on the same tank of gas. And yet only the GV has an ETOPS issue for the KSFO-PHNL city pair. Why?

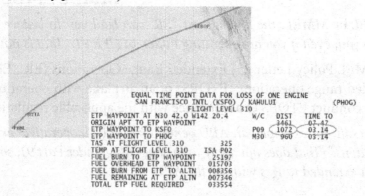

```
             EQUAL TIME POINT DATA FOR LOSS OF ONE ENGINE
              SAN FRANCISCO INTL (KSFO) / KAHULUI          (PHOG)
                          FLIGHT LEVEL 310
BITTA   ETP WAYPOINT AT N30 42.0 W142 20.4    W/C   DIST   TIME TO
        ORIGIN APT TO ETP WAYPOINT                  3461    07.47
PHNL    ETP WAYPOINT TO KSFO                   P09  1072    03.14
        ETP WAYPOINT TO PHOG                   M30   960    03.14
        TAS AT FLIGHT LEVEL 310         325
        TEMP AT FLIGHT LEVEL 310     ISA P02
        FUEL BURN TO   ETP WAYPOINT   25197
        FUEL OVERHEAD ETP WAYPOINT   015703
        FUEL BURN FROM ETP TO ALTN   008356
        FUEL REMAINING AT ETP ALTN   007346
        TOTAL ETP FUEL REQUIRED      033554
```

The ETPs between KSFO and PHNL flying a Challenger 604 will probably be less than 180 minutes, so no ETOPS issues when flying 14 CFR 135. This isn't the case for a GV.

Using standard drift down procedures, if you lose thrust on an engine you set the operating engine to its maximum continuous setting, allow the airplane to decelerate to an optimum speed, and then you allow the airplane to drift down to an altitude it can sustain on one engine. Most flight plan providers know this and program the equal time point calculations to do just that.

A normal airplane—one with more fuselage than wing—will have to drift down to the middle twenties and fly a speed around 250 or so. The Challenger 604, for example, may end up at 27,000 feet and 240 KIAS, which equates to 370 nautical miles per hour true airspeed. The airplane can make it to its divert airport in 2 hour 53 minutes, though it will be right at its minimum fuel.

31,000 feet	218 KCAS	352.1 KTAS	0.1317 NAM/LB fuel
29,000 feet	228 KCAS	355.1 KTAS	0.1266 NAM/LB fuel
27,000 feet	238 KCAS	358.2 KTAS	0.1214 NAM/LB fuel

Table: Example GV Engine-out Drift Down

With its massive wing, the Gulfstream V, only needs to descend to 31,000 feet and can slow down to 218 KCAS. It doesn't have to fly that slowly, but the chart says it can. So flight planners use these numbers; a higher altitude translates to a lower true airspeed, as does the lower calibrated airspeed. The airplane, if flown at this altitude and speed, makes it to the divert airport in 3 hours and 14 minutes. An FAA examiner who doesn't understand the topic well will go ballistic and start the violation paperwork. The pilot needs to understand why the flight planning software is wrong.

In this example, the pilot need only select an altitude 4,000 feet below optimum and a little faster to beat the 3 hour stop watch:

$$Time = 1072 / 358.2 = 179 \text{ minutes.}$$

The lower altitude will cost extra fuel, but the airplane has that to spare. So long as the pilot ensures there is fuel to do this, the aircraft doesn't need ETOPS certification.

Southeast Pacific: A Show Stopper

While not a common flight, a trip from New Zealand to Chile is well within the range of a GV but cannot be made under 14 CFR 135 because of ETOPS-180 requirements. The total flight time is under 10 hours and not much over 5,100 nm. There is only one suitable alternate between Christchurch, New Zealand (NZCH) and Santiago, Chile (SCEL): the Isle de Pascua (SCIP).

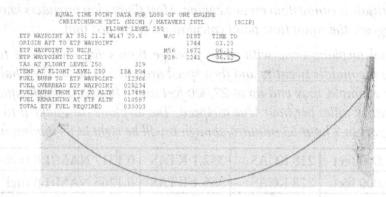

```
          EQUAL TIME POINT DATA FOR LOSS OF ONE ENGINE
          CHRISTCHURCH INTL (NZCH) / MATAVERI INTL      (SCIP)
                     FLIGHT LEVEL 250
ETP WAYPOINT AT 851 21.2 W147 20.8       W/C    DIST    TIME TO
ORIGIN APT TO ETP WAYPOINT                      1744    03.20
ETP WAYPOINT TO NZCH                     M56    1672    06.13
ETP WAYPOINT TO SCIP                     P29    2241    06.13
TAS AT FLIGHT LEVEL 250         329
TEMP AT FLIGHT LEVEL 250      ISA P04
FUEL BURN TO  ETP WAYPOINT     12366
FUEL OVERHEAD ETP WAYPOINT    028234
FUEL BURN FROM ETP TO ALTN    017499
FUEL REMAINING AT ETP ALTN    010597
TOTAL ETP FUEL REQUIRED       030003
```

The engine-out ETP is already calculated at an optimal altitude in terms for producing the highest available TAS, but even if the TAS is increased to the aircraft's maximum capable, the time to the ETP airport cannot be reduced to under 180 minutes. This flight cannot be accomplished in a GV under 14 CFR 135.

Chapter 21

Flight Operations Checklist

*W*henever you fly internationally there are a host of things you need to consider that may not be of primary concern when operating closer to home.
*You should develop a checklist that covers all the bases for your operation and
run that checklist before you start international operations and at least once
every year to make sure everything is up-to-date and nothing has changed in
the list of requirements. Here is my checklist to give you a head start.*

Aircraft Equipment

There are things you are required to have by regulation and others that you
should have, depending on where you are going.

* Aircraft tow bar or at least the tow head.

If you are going someplace that regularly handles your aircraft type, then
maybe you don't need this. Otherwise, you should consider bringing one.
Remember to consider all of your alternate, ETP, and ETOPS airports too.

* Emergency locator transmitter.

An ELT is not specifically required to fly oceanic, but you will find requirements for most operators in many locations around the world.

* First-aid kit. [ICAO Annex 6, Part II, Chapter 2.4, ¶2.4.2.2.]
* Fire extinguisher, portable. [ICAO Annex 6, Part II, Chapter 2.4,
  ¶2.4.2.2.]
* Fuel sample kit.

If your location will be dispensing fuel from 50 gallon drums or a fuel truck
caked in rust, you may want a fuel sample kit.

* Headphones, microphones.
* High frequency radios. [AC 91-70B, ¶3-3.c.] [ICAO Annex 2, ¶3.6.5.1.]

You have CPDLC and SATCOM and both can be used to make position reports. But you still need an HF radio in controlled airspace when out of the range of VHF communications.

- Life rafts, vests of sufficient quantity. [AC 91-70B, ¶5-6.]

- SATCOM.

SATCOM might be required in some regions when using Controller-Pilot Data Link Communications.

- SELCAL.

Certainly not required, but nice to have.

- Survival equipment appropriate to route. [AC 91-70B, ¶5-6]

- VHF 8.33 kHz. Required in various parts of Europe. [ICAO Doc 7030, Chapter EUR, ¶2.1.8.]

Aircraft Documentation

The documentation required for a trip will obviously vary by location and route of flight. Here are a few things you should consider for every trip:

- Air carrier certificate (14 CFR 135 operations). [ICAO Annex 6, Part I, ¶4.2.1.1] An operator shall not engage in commercial air transport operations unless in possession of a valid air operator certificate issued by the State of the Operator.

- Aircraft flight manual and systems manuals. [ICAO Annex 6, Part II, ¶2.4.2.2.]

- Aircraft noise compliance certificates. [ICAO Annex 6, Part I, ¶6.13] An aeroplane shall carry a document attesting noise certification.

- Aircraft registration. [AC 91-70B, ¶5.4.1.1.]

The advisory circular notes "a temporary registration certificate is not acceptable for international travel," but some countries will accept a "fly wire," or equivalent. You have to ask to find out.

- Aircraft and engine logbook copies. [AC 91-70B, ¶5.4.1.1.]

The aircraft's most recent flight and aircraft log usually suffices, but some countries may require much more. Once again, you need to ask.

- Airplane Flight Manual (AFM) with Weight and Balance (W&B) infor-

470

mation and metric conversion tables, if applicable. [AC 91-70B, ¶5.4.1.1.]

- Airworthiness certificate. [AC 91-70B, ¶5.4.1.1.]

- Authorization letters from the operating company or owner, if applicable. [AC 91-70B, ¶5.4.1.1.]

Not many countries require this but some do. If you aren't traveling with the person who owns the aircraft or is somehow identified on the registration, you might need to consider this.

- Cargo manifest, if applicable. [AC 91-70B, ¶5.4.1.2.]

- Certificates of insurance. [AC 91-70B, ¶5.4.1.1.]

The operator is responsible for ensuring the need for airframe logbooks, the engine logbooks, and insurance certificates. For additional details for operations of corporate aircraft, contact the company's aviation underwriter. In operations of private aircraft, if the owner is the pilot or is onboard the aircraft, there are usually no insurance difficulties. However, if a private aircraft owner is not onboard the aircraft, many countries require a letter from the owner that authorizes international flight in that specific country before they will allow operations within their country (you can find specific information on this letter and other requirements in the AIPs of the countries concerned).

Insurance paperwork can be problematic, it should be a question you ask prior to traveling any place new.

- Customs decals, receipts.

[http://www.cbp.gov/xp/cgov/trade/basic_trade/uftd_info.xml] Decals are stickers that are placed on all private aircraft and private vessels (30 feet or more in length) as proof that the User Fee for entry into the U.S. has been paid for the calendar year. Any arriving vessel or aircraft that does not have an annual decal is required to pay a non-refundable per arrival User Fee of $27.50, and complete an application, which will be forwarded to the processing center.

- Import papers for aircraft of foreign manufacture. [AC 91-70B, ¶5.4.1.1.]

- Journey log book for the aeroplane. [ICAO Annex 6, Part II, Chapter 2.4, ¶2.4.2.2.]

This requirement comes from the 1944 Chicago Convention and is further explained in ICAO Annex 6, Part I and ICAO Annex 6, Part II. A journey logbook could be your aircraft flight and maintenance log, provided it contains all the necessary items.

- LOAs/MSpecs/OpSpecs for Special Areas of Operation, if applicable. [AC 91-70B, ¶5.4.1.1.]

- Minimum Equipment List. [AC 91-70B, ¶5.4.1.1.]

If you operate internationally, you probably need an MEL and cannot get by with an MMEL.

- Navigation charts suitable for the route and divert locations. [ICAO Annex 6, Part II, Chapter 2.4, ¶2.4.2.2.]

- Passenger manifest. [AC 91-70B, ¶5.4.1.2.]

- Radio licenses. [AC 91-70B, ¶5.4.1.1. and Chicago Convention, Article 29]

This is the aircraft radio station license.

Operational Approvals

Depending on where you are flying, you may need authorizations for:

- Automatic Dependent Surveillance-Broadcast (ADS-B) Out

Section V, Chapter 2

- Automatic Dependent Surveillance-Contract (ADS-C)

Section V, Chapter3

- Controller-Pilot Data Link Communications (CPDLC)

Section IV, Chapter 5

- Extended Diversion Time Operations (EDTO / ETOPS)

Appendices , Chapter 20

- High Latitude and Northern Domestic Airspace

Appendices , Chapter 24

- North Atlantic High Level Airspace (NAT HLA)

Section III, Chapter 7

- Reduced Vertical Separation Minimum (RVSM)

Section II, Chapter 6

- Required Navigation Performance-1 (RNP-1)

Section III, Chapter 10

- Required Navigation Performance-4 (RNP-4)

Section III, Chapter 11

- Required Navigation Performance-10 (RNP-10)

Section III, Chapter 12

Crew Qualification and Training

Each of the operational approvals shown above have specific training requirements and some countries and airports have their own specific training requirements. You need to check with the country's Aeronautical Information Publication, the Jeppesen Airway Manual, or with your international service handler to be sure. Also consider:

- Aircrew ID cards.

(Nothing really mandates this, but these cards will make your life easier in some locations.)

- FAA Airman's Certificates. [ICAO Chicago Convention, Article 29.]

- FAA Medical Certificates. [AC 91-70B, ¶5.4.1.1]

Keep in mind that ICAO medical classes are slightly different and the valid dates are not like they are in the United States. The expiration isn't at the end of the sixth month following examination for a Class 1 Medical for example. (A medical completed on the 12th day of the month, for example, shall remain valid until the 12th day of the month of expiration.) Further, the 6 month / 12 month / 24 month expirations cannot be simply tied to the type of license or operation. See: ICAO Annex 1, ¶1.2.5.

- FCC Radiotelephone License. [AC 91-70B, ¶5.4.1.1]

While this isn't required flying within the United States, ICAO Annex 6, Part I, requires that one member of the flight crew hold a valid radio telephone operator's license. Keep in mind that Part I only constrains commercial operators but SAFA inspectors are instructed to check this for non-commercial operators as well.

- Immunization Records. (Some countries will require this.)
- Pilot's proof of qualification. Some countries require SICs to have type ratings. Some countries will not take you at your word and it pays to have a copy of your most recent training certificates.
- Passports. [ICAO Chicago Convention, Article 13.]
- Proof of Citizenship.

Paperless Note

There isn't much written about this but I have asked U.S. FAA and EASA SAFA inspectors and they have agreed that you can go paperless on everything except: Aircraft Registration, Airworthiness Certificate, Pilot's License, Pilot's Medical. Everything else can be electronically available. Keep in mind that the more quickly you can produce the document, say on your iPad, the more quickly the inspector is likely to move on.

Chapter 22

Flight Plans

*O*rdinarily the only time you have to worry about this is when you set up *an account with a flight planning service. But there are times in some locations you will have to fill one of these out manually, or check the work of a handler who did that for you. If called upon to fill out an International Flight Plan you may wish to copy the filed flight plan portion of your computer flight plan as a guide.*

General

[ICAO Doc 4444, Appendix 2] All clock times are in four figures, UTC. All estimated elapsed times are in four figures (hours and minutes). Area preceding Item 3 is to be completed by ATS and COM services.

Instructions for Items 7 through 9

[ICAO Doc 4444, Appendix 2]

7.   **Aircraft Identification.** Normally the aircraft call sign, if used, or the registration marking of the aircraft. (i.e., "TAG5")

8.   **Flight Rules.** "I" for IFR, "V" for VFR.

    Type of Flight. "N" for non-scheduled air transportation operation, "G" for general aviation.

9.   **Number of Aircraft.** Leave blank for one aircraft only.

    Type of Aircraft. Designator as specified in ICAO Doc 8643. (i.e., "GLF5").

    Wake Turbulence Category. "H" if aircraft MTOW is greater than 136,000 kg, "M" if less than 136,000 kg but more than 7,000 kg, "L" if less than 7,000 kg.

Figure: International Flight Plan, FAA Form 7233-4

Instructions for Item 10a

[FAA ICAO FPL Quick Guide 2019]

- N - No capabilities (Include no other entries if filed)
- S - Standard (VOR, VHF, ILS)
- A - GBAS Landing Sys.
- B - LPV (APV w/SBAS)
- C - LORAN C
- D - DME
- E1 - FMC WPR (ACARS)
- E2 - D-FIS (ACARS)
- E3 - PDC (ACARS)
- F - ADF
- G - GNSS
- H - HF RTF
- I - INS
- J1 - VDL Mode 2 (CPDLC ATN)
- J2 - HFDL (CPDLC FANS 1/A)
- J3 - VDL Mode A (CPDLC FANS 1/A)
- J4 - VDL Mode 2 (CPDLC FANS 1/A)
- J5 - Satellite Inmarsat (CPDLC FANS 1/A)
- J6 - Satellite MTSAT (CPDLC FANS 1/A)
- J7 - Satellite Iridium (CPDLC FANS 1/A)
- K - MLS
- L - ILS
- M1 - Inmarsat (ATC Satvoice - Item 18 CODE/ address)
- M2 - MTSAT (ATC Satvoice - Item 18 CODE/ address)
- M3 - Iridium (ATC Satvoice - Item 18 CODE/ address)
- O - VOR

- P1 - RCP400 (Requires Ops Approval Auth.)
- P2 - RCP240 (Requires Ops Approval Auth.)
- P3 - RCP400 (Satvoice) (Requires Ops Approval Auth.)
- R - PBN (Include type of PBN in Item 18 PBN/)
- T - TACAN
- U - UHF RTF
- V - VHF RTF
- W - RVSM (Do not include unless authorized)
- X - MNPS
- Y - 8.33 kHz VHF
- Z - Other Cap. (Requires NAV/, COM/, or DAT/ in Item 18)

Instructions for Item 10b

[FAA ICAO FPL Quick Guide 2019]

- N - No capability- include no other entries if filed
- Transponder (file no more than one letter)
    - A - Mode A
    - C - Mode A and C
    - S - Mode S, ACID and Altitude
    - P - Mode S, Altitude, no ACID
    - I - Mode S, ACID, no Altitude
    - X - Mode S, no ACID, no Altitude
    - E - Mode S, ACID, Altitude, extended squitter
    - H - Mode S, ACID, Altitude, Enhanced Surveillance
    - L - Mode S, ACID, Altitude, Enhanced Surveillance, extended squitter
- ADS-B (Include Aircraft Address in Field 18 CODE/, When compliant with 14 CFR 91.227 and AC 20-165, also include in Field 18 SUR/: 260B for 1090 MHz, 282B for UAT)

- B1 - 1090 MHz out capability, or

- B2 - 1090 MHz out and in capability U1 UAT out capability, or

- U2 - UAT out and in capability V1 VDL Mode 4 in capability, or

- V2 - VDL Mode 4 out and in capability

- ADS-C (File aircraft registration in Item 18 REG/)

  - D1 - ADS-C FANS-1/A, and/or

  - G1 - ADS-C ATN

Instructions for Items 13 through 17

[ICAO Doc 4444, Appendix 2]

13. **Departure Aerodrome.**

    The four letter identifier of the departure airport, or "ZZZZ" if no identifier (then specify in Item 18 with "DEP/" followed by name).

15. **Speed.**

    Cruising Speed. Enter the "N" followed by four figures to specify true airspeed in knots (e.g., "N0485"), or "M" followed by three figures to specify true Mach Number (e.g., "M083").

    Cruising Level. Enter "F" followed by three figures to specify a flight level (e.g., "F450"), or "A" followed by three figures to specify altitude in hundreds of feet (e.g., "A100").

    Route.

    Flights along designated ATS routes. Insert the route designator if the departure airport is located on the route, otherwise insert "DCT" followed by the point of joining the first ATS route, followed by the designator of the route. Then, insert each point at which either a change of speed or level, a change of ATS route, and/or a change of flight rules is planned. Followed in each case by the designator of the next route segment, even if same as the previous one, or by "DCT" if the next point will be outside a designated route, unless both points are specified by geographic coordinates.

    Flights outside designated ATS routes. Insert points normally not more than 30 minutes flying time or 200 nm apart, including each point at which a change of speed or level, a change of track, or a change of flight rules is planned. Insert "DCT" between successive points unless both points are defined by geographic coordinates or by bearing and distance.

ATS routes. The coded designator (2 to 7 characters), i.e., "UB10."

Significant points. The coded designator (2 to 5 characters) of the assigned point, i.e., "HADDY." Degrees only (7 characters) will be two figures describing latitude in degrees followed by "N" or "S" and three figures describing longitude in degrees followed by "E" or "W," i.e., "46N078W." Degrees and minutes (11 characters) will be four figures describing latitude in degrees and minutes followed by "N" or "S" and five figures describing longitude in degrees and minutes followed by "E" or "W," i.e., "4620N07805W." Bearing and distance from a navigation aid will be described by two or three characters, then the bearing in three figures (degrees magnetic), then the distance in three figures (nautical miles), i.e., "DUB180040."

Change of speed or level (maximum 21 characters). The point at which a change of speed (5% TAS or 0.01 Mach or more) or a change of level is planned will be followed by an oblique stroke and both the cruising speed and cruising level without a space. I.e., "DUB180040/M082F330."

16.   **Destination Aerodrome.** The four letter ICAO location identifier or "ZZZZ" if no identifier (then specify airport in Item 18 with "DEST/" followed by name).

       Total Elapsed Time. In four digits (hours and minutes).

       Alternate Aerodrome. The four letter ICAO identifier or "ZZZZ" if no identifier (then specify in Item 18 with "ALTN/" followed by name).

Instructions for Item 18

[FAA ICAO FPL Quick Guide 2019]

- STS/ Special Handling

  - ALTRV - Altitude reservation

    - ATFMX - Exempt from ATFM

- FLTCK - Flight check
- HAZMAT - Hazardous materials
- MEDEVAC - Life-critical medical flight
- MARSA - Military assumes responsibility for separation of aircraft
- NONRVSM - Non-RVSM requesting operations in RVSM airspace
- STATE - Military, customs, or police
- HUM - Humanitarian
- FFR - Fire fighting
- HEAD - Head of state
- SAR - Search and Rescue
- HOSP - Medical flight

- PBN/ Performance Based Navigation (list 8 maximum) Note: There is no PBN/ code for RNP2; file as NAV/RNP2
  - A1 - RNAV 10 (RNP10)
  - B1 - RNAV 5 All
  - B2 - RNAV 5 GNSS
  - B3 - RNAV 5 DME/DME
  - B4 - RNAV 5 VOR/DME
  - B5 - RNAV 5 INS or IRS
  - B6 - RNAV 5 LORANC
  - C1 - RNAV 2 All
  - C2 - RNAV 2 GNSS
  - C3 - RNAV 2 DME/DME
  - C4 - RNAV 2 DME/DME/IRU
  - D1 - RNAV 1 All
  - D2 - RNAV 1 GNSS
  - D3 - RNAV 1 DME/DME

- - D4 - RNAV 1 DME/DME/IRU
  - L1 - RNP 4
  - O1 - RNP1 All
  - O2 - RNP 1 GNSS
  - O3 - RNP 1 DME/DME
  - O4 - RNP 1 DME/DME/IRU
  - S1 - Approach RNP APCH
  - S2 - Approach RNP APCH w/BARO VNAV
  - T1 - AR Approach RNP AR APCH With RF
  - T2 - AR Approach RNP AR APCH WithoutRF
- NAV/ Other Navigation Capability (see advanced services, below)
- COM/ Other Comm. Capability
- DAT/ Other Data Application (See AC 90-117)
- SUR/ Other Surv. Capability (e.g. 260B RSP180)
- DEP/ Non-standard Departure (e.g. MD24)
- DEST/ Non-standard Destination (e.g. EMI090021)
- DOF/ Date of Flight (YYMMDD, e.g. 121123)
- REG/ Registration (e.g. N123A)
- EET/ Estimated Elapsed Times (e.g. KZNY0124)
- SEL/ SELCAL (e.g. BPAM)
- TYP/ Non-standard AC Type
- CODE/ Aircraft/Mode S address in hex (e.g. A519D9)
- DLE/ Delay (at a fix) (e.g. EXXON0120)
- OPR/ Operator
- ORGN/Flight Plan Originator (e.g. KHOUARCW)
- PER/ Performance Category (Categories based on Vref if specified, or 1.3Vso, each at maximum certificated landing weight per CFR 97.3)
  - A less than 91 knots IAS
  - B at least 91 and less than121 knots IAS

- C at least 121 and less than 141 knots IAS
- D at least 141 and less than 166 knots IAS
- E greater than 166 and less than 211 knots IAS
- H Helicopters

- ALTN/ Non-standard Alternate(s) (e.g. 61NC)
- RALT/ EnrouteAlternate(s) (e.g.EINN CYYR KDTW)
- TALT/ Take-off Alternate(s) (e.g. KTEB)
- RIF/ Route to revised Destination
- RMK/ Remarks- include any information instructed to include in Remarks (e.g. for NAS Field 11)

Filing for advanced services

[FAA ICAO FPL Quick Guide 2019]

Oceanic 50 NM lateral separation (AC 90-105A)

- R in Fld 10a
- A1 or L1 in Fld 18 PBN/

Oceanic 50 NM longitudinal separation (AC 90-105A)

- R and (J5, J6, or J7) in Fld 10a
- D1 in Fld 10b
- A1 or L1 in Fld 18 PBN/

Oceanic 30 NM Longitudinal or Lateral separation (AC 90-105A)

- R and (J5, J6, or J7) in Fld 10a
- D1 in Fld 10b
- L1 in Fld 18 PBN/

Note: The ADS-C contract requirements differ for longitudinal and lateral. See AC 90-105 for details.

Performance Based Oceanic Separation:

- R, P2, and (J5, J6, or J7) in Fld 10a

- D1 in Fld 10b
- RSP180 in Fld 18 SUR/

In addition to the above, also include:

For 23 NM lateral: L1 in Fld 18 PBN/

For 5 minutes longitudinal: A1 or L1 in Fld 18 PBN/; or RNP2 in Fld 18 NAV/

For 30 NM longitudinal: L1 in Fld 18 PBN/, or RNP2 in Fld 18 NAV/

For 50 NM longitudinal: A1 or L1 in Fld 18 PBN/

RNAV Route Assignment

- Q Route: C1, C2, or C4 in Fld 18 PBN/ ; R in Fld 10a
- T Route: C1, C2, or C4 in Fld 18 PBN/ ; R and G in Fld 10a
- RNAV DP or STAR: D1, D2, D4 in Fld 18 PBN/ ; R in Fld 10a
  Include a NAV/ entry to exclude an arrival or departure:
  - Can fly the RNAV departure only: NAV/RNVD1E2A0
  - Can fly the RNAV arrival only: NAV/RNVD0E2A1

Datacomm DCL (basic options):

Include Z in Fld 10a and Include in Fld 18 DAT/:

- PDC- for ACARS PDC
- FANS- for FANS DCL Only
- FANSP- for FANS 1/A+ DCL

Note: DCL does not require a "J" code In item 10a. Codes J1-J7 indicate en route/oceanic CPDLC (not DCL). See AC 90-117 Appendix D for full details and all options.

Datacomm En Route Services:

Include appropriate codes in Fld 10a and Fld 18 DAT/ According to AC 90-117 Appendix D.

Instructions for Item 19

[ICAO Doc 4444, Appendix 2]

Endurance

After E/ INSERT a 4-figure group giving the fuel endurance in hours and minutes.

Persons on board

After P/ INSERT the total number of persons (passengers and crew) on board, when required by the appropriate ATS authority. INSERT TBN (to be notified) if the total number of persons is not known at the time of filing.

Emergency and survival equipment

R/ (RADIO) - CROSS OUT U if UHF on frequency 243.0 MHz is not available. CROSS OUT V if VHF on frequency 121.5 MHz is not available. CROSS OUT E if emergency locator transmitter (ELT) is not available.

S/ (SURVIVAL EQUIPMENT) - CROSS OUT all indicators if survival equipment is not carried. CROSS OUT P if polar survival equipment is not carried. CROSS OUT D if desert survival equipment is not carried. CROSS OUT M if maritime survival equipment is not carried. CROSS OUT J if jungle survival equipment is not carried.

J/ (JACKETS) - CROSS OUT all indicators if life jackets are not carried. CROSS OUT L if life jackets are not equipped with lights. CROSS OUT F if life jackets are not equipped with fluorescein. CROSS OUT U or V or both as in R/ above to indicate radio capability of jackets, if any.

D/ (DINGHIES) (NUMBER) - CROSS OUT indicators D and C if no dinghies are carried, or INSERT number of dinghies carried; and

(CAPACITY) - INSERT total capacity, in persons, of all dinghies carried; and

(COVER) - CROSS OUT indicator C if dinghies are not covered; and

(COLOUR) - INSERT colour of dinghies if carried.

A/ (AIRCRAFT COLOUR AND MARKINGS) - INSERT colour of aircraft and significant markings.

N/ (REMARKS) - CROSS OUT indicator N if no remarks, or IN-DICATE any other survival equipment carried and any other remarks regarding survival equipment.

C/ (PILOT) - INSERT name of pilot-in-command.

486

Fueling

*B*efore you let the fuel truck pull away, in fact before you allow the truck to hook up, there are two critical questions you need to ask:

- *Is the amount of fuel coming out of the truck the same as what the engines are expecting?*

- *Is the fuel containated?*

The reason we measure fuel in the cockpit by weight and not volume is that is how the engines burn fuel. The pump sends a volume of fuel but the engine consumes less fuel when it is dense, more when it isn't. This density equation works out so that if we think of the engine burning pounds (or kilos) of fuel versus gallons (or liters), we are better off. So you need to understand variations in fuel density around the world.

We tend to rely on the FBO for fuel quality testing but sometimes you aren't familiar with the FBO, sometimes the fuel truck causes you to wonder if those engines will keep running once full thrust is added on takeoff. In either case, you may want to sump and test the fuel in your tanks. There are commercially available fuel test kits that can detect some contaminants and some amounts of water. While they are not as good as a lab test, they are certainly better than relying on the word of the guy doing the pumping. But what if you don't have a fuel test kit available? There are two other options.

Fuel Density Variations

We often think of fuel density as a function only of temperature, but temperature isn't the largest factor in determining how much "bang" you get per drop of fuel. To understand what is, consider this riddle. Why can a Gulfstream V almost always fly from San Francisco to Tokyo non-stop even with a headwind, but sometimes not be able to make the return trip, even with a tailwind?

As it turns out, fuel density in California is about the highest in the world while density in Japan is about the lowest. If you are planning on flying to the airplane's maximum range you need to understand fuel density, especially if operating out of Asia.

[PetroValue, ¶1.6]

- Scientific definition of density: density (ρ) of a body is the ratio of its mass (m) to its volume (V).

- Density of fuel is "the mass of fuel per unit volume."

- In some cases the density is expressed as a specific gravity or relative density, in which case it is expressed in multiples of the density of some other standard material, usually water or air.

- Reference: ASTM D1655 specification, Jet A-1 fuel has a density of between 775.0 and 840.0 kg/m3. Density ranging from 37 to 51 °C API corrected to 15 °C or 60 °F.

When it comes to fuel, higher density means more "bang for the buck." The density is determined by the quality of the crude used to produce the fuel and the refining process.

Jet-A fuel density limits are established by the American Society for Testing and Materials (ASTM) Specification D1655. At 60°F the density limits are from 6.46 to 6.99 lbs/gallon.

In a G450, this equates to a range of:

- *28,230 lbs at 6.46 lbs/gallon*

- *30,546 lbs at 6.99 lbs/gallon*

A variation of 2,316 lbs.

Fuel Contamination

If you are flying out of a major international airport with a reputable fuel dealer, you probably have nothing to worry about. What about those lesser travelled destinations? Perhaps a fuel contamination test kit is in order.

White Bucket Test

[PetroValue]

The white bucket is a simple but reliable test for detection of significant amounts of water and particulates. Water occurs in different forms in the fuel;

- Dissolved in the fuel, normally this water can not be removed from the fuel.

- Suspended or entrained in the fuel. Entrained water can be detected with the naked eyes. The fine droplets of water in fuel reflect light and in high concentration give the fuel a cloudy or hazy appearance.

- Water in high quantity into fuel may be caused by leakage into storage tanks, delivery of water-laden fuel, condensation or the coalescence and subsequent settling of entrained water.

Particulate or dirt is normally found in fuel in the form of rust, scale, lint, dust, particles from gaskets and hoses which have been released from the side of the tanks, piping and transportation vehicles.

A bucket, white porcelain lined or stainless steel of a capacity of seven liters (7 L) and with a bonding cable (a separate cable if not equipped, must be provided). A shiny coin with well-defined feature is an additional tool. Bucket must be clean and dry.

- A static bonding cable must be connected between bucket and the source of sample container, pipe or valve as required.

- Take a sample at system operating pressure (except samples from a storage tank or transport trailer). Fuel in the drain or line should be removed or displaced before taking sample. Valve should be completely open without causing spill.

- Fill bucket at least 15 cm of its depth.

- Place bucket on a level surface and allow it to stand for few minutes to settle sample to ensuring no air bubbles present.

- Visually inspect and observe the fuel sample to determine presence of free water, particulates, unusual colour, haze, floating material and lacy substance layers.

- Swirling of sample will cause dirt or water to collect at the centre of bucket for easier examination.

- Drop a coin with well-defined features into the fuel sample bucket to assist visual detection of haze.

Evaluation

- Observed colour of jet fuel should be colourless to a light straw. Colour should be similar to previously acceptable test if any.

- A cloudy or haziness condition in appearance of the fuel sample suggests water contamination.

- If sample does not appear cloudy, a drop of food colouring or coffee added to the sample will ensure absence of water when coloured drop settles at the bottom. If it dissolves in the sample the fuel is not pure and contaminated with unacceptable amount of water.

- Slime on the bottom surface of container or lacy substance is an indication of Microbiological Contamination.

Clear and Bright Test

[PetroValue]

Delivered fuel must be clean, bright and not contaminated with free water.

"Clear" is a visual condition of fuel with the absence of cloud, emulsion, visible particulate matter or entrained water. "Bright" is the quality of fuel refers to the shiny and sparkling appearance of clean and dry fuel.

The "bright and clear" condition of the fuel is not dependent on the natural colour of the fuel.

The "Clear and Bright" test is a visual check and conducted to detect water or other solid contaminants in the fuel. An evidence of external contaminants renders the fuel as "not suitable for use" and points to a requirement of further laboratory analysis.

Glass Jar – a wide mouth glass jar of 7.5 cm (3 in.) in diameter or other similar transparent container. A white paper sheet or light background surface material is a great tool to enhance detection of contaminants.

Evaluation is completed as given earlier, in the White Bucket Test.

Contaminants found in fuel sample would suggest a need to inspect the source of contaminants and could also be attributed to the failure of equipment or procedures.

Free water contamination in fuel can go undetected using visual test methods. There are number of free water detection kits available for field use such as the Velcon Hydrokit® and the Shell Water Detector®. A water sensitive chemical product is used with the fuel sample which reacts with the suspended water content in the fuel by changing its color.

Other Contaminants

There are several other worrisome contaminants that may escape visual detection. Unfortunately, you are pretty much at the mercy of the fuel provider to do the necessary tests. It is to your advantage to make sure the fueler is busy; there is no better reassurance than knowing airplanes have been successfully flying using the same fuel all day. Here are a few things to worry about and a thought or two about each.

[Fuel Handling Jet Quality and Test Procedure, ¶1.3] Rust is generally the leading source of particulate contamination. Frequently the sand or dust could also be present. The main source of this kind of contamination is erosion and corrosion of container surfaces, pipes, fittings, pumps cavity erosion and any other source which come in contact with the fuel.

The best test is force fuel under pressure through a filter membrane with pores as small as 0.8 microns. A collection of rust or sand will discolor the membrane. The FBO should be doing this. I don't think any commercially available portable pilot-operated fuel testing kits have this capability.

[PetroValue, ¶1.4] Micro-organisms may enter in aviation fuel in many ways such as air, sea or fresh water, soil or by other means. Micro-organism causes significant damage to the fuel system by means of slime formation, sludge and corrosion.

These micro-organisms feed on the fuel and produced more micro-organisms. Once they've multiplied enough they can be seen in the fuel as a black gelatinous matter. To detect them early, you need a laboratory test. There are commercially available kits but they aren't really suitable for pilot usage on the road.

Fuel Servicing Checklist

The following is procedure for some companies, a recommended technique from others.

Conduct Briefing with Fueler:

- Specify amount of fuel desired.
- Type of fuel desired.
- Location of where it is to be placed.
- Ensure proper grounding and safety equipment available.
- Instruct fueler about any special procedures needed.

Verify with fueler:

- Filter date (within 1 year).
- Sump drain (daily).
- Water test (daily).

Overall Vendor Quality:

- If vendor quality is acceptable, proceed with fueling.
- If vendor quality is unacceptable, use a fuel test kit. If the fuel passes, proceed with fueling and document results.
- If fuel test fails, do not fuel the aircraft.

Post Fueling Check:

- Check type fo fuel and quanity against receipts.
- Ensure fueling equipment is stowed or clear of aircraft.
- Check servicing caps and doors are secure.

Chapter 24

High Latitude Operations

If you fly anywhere near the poles under 14 CFR 135, you need to understand everything written below about high latitude operations. It could very well be that you can't legally do what your airplane is physically capable of doing. Flying near the poles under 14 CFR 91? You still need to understand this stuff, but you might not be prevented from doing something stupid. Me? I would make sure we had all our ducks in line first.

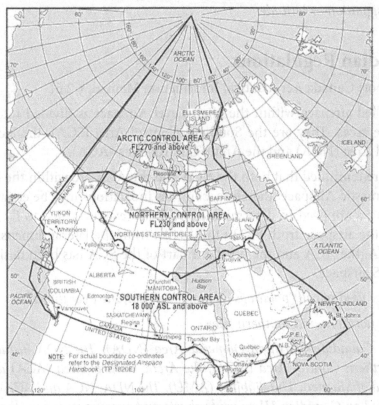

Figure: Southern, Northern, and Arctic Control Areas, from Transport Canada Aeronautical Information Manual, Figure 2.3.

Location

U.S. Regulations

[Advisory Circular 120-42B, ¶601.]

- The North Polar Area is defined as the entire area north of latitude 78° North.

- The South Polar Area is defined as the entire area south of latitude 60° South.

The worst magnetic compass performance is probably in the center of the Northern Control Area, home to the magnetic north pole. This position creates a notch in the circle of magnetic unreliability, often called a "key hole." Charts should be checked for the presence of a "T" denoting the use of True Heading instead of Magnetic. Some aircraft automatically switch to True based on airway designation or latitude.

Canadian Regulations

[Transport Canada Aeronautical Information Manual, ¶ 2.6]

Controlled airspace within the High Level Airspace is divided into three separate areas. They are the Southern Control Area (SCA), the Northern Control Area (NCA) and the Arctic Control Area (ACA).

Pilots are reminded that both the NCA and the ACA are within the Northern Domestic Airspace; therefore, compass indications may be erratic, and true tracks are used in determining the flight level at which to fly. In addition, the airspace from FL330 to FL410 within the lateral dimensions of the NCA, the ACA and the northern part of the SCA has been designated CMNPS airspace.

What we used to call "polar ops" is now "high latitude operations."

- *The northern and southern poles.*

- *The Canadian Northern Domestic Area (NDA). The NDA includes the Northern Control Area (NCA), the Arctic Control Area (ACA) and the Area of Magnetic Unreliability (AMU). The NDA, NCA and ACA are depicted on Canadian HI en route charts and encompass the northernmost Canadian airspace.*

Documentation / Certification

[14 CFR 135, §135.98 Operations in the North Polar Area.] After February 15, 2008, no certificate holder may operate an aircraft in the region north of 78° N latitude ("North Polar Area"), other than intrastate operations wholly within the state of Alaska, unless authorized by the FAA. The certificate holder's operation specifications must include the following:

- The designation of airports that may be used for en-route diversions and the requirements the airports must meet at the time of diversion.

- Except for all-cargo operations, a recovery plan for passengers at designated diversion airports.

- A fuel-freeze strategy and procedures for monitoring fuel freezing for operations in the North Polar Area.

- A plan to ensure communication capability for operations in the North Polar Area.

- An MEL for operations in the North Polar Area.

- A training plan for operations in the North Polar Area.

- A plan for mitigating crew exposure to radiation during solar flare activity.

- A plan for providing at least two cold weather anti-exposure suits in the aircraft, to protect crewmembers during outside activity at a diversion airport with extreme climatic conditions. The FAA may relieve the certificate holder from this requirement if the season of the year makes the equipment unnecessary.

[FAA Order 8900, Volume 4, Chapter 1, §5, ¶4-103.D] All approvals for operations into AMUs are granted by issuing OpSpec B040, and by adding that area of en route operation to the standard OpSpec B050. A checklist for operations in AMUs is available in the guidance subsystem in association with OpSpec B040.

Crews operating under 14 CFR 135 require operations specification approval (B040 and B050).

Crews operating under 14 CFR 91 should consider the many challenges involved and the potential safety risks illustrated below.

Equipment

[Advisory Circular 135-42, Appendix 3, ¶3.f.] Certificate holders must have at least two cold weather anti-exposure suit(s) for the crewmembers on the airplane if outside coordination by a crewmember at a diversion airport with extreme climatic conditions is determined to be necessary. The certificate holder may be relieved of this requirement based on seasonal temperatures that would render the use of such suits unnecessary. This determination must be made with concurrence of the CHDO.

This isn't much of a list; you would be wise to consider adding the requirements of Advisory Circular 120-42B, which do not restrict 14 CFR 135 and 91, but offer sound operating practices.

[Advisory Circular 120-42B, ¶603.b.(5)]

- Fuel quantity indicating system (FQIS), including the fuel tank temperature indicating system;

- APU (when the APU is necessary for an airplane to comply with ETOPS requirements), including electrical and pneumatic supply to its designed capability,

- Autothrottle system;

- Communication systems relied on by the flight crewmember to satisfy the requirement for communication capability; and

- Except for all-cargo operations, an expanded medical kit to include automated external defibrillators (AED).

MEL

[Advisory Circular 135-42, Appendix 3, ¶3.c.] Before receiving approval to conduct polar operations, a certificate holder must review their MEL for such operations and should amend their MEL. The following systems and equipment should be addressed in the MEL based on specific needs applicable to this operation.

- Fuel Quantity Indicating System (to include a fuel tank temperature indicating system).

- Communication system(s) needed for effective communications by the flight crewmember while in flight.

- Expanded medical kit.

Training

[Advisory Circular 135-42, Appendix 3, ¶3.e.] Before conducting polar operations, certificate holders must ensure that flight crewmembers are trained on any applicable passenger recovery plan used in this operation. Certificate holders should also ensure that flight crewmembers are trained on the following items, which should be included in a certificate holder's approved training programs:

- Atmospheric pressure at Field Elevation/Barometric pressure for Local Altimeter Setting and meter/feet conversion issues (flight crewmember training).

- Training requirements for fuel freeze (maintenance and flight crewmember training).

- General polar-specific training on weather patterns and aircraft system limitations (flight crewmember training).

- Proper use of the cold weather anti-exposure suit, if required (flight crewmember training).

- Radiation exposure (see AC 120-61B, In-Flight Radiation Exposure).

Communications Issues

[AC 120-42B, ¶303.c.(7)] The FAA recognizes the limitations of satellite communications (SATCOM) in the North Polar Area above this latitude, and in such an area an alternate communication system such as HF voice or data link is to be used. The relatively short period of time that the flight is above latitude 82 degrees North in relation to the total planned flight time is a small fraction of the total flight. The ability to use SATCOM for all other portions of the flight, which for some routes could be longer than 15 hours duration, is advantageous to the flight. For flights above 82 degrees North latitude, the operator must also ensure that communications requirements can be met by the most reliable means available, taking into account the potential communication disruption due to solar flare activity. The same philosophy and commensurate requirements apply for ETOPS in the South Polar Area.

VHF, HF, INMARSAT, CPDLC

You can find frequencies, phone numbers, and CPDLC addresses on en route charts. To do this in JeppFD, you scroll and zoom to the region in question and tap on any point away from the existing route or waypoints. You should get a flag with the FIR name. Click that to get the FIR contact information, as shown in the photo.

I am told that VHF is sparse, HF quality is generally good, though signals may be impacted by solar activity. You may need to use either AM, USB or LSB to achieve the best clarity.

Inmarsat

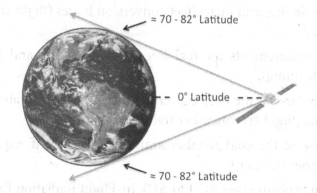

Figure: INMARSAT Line of Sight.

Keep in mind that Inmarsat satellites are geostationary, generally near the equator. They may not have good line-of-sight near the poles. Geosynchronous satellites, such as Iridium, have better coverage at the poles.

Navigation Issues

Magnetic Variation and Convergence of the Meridians

The following from an outdated navigation manual that still makes sense:

- Conventional magnetic compasses sense magnetic direction by detecting the horizontal component of the earth's magnetic field. Since this horizontal component vanishes near the magnetic poles, magnetic compasses are highly unreliable and unusable in an area approximately 1,000 nm from each magnetic pole. Within these areas, air navigation tasks are further complicated by very rapid changes in magnetic variation over small distances.

- Since these two major AMUs also occur near the earth's geographic poles, the convergence of the meridians also presents additional directional complications. When flying "great circle" courses at latitudes greater than 67 degrees, convergence of the meridians can create rapid changes in true headings and true courses with small changes in aircraft position. As a result, relatively small errors in determining the aircraft's actual position can produce very large errors in determining the proper heading to fly and maintain the assigned flight path.

True Heading

Navigating near the poles presents several issues not found anywhere else in the world. Because of these issues, the only acceptable method of navigating through the NCA and high latitude region is through the use of long-range navigation systems using inertial and GPS based FMS systems referenced to True North only. Back when I was a Strategic Air Command trained killer, our navigators would use grid navigation to head from here to there and I do believe we got lost a few times.

Other methods of navigation in the NCA are impractical or unreliable because of the inherent limitations of magnetic compasses near the magnetic and geographic North Poles, and because of the geometric problem caused by meridian convergence.

Some aircraft make the switch automatically by reference to latitude or airway, while for others the switch must be made manually. You need to dive into your aircraft manuals to find out.

GPS Navigation

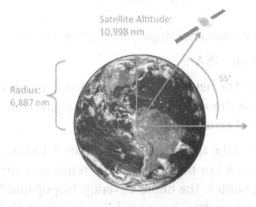

Figure: GPS Satellite Line of Sight.

Each GPS satellite traces a track over the earth from 55° North to 55° South every twelve hours. At their maximum latitudes they are actually "looking down" on the poles:

Height Above Pole = 10998 cos 55 − 6887 = 2122

Of course you have no guarantee you will have at least one satellite that high in its orbit. In order to have line of sight on the pole, a satellite would have to be at least 39° latitude:

Minimum Latitude to See Pole = arcsin(6887 / 10998) = 39

I've not found anything in writing that tells you there will always be at least four satellites above 39° North and 39° South, but it appears so. You should have a good GPS position at either pole. See Part II, Chapter 8, GNSS.

Temperature Issues

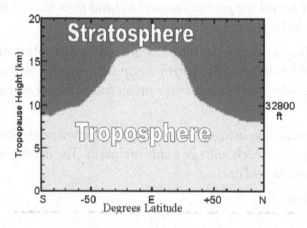

Figure: Tropopause Height, from Geerts and Linacre.

Tropopause Height and ISA

[Geerts and Linacre] The height of the tropopause depends on the location, notably the latitude, as shown in the figure on the right (which shows annual mean conditions). It also depends on the season.

At latitudes above 60°, the tropopause is less than 9-10 km above sea level; the lowest is less than 8 km high, above Antarctica and above Siberia and northern Canada in winter. The highest average tropopause is over the oceanic warm pool of the western equatorial Pacific, about 17.5 km high, and over Southeast Asia, during the summer monsoon, the tropopause occa-

500

sionally peaks above 18 km. In other words, cold conditions lead to a lower tropopause, obviously because of less convection.

Deep convection (thunderstorms) in the Intertropical Convergence Zone, or over mid-latitude continents in summer, continuously push the tropopause upwards and as such deepen the troposphere.

On the other hand, colder regions have a lower tropopause, obviously because convective overturning is limited there, due to the negative radiation balance at the surface. In fact, convection is very rare in polar regions; most of the tropospheric mixing at middle and high latitudes is forced by frontal systems in which uplift is forced rather than spontaneous (convective). This explains the paradox that tropopause temperatures are lowest where the surface temperatures are highest.

The tropopause at the poles is lower than at the equator; that means the altitudes where most polar-capable aircraft cruise is warmer. Knowing this, altitude selection may not be straightforward.

Surface Temperatures

If a descent into lower altitudes is required, fuel freezing and other aircraft systems limitations can become issues. If an emergency landing is required, surface temperatures can be life threatening.

Fuel Freezing

[Advisory Circular 135-42, Appendix 3, ¶3.c.] Fuel Freeze Strategy and Monitoring Requirements for Polar Operations. Certificate holders must develop a fuel freeze strategy and procedures for monitoring fuel freezing for operations in the North Polar Area. A fuel freeze analysis program in lieu of using the standard minimum fuel freeze temperatures for specific types of fuel may be used. In such cases, the certificate holder's fuel freeze analysis and monitoring program for the airplane fuel load must be acceptable to the FAA Administrator. The certificate holder should have procedures for determining the fuel freeze temperature of the actual fuel load on board the airplane. These procedures relative to determining the fuel freeze temperature and monitoring the actual temperature of the fuel on board should require appropriate levels of coordination between maintenance and the flight crewmember.

Should fuel temperatures approach the aircraft's freezing limit you should con-

501

sider:

- *Climbing or descending into a level of warmer air,*
- *Altering the route into a region of warmer air, and/or*
- *Increasing cruise airspeed (A Boeing study says an increase of 0.01 Mach results in an increase of 0.5° to 0.7° C total air temperature.)*

Your flight planning vendor should provide a temperature chart to help you plan for these contingencies. Remember, any changes in flight level, speed or route must be coordinated with ATC.

Polar Radiation

[Advisory Circular 120-61A, ¶6.] Radiation received on a lower-latitude flight will be lower because of the greater amount of radiation shielding provided by the earth's magnetic field. This shielding is maximum near the equator and gradually decreases to zero as one goes north or south. Radiation levels over the polar regions are about twice those over the equator at the same altitudes.

[NASA Study, Michael Finneran] Space radiation on the ground is very low, but increases significantly with altitude. At 30,000 to 40,000 feet, the typical altitude of a jetliner, exposure on a typical flight is still considered safe – less than a chest X-ray.

Exposure is considerably higher, however, over the Earth's poles, where the planet's magnetic field no longer provides any shielding. And with a thousand-fold rise in commercial airline flights over the North Pole in the last 10 years, exposure to radiation has become a serious concern.

A study by Mertens of polar flights during a solar storm in 2003 showed that passengers received about 12 percent of the annual radiation limit recommended by the International Committee on Radiological Protection. The exposures were greater than on typical flights at lower latitudes, and confirmed concerns about commercial flights using polar routes.

People who work on commercial airline flights are technically listed as "radiation workers" by the federal government – a classification that includes nuclear plant workers and X-ray technicians. But unlike some others in that category, flight crews do not quantify the radiation they are exposed to.

Flights in the Polar Region at typical business jet operating altitudes are well above the tropopause where much of the atmospheric protection from solar storms is lost, increasing crew and passenger exposure to solar radiation.

For example, one New York-Tokyo flight during a solar storm could expose the passengers and crew to the normal annual exposure (1mSv) of someone who remained on the surface. If an S4 solar storm is active or predicted, polar operations are generally considered not suitable at any altitude, while operations at FL310 or below are considered acceptable in S3 storm conditions.

Some flight plan vendors will include predicted solar activity for flights through the high latitude airspace. Additionally, Space Weather Now from the NOAA and spaceweather.com are useful when planning a polar flight.

Alternate Airports

[Advisory Circular 135-42, Appendix 3, ¶3.a.] Before each flight, certificate holders must designate alternate airports that can be used in case an en route diversion is necessary. The airplane should have a reasonable assurance that the weather during periods when the certificate holder would need the services of the airport are within the operating limits of the airplane. The airplane should be able to make a safe landing and maneuver off the runway at the diversion airport. In addition, those airports identified for use during an en route diversion should be capable of protecting the safety of all personnel by allowing:

- Safe offload of passengers and crewmember during possible adverse weather conditions;

- Providing for the physiological needs of the passengers and crewmember until a safe evacuation is completed; and

- Safe extraction of passengers and crewmember as soon as possible (execution and completion of the recovery should be within 12 to 48 hours following landing).

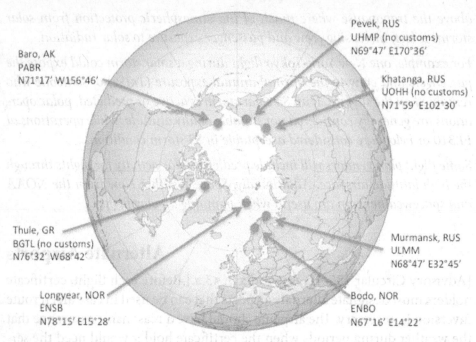

Pevek, RUS
UHMP (no customs)
N69°47' E170°36'

Baro, AK
PABR
N71°17' W156°46'

Khatanga, RUS
UOHH (no customs)
N71°59' E102°30'

Thule, GR
BGTL (no customs)
N76°32' W68°42'

Murmansk, RUS
ULMM
N68°47' E32°45'

Longyear, NOR
ENSB
N78°15' E15°28'

Bodo, NOR
ENBO
N67°16' E14°22'

The requirements for the passenger recovery plan are quite extensive and must be detailed for each airport listed as a possible alternate airport. More on this: Advisory Circular 135-42, Appendix 3, ¶3.b.

There aren't many airports with paved runways in the Arctic, and many of those do not have regular airline service or customs. If you are flying under 14 CFR 135 your Operations Specification approval will require a list of alternates and a plan for getting passengers from the alternates within 48 hours.

Insurance

*Y*our insurance paperwork needs to be in order whenever you depart for foreign shores, there are places where they will be asking to see them.

Sources

Aeronautical Information Publications (AIPs)

Theoretically, you should be able to find everything about a country's insurance requirements in their Aeronautical Information Publication, and that should be in section GEN 1.2 ENTRY, TRANSIT AND DEPARTURE OF AIRCRAFT. Here is a sampling:

Australia Example: [Australia AIP. GEN 1.2, ¶1.17.2] Commercial passenger transport operations are required to maintain appropriate insurance arrangements in accordance with the requirements of the Act and the operator's licence(s).

Hong Kong Example: [Hong Kong AIP. GEN 1.2, ¶2.1] Under the Civil Aviation (Insurance) Order (Cap. 448 sub. leg. F), all civil aircraft, whether operating commercial or non-revenue flights, are required to have a Combined Single Limit (CSL) insurance meeting the following requirements: a) Subject to para c) below, the CSL should cover the operators' liabilities in respect of third party, passenger, baggage, cargo and mail. b) It may include other liability items except the liability in respect of damage to the hull of the operators' aircraft. c) If an operator declares in writing that the aircraft does not carry any passenger, baggage, cargo or mail, as the case may be, they will be allowed not to include those items in the CSL. d) The insurance cover must be on a per occurrence basis. [. . .] Any aircraft not complying with these insurance requirements will not be allowed to land or take off in Hong Kong. However, this does not apply to an aircraft in emergency.

This would be helpful if every country (a) listed their insurance requirements in their AIPs and (b) had their AIPs readily available. But that isn't always so:

United Kingdom Example: We are told flight to a United Kingdom civil/military airport requires a Crown Indemnity Waiver, but that information is absent from their AIP.

Mexico Example: We know from experience that Mexico requires a standard worldwide insurance policy and a Mexican insurance policy drawn on a Mexican insurance company. But we cannot get the Mexican AIP without a paid subscription which gives us a mailed copy on a CD-ROM.

So the AIP is not always available and doesn't always include critical insurance information.

Jeppesen

The Jeppesen "State" pages are generally good about positing insurance requirements in the "Aircraft Entry Requirements" section. For example:

Mexico Entry Requirements: [Jeppesen, Mexico, Entry Requirements] [...] The applicant has proof of insurance policies in accordance with the Varsovia Convention, or has contracted insurance with Mexican companies authorized to practice liability and transport insurance, or has coverage with a foreign subsidiary company authorized to operate in Mexico.

Experience and/or Contacts

Asking about insurance requirements should be one of your Checklist items whenever setting up an international trip. If you don't have an in-country handler or contact with anyone who has recent experience, you should phone contacts at the airport.

Documentation of Insurance

[Insurance Considerations For Overseas Missions] A copy or a certified copy of your policy is usually sufficient, but not always.

[Dealing With the New Rules of Worldwide Documentation] Insurance requirements can be persnickety at some locations. The European Union (EU) has special insurance mandates, liability limits and formats that must be followed. Mexico, in most cases, requires liability policies from providers in Mexico and these documents must be in Spanish. Hong Kong is particularly obsessive in terms of insurance requirements, liability limits and specific wording/format of policies. "We had a case of a Hong Kong landing permit request denied because one comma was missing on the insurance policy."

[EASA Rules of Air Operations, AMC2 CATR.GEN.MPA.141(b)] The following EFB application should be considered type A EFB applications: [...] the third-party liability insurance certificate(s).

Most countries will accept a look at an insurance policy on an iPad but not all. Mexico, for example, requires a hard copy in color. (They have in the past required an original policy, but have gradually accepted copies that "look original."

War Risk Insurance

The insurance mandated by European Union Regulation 785-2004 must include coverage for war, terrorism, hijacking, sabotage, unlawful seizure of aircraft, and civil commotion. In addition, the third party element of the cover must be on an 'each accident, each and every aircraft' basis.

["Flying to Europe? Think Again"] There are no war risk insurance requirements in the United States but if you fly internationally you need to check. For example, Germany requires €60,000,000, China (Hong Kong) requires $200,000,000, and Poland requires €60,000,000.

Incognito LLC
Flight / Maintenance Log

Aircraft Reg.: 7700C

Log Number:

Oil
L:
R:

Crew, Duty Times, PIC Signature		On Duty	Off Duty	Total
PIC:				
SIC:				
ACM:				
Signature				

Leg	Z-Date	From / To	Out / In	Block Time	NM Distance	Off / On	Flight Time	Crew L / R	T/O D / N	Landing D / N	Apchs P / NP	Inst Time Hrs / PF	Night
1													
2													
3													
4													
5													

Totals This Log		Left Engine			Right Engine			VOR Check		RVSM
Aircraft	Landings	Hours	Cycles	Hours	Cycles	Hours	APU	Station	Type	Altimeter Check
Hours	Landings						03-08 → 0.1	33-38 → 0.6	Left
Log							09-14 → 0.2	39-44 → 0.7	Stby
Fwd							15-20 → 0.3	45-50 → 0.8	VOR #1	Right
Tot							21-26 → 0.4	51-56 → 0.9	VOR #2
							27-32 → 0.5	57-02 → 1.0		

Fuel/Passenger Data			Weight and Balance				
Leg	Uploaded	Start (#)	End (#)	Pax	T/O Wt	Max Wt	Fwd Limit	T/O CG	Aft Limit
1									
2									
3									
4									
5									

Discrepancy Report
No: ____ Leg: ____ Z-Date: ____ Signature: ____ Corrective Action ____ Mechanic Cert ____ Date

Sign/Certificate Number

Type Inspection.

I certify that this aircraft has been inspected in accordance with the inspection program identified in 14 CFR 91.409 and was determined to be in airworthy condition with respect to the work performed and is approved for return to service.

Discrepancy Report
No: ____ Leg: ____ Z-Date: ____ Signature: ____ Corrective Action ____ Mechanic Cert ____ Date

White Copy - Operations / Yellow Copy - Maintenance / Pink - Remains With Aircraft

Sample Flight and Maintenance Logbook

Chapter 26

Journey Logbook

*T*here was once a huge controversy over what exactly constitutes a journey logbook. Everybody agreed you had to have one, but what is it? The original requirement was set out in 1944 without a precise definition. ICAO Annex 6 changed all that a few years ago, but we are still left with a decision on where the book should be kept.

The only document we have that comes even close to satisfying all the requirements is the Flight and Maintenance Log that we complete for every flight. You will have to examine your version to see if it also satisfies the ICAO.

As for how long you need to keep it on the aircraft, that's where it gets tricky. More on that below.

Where (and when) it all started . . .

[1944 ICAO Chicago Convention, Article 34] There shall be maintained in respect of every aircraft engaged in international navigation a journey log book in which shall be entered particulars of the aircraft, its crew and of each journey, in such form as may be prescribed from time to time pursuant to this Convention.

Updated Guidance for Commercial Operators

[ICAO Annex 6 Part I]

11.4.1. The aeroplane journey log book should contain the following items and the corresponding roman numerals:

I.   Aeroplane nationality and registration.

II.   Date.

III.   Names of crew members.

IV.   Duty assignments of crew members.

V.   Place of departure.

VI.   Place of arrival.

VII. Time of departure.

VIII. Time of arrival.

IX.   Hours of flight.

X.   Nature of flight (private, aerial work, scheduled or non-scheduled).

XI.   Incidents, observations, if any.

XII. Signature of person in charge.

11.4.2 Recommendation.— Entries in the journey log book should be made currently and in ink or indelible pencil.

11.4.3 Recommendation.— Completed journey log book should be retained to provide a continuous record of the last six months' operations.

Paragraph 11.4.3 recommends the journey log book be "retained" but doesn't say it has to be on the aircraft. I think if you have electronic access to them you should be okay.

[EASA Air Ops Annex 1 to VIII] §AMC1 ORO.MLR.110]

a.   The aircraft journey log, or equivalent, should include the following items, where applicable:

1.   aircraft nationality and registration,

2.   date,

3.   name(s) of crew member(s),

4.   duty assignments of crew member(s),

5.   place of departure,

6.   place of arrival,

7.   time of departure,

8.   time of arrival,

9.   hours of flight,

10.   nature of flight (scheduled or non-scheduled),

11.   incidents, observations, if any,

12.   signature of person in charge.

510

b.　　The information, or parts thereof, may be recorded in a form other than on printed paper. Accessibility, usability and reliability should be assured.

c.　　'Journey log, or equivalent' means that the required information may be recorded in documentation other than a log book, such as the operational flight plan or the aircraft technical log.

d.　　'Series of flights' means consecutive flights, which begin and end:

　　1.　　within a 24-hour period;

　　2.　　at the same aerodrome or operating site or remain within a local area specified in the operations manual; and

　　3.　　with the same pilot-in-command/commander of the aircraft.

Updated Guidance for General Aviation

[ICAO Annex 6 Part II]

2.8.2 A journey log book shall be maintained for every aeroplane engaged in international air navigation in which shall be entered particulars of the aeroplane, its crew and each journey.

2.8.2.2. Recommendation.—The aeroplane journey log should contain the following items:

a.　　aeroplane nationality and registration;

b.　　date;

c.　　crew member names and duty assignments;

d.　　departure and arrival points and times;

e.　　purpose of flight;

f.　　observations regarding the flight; and

g.　　signature of the pilot-in-command.

[EASA Air Ops Annex 1 to VIII] §AMC1 ORO.MLR.110] Particulars of the aircraft, its crew and each journey shall be retained for each flight, or series of flights, in the form of a journey log, or equivalent.

We scan every flight log and have it electronically available at our home base on a full time, secured, network drive. We can download any log from any-

where with an Internet connection. We only carry enough past flight logs on the aircraft to prove a maintenance airworthiness release, a valid VOR check, and an RVSM check. Will this pass muster? I think so. I have been SAFA ramp checked and the subject never came up.

If you would like an example of a Flight and Maintenance Log that I believe satisfies all these Journey Logbook requirements, look at the first page of this chapter.

Chapter 27

Mach Number Technique

It is called "Mach Number Technique" but it is actually "Mach Number Procedure" because if you don't follow it you could lose your oceanic pilot's privileges. The procedure is required around much of the world, though the ICAO manual description is rather sparse.

If you have auto throttles you are pretty much set. Tune those puppies to the filed oceanic Mach and leave them there. If your ETA to the next waypoint varies by the required tolerance, 3 minutes or more for most of the world, update your ETA. Do not change your target Mach. Why? Read on . . .

Mach Number Technique Defined

[ICAO NAT Doc 007, ¶7.1.1.] Mach Number Technique (MNT) is a technique whereby aircraft operating successively along suitable routes are cleared by ATC to maintain a Mach number for a portion of the enroute phase of flight.

Objective

[ICAO NAT Doc 007, ¶7.2.1.] MNT is used to improve the utilisation of airspace on long route segments where ATC has only position reports to ensure longitudinal separation between flights is maintained. When two or more aircraft are operating along the same route at the same flight level and maintaining the same Mach number, the time interval between them is more likely to remain constant than by using any other method.

Longitudinal Separation

[ICAO Doc 4444, ¶5.4.2.1.1.] Longitudinal separation shall be applied so that the spacing between the estimated positions of the aircraft being separated is never less than a prescribed minimum. Longitudinal separation between aircraft following the same or diverging tracks may be maintained by application of speed control, including the Mach number technique. When applicable, use of the Mach number technique shall be prescribed on the basis of a regional air navigation agreement.

[ICAO NAT Doc 007, ¶7.3.] Oceanic clearances include assigned Mach numbers (when required) which are to be maintained. Aircraft capable of maintaining an assigned Mach must flight plan their requested Mach number. ATC uses assigned Mach number along with position reports to calculate estimated times along the cleared route. These times are used as the basis for longitudinal separation and for coordination with adjacent units.

ATC will try to accommodate flight crew/dispatcher requested or flight planned Mach numbers when issuing oceanic clearances. It is rare that ATC will assign a Mach number more than 0.01 faster or 0.02 slower than that requested.

The monitoring and maintenance of longitudinal separation is dependent upon the provision of accurate times in position reports.

The assigned Mach number must be maintained. If an immediate temporary change in the Mach number is essential (due to turbulence for example), ATC must be so informed.

[ICAO Annex 2, ¶3.6.2.2. c)] Change in time estimate: if the time estimate for the next applicable reporting point, flight information region boundary or destination aerodrome, whichever comes first, is found to be in error in excess of 3 minutes from that notified to air traffic services, or such other period of time as is prescribed by the appropriate ATS authority or on the basis of air navigation regional agreements, a revised estimated time shall be notified as soon as possible to the appropriate air traffic services unit.

Chasing ETAs

Imagine in the drawing you are the airplane in the middle. Your spacing is designed with the varying speeds taken into consideration. If all three airplanes are hit with less than forecast headwinds, all three airplanes will start arriving at their waypoints early. If you, in the middle, slow down to arrive at your waypoint on time while the faster airplane behind you correctly maintains his Mach number, you could have loss of separation. If the other two airplanes update their ETA's and you don't, it will be obvious to ATC who gets the violation.

M 0.83   M 0.80   M 0.80

The correct procedure:

- *Fly the assigned Mach Number if at all possible, if your ETA varies by 3 minutes or more, inform ATC.*

- *If you cannot maintain the assigned Mach Number for any reason (performance, turbulence, etc.), inform ATC before making an adjustment. If you cannot get clearance first, consider broadcasting your actions on 123.45 and 121.5 to ensure aircraft ahead and behind you are aware.*

Climbs

[ICAO NAT Doc 007, ¶7.3.5.] Flight crews should maintain their last assigned Mach number during climbs in oceanic airspace. If due to aircraft performance this is not feasible ATC should be advised at the time of the request for the climb.

If you can't make the climb at your assigned Mach number, you shouldn't be making the climb.

Procedures After Leaving Oceanic Airspace

[ICAO NAT Doc 007, ¶7.4.] After leaving oceanic airspace pilots must maintain their assigned Mach Number in domestic controlled airspace unless and until the appropriate ATC unit authorises a change.

Resume Normal Speed

[NAT Ops Bulletin 2019-001]

The requirement to issue an assigned fixed Mach to all flights has been removed from NAT SUPPs (ICAO Doc7030), however, due to the technical design of the ACARS Clearance (CLX) message and NAT Air Navigation Service Providers (ANSP) application of longitudinal separation using the Mach number technique, nearly all oceanic clearances issued to turbojet aircraft in the NAT Region include an assigned Mach. If any variation to the assigned Mach is desired, flight crews must request such changes from ATC.

All aircraft, regardless of FANS equipage, will be eligible for the application of OWAFS in both ATS surveillance and non-surveillance airspace. Oceanic clearance procedures will remain unchanged. A fixed Mach will continue to be part of the oceanic clearance. ATC may remove the speed restriction via voice or CPDLC by issuing "Resume normal speed" instructions.

If the aircraft then receives RESUME NORMAL SPEED (via CPDLC or Voice), the flight crew no longer needs to comply with a previously issued Mach. However, the flight crew shall advise ATC if, as the result of the RESUME NORMAL SPEED message, they intend to adjust their speed by plus or minus Mach 0.02 or more from their last assigned speed.

Where Mach Number Technique is Used

The Mach Number Technique is required in various parts of the world, for example:

- Africa (Canarias, Dakar, Recife, Sal Oceanic FIRs, and designated RNP-10 routes): [ICAO Doc 7030, ¶AFI 6.2.2.]

- Caribbean (specified areas in Houston Oceanic, Merida and Monterrey CTAs, Miami Oceanic, San Juan CTA, and New York Oceanic): [ICAO Doc 7030, ¶CAR 6.2.2.]

- Middle East/Asia (specified routes): [ICAO Doc 7030, ¶MID/ASIA 2.1.11.]

- North America (Anchorage Arctic CTA): [ICAO Doc 7030, ¶NAM 6.2.2.]

- North Atlantic: [ICAO Doc 7030, ¶NAT 6.2.2.]

- Pacific (Anchorage and Oakland Oceanic FIRs): [ICAO Doc 7030, ¶PAC 6.1.1.]

- South America (Dakar, Recife, and Sal Oceanic FIRs): [ICAO Doc 7030, ¶SAM 6.2.2.]

ICAO Doc 7030 is rarely updated and airspace around the world is getting more crowded so you can expect to see the use of Mach Number Technique expand. It might be a good idea to use it everywhere when not in radar contact.

Oceanic Checklist and RVSM/NAV Performance Log

Preflight

☑ Label one copy of the computer flight plan "Master Document"
☑ Plot route over Class II airspace and any relevant tracks
☑ Add ETPs (loss of pressurization, all-engine cruise, loss of engine) if required
☑ Position Check: Ramp (GPS) N/S ___42°27.6___ E/W ___71°17.4___

IRS #1	IRS #2	IRS #3	GPS #1	GPS#2
Diff 0.0	Diff 0.0	Diff 0.0	Diff 0.0	Diff 0.0

☑ Altimeter Check: QNH 2992 Pilot's 120 Stby 130 Copilot's 120
☑ Time Check: Source (circle) WWV GPS ATC +/- 10 sec ✓
☑ Compare Master Document course/distance with plotting or en route chart, circle waypoint
☑ Compare Master Document course/distance with FMS, draw diagonal over waypoint
☑ Record fuel onboard on the Master Document

Coast Out

☑ Check both HFs, check SELCAL prior to entering oceanic airspace
☑ Nav Accuracy Check:

RAW: Fix ___YQX___ Radial ___270___ Distance ___113___
FMS: Fix ___YQX___ Radial ___270___ Distance ___112___

☑ Altimeter Check: QNH 2992 Pilot's 41000 Stby 40900 Copilot's 41020
☑ Record oceanic clearances on the Master Document

At Each Waypoint

☑ Record ATA, fuel remaining, winds/temperature (if required), next ETA, HF frequencies, three altimeters on Master Document
☑ Make the position report, draw a second diagonal over waypoint on Master Document
☑ Check distance, time, heading, and fuel remaining to the next waypoint against the Master Document
☑ Plot aircraft position approximately 10 minutes after waypoint passage

Coast In

☑ Nav Accuracy Check:

RAW: Fix ___CRK___ Radial ___240___ Distance ___130___
FMS: Fix ___CRK___ Radial ___240___ Distance ___129___

Post-flight

☑ Position Check: Ramp (GPS) N/S ___46°13.0___ E/W ___06°06.4___

IRS #1	IRS #2	IRS #3	GPS #1	GPS#2
Diff 0.4	Diff 0.2	Diff 1.2	Diff 0.0	Diff 0.0

☑ Altimeter Check: QNH 1010 Pilot's 1410 Stby 1440 Copilot's 1430

Figure: Completed Oceanic Checklist and RVSM/NAV Performance Log

Chapter 28

Navigation Accuracy Check

The book — AC 91-70B — no longer requires you do navigation accuracy checks, but still says you should.

The Why?

The requirement to do a navigation accuracy check prior to coast-out and prior to coast-in went away with the adoption of AC 91-70B in 2016, but it remains a very good idea. We are continuing to see aircraft violated for things a good navigation accuracy check would have caught. A few reasons:

- A Navigation Accuracy Check will detect when the database has an error. I've seen this twice, though both time were over continental Europe. But it can happen.

- Every now and then you hear about the GPS system being intentionally or unintentionally being taken down or made inaccurate regionally. There tend to be NOTAMs about this kind of thing, but a navigation accuracy check can save you if you missed the NOTAM or they didn't publish it.

- Record of your Navigation Accuracy Check will impress upon an inspector that you are a careful and diligent pilot, when he or she asks for your paperwork because of a loss of separation caused by the other aircraft.

The How?

Paper or PDF Chart

You can check your FMS's "claimed" position on a chart and compare that to your "reported" position off a VOR's radial / dme.

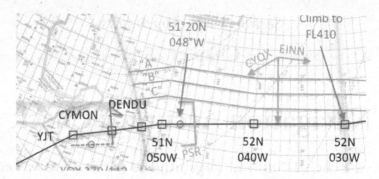

For example, the Gander VOR can be used for a coast-out NAV accuracy check. The VOR should be drawn on the plotting chart with a magnetic north flag which would be drawn in this case 22° to the west. (This flag points to magnetic north and can be labeled "360°M / 348°T") The latitude and longitude from the FMS is plotted directly on the chart. A compass plotter measures the angle from the magnetic north flag to determine the aircraft is on a 270° radial and the distance is measured to be 112 nm. (We were cleared direct 51°N 050°W so didn't overfly YJT, CYMON, or DENDU.)

iPad Application

Many iPad navigation applications can simplify the process of a navigation accuracy check. Using ForeFlight, for example:

Using two fingers (using two hands makes this easier), simultaneously press the applicable VOR and the approximate aircraft position, fine tune the VOR position so it is exact, adjust the other until the radial and DME agree with your raw data, release both fingers. The resulting point should be right on the course line. You can take a "screen grab" on most iPads by pressing the "Home" and "Power" buttons simultaneously. The resulting photo can be saved as proof you did the navigation accuracy check.

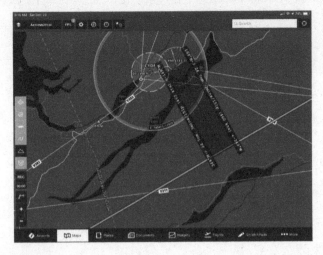

FMS Cross-Points

Some FMS installations include a "cross points" function that computes the position of the aircraft relative to a waypoint or VOR. The applicable VOR is inputted and compared to a raw data instrument tuned to the same VOR.

In the example photo, we see that we are on the 270° radial, 112 NM from YQX.

Tuning the YQX VOR we can see the raw data on the EBDI.

In the example photo, we see that we are on the 270° radial, 113 NM from YQX.

Of course the raw data distance is greater than the actual distance because it is the slant range.

Photos: G450 PPOS page and Electronic Bearing/Distance Indicator.

Chapter 29

Navigation Worksheet

*I*f you get a reclearance that is significantly different than what is on your
*master document, you will need to update the master document, get a new
one sent to you, or you will have to compute a new one on your own. The math
isn't that hard, but you are likely to be in a rush when this happens and that
means you will be prone to making math errors. You should carry a supply of
blank navigation worksheets on every oceanic flight. You can find a blank navigation worksheet at the end of this chapter. Now that you have the worksheet,
here are your options:*

- *If you have an Internet connection, have your flight planning service send
  you a new flight plan.*

- *If you have a fax machine, have them fax it to you.*

- *Got a phone? Have them read off the pertinent information. You don't
  need the entire flight plan, just the oceanic portion that has changed.*

- *Failing all that, get your trusty calculator and plotter and be careful. For
  how to do this, see the Appendices, Chapter 33.*

*I've only had to do this a few times and each time it was with the plotter and
circular slide rule. It was tedious and it was not as easy as I remember from my
lieutenant days. The next time I will pick up the phone. Why bother? There are
reports every month of a crew that got a reclearance and ended up flying into
the wrong airspace. It is nice having an accurate master document to check the
electrons flying the jet.*

The Requirement

[AC 91-70B, ¶D.2.5.7]

The number one scenario that leads to a pilot deviation from the assigned
routing is a reclearance (that is different from the oceanic route requested
with the filed flight plan).

You should be particularly cautious when receiving a reclearance.

Both pilots should separately copy and confirm the new routing, comparing with each other and confirming any inconsistencies with the ATS provider.

One pilot reprograms (and executes) your LRNS and updates the master document and plotting/orientation chart, crossing out the old waypoints and plotted route and replacing them with the updated information.

A second pilot cross-checks the newly effective route clearance with the re-programmed route in the FMS (checking the expanded coordinates: degrees and minutes), the updated master document, and the updated chart.

You should check the magnetic course and distance between the new way-points. To update the master document course and distance, use commercially available tables, or obtain from dispatch an updated master document. It is also possible to use an onboard flight planning system to independently calculate course and distance, and check that against the FMS.

[AC 91-70B, ¶6.1.2.3.1] Incorrect waypoint entry procedures, particularly if the waypoints are not named and flightcrews must enter the full latitude and longitude.

Note: Waypoints entered via full latitude and longitude can produce misleading display names, where minutes are truncated or rounded and/or generic names are generated.

Navigation Worksheet

Navigation Worksheet

Date: _____

From: _____

To: _____

Time Off: _____

Time On: _____

Waypoint	Route	FL	Wind	TC / Var	MC / Drift	MH / GS	Fuel Est / Fuel Act	Est T Rem / Act T Rem	Leg Dist / Tot Dist	Leg Time / Tot Time	ETA / ATA	Time Dif

Oceanic Checklist and RVSM/NAV Performance Log

Preflight

☐ Label one copy of the computer flight plan "Master Document"
☐ Plot route over Class II airspace and any relevant tracks
☐ Add ETPs (loss of pressurization, all-engine cruise, loss of engine) if required
☐ Position Check: Ramp (GPS) N/S _____   E/W _____

	IRS #1	IRS #2	IRS #3	GPS #1	GPS#2
Diff _____	Diff _____	Diff _____	Diff _____	Diff _____	

☐ Altimeter Check: QNH _____ Pilot's _____ Stby _____ Copilot's _____
☐ Time Check: Source (circle) WWV/GPS/ATC +/- 10 sec _____
☐ Compare Master Document course/distance with plotting or en route chart, circle waypoint
☐ Compare Master Document course/distance with FMS, draw diagonal over waypoint
☐ Record fuel onboard on the Master Document

Coast Out

☐ Check both HFs, check SELCAL prior to entering oceanic airspace
☐ Nav Accuracy Check:

RAW: Fix _____   Radial _____   Distance _____

FMS: Fix _____   Radial _____   Distance _____

☐ Altimeter Check: QNH _____ Pilot's _____ Stby _____ Copilot's _____
☐ Record oceanic clearances on the Master Document

At Each Waypoint

☐ Record ATA, fuel remaining, winds/temperature (if required), next ETA, HF frequencies, three altimeters on Master Document
☐ Make the position report, draw a second diagonal over waypoint on Master Document
☐ Check distance, time, heading, and fuel remaining to the next waypoint against the Master Document
☐ Plot aircraft position approximately 10 minutes after waypoint passage

Coast In

☐ Nav Accuracy Check:

RAW: Fix _____   Radial _____   Distance _____

FMS: Fix _____   Radial _____   Distance _____

Post-flight

☐ Position Check: Ramp (GPS) N/S _____   E/W _____

	IRS #1	IRS #2	IRS #3	GPS #1	GPS#2
Diff _____	Diff _____	Diff _____	Diff _____	Diff _____	

☐ Altimeter Check: QNH _____ Pilot's _____ Stby _____ Copilot's _____

Chapter 30

Oceanic Checklist and RVSM/NAV Performance Log

*Y*ou can make your oceanic checklist as detailed as you wish or fit just the important things on one page. If you are new to this, you should start out with details and start paring down as you become comfortable with the procedures.

If you have data link, don't forget to include those operations or keep a CPDLC checklist handy too. See Section IV, Chapter 6, CPDLC Checklist.

Over the years I've settled on the oceanic checklist on the facing page.

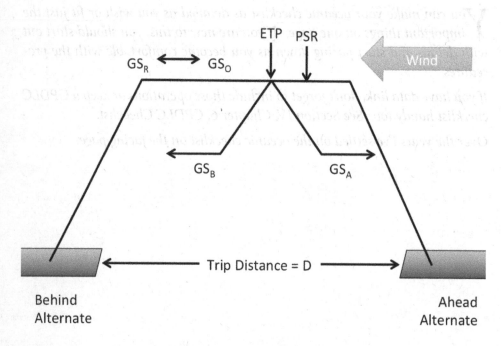

Figure: Equal Time Point and Point of No Return.

Chapter 31

Point of Safe Return (PSR)

*T*he Point of Safe Return is seldom discussed because it is rarely critical with modern aircraft designed for oceanic travel. It is, however, applicable even with lots of range and reliability.

You may need a PSR if you think your passengers may, for some reason, need to cancel their plans across the pond and return immediately. Of course this may not be possible because the skies are filled with airplanes behind you who may object. But, in case you need one, here's how to do that.

PSR Explained

The Point of Safe Return (PSR) provides the pilot with the farthest point to which the aircraft can go and be able to return safely to the departure point with adequate holding, approach, landing, and alternate fuel. It is normally used when flying to remote island destinations with no diversion possibilities en route but can be useful even when alternates are available.

Point of Safe Return, The Math

The diagram on the facing page describe both Equal Time Points (ETPs) and the Point of Safe Return (PSR).

- *Unlike the ETP, the Point of Safe Return should be based on your original departure airport, since that is where you are likely to want to go if it becomes an issue.*

- *The terms GS_A, GS_B, and ETP are for the "Equal Time Point." See the Appendices, Chapter 19, Equal Time Points.*

The following formula is used to calculate the ground distance from the departure airport to the Point of Safe Return:

$$\text{Ground distance to PSR} = \frac{(\text{Endurance}) \, (\text{GS}_\text{R}) \, (\text{GS}_\text{O})}{\text{GS}_\text{O} + \text{GS}_\text{R}}$$

Where:

Endurance = Total Fuel Quantity / Average Fuel Flow

GS_O = Normal Outbound Ground Speed at Cruise Altitude

GS_R = Return Ground Speed at Normal Cruise Altitude

Example PSR

Figure: Master Document Example, PNR.

The example flight used in Section VII, Tutorial, is from KBED to LSGG on a G450 which has more than ample range. The flight planning service automatically computed a "PNR" which came to 1,161 nm from KBED.

```
                    CRITICAL FUEL SUMMARIES

PNR
LAT/LONG      N51 26.5/W046 36.0            KBED
TIME TO ETP DIVRSN PT          02.11
DIST TO ETP DIVRSN PT          01161
FUEL TO ETP DIVRSN PT/RMNG  008170 /20930
FL/BURN/TIME TO ETP AP      200/20928/04.46
TAS/ETA/DIST TO ETP AP      308/2357/001141
MAG CRS/AVG WIND COMP TO ETP AP    262/M072
ISA TEMP DEV TO ETP AP                M003
TOTAL FUEL TO ETP AP /RMNG     29098/00001
```

If any of our passengers, for some reason, decide they need to go back to our departure airport (KBED), the last moment you can do this without having to make a fuel stop if you haven't passed the Point of Safe Return. Keep in mind that if you return at this point, you will need to fly direct to the airport, the PSR does not use normal routings that anyone less than an emergency aircraft will be offered.

Chapter 32

Post-Position Plot

A post-position plot is simply a check made after enough time has elapsed since crossing the waypoint to detect a navigation error, but soon enough to fix things before a loss of separation with other traffic occurs.

We started doing these after inertial reference systems replaced our navigators, and started wondering about the requirement when we installed our first GPS. Well here we are years later and guys are still getting violated even with hybrid IRUs and six satellites hooked up to two GPS. We still need to do these.

The rules were originally written to say 10 minutes after passing an oceanic waypoint. Many of us decided it was easier and more accurate to pick an even longitude going east or west so we adopted a 2° check. This simply eliminates having to interpolate twice. The Feds adopted this a few years back but failed to note this only works when the course is more or less east or west. If you are flying north or south make sure you get some kind of post position plot around 10 minutes after waypoint passage.

Requirement

[AC 91-70B, ¶D.2.9.2] Ten Minutes After Waypoint Passage. Cross-check navigational performance and course compliance by one of the following methods:

The old school method . . .

D.2.9.1 The "plotting" method is appropriate for all aircraft navigation configurations.

1.   Verify your plotting/orientation chart reflects the currently effective route clearance.

2.   Plot your present latitude/longitude and record the time on your chart.

3.   You should plot your position using coordinates from the nonsteer-

ing LRNS.

4. Investigate/take corrective action if your plotted position does not agree with your currently effective route clearance.

5. Using the steering LRNS, verify the next waypoint is consistent with the currently effective route clearance.

6. Verify your autopilot steering mode is in LNAV/VNAV or other appropriate mode to ensure steering to the next intended waypoint.

The new school method

D.2.9.2 The "navigation display" method is appropriate for and available for use in aircraft equipped with an operable FMS:

1. Confirm the aircraft symbol is on the programmed route on the navigation display (at smallest scale).

2. Check system-generated cross-track deviation or similar indication of any deviation from the programmed route of flight.

This will protect you against problems between the autopilot and the FMS, but not against an improperly programmed waypoint. Let's say you entered 5230N instead of 5330N, the classic "one degree" error that will throw you 60 nm off course. Since the line drawn by the FMS on your display is looking for a latitude of 52 degrees it will draw that as a point and you will think you are on course, no matter how small the display scale is set. I recommend that if you are not going to plot, you should at the very least bring up the GPS present position display and verify you cross the correct waypoint first, and that your course to the next waypoint agrees with the master document. (Check the magnetic course, not the heading.)

3. Using the steering LRNS verify the "TO" waypoint is consistent with your currently effective route clearance.

Do not rely on the ARINC shorthand codes here. If you don't have a way of displaying the flight plan waypoints as latitude/longitude pairs, try bringing the waypoint into the scratch pad and then to a waypoint page to ensure your "TO" latitude and longitude points are correct.

4. Investigate/take correction action to address any anomalies or unexpected deviations.

5. Verify your autopilot steering mode is LNAV/VNAV or other appropriate mode to ensure steering to the next intended waypoint.

[NAT Doc 007, ¶8.4.18.] A position check should be made at each waypoint and the present position plotted 10 minutes after passing each waypoint. For a generally east-west flight, this 10 minute point will be approximately 2 degrees of longitude beyond the oceanic waypoint. It may therefore in fact be simpler to plot a present position 2 degrees of longitude after each 10 degree waypoint. There may be circumstances, (e.g. when, due to equipment failure, only one LRNS remains serviceable) in which additional plots midway between each waypoint may be justified.

The point is to plot the aircraft's position after about ten minutes to ensure the next waypoint wasn't entered in error. If, for example, the flight plan download (or manual entry) entered the next waypoint as 51N 040W, one degree south of the clearance, it would look perfectly normal on the cockpit displays but plotting the position would alert the crew that something is amiss, as shown on the chart. Don't think this is possible? Modern G550s continue to get caught in just this type of Gross Navigational Error.

Plotting on Paper Charts

Plotting is covered in Section II, Chapter 5. It is a basic pilot skill, one thinks, but there are easier ways using an iPad App with plotting capabilities. For the sake of example, we'll use JeppFD here.

Plotting on an iPad

Making a post-position plot using JeppFD with the iPad is quite easy. You derive the coordinates from your FMS and then press the course line in the approximate position. Then it is just a matter of correcting the approximate latitude and longitude with exact numbers and pressing "done." Do not press "Add to Route" or "Direct To."

You can either save the entire chart on your iPad, with the post position plot, or do a "screen grab" of the particular plot by pressing the "Home" and "Power" buttons simultaneously. The shot will be saved in your Photos app.

Plotting on an iPad Using a Portable GPS

An even easier method is to link your iPad to a portable GPS and do a screen grab, as with the previous example. In the photo below the GPS symbol is 2nm right of course, reflecting the aircraft's strategic lateral offset.

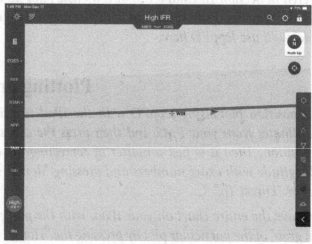

Chapter 33

Reroute

*I*t *is a common fear of inexperienced oceanic travelers: the FMS is pro-grammed, the charts are plotted, and you are wondering what to do with yourself for the next three hours. Then the oceanic clearance comes in and it doesn't look anything like what you had planned; you have been rerouted. You know a reroute is an invitation to a gross navigational error so you obviously want to take all of this seriously and if you ever needed to do navigation accuracy checks, the time is now. But how you are you going to do all this without a computer flight plan?*

I used to wax poetic about how now is the time to get out your plotter and a sharp pencil and get to work. But these days you are better off picking up the phone and calling your flight planning service provider. See the "Preferred Method," below.

If you can't do that for some reason, there is still no reason to panic. You can get this done manually. You really ought to practice this once or twice. What follows is a walk through on how we used to do this routinely.

Preferred Method: E-mail, App Upload, Fax, Phone

The easiest and most accurate method is to email or phone your flight plan-ning service and ask them to run the flight plan using the reroute points. If you have the technology you can have them upload the new flight plan to your App or email the PDF to you. Even if you don't have an Internet con-nection, you can have them read you the particulars for the oceanic legs that matter and save yourself from having to do the math.

As is true with your original flight plan, you should understand which legs the numbers apply to and if they are based on initial or midpoint course lines. Many of the default formats provided by international flight plan ser-vices do not arrange each item on a line of the flight plan as you would ex-pect. See Section II, Chapter 3, Initial vs. Midpoint Course.

With this example:

- The data given on a particular line are the numbers needed to fly from the previous line.

- The course line is measured from the midpoint.

- Specifically: Flying between 55°N 050°W and 58°N 040°W will require a true course of 062° as measured at 045°W (the midpoint) and is 378 nautical miles in length.

At this point, you should plot the new course and you are ready to continue as before. If you can't print it or are not using an iPad Master Document, you really should transpose the data to a navigation worksheet, shown below, as a part of your master document. If you don't have the data, you will have to compute it on your own. Read on . . .

```
M83     / FLIGHT LEVEL 450 / ETP APTS: BIKF-EINN
ORIGIN/ETP ALTN ETP COORDINATE                      W/C    DIST   TIME TO
KASH TO ETP      N58 16.6 W015 46.5                         2274   04.52
ETP TO OPT APT EINN                                 M008   0408    01.03
TAS / TEMP AT FL 450     400 / ISA M10
FUEL BURN TO    ETP           014428
FUEL REMAINING AT ETP         010072
FUEL BURN FROM ETP TO ALTN 002188
FUEL REMAINING AT ETP ALTN 007884

CPT    FLT OAT WIND   TAS MCS  TCS  ZDST   ZT  FF/E  ZFU   EFR   ETA
FREQ   TP  DEV  S     GRS MH   TB   DGTR   CT  LB/NM CFU   AFR   ATA
                                          ETR

MHT    ...  ...  .....  ... 066M 051T 0008   002 .... 00218 24282 .....
114.40 ...  ...  01    ... 064M 048T 2929 00.02 ... 00218 ..... .....
                                          06.24

ENE    ...  ...  .....  ... 061M 045T 0047   008 .... 00976 23306 .....
117.10 ...  ...  01    ... 055M 038T 2882 00.10 ... 01194 ..... .....
                                          06.16

BGR    450 -61 30055 474 058M 041T 0113   018 3029 01832 21474 .....
114.80 383 M05 01    480 053M 035T 2769 00.28 078 03026 ..... .....
                                          05.58

TOPPS  450 -57 30033 475 076M 058T 0057   007 1386 00323 21151 .....
       376 M01 01    487 073M 055T 2712 00.35 171 03349 ..... .....
                                          05.51

STEAM  450 -55 31016 478 063M 042T 0614   078 1362 03506 17645 .....
       353 P02 00    477 061M 040T 2098 01.53 175 06855 ..... .....
                                          04.33

OYSTR  450 -52 16008 481 083M 059T 0100   012 1355 00554 17091 .....
       354 P04 00    482 084M 059T 1998 02.05 177 07409 ..... .....
                                          04.21

55050  450 -52 14010 481 094M 069T 0187   024 1323 01035 16056 .....
       346 P04 00    478 096M 070T 1811 02.29 182 08444 ..... .....
                                          03.57

58040  450 -51 14012 479 081M 062T 0378   047 1294 02048 14008 .....
       345 P03 00    478 088M 082T 1433 03.16 185 10492 ..... .....
                                          03.10

59030  450 -58 19018 474 091M 079T 0320   040 1254 01674 12334 .....
       385 M01 02    480 104M 092T 1123 03.56 189 12166 ..... .....
                                          02.30

59020  450 -53 22023 468 101M 090T 0310   039 1221 01564 10770 .....
       411 M06 02    484 110M 092T 2200 04.35 192 13730 ..... .....
                                          01.51
```

Figure: Example Flight Plan (GV)

Classic ("Back in the Old Days") Method

If you can't get a hard, printed copy of the reroute using the preferred method, above, you will have to write one of your own. You should keep a number of blank navigation worksheets for just this purpose. Copies are available in the Appendices, Chapter 29, Navigation Worksheet. It isn't hard if you are methodical about it.

Step 1: Plot the New Oceanic Points

Plot the new points on your existing chart unless it would be too hard to read, in which case you should get a fresh chart. See Part II, Chapter 5, Plotting.

Figure: Reroute plotted

Step 2: Enter Known Data

You can guess the winds from your existing flight plan or download them from data link if available. The variation can be read directly from the en route chart. Note that the chart's plotted variation lines are likely to be out of date, your FMS may provide more timely variation data.

Navigation Worksheet

Date:	Oct 8, 2007
From:	KTASH
To:	EGGW
Time Off:	1220 Z
Time On:	

Waypoint	Route	FL	Wind	TC Var	MC Drift	MH GC	Fuel Est Fuel Act	Est T Rem Act T Rem	Leg Dist Tot Dist	Leg Time Tot Time	ETA GTA	Time Dif
55N 50W	D	450	140/10	+24								
58N 40W	D	450	140/10	+23								
59N 30W	D	450	190/20	+19								
59N 20W	D	450	220/20	+14								
60HUP	D	450	250/10	+8								

Figure: Navigation Worksheet (known data entered).

Step 3: Determine True Courses

Using 10 Degree Tables

Using True Course 10 Degree tables you can find courses and distances between major latitudes and longitudes. A major latitude is one to a whole degree and a major longitude is one to the nearest 10 degrees. See the Appendices, Chapter 39, True Course 10 Degree Tables.

In the example we see that flying from 55°N 050°W to 58°N 040°W will require a true course of 062° as measured from the midpoint and a distance of 376 nautical miles. (The 050°W and 040°W are not needed in the table, the answer will be the same at any pair of latitudes 55° - 58°N in the world, so long as the longitudes are 10 degrees apart.)

From 55° Latitude

To determine the average true course and distance between two points which are ten degrees apart in longitude:

1. Find the table with the starting latitude (North or South doesn't matter)
2. Find the corresponding latitude in the second column. (If there are two choices, the latitude on top is in the same hemisphere (North or South)
3. Read the true course underneath the desired hemisphere and direction of travel (east or west)
4. Read the distance in the last column

To Latitude	Northern Hemisphere		Southern Hemisphere		Distance (nm)
	East	West	East	West	
65	027	333	153	207	669
64	030	330	150	210	618
63	033	327	147	213	570
62	037	323	143	217	523
61	042	318	138	222	479
60	047	313	133	227	440
59	054	306	126	234	405
58	062	298	118	242	376
57	070	290	110	250	356
56	080	280	100	260	345
55	090	270	090	270	344
54	100	260	080	280	353
53	109	251	071	289	372
52	117	243	063	297	399
51	124	236	056	304	433
50	129	231	051	309	472
49	134	226	046	314	515
48	138	222	042	318	561
47	142	218	038	322	610
46	145	215	035	325	660
45	147	213	033	327	712

Figure: 55° True Course 10° Table, from the Appendices, Chapter 39, True Course 10 Degree Tables / 55°.

Using a Chart and Plotter

If you do not have 10-degree tables or if your waypoints are not covered in the tables, you can determine the courses and distances right off the chart.

In our example we measure a course of 062° and a distance of around 375 nautical miles. We repeat the process for each oceanic waypoint.

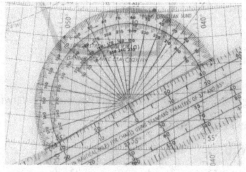

Figure: Reroute en route chart, plotting first leg.

Step 4: Determine Magnetic Courses

Compute each leg's magnetic course by adding the magnetic variation to the true course. Westerly variation is added, easterly is subtracted.

The navigation worksheet now includes magnetic courses based on the variation we provided. (The plotting chart was a few years out of date and some of the variation figures were off by a few degrees. We need to keep that in mind when checking navigation performance.)

Step 5: Determine Drift, Heading, and Ground Speed

The higher your TAS in relation to your wind speed the less of a factor it will be, in fact the harder it will be to visualize on a wind computer such as the Jeppesen CR-2. For the purpose of demonstrating the method, we will use the highest wind in the example, on the leg to 59°N 020°W: 220/20. The method is similar for each leg.

- Set the true airspeed (i.e., 480) under the TAS index.

- Set the true course (i.e., 090°) under the TC index.

- Find the wind direction (i.e., 220°) on the wind slide.

- Draw a dot over the windspeed on the wind direction line. You may have a choice of scales. In our case, we use the largest scale available for ease of legibility.

- Draw a line from the wind dot parallel to the horizontal scale to read the tailwind on the vertical scale (i.e., 12 knots, which means our ground-speed will be 490 + 12 = 492 knots)

- Draw a line from the wind dot parallel to the vertical scale to read the crosswind on the horizontal scale (i.e., 16 knots)

- Find the crosswind, in knots, on the outer scale. Remember that since we entered this outer scale with 480 knots, our 16 knot crosswind is actually 1.6 when read against the 16 number.

- Read the drift angle on the inner scale. (i.e., 1.9°)

- Since true course = 090° and magnetic variation = +14°, magnetic course = 090 + 14 = 104°. Adding drift angle gives us a magnetic heading of 104 + 2 = 106°)

The navigation worksheet now includes drift and groundspeed. We can then figure magnetic heading by adding the drift to magnetic course.

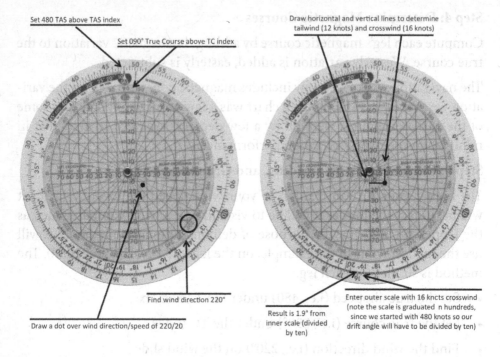

Set 480 TAS above TAS index

Set 090° True Course above TC index

Draw horizontal and vertical lines to determine tailwind (12 knots) and crosswind (16 knots)

Find wind direction 220°

Draw a dot over wind direction/speed of 220/20

Result is 1.9° from inner scale (divided by ten)

Enter outer scale with 16 kncts crosswind (note the scale is graduated n hundreds, since we started with 480 knots so our drift angle will have to be divided by ten)

Note: Each step of this process involves the width of your pencil on the wind side of the circular computer and small errors early magnify themselves. This navigation worksheet will get you in the ballpark.

Navigation Worksheet

Date: Oct 8, 2007

From: KASH

To: EGGW

Time Off: 1220 Z

Time On:

TAS 480

Waypoint	Route	FL	Wind	TC / Var	MC / Drift	MH / GS	Fuel Est / Fuel Act	Ht T Rem / Act T Rem	Leg Dist / Tot Dist	Leg Time / Tot Time	ETA / ATA	Time Off
55N 50W	D	450	140/10	124								
58N 40W	D	450	140/10	062 +23	085 +1	086 480			376			
59N 30W	D	450	198/20	079 +19	098 +2	106 485			319			
59N 20W	D	450	220/20	090 +14	104 +2	106 490			309			
60 HUP	D	450	280/10	112 +8	120 +3	123 495			335			

Figure: Navigation Worksheet (drift, heading, ground speed added).

Safety Assessment of Foreign Aircraft (SAFA)

The Safety Assessment of Foreign Aircraft (SAFA) program has been with us since 1996 and we have been expecting ramp inspections throughout Europe ever since. The European Union made it mandatory for its member states to do these SAFA checks and they seem to trip us up now and then. The SAFA is a part of the European Union (EU) Ramp Inspection Program (RIP); the other part is the SACA, where the "C" is for Community aircraft.

Background

[InFO 20003] The SAFA RIP began in the EU community in 1996 and has evolved into a ramp inspection tool that is utilized by at least 49 countries. The EU RIP is managed by the European Aviation Safety Agency (EASA) and continues to focus on EU and non-EU aircraft landing at airports within EU member states and other non-EU participating states. The FAA signed a cooperative arrangement with EASA to receive safety information and notices from the SAFA RIP in 2011. Aircraft suspected of noncompliance with safety standards established by the International Civil Aviation Organization (ICAO) have a greater chance of a ramp inspections.

The ramp inspections carried out by EU RIP participating member states follows a common procedure, using a checklist covering the array of inspection areas based on ICAO standards. It is EASA policy that ramp inspections will not delay aircraft except for safety reasons. Ramp Inspection Programme inspectors may not be able to complete all checklist items if an aircraft has a short turnaround time. Regardless of if an EU RIP inspection is completed in its entirety or not, it is an on-the-spot ramp inspection that does not substitute regulatory oversight of the state of the operator or the state of registry, as applicable. A completed RIP inspection does not guarantee the aircraft is airworthy; instead, it focuses on evaluating compliance with 53 inspection areas that consist of ICAO requirements and specific EASA criteria.

When an EU RIP ramp inspection results in a finding identified within a checklist item, it is categorized as a 1, 2, or 3. The category is dependent upon the magnitude of the deviation from the international requirements and the impact on safety associated with the noncompliance.

- Category 1 Finding. A Category 1 finding is considered a minor deviation and is reported to the pilot-in-command (PIC) (operator).

- Category 2 Finding. A Category 2 finding is considered a significant deviation from safety standards. The findings are reported to the operator and the oversight authority of the operator. For U.S. operators, Category 2 findings are reported to the Federal Aviation Administration (FAA).

- Category 3 Finding. A Category 3 finding is one that has a major impact on safety. The reporting requirements are the same as Category 2. Category 3 findings are expected to be corrected by the operator before the aircraft departs either by correcting the deficiency or by imposing limitations or restrictions on the operation of the aircraft. These limitations may be imposed by the inspecting authority.

Any U.S. operator who receives a EU RIP ramp inspection and is issued a Category 1, 2, or 3 finding is responsible for all immediate and future actions required to clear the finding to the satisfaction of the EU RIP pursuant to and in accordance with the requirements of Title 14 of the Code of Federal Regulations part 91, § 91.703. Failure by the operator to respond within 60 days of notification of inspection findings, failure to address repetitive findings, or failure to address safety items could result in operational restriction(s) applied to that operator, up to and including rescinding flight authorizations and barring the operator from future operations into applicable state(s).

A ramp inspection is possible anywhere in the world, an EU RIP is possible at: Albania, Armenia, Australia, Austria, Azerbaijan, Belgium, Bosnia and Herzegovina, Bulgaria, Croatia, Cyprus, Czech Republic, Denmark, Estonia, Finland, France, Georgia, Germany, Greece, Hungary, Iceland, Ireland, Israel, Italy, Latvia, Lithuania, Luxembourg, Malta, Republic of Moldova, Monaco, Montenegro, Netherlands, Norway, Poland, Portugal, Romania, Serbia, Slovak Republic, Slovenia, Spain, Sweden, Switzerland, The Republic of North Macedonia, Turkey, Ukraine, and United Kingdom. Also participating: Canada, Morocco, Singapore, United Arab Emirates.

How it Normally Goes Down

[Ops.Group]

As you pull on to the stand, you will notice more yellow vests than normal hanging around.

Two of these will be your friendly ramp inspection team (to be fair, they almost always are). A short time later, those yellow vests will be in the cockpit, and the first request will be for a look at your license, medical, aircraft documents (like Insurance, Airworthiness), and flight paperwork. Make sure you've done your fuel checks and there are a few marks on the flight plan.

If you get a good cop, bad cop scenario, one will disappear down the back (this will be the nice guy) and check the cabin, while the first will stay and ask you tough questions about the TCAS system.

Some time later, you'll get a list of findings. The average check is probably about 30 minutes.

You can be guaranteed they will always have at least one finding – which will probably be obscure.

Sign off the checklist, and you're on your way.

The Inspectors can ask you for manuals, documents, or guidance – but they are not supposed to test your knowledge of procedures, regulations, or technical matters. This doesn't always happen in practice – so if you get a tough question – just say "I don't know" – and let them note it if they want to.

Remember, it's not you that's being inspected. It's your aircraft. If you're uncomfortable with the questions, get them noted and allow your operator to discuss later.

Every inspector is a little different. Work with them and you'll find that 90% of your ramp checks will be over in 20 minutes with little issue.

Private Operators – especially in GA (even more so under the 5700kg mark) – are far less likely to get ramp checked. EASA guidelines do apply to General Aviation, but they are far more interested in Commercial Operators.

The items checked during ramp checks are based on a risk based approach and can differ from operator to operator. Operators who get ramp checked with findings will most likely get ramp checked again, to see if they've sorted out the problems!

An Abbreviated Checklist

You will find the following in many places as "the" SAFA inspection checklist. It is little more than a list of topics, but at least it gives you an idea of what will be examined.

A. Flight Deck A01   General condition

    A02   Emergency exit

    A03   Equipment

Documentation   A04   Manuals

    A05   Checklists

    A06   Navigation/instrument charts

    A07   Minimum equipment list

    A08   Certificate of registration

    A09   Noise certificate (where applicable)

    A10   AOC or equivalent

    A11   Radio license

    A12   Certificate of Airworthiness

Flight Data   A13   Flight preparation

    A14   Mass and balance calculation

Safety Equipment   A15   Hand fire extinguishers

    A16   Life jackets / flotation device

    A17   Harness

    A18   Oxygen equipment

    A19   Independent portable light

Flight Crew   A20   Flight crew license/composition

    A21   Journey log book or equivalent

    A22   Maintenance release

    A23   Defect notification and rectification (Int. Tech Log)

    A24   Preflight inspection

B. Safety / Cabin   B01   General internal condition

	B02	Cabin crew station and crew rest area
	B03	First aid kit / emergency medical kit
	B04	Hand fire extinguishers
	B05	Life jackets / flotation device
	B06	Seat belts and seat condition
	B07	Emergency exit, lighting and independent portable light
	B08	Slides / life-rafts (as required), ELT
	B09	Oxygen supply (cabin crew and passengers)
	B10	Safety instructions
	B11	Cabin crew members
	B12	Access to emergency exits
	B13	Stowage of passenger baggage
	B14	Seat capacity
Aircraft Condition	C01	General external condition
	C02	Doors and hatches
	C03	Flight controls
	C04	Wheels, tyres and brakes
	C05	Undercarriage, skids/floats
	C06	Wheel well
	C07	Powerplant and pylon
	C08	Fan blades / propellers, rotors (main/tail)
	C09	Obvious repair
	C10	Obvious un-repaired damage
	C11	Leakage
Cargo	D01	General condition of cargo compartment
	D02	Dangerous goods
	D03	Cargo stowage
General	E01	General

A Detailed Checklist

The Inspector's Guidance

The inspector's guidance, *EU SAFA Inspection Instructions*, all 432 pages of it, can be quite intimidating, hard to read, and tempt one to give up on making sense of it all. The key to understanding the new methodology is that there are "Pre-Described Findings," or PDF's. The inspector will have a PDF, such as "Landing gear safety lock pin(s) missing or defective," but written in the inspector's native language. You will be cited in that case for a SAFA-C05-02. Your finding will be translated into your native language.

My Expanded Checklist

Rather than present a list of PDFs or citing documents, I've grouped PDFs into issues, listed the PDF numbers, and included the citing document codes. Reading the categories tells you how to prepare, doing a page search for the PDFs helps you find the item you have been accused of violating, and the citations show you which document controls it. My operation's checklist will have photos and supporting documentation. For this example, I've deleted those and leave it to you to insert your own photos and documents.

A Note to Non-Commercial Operators

First off, you may have heard that as a general aviation (Part 91) operator, the SAFA inspectors don't care about you. Not true. They are usually busy with commercial operators but they are authorized to inspect you. In fact, they have told me that in so many words. So don't think you are off the hook.

Secondly, one of the most often cited documents, Annex 6, Volume 1, is devoted to commercial operators. Annex 6, Volume II, which applies to general aviation, isn't nearly as complete. So where only Volume I is cited, I have this asterisk:

* The given standards from Annex 6, Volume I, which pertain to commercial aircraft, and are not duplicated in Annex 6, Volume II, which apply to general aviation aircraft.

That doesn't mean you are off the hook. Inspectors will cite you even if there isn't a non-commercial document to do so. They've done this many times with MELs, for example. In the examples that follow, I'll simply say it doesn't apply to us. But if I can prove we comply nevertheless, I'll do so.

Citing Documents

What follows are the references used by the inspectors to determine a Pre-Described Finding (PDF). The two main categories are called "Documents" or "Annexes." You can find them at: https://store.icao.int/en/annexes.

Convention on International Civil Aviation (ICAO) (also known as Chicago Convention). It is made available as CAO Doc 7300/0, Convention on International Civil Aviation (ICAO) (also known as Chicago Convention), 9th Edition, 2006.

ICAO Annex 1 (12th Edition July 2018, Amendment 175, 16 July 2018). Referred to as "A1" in the PDFs.

ICAO Annex 2 (10th Edition July 2005, Amendment 46, 16 July 2018). Referred to as "A2" in the PDFs.

ICAO Annex 6, Part I (11th Edition July 2018, Amendment 43, 16 July 2018). Referred to as "A6" in the PDFs.

ICAO Annex 7 (6th Edition, July 2012, Amendment 6, 16 July 2012). Referred to as "A7" in the PDFs.

ICAO Annex 8 (12th Edition, July 2018, Amendment 106, 08 November 2018). Referred to as "A8" in the PDFs.

ICAO Annex 10, Volume III (Second Edition July 2007, Amendment 90, 11 July 2016) and Volume IV (Fifth Edition July 2014, Amendment 90, 16 July 2018). Referred to as "A10" in the PDFs.

ICAO Annex 15 (16th Edition, July 2018, Amendment 40, 16 July 2018). Referred to as "A15" in the PDFs.

ICAO Annex 16, Volume I (8th Edition, July 2017, Amendment 12, 21 July 2017). Referred to as "A16" in the PDFs.

ICAO Annex 18, (4th Edition, July 2011, Amendment 12, 13 July 2015). Referred to as "A18" in the PDFs.

European (EUR) Regional Supplementary Procedures (ICAO Doc 7030) (5th Edition, 2008, Amendment 9, 25 April 2014). Referred to as "EUR" in the PDFs.

ICAO Doc 4444, Procedures for Air Navigation Services (16th edition, 2016, Amendment 9, 15 June 2020).

ICAO Doc 9284, Technical Instructions for the Safe Transport of Dangerous

Goods by Air (2017-2018 Edition, Addendum No. 2/Corrigendum No. 1).

Commission Implementing Regulation (EU) No 923/2012 laying down the common rules of the air and operational provisions regarding services and procedures in air navigation and amending Implementing Regulation (EU) No 1035/2011 and Regulations (EC) No 1265/2007, (EC) No 1794/2006, (EC) No 730/2006, (EC) No 1033/2006 and (EU) No 255/2010.

In some cases no citing document is given, in these cases I leave the entry blank.

What you need to know: You don't necessarily need a copy of every ICAO Annex and Document to fly internationally, the extracts in your Jeppesen series may be good enough. But having them will give you the real answers rather than someone's interpretation.

ACAS

SAFA-A03-02: ACAS II N/A or U/S (outside dispatch limits/conditions).

SAFA-A03-03: Aeroplane not equipped with ACAS II collision avoidance logic version 7.1, but mitigating measures in place.

SAFA-A03-10: Aeroplane not equipped with ACAS II collision avoidance logic version 7.1.

Our Proof of Compliance:

The aircraft is equipped with a Honeywell TPA-100 TCAS, Part Number 940-0452-001, Installed in the RH Radio Rack.

Photo: Touch Screen Controller Traffic page.

Citing Documents:, A6-I-6.19.1, AUR.ACAS.1005(1), A10-IV-4.3.5.3.1, A10-IV-4.3.5.3.3.

Airworthiness / Registration

SAFA-A01-13: Equipment installations obviously not in compliance with Annex 8, Part IIIA/B, Chapter 4.

SAFA-A01-15: Unsafe features and characteristics. Under all anticipated operating conditions, the aeroplane shall not possess any feature or characteristic that renders it unsafe.

SAFA-A08-01: CofR format not in accordance with Annex 7.

SAFA-A08-02: No English translation of the CofR.

SAFA-A08-03: No fireproof identification plate or mismatch of data on CofR and identification plate.

SAFA-A08-04: No valid CofR or cannot be shown by crew.

SAFA-A08-05: A valid CofR was issued but not carried on board.

SAFA-A12-01: Format of CofA not in accordance with Annex 8 requirements.

SAFA-A12-02: No English translation of the CofA.

SAFA-A12-03: CofA not issued/rendered valid by the State of registry.

SAFA-A12-04: A valid CofA was issued but not carried on board at the time of the inspection.

SAFA-A12-05: Endorsed CofA without permission of the State of inspection.

SAFA-A12-06: No valid CofA issued or CofA invalid/expired.

Our Proof of Compliance:

This aircraft has not been modified since initial type certification except by certified means, such as an STC. The aircraft is inspected regularly and no unsafe characteristics have been found. The certificate of registration is written in accordance with U.S. criteria.

Photos: Airworthiness Certificate and Certificate of Registration on cockpit wall, aircraft identification plate.

Citing Documents:, A, A7-7.2, A7-8, CC-29a, CC-29b, CC-31, CC-39a, CC-40, A8-II-3.3.1, A8-II-3.3.2, A8-IIIA-1.4, A8-IIIB-1.3, A8-IIIA-1.5.1, A8-II-IA-1.5.2, A8-IIIB-1.4.

AOC

SAFA-A10-01*: Layout of the AOC and/or the operations specifications not in accordance with provisions of Annex 6.

SAFA-A10-02*: Information in the operations specifications not in accordance with Annex 6.

SAFA-A10-03*: Information in AOC incorrect.

SAFA-A10-04*: No English translation of the AOC and/or operations specifications.

SAFA-A10-05*: Commercial Air Transport operations not in accordance with the operations specifications.

SAFA-A10-06*: Commercial Air Transport operations without a valid AOC.

SAFA-A10-08*: A valid AOC (either original or certified true copy) and/or operations specifications for the flights performed was issued but not carried on board at the time of the inspection.

SAFA-A10-09*: Third Country Operator not holding a valid TCO Authorisation (operations to/from/within EU).

SAFA-A10-10*: Third Country Operator performing operations not in accordance with the operations specifications associated to the TCO Authorisation (operations to/from/within EU).

SAFA-A10-11*: Third Country Operator holding a valid TCO Authorisation (operations to/from/within EU) but operating an aircraft not listed on the TCO web interface.

Our Proof of Compliance:

Citing Documents:, A6-I-4.2.1.5/ A6-I-4.2.1.6/ A6-I-4.2.1.7, A6-I-4.2.2.2, A6-I-4.2.2.3, A6-I-6.1.2, Regulation 2018/1139 Art. 60, TCO.200.

Baggage

SAFA-B13-01*: Hard or heavy baggage stored in open hat-racks.

SAFA-B13-02*: Baggage stowed in unserviceable overhead bins.

SAFA-B13-03*: Oversized baggage transported in the cabin not adequately secured.

SAFA-B13-04*: Baggage not stowed securely.

SAFA-B13-05*: Overhead bins loaded in excess of the placarded weight limitation.

Our Proof of Compliance:

We do not have hat racks or overhead bins. We do not permit carry on baggage other than hand held items in the cabin. If oversized baggage is transported in the cabin, it will be secured to an adjacent and unoccupied seat.

Citing Documents:, A6-I-4.8.

Cabin Crew and Stations

SAFA-B02-01*: Strap or buckle worn or damaged.

SAFA-B02-02*: Cabin crew seat(s) not equipped with safety harness (only seat belt).

SAFA-B02-03*: Cabin crew life jackets (when required) not easily accessible.

SAFA-B02-04*: Cabin crew seat(s) unserviceable (outside dispatch limits/conditions).

SAFA-B02-05*: Cabin crew harness/seat belt not available or unserviceable on required cabin crew seats (outside dispatch limits/conditions).

SAFA-B02-06*: Cabin crew seats not correctly located.

SAFA-B02-07: Communication equipment unserviceable (outside dispatch limits/conditions).

SAFA-B11-01*: Cabin crew member(s) not familiar with the cabin emergency procedures.

SAFA-B11-02*: Cabin crew not familiar with the location and/or operation of emergency equipment.

AFA-B11-03*: Insufficient number of cabin crew members.

SAFA-B11-07*: Cabin crew member not in compliance with the flight and duty time rules.

Our Proof of Compliance:

We do not have a cabin attendant's station or crew rest area. Cabin attendants attend regular emergency procedure training. Cabin crew member flight and duty time rules are identical to pilot rules, specified in the Company Operations Manual section 4.2.

Citing Documents:, A6-I-6.16.1, A6-I-6.16.3, A6-I-12.1, A6-I-4.10.2, A6-I-Appendix 2, 2.

Cargo Compartment

SAFA-D01-01: Minor defects with limited effect on safety.

SAFA-D01-02: Equipment installations obviously not in compliance with Annex 8, Part IIIA/B, Chapter 4.

SAFA-D01-03: Ground servicing markings not applied or unreadable.

SAFA-D01-04: Cargo bay smoke detection test fail or outside dispatch limits/conditions.

SAFA-D01-05: Blow-out panels pushed, damaged or missing (outside dispatch limits/conditions).

SAFA-D01-06: Damage to panelling and/or lining outside limits.

SAFA-D01-07: Unserviceable fire extinguishing system and the affected cargo compartment is used.

SAFA-D01-08: Floor locks unserviceable outside dispatch limits/conditions (with cargo).

SAFA-D01-09: No or unserviceable required barrier net.

SAFA-D01-10: No smoke barrier/curtain (if applicable).

SAFA-D01-11: Structural or floor damage outside dispatch limits/conditions.

SAFA-D01-12: Cargo compartment (s) not equipped with fire suppression systems.

SAFA-D01-13: Cargo compartment lighting damaged outside dispatch limits/conditions.

Our Proof of Compliance:

The aircraft does not have a cargo compartment.

Citing Documents:, A8-II-3.5, A8-IIIA-1.4,, A8-IIIA-1.5, A8-IIIA-4.1.6.(g), A8-IIIA-9.6.2, A8-IIIB-1.3, A8-IIIB-1.4, A8-IIIB-4.2 (g), A8-IIIB-7.6.2, A8-V-7.6.2.

Cargo Stowage

SAFA-D03-01*: Minor damage to lashing, tie-down equipment, pallets, lock assemblies and/or containers.

SAFA-D03-02*: Incomplete equipment like lashing, tie-down equipment, pallets, lock assemblies and/or containers.

SAFA-D03-03*: Cargo Area not used in accordance with classification.

SAFA-D03-04*: Cargo not correctly secured and restrained in all directions.

SAFA-D03-05*: Major damage to lashing, tie-down equipment, pallets, lock assemblies and/or containers affecting the structural integrity and their intended function.

SAFA-D03-06*: Dividing net or protection net damaged outside dispatch limits/conditions.

SAFA-D03-07*: Load distribution/load limit (floor and/or height) exceeded.

Our Proof of Compliance:

We do not have a cargo compartment. The baggage compartment is inspected regularly for damage to lashing and other securing devices and any deficiencies are addressed immediately. We check the load distribution and limit prior to every flight.

Citing Documents:, A6-I-4.3.1e.

Checklists

SAFA-A05-01*: Checklists do not conform with the checklist details in the operations manual.

SAFA-A05-02*: No checklist details in the operations manual.

SAFA-A05-03*: Normal and emergency checklists not readily accessible to all relevant flight crew members.

SAFA-A05-04*: Checklists not covering all flight phases.

SAFA-A05-05*: Different versions of checklists used by captain and co-pilot.

SAFA-A05-06*: No normal and emergency checklists available.

SAFA-A05-07*: Checklists not matching the current aircraft configuration.

SAFA-A05-08*: Checklists revision number/reference missing, but content in accordance with operations manual.

SAFA-A05-09*: Checklists do not take into account latest relevant documentation from the aircraft manufacturer.

Our Proof of Compliance:

The aircraft operating manual is located in the PlaneBook App on each pilot's iPad.

Photo: Electronic checklist.

Our electronic checklists are manufacturer approved and taken directly from the AFM. The electronic checklist is accessible to both pilots.

Citing Documents:, A6-I-4.2.6, A6-I-6.1.4.

CVR

SAFA-A03-07*: Cockpit Voice Recorder inoperative (outside dispatch limits/conditions).

Our Proof of Compliance:

A CVR is installed and operative as required by the MEL.

Photo: G500 Product Specification, CVR Section 12.4.2.

Citing Documents:, A6-I-6.3.2.1.1, A6-I-6.3.2.1.3, A6-I-6.3.2.1.4.

Dangerous Goods

SAFA-A04-08: No information and instructions in operations manual on the actions to be taken in the event of an emergency (DG on board).

SAFA-D02-01: Incorrect or incomplete information in NOTOC [Notification to Captain], not concerning CAO packages.

SAFA-D02-02: Incorrect or incomplete information in NOTOC, concerning CAO packages.

SAFA-D02-03: CAO-cargo (Cargo Aircraft Only) carried on passenger flights.

SAFA-D02-04: Damaged and/or leaking packages/overpacks containing DG.

SAFA-D02-05: Dangerous goods not correctly loaded and/or secured.

SAFA-D02-06: DG label incorrect or missing.

SAFA-D02-07: Required identification tag not properly filled in or partly invisible (no CAO packages inside).

SAFA-D02-08: Required identification tag missing (CAO packages inside).

SAFA-D02-09: DG identification tag improperly used.

SAFA-D02-10: DG identification tag not compliant with technical instructions.

SAFA-D02-11: Dangerous goods carried as limited quantities or excepted quantities but limits exceeded.

SAFA-D02-12: Dangerous goods not packed in accordance with proper packing instructions.

SAFA-D02-13: DG not stowed and/or separated in accordance with the Technical Instructions.

SAFA-D02-14: Hazardous and/or radioactive contamination not removed.

SAFA-D02-15: Required NOTOC missing.

SAFA-D02-16: DG carried in the cabin or on the flight deck not permitted by the provisions of the technical instructions.

SAFA-D02-17: No access to DG packages labeled "Cargo aircraft only" where required.

SAFA-D02-18: Transport of forbidden dangerous goods.

SAFA-D02-19: Dangerous goods not accompanied by shipper's declaration when so required.

Our Proof of Compliance:

We do not carry dangerous goods. The dangerous goods program is located in COM section 11.

Citing Documents:, A18-5.1, A18-8.1, A18-8.3, A18-8.4, A18-8.7, A18-8.8, A18-8.9, A18-9.1, A18-9.2.

EFBs

SAFA-A03-08*: EFB functions affecting the safe operation of the aircraft used without back-up.

SAFA-A03-11*: EFB mounting device or viewable stowage device obstructing forward visual or physical access to controls, display or external vision.

SAFA-A03-12*: The viewable stowage device used does not adequately secure the EFB.

SAFA-A03-13*: No operational approval of EFB functions affecting the safe operation of the aircraft.

Our Proof of Compliance:

Each pilot carries an iPad fully loaded with the operations manual, the flight manual, performance apps, and suitable charts for the route. Each pilot also carries an iPhone with several backup apps. The cockpit includes two USB power ports on each side to provide power to each pilot's iPad and iPhone. the cockpit displays also contain the suitable instrument charts, as shown:

Photo:s Typical iPad and iPhone backup, view of EFB storage.

The GVII-G500 / GVII-G-600 Type Certification Data Sheet (T00021AT, Revision 3) documents the aircraft's PED tolerance.

Photo: Extract of aircraft's Type Certification Data Sheet.

Citing Documents:, A6-I-6.2.3, A6-I-6.25.1, 6-I-6.25.3.

Emergency Exits / Lighting

SAFA-A02-01: Access to emergency exit impeded.

SAFA-A02-02: Emergency exits U/S.

SAFA-A02-03: If applicable, flight deck escape facilities (ropes, hatches, harnesses) not available or unserviceable (outside dispatch limits/conditions).

SAFA-B07-01: Emergency exit sign(s) lens/cover missing or broken.

SAFA-B07-02: Some of the cabin crew members have no serviceable portable lights available/readily accessible during night operations.

SAFA-B07-03: None of the cabin crew members have a serviceable portable light available/readily accessible during night operations.

SAFA-B07-04: Emergency exit sign(s) out of order (outside dispatch limits/conditions).

SAFA-B07-05: No means for illuminating the escape paths.

SAFA-B07-06: System for visually indicating the escape path(s) unserviceable (outside dispatch limits/conditions).

SAFA-B07-07: Emergency exit(s) not marked with the appropriate operating instructions.

SAFA-B07-09: Emergency exit(s), lighting and marking unserviceable (outside dispatch limits/conditions).

SAFA-B07-10: Number of passengers on board exceeds the maximum allowed in case of unserviceable emergency exit(s).

SAFA-B12-01: [Access to emergency exits] Floor/carpet in poor condition affecting the rapid evacuation.

SAFA-B12-02: Damaged wall panel or cabin crew seat lower stowage container access door latches not secure or unserviceable in the vicinity of emergency exit, possibly obstructing the exit.

SAFA-B12-03: Not-recessed tray table latch can be opened in the direction of evacuation (no one-way lock).

SAFA-B12-04: Not-recessed tray table latch can be opened in the direction of evacuation (for retrofitted aircraft).

SAFA-B12-05: Access to emergency exits impeded by baggage or cargo.

SAFA-B12-06: Access to emergency exits impeded by seats (total rows).

SAFA-B12-07: Cabin crew seat does not retract automatically impeding the access to emergency exit.

SAFA-B12-08: Access to emergency exits impeded by seats (oversized seat cushions).

SAFAB12-09: Tray table locks fail to maintain the tables in upright position in case of deceleration, shocks (for seats not adjacent to emergency exits).

SAFA-B12-10: Tray table locks fail to maintain the tables in upright position in case of deceleration, shocks (for seats adjacent to emergency exits).

Our Proof of Compliance:

The four exits are clearly marked and seating areas are as certified; the crew inspects the area as passengers embark and are seated.

Photos: Emergency Exits, path lighting, flashlight locations.

Emergency equipment (fire extinguishers, life vests, rafts, PBE, first aid and medical kits) are in clearly marked locations. Emergency exits are inspected prior to every flight as pilots remove locks.

Photos: Example life preserver placard, fire extinguishers, PBE placard, emergency exit signs.

Our configuration is as originally designed. We do not allow baggage or cargo near the emergency exits. Our tray tables are recessed and are not behind seats that would impact egress.

Citing Documents:, A6-I-6.10(f), A8-IIIB-4.6.2, A8-IIIB-4.6.2-4, A8-IIIB-6.3, A8-IIIB-4.6.4, A8-IIIA-4.1.7, A8-IIIA-4.1.7.2, A8-IIIA-4.1.7.3, A8-IIIA-8.3, A8-IIIB-8.4, A8-IIIB-8.5, A8-V-6.3, A8-IIIB-6.3, A8-V-6.3.

Equipment

SAFA-A03-01*: Required equipment installed but not being used during operation by crew.

SAFA-A03-06*: Required navigation equipment N/A or U/S (outside dispatch limits/conditions).

Our Proof of Compliance:

The instruments and equipment are as originally delivered.

Photos: Our cockpit, installed apps.

All flight documents are maintained in apps on iPads issued to all pilots.

Primary documents are kept in an app called ARINC Flight Operations Software (FOS) that are maintained by a full time dispatcher, updated automatically online and available off line.

Instrument charts are maintained on an App called JeppFD, updated regularly and available off line. Aircraft specific documents are maintained by an app called PlaneBook, updated regularly and available offline.

Citing Documents:, A6-I-4.3.1, A6-I-6.15.4, A6-I-6.15.6, A6-I-6.15.8, A6-I-7.5.2.

Fatigue / Duty Day / Rest

SAFA-A04-03: No rules on flight time, flight duty and rest time limitations in the operations manual.

SAFA-A20-20*: Flight crew member not in compliance with the flight and duty time rules.

Our Proof of Compliance:

The flight time, flight duty period, duty period and rest period limitations are located in COM section 4.3. The Fatigue Risk Management System is located in COM section 2.11.

Citing Documents:, A6-I-4.10.2abc, A6-I-Appendix 2, 2.

First Aid / Medical

SAFA-B02-01*: Medical supplies not at the indicated location.

SAFA-B02-02*: Contents of the medical kit past expiration date.

SAFA-B02-03*: Contents of the first-aid kit and/or universal precaution kit past expiration date.

SAFA-B02-04: Medical supplies not identified as such.

SAFA-B02-05*: Medical supplies not available or not accessible during flight.

Our Proof of Compliance:

Photo: G500 First Aid kit location example

Citing Documents:, A6-I-6.2.2, A6-I-4.2.12.2, A6-I-6.5.2, A8-IIIA-8.3, A8-V-6.3, A8-IIIB-6.3.

Flight Controls

SAFA-C03-02: Hydraulic leak outside dispatch limits/conditions.

SAFA-C03-03: Static discharger(s) missing (outside dispatch limits/conditions).

SAFA-C03-04: Flight controls unserviceable.

SAFA-C03-06: Loose and/or missing fastener on secondary structure with minor influence on safety.

SAFA-C03-07: Loose and/or missing fastener on secondary structure with significant influence on safety.

SAFA-C03-08: Loose and/or missing fastener on secondary or primary structure elements with major influence on safety.

SAFA-C03-09: Bonding wires broken or missing with minor impact on flight safety.

SAFA-C03-10: Bonding wires broken or missing with significant impact on flight safety.

SAFA-C03-11: Bonding wires broken or missing with major impact on flight safety.

Our Proof of Compliance:

The aircraft is inspected regularly for hydraulic leaks, loose or missing static dischargers, fasteners, bonding wires, as well as properly operating flight controls. Any discrepancies are corrected immediately.

Citing Documents:, A8-II-3.5.

Flight Crew

SAFA-A20-01: Form and/or content not in compliance with ICAO standard (licence, medical certificate).

SAFA-A20-02*: No crew member holds a valid R/T licence/rating.

SAFA-A20-04: Language proficiency endorsement expired.

SAFA-A20-05: Language proficiency endorsement missing or lower than the required operational level (Level 4).

SAFA-A20-06: Flight crew member(s) having obvious difficulty speaking in English, despite holding a valid ELP endorsement.

SAFA-A20-07: No endorsement of the required English language proficiency, but the flight crew member can obviously communicate effectively in English.

SAFA-A20-08: No English translation of ICAO required items of the licence.

SAFA-A20-09: No mention of ICAO medical class.

SAFA-A20-10: No proper validation issued by the State of registry.

SAFA-A20-11*:Spare correcting spectacles not available (for multi-pilot operations).

SAFA-A20-12: Flight crew member without appropriate licence/rating.

SAFA-A20-13: Medical certificate invalid for the privileges being exercised.

SAFA-A20-14*: No correcting lenses available and/or used when required.

SAFA-A20-15: PIC aged 60 or more engaged in single pilot commercial air transport.

SAFA-A20-16: Pilot aged 65 or more in commercial air transport.

SAFA-A20-17: Spare correcting spectacles not available (for single pilot operations).

SAFA-A20-18: A valid and appropriate flight crew licence and/or medical certificate was issued but not carried on board at the time of the inspection.

SAFA-A20-19*: Insufficient number of flight crew members.

Our Proof of Compliance:

Each pilot will have in his or her possession a valid license, medical certificate, valid radio transmitting license. Each pilot is evaluated at least annually during a type specific recurrent evaluation for language proficiency. Each pilot requiring the use of correcting spectacles will have a spare set.

Citing Documents:, A1-1.2.1, A1-1.2.5.2, A1-1.2.5.2.2, A1-1.2.5.2.3, A1-1.2.9.1, A1-1.2.9.5, A1-2.1.10, A1-6.1.1a,b, A1-5.1.1.1, A1-5.1.1.2, A1-5.1.3, A1-APP 1, A6-I-3.1.8, A6-I-9.1.1, A6-I-9.1.2, A1-6.3.3.2, A1-6.3.3.2.1, CC-29c, CC-32a, CC-40.

Flight Deck Condition

SAFA-A01-18: Cockpit seats in poor condition.

Our Proof of Compliance:

Our seats are like new.

Photos: Photo of left and right cockpit seats.

Citing Documents:

Flight Deck Markings

SAFA-A01-14: Operational flight deck markings and/or placards missing or incorrect.

Our Proof of Compliance:

The aircraft was certified with some limitations on the center windshield pos and and we have one serial-number specific placard in the cockpit:

Photos: Aircraft limitations on windshield post.

Photo: Aircraft limitations on left windshield post, cockpit internal placard

Citing Documents:, A8-IIIB-7.1, A8-IIIA-9.1.

Flight Deck Windows

SAFA-A01-07: Damage and/or delamination to flight deck windows (outside dispatch limits/conditions).

Our Proof of Compliance:

Our cockpit windows are inspected regularly and have not shown any signs of damage or delamination.

Photo: Cockpit windows.

Flight Planning

SAFA-A13-01*: No copy of the operational flight plan retained on the ground.

SAFA-A13-02*: Fuel calculation not in accordance with ICAO requirements, but total fuel on board at or above minimum ICAO requirements.

SAFA-A13-03: ATC Flight plan incorrect.

SAFA-A13-05: Content and use of the Operational Flight plan not in accordance with the operations manual.

SAFA-A13-06: Fuel on board less than minimum ICAO requirements.

SAFA-A13-07*: Flight crew unaware of the applicable departure, destination or alternate airports NOTAMs.

SAFA-A13-10*: Incorrect Operational Flight Plan.

SAFA-A13-11*: No Operational Flight Plan.

SAFA-A13-12*: Less than required or unsuitable alternate(s) airports selected.

SAFA-A13-15: Performance and/or fuel calculation not available or significantly incorrect for the flight.

SAFA-A13-16*: Required en-route alternate(s) (EDTO/ETOPS) not available.

SAFA-A13-19*: Weather on required en-route alternate(s) below EDTO/ETOPS minima.

SAFA-A13-20*: Required alternate airport(s) considered in OFP but not specified in the ATS flight plan.

Our Proof of Compliance:

Our flight plans are filed automatically by ARINCDirect and the master flight plan does comply with the Annex 2 and EU requirements. Our fuel planning policies are in our Company Operations Manual section 4.5.

Citing Documents:, A2-2.3.2, A6-I-4.1.1, A6-I-4.3.3.1, A6-I-4.3.4.2, A6-I-4.3.6.2, A6-I-4.3.6.3, A6-I-4.3.6.5, A6-I-4.7.1.1, A6-I-5.2.5, EUR 2.1.5.1, EUR 2.1.5.2, EUR 2.1.6.1.

Fuel Checks / Fueling Operations

SAFA-A04-10: No procedures ensuring that in-flight fuel checks/fuel management checks are performed.

SAFA-A13-21*: Fuel consumption monitoring not recorded or not performed in accordance with the approved procedures.

SAFA-A13-23*: Qualified personnel not at their required positions when refuelling with passengers on board.

SAFA-A13-25*: No two-way communication established with the ground crew during refuelling with passengers on board.

Our Proof of Compliance:

The International Operations Manual (IOM) is located in the FOS App Documents folder:

Photo: Company Operations Manual (COM) in FOS App.

Fuel management tasks are located in the IOM Sections 2.1.5.3.

Citing Documents:, 6-I-4.2.10.1, A6-I-4.3.7.1, A6-I-4.3.7.2, A6-I-4.3.8.1, A6-I-4.3.8.2, A6-I-4.3.8.12.

General External Condition

SAFA-C01-01: Markings and/or placards not related to ground servicing required by the manufacturer not applied or unreadable.

SAFA-C01-02*: Break-in point markings (if applied) faded or incorrectly marked.

SAFA-C01-03: Paint damage with exposed composite (outside dispatch limits/conditions).

SAFA-C01-04: Poor condition of de-icing system.

SAFA-C01-05: Ground servicing placards and markings not applied or unreadable.

SAFA-C01-06: Significant corrosion.

SAFA-C01-07: Major corrosion (outside dispatch limits/conditions).

SAFA-C01-08: Required aircraft lights unserviceable (outside dispatch limits/conditions) or not displayed.

SAFA-C01-10: Static discharger(s) missing or damaged outside dispatch limits/conditions.

SAFA-C01-11: Antenna(s) missing or damaged outside dispatch limits/conditions.

SAFA-C01-12: Pressure port (and/or RVSM area) damaged or contaminated (outside dispatch limits/conditions).

SAFA-C01-13: Tail skid wear outside dispatch limits/conditions.

SAFA-C01-16: Loose and/or missing fastener on secondary structure with minor influence on safety.

SAFA-C01-17: Loose and/or missing fastener on secondary structure with significant influence on safety.

SAFA-C01-18: Loose and/or missing fastener on secondary or primary structure elements with major influence on safety.

SAFA-C01-19: Bonding wires broken or missing with minor impact on flight safety.

SAFA-C01-20: Bonding wires broken or missing with significant impact on flight safety.

SAFA-C01-21: Bonding wires broken or missing with major influence on safety.

SAFA-C02-02: Door handle(s), lever(s), access panel(s) not flush.

SAFA-C02-03: Door operation instructions missing or unclear.

SAFA-C02-04: Cargo door lock inspection glasses blind and no other means to verify locking position(s).

SAFA-C02-05: Door seal damaged outside dispatch limits/conditions.

SAFA-C02-06: Door(s) unserviceable outside dispatch limits/conditions.

SAFA-C02-07: Bonding wires broken or missing with minor impact on flight safety.

SAFA-C02-08: Bonding wires broken or missing with significant impact on flight safety.

SAFA-C02-09: Bonding wires broken or missing with major impact on flight safety.

SAFA-C02-10: Loose and/or missing fastener on secondary structure with minor influence on safety.

SAFA-C02-11: Loose and/or missing fastener on secondary structure with significant influence on safety.

SAFA-C02-12: Loose and/or missing fastener on secondary or primary structure elements with major influence on safety.

Our Proof of Compliance:

The aircraft is inspected annually by the manufacturer and any missing markings or placards are reapplied as needed.

The aircraft is inspected regularly and any corrosion, paint damage, inoperative lights, missing or damaged static dischargers, missing or damaged antennas, broken or missing bonding wires, damaged pressure ports or RVSM areas, loose or missing fasteners, or problems with the de-icing system is corrected immediately.

The aircraft does not have a tail skid.

Photos: GVII-G500 main entrance door placard, water and waste service placards, fuel service placards.

The aircraft was certified without any break-in marks.

Citing Documents:, A6-I-6.2.4.1, A6-I-6.10, A8-IIIB-7.6.2, A8-V-7.6.2, A8-IIIA-9.6.2, SERA.3215.

General Internal Condition

SAFA-B01-01: Equipment installations obviously not in compliance with

564

Annex 8, Part IIIA/B, Chapter 4.

SAFA-B01-02: Cabin interior layout obviously not furnished in accordance with certified.

SAFA-B01-03: Smoke detection system not installed or inoperative (outside dispatch limits/conditions) and lavatory not placarded in compliance with MEL.

SAFA-B01-04: Disposal receptacles not equipped with a serviceable built-in fire extinguisher system.

SAFA-B01-05*: Crew carry-on baggage not adequately and securely stowed during flight.

SAFA-B01-06: Loose or heavy objects in the cabin/galleys.

SAFA-B01-07: Cabin equipment not properly secured.

SAFA-B01-08*: Stowage of luggage or loose articles in the toilets.

SAFA-B01-09*: Lavatory smoke detection system obstructed.

SAFA-B01-10*: Lavatory inoperative (not placarded as such and not confirmed with MEL restrictions if any).

SAFA-B01-11: Galley or trolley (when used) waste receptacle access door cover inoperative.

SAFA-B01-12: Damaged wall panels.

SAFA-B01-13: Unserviceable brakes of service cart(s).

SAFA-B01-14: Covers damaged/missing exposing sharp edges and/or cables and wires.

SAFA-B01-16: Lavatory waste receptacle access door cover inoperative.

SAFA-B01-17: Safety markings and placards not applied or unreadable.

SAFA-B14-01*: Passengers on board in excess of the number of available seats.

Our Proof of Compliance:

The aircraft interior was designed and outfitted by Gulfstream, the aircraft manufacturer. No subsequent modifications have been made. The aircraft is maintained according to the Gulfstream maintenance program by two full time mechanics. Disposal receptacles are as originally installed. Pilots perform a visual scan of the cabin prior to engine start and prior to landing to verify the cabin is secure and undamaged. We do have a Minimum Equipment List . We do not have galley carts.

Citing Documents:, A6-I-6.1.3, A6-I-6.2.2(c)(1), A6-I-4.3.1, A6-I-4.8, A8-IIIA-1.4, A8-IIIA-1.5, A8-IIIA-4.1.6 (f), A8-IIIA-4.1.7.1, A8-IIIA-8.2, A8-IIIA-9.6.2, A8-IIIB-1.3, A8-IIIB-4.2 (f), A8-IIIB-4.6., A8-IIIB-4.6.1, A8-IIIB-6.2, A8-IIIB-7.6.2, A8-V-7.6.2, (E)TSO-C175 SAE AS8056 EUROCAE ED-121.

General Operations

SAFA-E01-01: Aircraft not operated according to the manufacturer's operating instructions during push-back, towing and/or taxiing.

Our Proof of Compliance:

Our crews are trained and evaluated every six months for proper operating procedures.

Citing Documents:

GPWS

SAFA-A03-04*: GPWS with forward looking terrain avoidance function not installed or unserviceable (outside dispatch limits/conditions).

Our Proof of Compliance:

The aircraft's original certification includes EGPWS, as evidenced by the following product specification extract:

Photo: G500 Product Specification extract, item 12.3.14, October 2017.

The EGPWS database is updated regularly in accordance with the aircraft's Computerized Maintenance Program and the dates are checked prior to every flight via the cockpit Touch Screen Controllers:.

Citing Documents:, A6-I-4.3.1, A6-I-6.15.4, A6-I-6.15.6,, A6-I-6.15.8, A6-I-7.5.2.

Hand Fire Extinguishers

SAFA-A15-01: HFE not at indicated location.

SAFA-A15-02: HFE not marked with the appropriate operating instructions.

SAFA-A15-03: Insufficient number of serviceable HFE.

SAFA-A15-04: HFE not accessible.

SAFA-B04-01: HFE not at indicated location.

SAFA-B04-02: HFE not marked with the appropriate operating instructions.

SAFA-B04-03*: Insufficient number of serviceable HFE.

SAFA-B04-04: HFE not correctly secured.

SAFA-B04-05: HFE not readily accessible.

Our Proof of Compliance:

Photos: Hand Fire Extinguisher locations, cockpit fire extinguisher, cabin fire extinguisher, lav fire extinguisher, placards.

Citing Documents:, A6-I-6.2.2b, A6-I-6.2.2(b)(2), A8-IIIA-4.1.7.1, A8-II-IA-8.3, A8-IIIB-4.6.1, A8-IIIB-6.3,, A8-V-6.3.

Icing

SAFA-A13-08*: Flight operated in known icing conditions without suitable certification and/or equipment.

SAFA-A13-09*: No icing inspection performed by crew or ground staff with ground icing conditions.

SAFA-A13-22*: No intentions to request appropriate de-icing treatment.

Our Proof of Compliance:

Citing Documents:, A6-I-4.3.5.5, A6-I-4.3.5.6.

Journey Log Book

SAFA-A21-01: Inconsistent data entered into the Journey log book.

SAFA-A21-02: Flight details not recorded in a journey log book or General Declaration.

SAFA-A21-03: Journey log book or equivalent not on board.

SAFA-A21-04: Flight details not updated on EFB.

Our Proof of Compliance:

Our logbook is maintained in our Flight Operations Software App and can be viewed by selected the particular flight date in the calendar and then selecting "Post Flight."

Photo: Journey Logbook example in FOS (First page of many).

Citing Documents:, A6-I-4.5.5, CC-29d, CC-34.

Leakage

SAFA-C11-01: Leakage outside dispatch limits/conditions.

SAFA-C11-02: Servicing doors/panels, drains blocked by ice or other debris.

Our Proof of Compliance:

The aircraft is inspected regularly and any leakage or blocked drains are addressed immediately.

Citing Documents:

Life Jackets / Flotation Devices / Harnesses

SAFA-A16-01*: Life jackets/flotation devices not easily accessible when required for the type of flight.

SAFA-A16-02*: Insufficient number of life jackets/flotation devices available and required for the type of flight.

SAFA-A17-01*: Pilot harness does not incorporate an automatic restraining device.

SAFA-A17-03*: No or unserviceable safety harness for each flight crew seat (outside dispatch limits/conditions).

SAFA-B05-01: Life jackets / flotation devices not easily accessible and required for the type of flight.

SAFA-B05-02: Insufficient number of serviceable Life jackets / Flotation devices available and required for the type of flight.

SAFA-B08-01*: No equipment for making the pyrotechnical distress signals when required for long-range over-water flights.

SAFA-B08-02: Insufficient number of serviceable slides/slide rafts.

SAFA-B08-03*: Insufficient number of serviceable rafts and required for long-range over water flights.

SAFA-B08-04*: Insufficient number of compliant ELTs (outside dispatch limits/conditions).

SAFA-B08-05: ELT(s) not capable of simultaneously transmitting on 406 MHz and 121.5 MHZ.

SAFA-B08-06*: No automatic ELT available when required.

SAFA-B08-07: Portable ELT not at indicated location.

Our Proof of Compliance:

The aircraft is equipped with a life vest for each seat.

Photos: Life jacket locations, life vest under seat location, typical, life rafts location, cockpit seats.

Photo: Photo of right cockpit seat.

Citing Documents:, A6-I-6.2.2.c3, A6-I-6.5.2, A6-I-6.5.3.1(a), A8-II-IA-4.1.7, A8-IIIA-8.3, A8-V-6.3, A8-IIIB-6.3, A8-IIIB-8.4, A6-I-6.5.2.1, A6-I-6.5.1(a), A6-I-6.5.2.2, A8-IIIA-8.3, A8-IIIB-8.4, A8-IIIB-6.3, A8-V-6.3, A6-I-6.17.2, A6-I-6.17.3, A6-I-6.17.4, A6-I-6.17.5, A6-I-6.17.6.

Lights U/S

SAFA-A01-10: Lights U/S in warning panel (outside dispatch limits/conditions).

Our Proof of Compliance:

The aircraft is inspected regularly and any inoperative lights are replaced prior to flight.

Citing Documents:

Locking Crew Compartment Door

SAFA-A01-01*, SAFA-A01-09*: One or more door locking/un-locking mechanism not serviceable or present.

SAFA-A01-02*, SAFA-A01-06*: No means for cabin crew to discretely notify cockpit crew of suspicious activity.

SAFA-A01-03*, SAFA-A01-04*, SAFA-A01-05: No means for cockpit crew to monitor area behind door.

Our Proof of Compliance:

Citing Documents:, A6-I-13.2.1, A6-I-13.2.2, A6-I-13.2.3.

Maintenance Release / Deferred Items

SAFA-A22-01*: PIC did not certify that s/he is satisfied that a maintenance release has been issued.

SAFA-A23-01*: Defect deferred with a wrong AMM/SRM/MEL/CDL reference.

SAFA-A23-02*: Item closed but not reported as such in the deferred defect list / hold item list.

SAFA-A23-03*: Maintenance action not properly reported.

SAFA-A23-04*: Maintenance action not properly reported.

SAFA-A23-05*: Known defect not reported/assessed.

SAFA-A23-06*: No evidence of identification nor monitoring of significant defect.

SAFA-A23-07*: Deferred defect open while the MEL rectification interval has expired.

SAFA-A23-08*: Technical logbook entry not understood by the flight crew members.

SAFA-A23-09*: Incorrect rectification interval applied (but still within the prescribed MEL interval).

SAFA-A23-10*: Required maintenance action not performed or not in accordance with applicable (MEL/AMM/SRM) instructions.

SAFA-A23-11*: Maintenance action not performed by appropriately qualified personnel.

SAFA-A23-12*: Defect deferred but without applying (correctly) the required (M), (O) and/or other procedures prescribed by the MEL.

SAFA-A23-13*: Maintenance personnel working on the aircraft without using appropriate tooling.

SAFA-A23-15*: Technical logbook not updated on the EFB.

Our Proof of Compliance:

Our MEL policies are located in the Company Operations Manual section 3.3. Our MEL is located in our ARINCDirect App:

Photo: Aircraft MEL found in ARINCDirect App Documents.

Citing Documents:, A6-I-4.3.1(a)(c), A6-I-4.5.4, A6-I-8.1.2, A6-I-6.1.3, A6-I-8.1.4, A6-I-8.4, A6-I-8.5, A6-I-8.7.5.2, A6-I-8.7.6.2.

Manuals

SAFA-A04-01*: Incomplete parts of the operations manual pertaining to flight operations on board.

SAFA-A04-02*: No operations manual (parts pertaining to flight operations) or Flight manual on board.

SAFA-A04-04*: Operations manual not up to date.

SAFA-A04-05*: Operations manual not issued by the current operator.

SAFA-A04-07*: No or incomplete performance and limitations data on board.

SAFA-A04-09*: Operations manual published in a language not understood by any of the flight crew members.

SAFA-A04-11*: Flight crew not familiar with approved company procedures and manuals.

Our Proof of Compliance:

The operations manual is located in the FOS Documents folder on each pilot's iPad. The manual has been vetted by several Safety Management System audits, including an initial and several recertifying Stage III compliance. The operations manual is issued by the operator. The operations manual is issued in English. The manual is automatically kept up-to-date through FOS. Performance and limitations are included in the AFM contained in each pilot's iPad. The airplane flight manual is located in the PlaneBook App on each pilot's iPad.

Photo: AFM and Company Operations Manual (COM) in FOS App.

Citing Documents:, A6-I-6.2.3ab, A6-I-4.2.3.1, A6-I-3.1.2.

MEL

SAFA-A07-01*: MEL does not reflect aircraft configuration or the operations specifications.

SAFA-A07-02*: MEL lacking (M) and/or (O) procedures when required (no deferred defect requiring such procedure).

SAFA-A07-03*: MEL lacking (M) and/or (O) procedures when required (with deferred defect requiring such procedure).

SAFA-A07-04*: MEL less restrictive than the MMEL (with deferred defects affected by the lower restrictions).

SAFA-A07-05*: MEL less restrictive than the MMEL (without deferred defects affected by the lower restrictions).

SAFA-A07-06*: MEL not available (no deferred defects).

SAFA-A07-07*: Some MEL items not fully customised (but no defects affecting those items).

SAFA-A07-08*: MMEL instead of MEL.

SAFA-A07-09*: Some MEL items not fully customised (with defects affecting those items).

SAFA-A07-10*: MEL not available (with deferred defects).

Our Proof of Compliance:

The aircraft's MEL (D195) was written by the manufacturer and is kept up-to-date following any configuration changes.

Photo: Aircraft MEL found in ARINCDirect App Documents.

Citing Documents:, A6-I-6.1.3.

Navigation

SAFA-A06-01: Navigation database out of date, within limits but not recognised as such (prescribed operational procedures not applied).

SAFA-A06-02: Navigation database out of date (outside dispatch limits/conditions).

SAFA-A06-03: Navigation database with incorrect routes/ procedures/ waypoints/ reporting points pertaining to the performed/intended flight.

SAFA-A06-04: Required en-route charts out of date (navigation database up to date).

SAFA-A06-05: Required en-route charts and navigation database out of date.

SAFA-A06-06: Required instrument charts not on board, or not available during critical phases of the flight.

SAFA-A06-07: Required instrument charts (except en-route) out of date.

SAFA-A06-08: Several sets of required instrument charts available in the flight deck, of which one (not in use) is out of date.

Our Proof of Compliance:

The navigation database is updated regularly in accordance with the aircraft's Computerized Maintenance Program and the electronic navigation data is checked by the aircraft itself on a Touch Screen Controller and checked by pilots prior to every flight.

Photo: G500 TSC FMS Init Page, installed iPad Apps.

Citing Documents:, A6-I-6.2.3c, A6-I-7.5.2, A15-6.1.1.

Noise

SAFA-A09-01: Documents attesting noise certification inaccurate, not on board or cannot be produced by the crew.

SAFA-A09-02: No English translation of the noise certificate.

Our Proof of Compliance:

Our noise certificate is kept under the documents/gvii-g500 tab of our ARINCDirect App, available on each pilot's iPad.

Photo: Noise certificate located in ARINCS App Documents folder, example.

Citing Documents:, A6-I-6.13, A16-I-II-1.4, A16-I-II-1.5.

Oxygen / PBE

SAFA-A18-01: Oxygen equipment not readily accessible and required for the type of flight.

SAFA-A18-02*: Insufficient number of serviceable quick donning masks available.

SAFA-A18-03*: Insufficient oxygen and/or serviceable oxygen masks.

SAFA-A18-04*: Unserviceable oxygen system.

SAFA-B09-01: Protective breathing equipment not at indicated location.

SAFA-B09-02: Oxygen equipment not readily accessible and required for the type of flight.

SAFA-B09-03*: Aeroplane not equipped with an automatic deployable oxygen system (individual CofA issued on or after 9 November 1998) and flight planned above FL 250.

SAFA-B09-04*: Insufficient number of required serviceable automatic deployable oxygen dispensing units - individual CofA issued on or after 9 November 1998 (outside dispatch limits/conditions).

SAFA-B09-05: Oxygen equipment not adequately marked with its operating instructions.

SAFA-B09-06: Insufficient oxygen quantity and/or serviceable oxygen masks required for the type of flight.

SAFA-B09-07*: Insufficient oxygen (quantity and/or dispensing units) for all cabin crew and 10% of passengers (and required for the type of flight) – non-pressurized flight between FL 100 and FL 130, in excess of 30 min.

SAFA-B09-08*: Automatic oxygen deploying system unserviceable (damaged/taped drop-out panels) outside dispatch limits/conditions.

SAFA-B09-09*: Oxygen dispensing equipment unserviceable (low pressure, clearly overdue, damaged) and not identified as.

SAFA-B09-10: Oxygen bottles not correctly secured.

Our Proof of Compliance:

Photos: Passenger oxygen mask instructions (from information card), oxygen duration chart at 15,000' after a 6 minute descent, pilot seat oxygen mask location, therapeutic oxygen location, PBE Locations.

Citing Documents:, A6-I-4.4.5.2, A6-I-6.7.1, A6-I-6.7.2, A6-I-6.7.5, A6-I-4.3.9.1, A6-I-4.3.9.2, A8-IIIA-8.3, A8-IIIB-6.3, A8-V-6.3.

Passenger Seats

SAFA-B06-01: No extension belts available on board when necessary.

SAFA-B06-02: Passenger seats in poor condition.

SAFA-B06-03: Strap or buckle worn out or damage.

SAFA-B06-04: No serviceable seat belt available for each passenger on board.

SAFA-B06-05: Seat(s) unserviceable and not identified as such (outside dispatch limits/conditions).

SAFA-B06-06: Seat(s)/berth(s) not certified to be installed on board of aircraft.

SAFA-B06-07: Baby berth(s) used without restraining belts.

Our Proof of Compliance:

We keep two seatbelt extension belts under the forward divan in the middle section cabinet. We do not have baby berth(s).

Photos: Seatbelt extenders, cabin interior.

Citing Documents:, A6-I-6.2.2(c), A8-IIIB-4.4.1.

Pilots' vision

SAFA-A01-11: Cockpit installations significantly decreasing pilots vision.

SAFA-A01-12: Windshield wipers/cleaning/drying system not installed or inoperative (outside dispatch limits/conditions).

Our Proof of Compliance:

Photo: View of cockpit.

The aircraft was certified without a wipers/cleaning/drying system.

Citing Documents:, A8-IIIA-4.1.6d, A8-IIIB-4.2d.

Portable Lights

SAFA-A19-01: Serviceable independent portable light available to both pilots but not for other flight crew members during night operation.

SAFA-A19-02: Independent portable lights not serviceable or readily available during night operation.

SAFA-A19-03: Insufficient number of serviceable independent portable lights for all pilots during night operation.

Our Proof of Compliance:

Photo: Flashlight locations.

Citing Documents:, A6-I-6.10f, A8-IIIA-8.3, A8-IIIB-6.3, A8-V-6.3.

Powerplant and Pylon

SAFA-C07-01: Markings and/or placards not related to ground servicing required by the manufacturer not applied or unreadable.

SAFA-C07-02: Ground servicing markings not applied or unreadable.

SAFA-C07-03: Significant damage in the intake and exhaust area.

SAFA-C07-04: Damage (dents, nicks, cracks) outside dispatch limits/conditions.

SAFA-C07-05: Intake acoustic liners damaged outside dispatch limits/conditions.

SAFA-C07-06: Leakage (oil, fuel, hydraulics) outside dispatch limits/conditions.

SAFA-C07-07: Panels/fairings/cowlings/handles misaligned or not flush outside dispatch limits/conditions.

SAFA-C07-09: Thrust reverser/blocker doors not fully stowed.

SAFA-C07-10: Loose and/or missing fastener with minor influence on safety.

SAFA-C07-11: Loose and/or missing fastener on secondary structure with significant influence on safety.

SAFA-C07-12: Loose and/or missing fastener on secondary or primary structure elements with major influence on safety.

SAFA-C07-13: Safety markings not applied or unreadable.

SAFA-C08-01: Fan blade(s) LPT and HPT, IGV/OGV damaged outside dispatch limits/conditions.

SAFA-C08-02: Propeller de-icing system unserviceable (outside dispatch limits/conditions).

SAFA-C08-03: Propeller(s) damaged outside dispatch limits/conditions.

Our Proof of Compliance:

The aircraft is inspected regularly and any damage, leakage, and part misalignment is corrected immediately.

Photos: Water and waste service placards, fuel service placards.

Thrust reverser doors that have not fully closed will cause a Crew Alerting System message, prompting the crew to address the issue. The aircraft is inspected regularly and any fan blade damage is addressed immediately. The aircraft is not equipped with propellers.

Citing Documents:, A8-IIIA-9.6.2, A8-IIIB-7.6.2, A8-V-7.6.2.

Preflight Inspection

SAFA-A24-01*: Pre-flight inspection performed but the pilot in command did not certify that he is satisfied that the aircraft is airworthy.

SAFA-A24-02*: Pilot in command certified that he is satisfied that the aircraft is airworthy before the pre-flight inspection was performed.

SAFA-A24-03*: Pre-flight inspection performed but without identifying significant defects.

SAFA-A24-04*: Pre-flight inspection not performed.

Our Proof of Compliance:

Citing Documents:, A6-I-4.3.1(a)(c).

Radio License

SAFA-A11-01: Incorrect information on the Radio Station Licence.

SAFA-A11-02: A valid Radio Station Licence was issued but not carried on board at the time of the inspection.

SAFA-A11-03: No valid Radio Station Licence issued.

SAFA-A11-04: Radio Station Licence on board expired.

Our Proof of Compliance:

Our radio license is kept under the documents/gvii-g500 tab of our ARINC-Direct App, available on each pilot's iPad.

Photo: Radio license located in ARINCS App Documents folder, example.

Citing Documents:, CC-29e, CC-30a.

Repairs

SAFA-C09-01: Previous repair in poor condition.

SAFA-C09-02: Repairs obviously not carried out in accordance with the applicable AMM/SRM.

SAFA-C10-01: Obvious unrepaired damage, structural damage affecting the airworthiness of the aircraft.

Our Proof of Compliance:

All repairs are completed in accordance with Gulfstream maintenance manual best practices.

Citing Documents:

Safety Instructions

SAFA-B10-01*: Insufficient safety briefing cards for all passengers on board.

SAFA-B10-02*: Safety briefing cards in poor condition.

SAFA-B10-03*: Safety briefing cards contain inaccurate information.

SAFA-B10-04*: 'Fasten seat belt' sign(s) unserviceable.

SAFA-B10-05*: 'Return to Seat' signs in lavatory unserviceable (outside dispatch limits/conditions).

SAFA-B10-06*: No safety briefing cards on board.

SAFA-B10-07*: Safety briefing cards not for the correct aircraft type and/or configuration.

Our Proof of Compliance:

Photo: Location of briefing cards (forward armrest of forward divan).

The briefing cards were provided by the manufacturer and the cabin remains in its original configuration. The cards are in good condition. All signs are checked for operation on a regular basis.

Citing Documents:, A6-I-4.2.12.1, A6-I-6.2.2 (d).

Stowage of Loose Items in Cabin

SAFA-A01-08: Interior equipment and/or other object(s) not correctly secured or stowed during flight.

Our Proof of Compliance:

The crew monitors the interior to ensure nothing will impair egress following an abrupt stop.

Photo: Aircraft interior.

Citing Documents:, A8-IIIA-4.1.6.(c), A8-IIIB-4.2.(c), A8-IIIA-4.1.7.1, A8-IIIB-4.6.1.

Undercarriage

SAFA-C05-01: Markings and/or placards not related to ground servicing required by the manufacturer not applied or unreadable.

SAFA-C05-02: Safety lock pin(s) missing or defective.

SAFA-C05-03: Gear strut valve cap(s) missing.

SAFA-C05-04: Water/debris deflectors damaged or missing outside dispatch limits/conditions.

SAFA-C05-05: Lines, hoses electrical wiring chafed.

SAFA-C05-06: Ground servicing markings not applied or unreadable.

SAFA-C05-07: Significant corrosion.

SAFA-C05-08: Major corrosion (outside dispatch limits/conditions).

SAFA-C05-09: Seepage/leakage outside dispatch limits/conditions.

SAFA-C05-10: Strut pressure outside dispatch limit/conditions.

SAFA-C05-11: Safety markings not applied or unreadable.

Our Proof of Compliance:

Safety lock pins and other components are inspected regularly. Any missing or defective pins are replaced immediately.

Photos: Safety lock pins, eexample gear strut valve cap from right main landing gear, nose gear strut, with proper pressure. The aircraft does not have water/debris deflectors installed.

Citing Documents:, A8-IIIA-9.6.2, A8-IIIB-7.6.2, A8-V-7.6.2.

VHF 8.33

SAFA-A03-05: From 1 January 2018 an operator shall not operate an aircraft in airspace where carriage of radio is required unless aircraft radio equipment has the 8. 33 kHz channel spacing capability.

Our Proof of Compliance:

8.33 kHz channel spacing capability is installed, as is evidenced by a view of the radio settings shown here:

Photo: G500 TSC VHF Com1 Settings Page.

Citing Documents:, Reg. 1079/2012, Art. 5.

Weather

SAFA-A13-13*: Flight took off or continued beyond the point of in-flight replanning while data indicated that DES meteorological conditions were below minima.

SAFA-A13-14*: Take-off intended while data indicates that DEP/DES meteorological conditions are below minima (and in-flight replanning not allowed).

Our Proof of Compliance:

Citing Documents:, A6-I-4.1.1, A6-I-4.1.4, A6-I-4.1.5, A6-I-4.3.4.1, A6-I-4.3.4.2, A6-I-4.3.4.3.1, A6-I-4.3.4.3.2, A6-I-4.3.5.2.

Weight and Balance

SAFA-A14-01*: Incorrect mass and/or balance calculations, within a/c limits, and having minor effect on the performance calculations.

SAFA-A14-02*: Incorrect mass and/or balance calculations, within a/c limits, but significantly affecting the performance calculations.

SAFA-A14-03*: Insufficient data to enable the crew to check the Mass &

balance calculations.

SAFA-A14-04*: Mass and balance outside operational limits.

SAFA-A14-05*: Load sheet does not reflect actual load distribution but within A/C limits.

SAFA-A14-06*: No mass and balance calculations performed.

SAFA-A14-07*: No completed mass and balance sheet on board.

SAFA-A14-10*: Load sheet does not reflect actual load distribution with major impact on trim setting.

Our Proof of Compliance:
Citing Documents:, A6-I-4.3.1(d)(e), A6-I-5.2.7.

Wheel Well

SAFA-C06-01: Landing gear door(s) damaged outside dispatch limits/conditions.

SAFA-C06-02: Obvious lack of lubrication of hinge(s), actuator(s).

SAFA-C06-04: Significant corrosion.

SAFA-C06-05: Major corrosion (outside dispatch limits/conditions).

SAFA-C06-06: Landing gear emergency spring lock(s) broken/unserviceable.

SAFA-C06-07: Seepage/leakage outside dispatch limits/conditions.

SAFA-C06-08: Bonding wires broken or missing with minor impact on flight safety.

SAFA-C06-09: Bonding wires broken or missing with significant impact on flight safety.

SAFA-C06-10: Bonding wires broken or missing with major impact on flight safety.

SAFA-C06-11: Loose and/or missing fastener on secondary structure with minor influence on safety.

SAFA-C06-12: Loose and/or missing fastener on secondary structure with significant influence on safety.

SAFA-C06-13: Loose and/or missing fastener on secondary or primary structure elements with major influence on safety.

Our Proof of Compliance:

All aircraft structures are inspected regularly for damage, lubrication, corrosion, leakage, missing parts, or other anomalies and are corrected immediately.

Citing Documents:, A8-IIIA-4.1.4, A8-IIIB-4.1.5, A8-V-4.1.5.

Wheels, tires and brakes

SAFA-C04-01: Brake wear indicator pin(s) missing (at least one pin remaining) and not recorded.

SAFA-C04-02: Tyre inflation valve(s) cap missing.

SAFA-C04-03: Brake assembly bleed valve dust cap(s) missing.

SAFA-C04-04: Brake(s) unserviceable and not recorded.

SAFA-C04-05: Damaged or missing parts outside limits (i.e. bolts, heat sensors) and not recorded.

SAFA-C04-06: Leaking hydraulic braking system (outside dispatch limits/conditions).

SAFA-C04-07: Nose landing gear wheel snubbers worn outside dispatch limits/conditions.

SAFA-C04-08: Tyre pressure obviously outside dispatch limits/conditions.

SAFA-C04-09: Tyre(s) unserviceable (worn or damaged) and not recorded.

SAFA-C04-10: Rim damaged outside dispatch limits/conditions.

Our Proof of Compliance:

The aircraft brake assemblies are inspected regularly and any defects are corrected immediately.

Photos: Brake wear indicators, right main landing gear, tire inflation caps, left main landing gear, example brake assembly bleed valve, right main landing gear.

The tire pressures are available on cockpit Touch Screen Controllers. (Note, nose gear transducer wire on steering link must be connected first.)

Photo: Tire pressure indicators on TSC.

The aircraft was certified without nose landing gear wheel snubbers.

Slots (European Union)

*F*low control is a way of life in the EU; the skies have become so crowded that something had to be done. In 1988 the entire system was automated which enabled more airplanes to fill the sky more efficiently, but it made a complex system too complex for pilots to comprehend.

Even if a pilot was emersed into the system for complete familiarity, pilots aren't allowed to access the system directly. And there is that pesky problem with language. It really pays to have a local handler on your payroll everywhere you go in Europe. But there may be times the handler is unable or unwilling to help. In that case you need to be able to speak the CFMU lingo. There are a lot of acronyms. If you learn the terms, are patient, and remain calm on the phone and radio, you too can negotiate a slot in the European Union.

In a nutshell, here is how it is supposed to work:

- *You tell "them" when you are going to be ready with a "Target Off Block Time" (TOBT), when you will be ready with all passengers on board, doors closed, ready to start engines.*

- *"They" give you a "Target Start Up Approval Time" (TSAT).*

- *You call "them" when ready to start.*

- *"They" look at all the traffic throughout Europe to make sure the airways and airports do not become saturated during the time you are moving. If there is going to be any saturation, "they" will issue slot reservations to make sure the system isn't overwhelmed.*

- *"They" can simply delay you or even re-route you.*

- *Getting slotted may be no big deal, or it could ruin your day. Knowing how to handle it all improves your odds of avoiding that last possibility.*

583

When do I File my flight plan?

[ATFCM Users Manual, ¶2.2] As per ICAO rule from ICAO doc 7030, flight plans for flights which may be subject to ATFM shall be submitted at least 3 hours before the EOBT. You will get either:

- ACK (FPL accepted) or,
- MAN (errors in FPL; after manual processing you will get either ACK or REJ) or,
- REJ (FPL rejected)

Translation: You should file your flight plan at least three hours prior to your Estimated Off Block Time (EOBT), which is the time you plan on starting your taxi after engine start and before takeoff. You should be told the flight plan was accepted with an ACK message. They could come back and say they had to manually edit the flight plan with a MAN message and that sets you up again for either an ACK or REJ message. If you get a MAN and an ACK, you need to examine the flight plan because it may have changed. In any case, a REJ message means the flight plan you submitted isn't going to work and it is up to you to revise it.

When do I have to notify "them" of a delay or desire to go early?

[ATFCM Users Manual, ¶2.2] As per ICAO rule from ICAO doc 7030, any changes to the EOBT of more than 15 minutes for any IFR flight within the IFPZ shall be communicated to the IFPS.

Translation: If you think you will be more than 15 minutes early or late from the time you estimate your will be ready to taxi (Estimated Off Block Time), you have to let someone know. This applies to flights in the Integrated Initial Flight Plan Processing System (IFPS) Zone (IFPZ).

When do I find out I've been slotted?

[ATFCM Users Manual, ¶2.2] At the earliest, 2 hours before EOBT you will receive a SAM with a CTOT. However, if a regulation is applied after this time a slot will be issued immediately.

How do I improve my slot?

[ATFCM Users Manual, ¶7.1] The RFI status indicates that the flight can accept SRMs with CTOT improvements. All flight plans are by default in RFI status. In case an improvement is possible, flights in status RFI will immediately receive a Slot Revision Message (SRM).

Translation: Once you are slotted, you are automatically placed in "Request for Direct Improvement" (RFI) status and as soon as a better slots comes available, you should get it in the form of a Slot Revision Message (SRM).

How do I revise my flight plan or EOBT?

[ATFCM Users Manual, ¶2.2] Send a DLA / CHG message.

Translation: You can send a delay (DLA) message or a modification (CHG) message to communicate the need to change routing or timing.

What happens if I revise my EOBT after I've been slotted?

[ATFCM Users Manual, ¶2.2] If the new EOBT still enables the flight to depart according to its CTOT, the slot will not be recalculated. If a recalculation is necessary (e.g. DLA / CHG was received with an EOBT that places the ETOT after the CTOT tolerance window), the next available slot will be issued in a SRM. To avoid a substantial delay it is therefore important to update the EOBT as soon as practicable.

Translation: If your change doesn't impact the Calculated Takeoff Time (CTOT), then no problem. If it does, then they put you back into the process. You go to the bottom of the request list, but this isn't always bad. Let's say you want to go early and there happens to be an earlier slot that is empty because it was never assigned or someone else dropped out of it, well then it goes to you. But, on the other hand, if there are other airplanes who sent a CHG before you, well they get first crack at the new slot. Meanwhile the slot you were first given may be taken by someone else. The risk of sending a CHG is that you could end up with a slot that is worse than the one you started with.

What if I am ready early?

[ATFCM Users Manual, ¶7.3] For regulated flights being in a situation to depart before their CTOT / EOBT (doors closed and ready to depart), the AO may ask local ATC to send a Ready (REA) message or, in a CDM aerodrome, the TWR may send a TTOT (T-DPI-s) before the CTOT tolerance window (-5, +10). These actions will trigger the REA status for the concerned flight.

Translation: You, the Aircraft Operator (AO), can call up ground control or tower to send a REA (ready) message to let them know you are ready as much as 15 minutes early. If you want to go even sooner, I think you are supposed to submit a CHG message, but I've seen handlers work around this with an REA message.

What is my slot tolerance?

[ATFCM Users Manual, Annex 7] A slot is issued as a Calculated Take-Off Time (CTOT). The CTOT is defined as a time when the aircraft must take-off. The slot tolerance (-5' to +10') is available only to ATC and only to organise the departure sequence. If there is no departure sequence, the CTOT shall be strictly adhered to.

Translation: The slot tolerance is meant for tower to plan take off times as early as 5 minutes before and 10 minutes after the CTOT.

What happens if I miss my slot?

[ATFCM Users Manual, ¶2.2] If your new EOBT is known, send a DLA / CHG. You will receive either: SRM, SLC or FLS. If your new EOBT is not known, send a SMM. You will receive an FLS and will remain suspended until you send a DLA / CHG to provide your new EOBT.

Translation: If you can provide a new Estimated Off Block Time (EOBT), do that. They will respond with a Slot Revision Message (SRM), a Slot Cancellation Message (SLC), or a Flight Suspension Message (FLS). If you cannot provide a new EOBT, you get the FLS. A SRM gives you a new slot time. A SLC means the entire need for slots has gone away. An FLS means you probably have to refile.

Southern Border Overflight Exemption (SBOE)

There are only 58 qualified airports of entry in the United States and the rest that you might fly into are known as "landing rights" airports. You need permission from a customs officer with acknowledgment of the Immigration and Naturalization Service, the Public Health Service, and the Animal and Plant Health Inspection Service of the Agriculture Department. But it gets more complicated when your arrival back to the U.S. is from south of the border. You have to land at one of only 32 airports unless you have an exemption.

The exemption process has gotten easier over the years. You no longer need to have all of your pilots registered in the program or have at least one person in the cabin registered. But you do need to apply for this well in advance. The exemption letter is good for two years.

The Restriction

[19 CFR §122.23] Certain aircraft arriving from areas south of the U.S.

(a) Application.

(1) This section sets forth particular requirements for certain aircraft arriving from south of the United States. This section is applicable to all aircraft except:

(i) Public aircraft;

(ii) Those aircraft operated on a regularly published schedule, pursuant to a certificate of public convenience and necessity or foreign aircraft permit issued by the Department of Transportation, authorizing interstate, overseas air transportation; and

(iii) Those aircraft with a seating capacity of more than 30 passengers or a maximum payload capacity of more than 7,500 pounds which are engaged in air transportation for compensation or hire on demand. (See 49 U.S.C. App. 1372 and 14 CFR part 298).

(2) The term "place" as used in this section means anywhere outside of the inner boundary of the Atlantic (Coastal) Air Defense Identification Zone (ADIZ) south of 30 degrees north latitude, anywhere outside of the inner boundary of the Gulf of Mexico (Coastal) ADIZ, or anywhere outside of the inner boundary of the Pacific (Coastal) ADIZ south of 33 degrees north latitude.

(b) Notice of arrival. All aircraft to which this section applies arriving in the Continental United States via the U.S./Mexican border or the Pacific Coast from a foreign place in the Western Hemisphere south of 33 degrees north latitude, or from the Gulf of Mexico and Atlantic Coasts from a place in the Western Hemisphere south of 30 degrees north latitude, from any place in Mexico, from the U.S. Virgin Islands, or [notwithstanding the definition of "United States" in §122.1(l)] from Puerto Rico, must furnish a notice of intended arrival. Private aircraft must transmit an advance notice of arrival as set forth in §122.22 of this part. Other than private aircraft, all aircraft to which this section applies must communicate to CBP notice of arrival at least one hour before crossing the U.S. coastline. Such notice must be communicated to CBP by telephone, radio, other method or the Federal Aviation Administration in accordance with paragraph (c) of this section.

Note: Paragraph (c) lists the needed details, 19 CFR 122.22 refers to the "Electronic manifest requirement for all individuals onboard private aircraft arriving in and departing from the United States."

[19 CFR §122.24] Landing requirements for certain aircraft arriving from areas south of U.S.

(a) In general. Certain aircraft arriving from areas south of the United States that are subject to §122.23 are required to furnish a notice of intended arrival in compliance with §122.23. Subject aircraft must land for CBP processing at the nearest designated airport to the border or coastline crossing point as listed under paragraph (b) unless exempted from this requirement in accordance with §122.25. In addition to the requirements of this section, pilots of aircraft to which §122.23 is applicable must comply with all other landing and notice of arrival requirements. This requirement shall not apply to those aircraft which have not landed in foreign territory or are arriving directly from Puerto Rico, if the aircraft was inspected by CBP officers in the

U.S. Virgin Islands, or otherwise precleared by CBP officers at designated preclearance locations.

(b) List of designated airports.

Location	Name
Beaumont, Tex	Jefferson County Airport.
Brownsville, Tex	Brownsville International Airport.
Calexico, Calif	Calexico International Airport.
Corpus Christi, Tex	Corpus Christi International Airport.
Del Rio, Tex	Del Rio International Airport.
Douglas, Ariz	Bisbee-Douglas International Airport.
Douglas, Ariz	Douglas Municipal Airport.
Eagle Pass, Tex	Eagle Pass Municipal Airport.
El Paso, Tex	El Paso International Airport.
Fort Lauderdale, Fla	Fort Lauderdale Executive Airport.
Fort Lauderdale, Fla	Fort Lauderdale-Hollywood International Airport.
Fort Pierce, Fla	St. Lucie County Airport.
Houston, Tex	William P. Hobby Airport.
Key West, Fla	Key West International Airport.
Laredo, Tex	Laredo International Airport.
McAllen, Tex	Miller International Airport.
Miami, Fla	Miami International Airport.
Miami, Fla	Opa-Locka Airport.
Miami, Fla	Tamiami Airport.
Midland, TX	Midland International Airport.
New Orleans, La	New Orleans International Airport (Moissant Field).
New Orleans, La	New Orleans Lakefront Airport.
Nogales, Ariz	Nogales International Airport.
Presidio, Tex	Presidio-Lely International Airport.
San Antonio Tex	San Antonio International Airport.
San Diego, Calif	Brown Field.
Santa Teresa, N. Mex	Santa Teresa Airport.
Tampa, Fla	Tampa International Airport.
Tucson, Ariz	Tucson International Airport.
West Palm Beach, Fla	Palm Beach International Airport.
Wilmington, NC	New Hanover County Airport
Yuma, Ariz	Yuma International Airport.

Exemption

[19 CFR §122.25] Exemption from special landing requirements.

(a) Request. Any company or individual that has operational control over an aircraft required to give advance notice of arrival under §122.23 may request an exemption from the landing requirements in §122.24. Single overflight exemptions may be granted to entities involved in air ambulance type operations when emergency situations arise and in cases involving the non-emergency transport of persons seeking medical treatment in the U.S. All approvals of requests for overflight exemptions and the granting of authority to be exempted from the landing requirements are at the discretion of the port director. Exemptions may allow aircraft to land at any airport in the U.S. staffed by Customs. Aircraft traveling under an exemption shall continue to follow advance notice and general landing rights requirements.

(b) Procedure. An exemption request shall be made to the port director at the airport at which the majority of Customs overflight processing is desired by the applicant. Except for air ambulance operations and other flights involving the non-emergency transport of persons seeking medical treatment in the U.S., the requests shall be signed by an officer of the company or by the requesting individual and be notarized or witnessed by a Customs officer. The requests shall be submitted:

(1) At least 30 days before the anticipated first arrival, if the request is for an exemption covering a number of flights over a period of one year, or

(2) At least 15 days before the anticipated arrival, if the request is for a single flight, or

(3) In cases involving air ambulance operations when emergency situations arise and other flights involving the non-emergency transport of persons seeking medical treatment in the U.S., if time permits, at least 24 hours prior to departure. If this cannot be accomplished, Customs will allow receipt of the overflight exemption application up to departure time. In cases of extreme medical emergency, Customs will accept overflight exemption requests in flight through a Federal Aviation Administration Flight Service Station.

(c) Content of request. All requests for exemption from special landing requirements, with the exception of those for air ambulance operations and other flights involving the non-emergency transport of persons seeking medical treatment in the U.S., shall include the following information. Requests for exemptions for air ambulance operations and other flights involving the non-emergency transport of persons for medical treatment in the U.S. shall include the following information except for paragraphs (c)(5) and (c)(6) of this section:

(1) Aircraft registration number(s) and manufacturer's serial number(s) for all aircraft owned or operated by the applicant that will be utilizing the overflight exemption;

(2) Identification information for each aircraft including class, manufacturer, type, number, color scheme, and type of engine (e.g., turbojet, turbofan, turboprop, reciprocating, helicopter, etc.);

(3) A statement that the aircraft is equipped with a functioning mode C (altitude reporting) transponder which will be in use during overflight, that the overflights will be made in accord with instrument flight rules (IFR), and that the overflights will be made at altitudes above 12,500 feet mean sea level (unless otherwise instructed by Federal Aviation Administration controllers);

(4) Name and address of the applicant operating the aircraft, if the applicant is a business entity, the address of the headquarters of the business (include state of incorporation if applicable), and the names, addresses, Social Security numbers (if available), and dates of birth of the company officer or individual signing the application. If the aircraft is operated under a lease, include the name, address, Social Security number (if available), and date of birth of the owner if an individual, or the address of the headquarters of the business (include state of incorporation if applicable), and the names, addresses, Social Security numbers, and dates of birth of the officers of the business;

(5) Individual, signed applications from each usual or anticipated pilot or crewmember for all aircraft for which an overflight exemption is sought stating name, address, Social Security number (if available), Federal Aviation Administration certificate number (if applicable), and place and date of birth;

(6) A statement from the individual signing the application that the pilot(s) and crewmember(s) responding to paragraph (c)(5) of this section are those intended to conduct overflights, and that to the best of the individual's knowledge, the information supplied in response to paragraph (c)(5) of this

591

section is accurate;

(7) Names, addresses, Social Security numbers (if applicable), and dates of birth for all usual or anticipated passengers. An approved passenger must be on board to utilize the overflight exemptions.

Note: Where the Social Security number is requested, furnishing of the SSN is voluntary. The authority to collect the SSN is 19 U.S.C. 66, 1433, 1459 and 1624. The primary purpose for requesting the SSN is to assist in ascertaining the identity of the individual so as to assure that only law-abiding persons will be granted permission to land at interior airports in the U.S. without first landing at one of the airports designated in §122.24. The SSN will be made available to Customs personnel on a need-to-know basis. Failure to provide the SSN may result in a delay in processing of the application;

(8) Description of the usual or anticipated baggage or cargo if known, or the actual baggage or cargo;

(9) Description of the applicant's usual business activity;

(10) Name(s) of the airport(s) of intended first landing in the U.S. Actual overflights will only be permitted to specific approved airports;

(11) Foreign place or places from which flight(s) will usually originate; and

(12) Reasons for request for overflight exemption.

(d) Procedure following exemption. (1) If an aircraft subject to §122.23 is granted an exemption from the landing requirements as provided in this section, the aircraft commander shall notify Customs at least 60 minutes before:

(i) Crossing into the U.S. over a point on the Pacific Coast north of 33 degrees north latitude; or

(ii) Crossing into the U.S. over a point of the Gulf of Mexico or Atlantic Coast north of 30 degrees north latitude; or

(iii) Crossing into the U.S. over the Southwestern land border (defined as the U.S.-Mexican border between Brownsville, Texas, and San Diego, California). Southwestern land border crossings must be made while flying in Federal Aviation Administration published airways.

(2) The notice shall be given to a designated airport specified in §122.24. The notice may be furnished directly to Customs by telephone, radio or other means, or may be furnished through the Federal Aviation Administration to

Customs. If notice is furnished pursuant to this paragraph, notice pursuant to §§122.23 and 122.24 is unnecessary.

(3) All overflights must be conducted pursuant to an instrument flight plan filed with the Federal Aviation Administration or equivalent foreign aviation authority prior to the commencement of the overflight.

(4) The owner or aircraft commander of an aircraft subject to §122.23 granted an exemption from the landing requirements must:

(i) Notify Customs of a change of Federal Aviation Administration or other (foreign) registration number for the aircraft;

(ii) Notify Customs of the sale, theft, modification or destruction of the aircraft;

(iii) Notify Customs of changes of usual or anticipated pilots or crewmembers as specified in paragraph (c)(5) of this section. Every pilot and crewmember participating in an overflight must have prior Customs approval either through initial application and approval, or through a supplemental application submitted by the new pilot or crewmember and approved by Customs before commencement of the pilot's or crewmember's first overflight.

(iv) Request permission from Customs to conduct an overflight to an airport not listed in the initial overflight application as specified in paragraph (c)(10) of this section. The request must be directed to the port director who approved the initial request for an overflight exemption.

(v) Retain copies of the initial request for an overflight exemption, all supplemental applications from pilots or crewmembers, and all requests for additional landing privileges as well as a copy of the letter from Customs approving each of these requests. The copies must be carried on board any aircraft during the conduct of an overflight.

(5) The notification specified in paragraph (d)(4) of this section must be given to Customs within 5 working days of the change, sale, theft, modification, or destruction, or before a flight for which there is an exemption, whichever occurs earlier.

(e) Inspection of aircraft having or requesting overflight exemption. Applicants for overflight exemptions must agree to make the subject aircraft available for inspection by Customs to determine if the aircraft is capable of meeting Customs requirements for the proper conduct of an overflight.

Inspections may be conducted during the review of an initial application or at any time during the term of an overflight exemption.

Chapter 37

Strategic Lateral Offset Procedure (SLOP)

The world has gone to SLOP. You can (and should) employ a Strategic Lateral Offset Procedure (SLOP) in almost every oceanic area. There is a debate about using SLOP over land, but the legal and official answer is you cannot with only very rare exceptions. Most of the world only permits SLOP to the right and usually only of 1 or 2 NM. The ICAO has permitted "micro SLOP" in tenths since 2014, but only a few regions have adopted this. Remember that some aircraft may not SLOP: particularly those that do not have an automatic offset capability.

Clearly it can save your life and it is therefore worth using. But you need to know where it is authorized and how to apply it correctly. Also note that while usually no clearance is required to initiate SLOP and no call is needed when returning to centerline, this isn't the case worldwide.

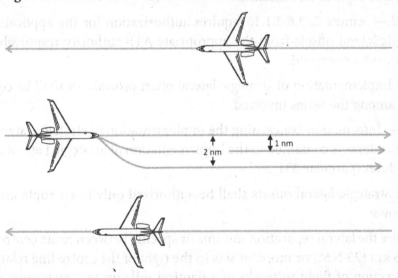

Why?

In the days before GPS, we would be lucky if our oceanic position was within a couple of miles of where we should have been. In the days before INS, being within 10 miles was a major accomplishment. But there were not a lot of airplanes flying oceanic and the accuracy wasn't all that important. These days, the skies are packed with airplanes but GPS allows us to navigate within a tenth or so of course centerline. It is almost all good.

It is almost all good because there is a chance a navigation or altitude error can end very badly. If someone programs the wrong course or levels off at the wrong altitude, they may be precisely on the wrong course, in position to hit someone who is properly and precisely on course.

ICAO Guidance

[ICAO Doc 4444, ¶16.5] Strategic Lateral Offset Procedures (SLOP)

Note 1.— SLOP are approved procedures that allow aircraft to fly on a parallel track to the right of the centre line relative to the direction of flight to mitigate the lateral overlap probability due to increased navigation accuracy and wake turbulence encounters. Unless specified in the separation standard, an aircraft's use of these procedures does not affect the application of prescribed separation standards.

Note 2.— Annex 2, 3.6.2.1.1, requires authorization for the application of strategic lateral offsets from the appropriate ATS authority responsible for the airspace concerned.

16.5.1 Implementation of strategic lateral offset procedures shall be coordinated among the States involved.

Note.— Information concerning the implementation of strategic lateral offset procedures is contained in the Implementation of Strategic Lateral Offset Procedures (Circular 331).

16.5.2 Strategic lateral offsets shall be authorized only in en-route airspace as follows:

a) where the lateral separation minima or spacing between route centre lines is 42.6 km (23 NM) or more, offsets to the right of the centre line relative to the direction of flight in tenths of a nautical mile up to a maximum of 3.7 km (2 NM); and

b) where the lateral separation minima or spacing between route centre lines is 11.1 km (6 NM) or more and less than 42.6 km (23 NM), offsets to the right of the centre line relative to the direction of flight in tenths of a nautical mile up to a maximum of 0.9 km (0.5 NM).

16.5.3 The routes or airspace where application of strategic lateral offsets is authorized, and the procedures to be followed by pilots, shall be promulgated in aeronautical information publications (AIPs). In some instances, it may be necessary to impose restrictions on the use of strategic lateral offsets, e.g. where their application may be inappropriate for reasons related to obstacle clearance. Route conformance monitoring systems shall account for the application of SLOP.

16.5.4 The decision to apply a strategic lateral offset shall be the responsibility of the flight crew. The flight crew shall only apply strategic lateral offsets in airspace where such offsets have been authorized by the appropriate ATS authority and when the aircraft is equipped with automatic offset tracking capability.

Note 1.— Pilots may contact other aircraft on the inter-pilot air-to-air frequency 123.45 MHz to coordinate offsets.

Note 2.— The strategic lateral offset procedure has been designed to include offsets to mitigate the effects of wake turbulence of preceding aircraft. If wake turbulence needs to be avoided, an offset to the right and within the limits specified in 16.5.2 may be used.

Note 3.— Pilots are not required to inform ATC that a strategic lateral offset is being applied.

North Atlantic Guidance

[NAT Doc 007, ¶8.5.8.] While ATC clearances are designed to ensure that separation standards are continually maintained for all traffic, errors do occur. Neither flight crews nor controllers are infallible. Gross Navigation Errors (usually involving whole or half latitude degree mistakes in route waypoints) are made, and aircraft are sometimes flown at flight levels other than those expected by the controller. Ironically, when such errors are made, the extreme accuracies of modern navigation and height keeping systems themselves increase the risk of a collision. Within an ATS Surveillance environment where VHF communications are available, controllers alerted to such errors will intervene using VHF voice communications. In areas (surveillance or otherwise) where VHF voice communication is not available, controllers rely on voice and data link position reports augmented by ADS-C and ADS-B transmissions to monitor conformance. Controllers, when alerted to errors, will intervene using HF, CPDLC, SATVOICE or any other means available. Given the potential delay in intervention, it has been determined that encouraging aircraft operating in the NAT to fly self-selected lateral offsets provides an additional safety margin and mitigates the risk of traffic conflict when non-normal events (such as aircraft navigation errors, height deviation errors and turbulence induced altitude-keeping errors) do occur. Collision risk is significantly reduced by application of these offsets. These procedures are known as "Strategic Lateral Offset Procedures (SLOP)."

[NAT Doc 007, ¶8.5.9.] This procedure provides for offsets within the following guidelines:

a) an aircraft may fly offsets right of centreline up to a maximum of 2 NM; and

b) offsets left of centreline are not permitted.

[NAT Doc 007, ¶8.5.10.] Distributing aircraft laterally and equally across all available positions adds an additional safety margin and reduces collision risk. SLOP is now a standard operating procedure for the entire NAT region and flight crews are required to adopt this procedure as is appropriate. In this connection, it should be noted that:

a) Aircraft without automatic offset programming capability must fly the centreline.

b) Aircraft able to perform offsets in tenths of nautical mile should do so as it contributes to risk reduction.

c) It is recommended that flight crews of aircraft capable of programming automatic offsets should randomly select flying centreline or an offset. In order to obtain lateral spacing from nearby aircraft (i.e. those immediately above and/or below), flight crews should use whatever means are available (e.g. ACAS/TCAS, communications, visual acquisition, GPWS) to determine the best flight path to fly.

d) An aircraft overtaking another aircraft should offset within the confines of this procedure, if capable, so as to minimize the amount of wake turbulence for the aircraft being overtaken.

e) For wake turbulence purposes, flight crews should fly one of the offset positions. Flight crews may contact other aircraft on the air-to-air channel, 123.450 MHz, as necessary, to coordinate the best wake turbulence mutual offset option. (Note. It is recognized that the flight crew will use their judgment to determine the action most appropriate to any given situation and that the pilot-in-command has the final authority and responsibility for the safe operations of the aircraft.)

f) Flight crews may apply an offset outbound at the oceanic entry point and must return to centreline prior to the oceanic exit point unless otherwise authorized by the appropriate ATS authority or directed by the appropriate ATC unit.

g) There is no ATC clearance required for this procedure and it is not necessary that ATC be advised.

h) Voice Position reports should be based on the waypoints of the current ATC clearance and not the offset positions.

i) Aircraft shall not apply SLOP below F285 in the Reykjavik CTA and Bodo OCA.

j) The offset should be applied from the time the aircraft reaches its cruising level until top of descent.

US FAA Guidance

[AC 91-70B, ¶D.2.6.5] Your SOPs should include SLOP for all oceanic crossings. NOTAMs, State AIPs, and other flight planning guidance will indicate where exceptions apply and where procedures differ.

This procedure was developed to reduce the risk associated with an altitude deviation and two highly accurate navigation systems navigating to the same point.

SLOP also replaced the contingency procedure developed for aircraft encountering wake turbulence. Depending upon winds aloft, coordination between aircraft to avoid wake turbulence may be necessary.

This procedure, which distributes traffic between the route centerline and up to 2 NM right of centerline, greatly reduces risk by the nature of its randomness.

Operators that have an automatic offset capability should fly up to 2 NM right of the centerline.

Aircraft that do not have an automatic offset capability (that can be programmed in the LRNS) should fly the centerline only.

Searching for SLOP

Using a Country's Aeronautical Information Publication

Theoretically, the best place to look is a country's AIP, but not all countries include any mention of SLOP and those that do are inconsistent about where they put this information. In general, look in the ENR section. If you have a PDF copy, do a word search for "lateral" and start from there.

Using JeppFD

Your JeppFD App on the iPad can help you find out the SLOP rules for the region you are flying. Let's say, for example, you are unsure about the rules off the coast of South Africa.

1. Bring up the JeppFD App, look at the High IFR map, and find the FIR label. The first two letters give you a clue as to what region you are in. In the example, the FACA FIR tells you this is in the Africa region and that the South Africa Republic would be a good place to look. You may have to hunt around countries that border the oceanic region. Not every country publishes SLOP rules, even if the region does allow it.

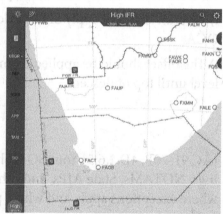

2. Press the text icon in the upper left. If the "Route" is in reverse video, you will want to select "Pubs" instead. At this point you might see whatever you had viewed previously; if so, go to higher menus by selecting the left arrow until you see "Route Notes" with various Regions shown below.

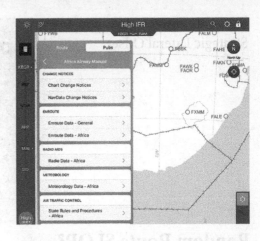

3. From here, select "Africa" from the list of regions. Look for the Air Traffic Control section and select State Rules and Procedures.

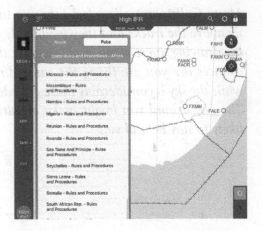

4. Scroll down the list and select your desired country. At this point you will see a page for the rules and procedures from that country.

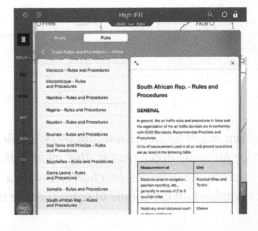

5. Scroll down until you see Strategic Lateral Offset.

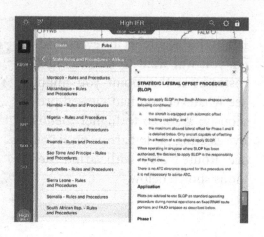

Random Route SLOP?

Many Gulfstream pilots feel immune to the SLOP issue, saying they always fly above the tracks and they usually fly random routing. As you can see from the drawing, there is one problem with that argument. If you are on the track, chances are you are flying the same direction as your nearest neighbor and while the sky is considerably more crowded, the chance of a collision is reduced. The guy behind you might make an altitude error but he is behind you and likely to stay behind you.

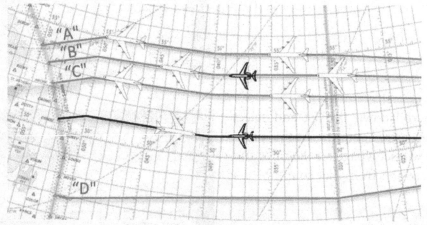

You might be on the random track because you are flying an unusual city pair or for some other reason. But what if there is somebody flying the same city pair in the opposite direction? Now what if that guy makes an altitude error? Wouldn't an extra mile of separation be nice?

Chapter 38

Traffic Information Broadcast by Aircraft (TIBA)

The IATA calls them "In-Flight Broadcast Procedures" or IFBP. The ICAO calls them Traffic Information Broadcasts by Aircraft" or TIBA. As pilots we've known them as "Broadcast in the Blind." Whatever you call them, they used to be the staple of remote flight operations in places like Africa, South America, India, and parts of Australia. There aren't many TIBA regions left but you still find them. So if you find a note on the chart calling for TIBA or IFBP, you should know this. So what's it all about?

You are broadcasting your position in space to everyone on an agreed upon frequency in hopes they are paying attention. You are listening to everyone else, hoping to decipher their English into figuring out if somebody else will be on the same airway and altitude about your time, or perhaps an intersection. If there is a conflict, you negotiate avoidance actions.

Of course all that is theory and you hope those deconflicting flight plans have done a good job. All this was really terrifying about twenty years ago. (In some parts of the world they didn't even make the pretense of speaking English.) Now your biggest fear is that they don't have TCAS or for some reason have it turned off.

Introduction and applicability of broadcasts

[ICAO Annex 11 Attachment B, para;1]

1.1 Traffic information broadcasts by aircraft are intended to permit reports and relevant supplementary information of an advisory nature to be transmitted by pilots on a designated VHF radiotelephone (RTF) frequency for the information of pilots of other aircraft in the vicinity.

1.2 TIBAs should be introduced only when necessary and as a temporary measure.

1.3 The broadcast procedures should be applied in designated airspace where:

- there is a need to supplement collision hazard information provided by air traffic services outside controlled airspace; or

- there is a temporary disruption of normal air traffic services.

1.4 Such airspaces should be identified by the States responsible for provision of air traffic services within these airspaces, if necessary with the assistance of the appropriate ICAO Regional Office(s), and duly promulgated in aeronautical information publications or NOTAM, together with the VHF RTF frequency, the message formats and the procedures to be used. Where, in the case of 1.3 a), more than one State is involved, the airspace should be designated on the basis of regional air navigation agreements and promulgated in Doc 7030.

1.5 When establishing a designated airspace, dates for the review of its applicability at intervals not exceeding 12 months should be agreed by the appropriate ATS authority(ies).

Details of broadcasts

[ICAO Annex 11 Attachment C, para;2]

VHF RTF frequency to be used

2.1.1 The VHF RTF frequency to be used should be determined and promulgated on a regional basis. However, in the case of temporary disruption occurring in controlled airspace, the States responsible may promulgate, as the VHF RTF frequency to be used within the limits of that airspace, a frequency used normally for the provision of air traffic control service within that airspace.

2.1.2 Where VHF is used for air-ground communications with ATS and an aircraft has only two serviceable VHF sets, one should be tuned to the appropriate ATS frequency and the other to the TIBA frequency.

Listening watch

A listening watch should be maintained on the TIBA frequency 10 minutes before entering the designated airspace until leaving this airspace. For an aircraft taking off from an aerodrome located within the lateral limits of the designated airspace listening watch should start as soon as appropriate after takeoff and be maintained until leaving the airspace.

Time of broadcasts

A broadcast should be made:

- 10 minutes before entering the designated airspace or, for a pilot taking off from an aerodrome located within the lateral limits of the designated airspace, as soon as appropriate after takeoff;
- 10 minutes prior to crossing a reporting point;
- 10 minutes prior to crossing or joining an ATS route;
- at 20-minute intervals between distant reporting points;
- 2 to 5 minutes, where possible, before a change in flight level;
- at the time of a change in flight level; and
- at any other time considered necessary by the pilot.

Forms of broadcast

2.4.1 The broadcasts other than those indicating changes in flight level, should be in the following form:

- ALL STATIONS (necessary to identify a traffic information broadcast)
- (call sign)
- FLIGHT LEVEL (number) (or CLIMBING* TO FLIGHT LEVEL (number))
- (direction)
- (ATS route) (or DIRECT FROM (position) TO (position))
- POSITION (position**) AT (time)
- ESTIMATING (next reporting point, or the point of crossing or joining a designated ATS route) AT (time)
- (call sign)
- FLIGHT LEVEL (number)
- (direction)

Fictitious example

"ALL STATIONS WINDAR 671 FLIGHT LEVEL 350 NORTHWEST BOUND DIRECT FROM PUNTA SAGA TO PAMPA POSITION 5040 SOUTH 2010 EAST AT 2358 ESTIMATING CROSSING ROUTE LIMA THREE ONE AT 4930 SOUTH 1920 EAST AT 0012 WINDAR 671 FLIGHT LEVEL 350 NORTHWEST BOUND OUT"

2.4.2 Before a change in flight level, the broadcast (referred to in 2.3 e)) should be in the following form:

- ALL STATIONS
- (call sign)
- (direction)
- (ATS route) (or DIRECT FROM (position) TO (position)
- LEAVING FLIGHT LEVEL (number) FOR FLIGHT LEVEL (number) AT (position and time)

2.4.3 Except as provided in 2.4.4, the broadcast at the time of a change in flight level (referred to in 2.3 f) should be in the following form:

- ALL STATIONS
- (call sign)
- (direction)
- (ATS route) (or DIRECT FROM (position) TO (position))
- LEAVING FLIGHT LEVEL (number) NOW FOR FLIGHT LEVEL (number) followed by:
- ALL STATIONS
- (call sign)
- MAINTAINING FLIGHT LEVEL (number)

2.4.4 Broadcasts reporting a temporary flight level change to avoid an imminent collision risk should be in the following form:

- ALL STATIONS
- (call sign)
- LEAVING FLIGHT LEVEL (number) NOW FOR FLIGHT LEVEL (number) followed as soon as practicable by:

- ALL STATIONS
- (call sign)
- RETURNING TO FLIGHT LEVEL (number) NOW

Acknowledgement of the broadcasts

The broadcasts should not be acknowledged unless a potential collision risk is perceived.

Related operating procedures

[ICAO Annex 11 Attachment C, para;3]

Changes of cruising level

3.1.1 Cruising level changes should not be made within the designated airspace, unless considered necessary by pilots to avoid traffic conflicts, for weather avoidance or for other valid operational reasons.

3.1.2 When cruising level changes are unavoidable, all available aircraft lighting which would improve the visual detection of the aircraft should be displayed while changing levels.

Collision avoidance

If, on receipt of a traffic information broadcast from another aircraft, a pilot decides that immediate action is necessary to avoid an imminent collision risk, and this cannot be achieved in accordance with the right-of-way provisions of Annex 2, the pilot should:

- unless an alternative manoeuvre appears more appropriate, immediately descend 150 m (500 ft), or 300 m (1,000 ft) if above FL 290 in an area where a vertical separation minimum of 600 m (2,000 ft) is applied;
- display all available aircraft lighting which would improve the visual detection of the aircraft;
- as soon as possible, reply to the broadcast advising action being taken;
- notify the action taken on the appropriate ATS frequency; and
- as soon as practicable, resume normal flight level, notifying the action on the appropriate ATS frequency.

Normal position reporting procedures

Normal position reporting procedures should be continued at all times, regardless of any action taken to initiate or acknowledge a traffic information broadcast.

Chapter 39

True Course 10-Degree Tables

*B*ack *in the old days if you were presented with a reroute when oceanic, you pulled out the charts and plotter and got to work building a new flight plan. If you were good, you could churn out three thousand miles of master document in about fifteen minutes. If you were really good, you had a book of ten-degree tables and could cut that time in half.*

These days I would just call in the change to my flight planning service and have them fax, e-mail, or just read them to me over the phone. What if you don't have that kind of connectivity or if you just want to be old school for a day?

Purpose

If required to fly an unplanned oceanic flight plan — you got a reroute just prior to coast out — you need to build a new master document with courses and distances between waypoints so you can still make all the necessary checks before each point and also so you can make your post position plot. The 10-degree tables below provide your true courses and distances between any two positions expressed as latitudes (to the nearest degree) and the next position expressed as a longitude 10 degrees east or west.

For example, say you are 50°N 030°W heading to Europe and your next position will be at 51°N 020°W. You could pull out a plotter and come up with a course, add the variation, and end up with the correct magnetic course. Then you could measure the distance, compare that to the nearest line of longitude and come up with a distance. You would probably do this a few times to make sure you didn't make a mistake, either with the plotter or your ad hoc measuring device. Or you could go to the From 50° Latitude table, check the course provided on the 51° row and Northern Hemisphere / East column and see your true course will be 081° and reading across see that the distance between these two points is 386 nautical miles.

The Tables

From 0° Lat	Northern Hemisphere		Southern Hemisphere		Distance
To Latitude	East	West	East	West	(nm)
10°	045°	315°	135°	225°	846
09	048	312	132	228	805
08	051	309	129	231	767
07	055	305	125	235	731
06	059	301	121	239	699
05	063	297	117	243	670
04	068	292	112	248	646
03	073	287	107	253	626
02	078	282	102	258	612
01	084	276	096	264	603
00	090	270	090	270	600

From 1° Lat	Northern Hemisphere		Southern Hemisphere		Distance
To Latitude	East	West	East	West	(nm)
11°	044°	316°	136°	224°	846
10	048	312	132	228	805
09	051	309	129	231	766
08	055	305	125	235	731
07	059	301	121	239	698
06	063	297	117	243	670
05	068	292	112	248	645
04	073	287	107	253	626
03	079	281	101	259	611
02	084	276	096	264	603
01	090	270	090	270	600
00	096	264	084	276	603
01	101	259	079	281	612
02	106	254	074	286	626
03	112	248	068	292	646
04	117	243	063	297	670
05	121	239	059	301	699
06	125	235	055	305	732
07	129	231	051	309	767
08	132	228	048	312	806
09	135	225	045	315	847

From 2° Lat	Northern Hemisphere		Southern Hemisphere		Distance
To Latitude	East	West	East	West	(nm)
12°	044°	316°	136°	224°	845
11	047	313	133	227	804
10	051	309	129	231	765
09	055	305	125	235	730
08	059	301	121	239	697
07	063	297	117	243	669
06	068	292	112	248	645
05	073	287	107	253	625
04	078	282	102	258	611
03	084	276	096	264	602
02	090	270	090	270	600
01	096	264	084	276	603
00	101	259	079	281	612
01	107	253	073	287	626
02	112	248	068	292	646
03	117	243	063	297	671
04	121	239	059	301	699
05	125	235	055	305	732
06	129	231	051	309	768
07	132	228	048	312	806
08	135	225	045	315	847

From 3° Lat	Northern Hemisphere		Southern Hemisphere		Distance
To Latitude	East	West	East	West	(nm)
13°	044°	316°	136°	224°	844
12	047	313	133	227	803
11	051	309	129	231	764
10	054	306	126	234	729
09	058	302	122	238	697
08	063	297	117	243	668
07	068	292	112	248	644
06	073	287	107	253	625
05	078	282	102	258	610
04	084	276	096	264	602
03	090	270	090	270	599
02	096	264	084	276	602
01	101	259	079	281	611
00	107	253	073	287	626
01	112	248	068	292	646
02	117	243	063	297	671
03	121	239	059	301	699
04	125	235	055	305	732
05	129	231	051	309	768
06	132	228	048	312	807
07	135	225	045	315	848

From 4° Lat	Northern Hemisphere		Southern Hemisphere		Distance
To Latitude	East	West	East	West	(nm)
14°	044°	316°	136°	224°	843
13	047	313	133	227	802
12	051	309	129	231	763
11	054	306	126	234	728
10	058	302	122	238	696
09	063	297	117	243	667
08	068	292	112	248	643
07	073	287	107	253	624
06	078	282	102	258	610
05	084	276	096	264	601
04	090	270	090	270	598
03	095	265	085	275	602
02	101	259	079	281	611
01	107	253	073	287	626
00	112	248	068	292	646
01	116	244	064	296	670
02	121	239	059	301	699
03	125	235	055	305	732
04	129	231	051	309	768
05	132	228	048	312	807
06	135	225	045	315	848

From 5° Lat	Northern Hemisphere		Southern Hemisphere		Distance
To Latitude	East	West	East	West	(nm)
15°	044°	316°	36°	224°	841
14	047	313	133	227	801
13	050	310	130	230	762
12	054	306	126	234	727
11	058	302	122	238	694
10	063	297	117	243	666
09	068	292	112	248	642
08	073	287	107	253	623
07	078	282	102	258	609
06	084	276	096	264	600
05	090	270	090	270	598
04	095	265	085	275	601
03	101	259	079	281	610
02	106	254	074	286	625
01	112	248	068	292	645
00	116	244	064	296	670
01	121	239	059	301	699
02	125	235	055	305	732
03	129	231	051	309	768
04	132	228	048	312	807
05	135	225	045	315	848

From 6° Lat	Northern Hemisphere		Southern Hemisphere		Distance
To Latitude	East	West	East	West	(nm)
16°	044°	316°	136°	224°	840
15	047	313	133	227	799
14	050	310	130	230	761
13	054	306	126	234	725
12	058	302	122	238	693
11	063	297	117	243	665
10	067	293	113	247	641
09	073	287	107	253	621
08	078	282	102	258	607
07	084	276	096	264	599
06	090	270	090	270	597
05	095	265	085	275	600
04	101	259	079	281	610
03	106	254	074	286	625
02	111	249	069	291	645
01	116	244	064	296	670
00	121	239	059	301	699
01	125	235	055	305	732
02	128	232	052	308	768
03	132	228	048	312	807
04	135	225	045	315	848

From 7° Lat	Northern Hemisphere		Southern Hemisphere		Distance
To Latitude	East	West	East	West	(nm)
17°	043°	317°	137°	223°	839
16	047	313	133	227	797
15	050	310	130	230	759
14	054	306	126	234	724
13	058	302	122	238	692
12	062	298	118	242	663
11	067	293	113	247	639
10	072	288	108	252	620
09	078	282	102	258	606
08	084	276	096	264	598
07	090	270	090	270	595
06	095	265	085	275	599
05	101	259	079	281	609
04	106	254	074	286	624
03	111	249	069	291	644
02	116	244	064	296	669
01	121	239	059	301	698
00	125	235	055	305	731
01	128	232	052	308	767
02	132	328	048	312	806
03	135	225	045	315	848

From 8° Lat	Northern Hemisphere		Southern Hemisphere		Distance
To Latitude	East	West	East	West	(nm)
18	044	316	136	224	837
17	047	313	133	227	797
16	051	309	129	231	758
15	055	305	125	235	722
14	059	301	121	239	690
13	063	297	117	243	665
12	068	292	112	248	639
11	073	287	107	253	620
10	078	282	102	258	607
09	084	276	096	264	598
08	090	270	090	270	597
07	096	264	084	276	600
06	101	259	079	281	612
05	106	254	074	286	624
04	111	249	069	291	645
03	116	244	064	296	669
02	121	239	059	301	698
01	125	235	055	305	732
00	129	231	051	309	767
01	132	228	048	312	807
02	135	225	045	315	848

From 9° Lat	Northern Hemisphere		Southern Hemisphere		Distance
To Latitude	East	West	East	West	(nm)
19	044	316	136	224	832
18	047	313	133	227	794
17	051	309	129	231	756
16	054	306	126	234	721
15	059	301	121	239	689
14	063	297	117	243	662
13	068	292	112	248	638
12	073	287	107	253	620
11	078	282	102	258	605
10	084	276	096	264	598
09	090	270	090	270	596
08	096	264	084	276	598
07	101	259	079	281	600
06	106	254	074	286	623
05	112	248	068	292	643
04	116	244	064	296	668
03	121	239	059	301	697
02	125	235	055	305	730
01	129	231	051	309	766
00	132	228	048	312	805
01	135	225	045	315	847

From 10° Lat	Northern Hemisphere		Southern Hemisphere		Distance
To Latitude	East	West	East	West	(nm)
20	044	316	136	224	834
19	047	313	133	227	793
18	051	309	129	221	754
17	054	306	126	234	719
16	058	302	122	238	686
15	063	297	117	243	658
14	068	292	112	248	634
13	073	287	107	253	615
12	078	282	102	258	601
11	084	276	096	264	593
10	090	270	090	270	590
9	096	264	084	276	595
8	101	259	079	281	605
7	107	253	073	287	620
6	112	248	068	292	641
5	117	243	063	297	666
4	121	239	059	301	696
3	125	235	055	305	729
2	129	231	051	309	765
1	132	228	048	312	805
0	135	225	045	315	846

From 11° Lat	Northern Hemisphere		Southern Hemisphere		Distance
To Latitude	East	West	East	West	(nm)
21	044	316	136	224	832
20	047	313	133	227	791
19	050	310	130	230	752
18	054	306	126	234	716
17	058	302	122	238	684
16	063	297	117	243	656
15	068	292	112	248	632
14	073	287	107	253	613
13	078	282	102	258	599
12	084	276	096	264	591
11	090	270	090	270	589
10	096	264	084	276	593
09	101	259	079	281	603
08	107	253	073	287	619
07	112	248	068	292	639
06	117	243	063	297	665
05	121	239	059	301	695
04	125	235	055	305	728
03	129	231	051	309	765
02	132	228	048	312	804
01	135	225	045	315	846

From 12° Lat	Northern Hemisphere		Southern Hemisphere		Distance
To Latitude	East	West	East	West	(nm)
22	044	316	136	224	830
21	047	313	133	227	788
20	050	310	130	230	750
19	054	306	126	234	714
18	058	302	122	238	682
17	063	297	117	243	654
16	068	292	112	248	630
15	073	287	107	253	610
14	078	282	102	258	597
13	084	276	096	264	589
12	090	270	090	270	587
11	096	264	084	276	591
10	102	258	078	282	601
09	107	253	073	287	617
08	112	248	068	292	638
07	117	243	063	297	663
06	121	239	059	301	693
05	125	235	055	305	727
04	129	231	051	309	763
03	132	228	048	312	803
02	135	225	045	315	845

From 13° Lat	Northern Hemisphere		Southern Hemisphere		Distance
To Latitude	East	West	East	West	(nm)
23	044	316	136	224	827
22	047	313	133	227	786
21	050	310	130	230	748
20	054	306	126	234	712
19	058	302	122	238	680
18	063	297	117	243	651
17	068	292	112	248	627
16	073	287	107	253	608
15	078	282	102	258	594
14	084	276	096	264	587
13	090	270	090	270	585
12	096	264	084	276	589
11	101	259	079	281	599
10	107	253	073	287	615
09	112	248	068	292	636
08	117	243	063	297	662
07	121	239	059	301	692
06	125	235	055	305	725
05	129	231	051	309	762
04	132	228	048	312	802
03	135	225	045	315	844

From 14° Lat	Northern Hemisphere		Southern Hemisphere		Distance
To Latitude	East	West	East	West	(nm)
24	044	316	136	224	825
23	047	313	133	227	784
22	050	310	130	230	745
21	054	306	126	234	709
20	058	302	122	238	677
19	063	297	117	243	649
18	068	292	112	248	625
17	073	287	107	253	605
16	078	282	102	258	592
15	084	276	096	264	584
14	090	270	090	270	582
13	096	264	084	276	587
12	102	258	078	282	597
11	107	253	073	287	613
10	112	248	068	292	634
09	117	243	063	297	660
08	121	239	059	301	690
07	125	235	055	305	724
06	129	231	051	309	761
05	132	228	049	312	801
04	135	225	045	315	843

From 15° Lat	Northern Hemisphere		Southern Hemisphere		Distance
To Latitude	East	West	East	West	(nm)
25	043	317	137	223	823
24	046	314	134	226	781
23	050	310	130	230	743
22	054	306	126	234	707
21	058	302	122	238	674
20	062	298	118	242	646
19	067	293	113	247	622
18	073	287	107	253	603
17	078	282	102	258	589
16	084	276	096	264	581
15	090	270	090	270	580
14	096	264	084	276	584
13	102	258	078	282	594
12	107	253	073	287	610
11	112	248	068	292	632
10	117	243	063	297	658
09	121	239	059	301	688
08	125	235	055	305	722
07	129	231	051	309	759
06	132	228	048	312	799
05	135	225	045	315	842

From 16° Lat	Northern Hemisphere		Southern Hemisphere		Distance
To Latitude	East	West	East	West	(nm)
26	043	317	137	223	820
25	046	314	134	226	779
24	050	310	130	230	740
23	054	306	126	234	704
22	058	302	122	238	672
21	062	298	118	242	643
20	067	293	113	247	619
19	073	287	107	253	600
18	078	282	102	258	586
17	084	276	096	264	578
16	090	270	090	270	577
15	096	264	084	276	581
14	102	258	078	282	592
13	107	253	073	287	608
12	112	248	068	292	630
11	117	243	063	297	656
10	122	238	058	302	686
9	126	234	054	306	720
8	129	231	051	309	758
7	133	227	047	313	798
6	135	224	044	316	840

From 17° Lat	Northern Hemisphere		Southern Hemisphere		Distance
To Latitude	East	West	East	West	(nm)
27	043	317	137	223	817
26	046	314	134	226	776
25	050	310	130	230	737
24	053	307	127	233	701
23	058	302	122	238	669
22	062	298	118	242	640
21	067	293	113	247	616
20	073	287	107	253	596
19	078	282	102	258	583
18	084	276	096	264	575
17	090	270	090	270	574
16	096	264	084	276	578
15	102	258	078	282	589
14	107	253	073	287	606
13	112	248	068	292	627
12	117	243	063	297	653
11	122	238	058	302	684
10	126	234	054	306	718
09	129	231	051	309	756
08	133	227	047	313	796
07	136	224	044	316	838

From 18° Lat	Northern Hemisphere		Southern Hemisphere		Distance
To Latitude	East	West	East	West	(nm)
28	043	317	137	223	815
27	046	314	134	226	773
26	049	311	131	229	734
25	053	307	127	233	698
24	057	303	123	237	666
23	062	298	118	242	637
22	067	293	113	247	613
21	072	288	108	252	593
20	078	282	102	258	580
19	084	276	096	264	572
18	090	270	090	270	571
17	096	264	084	276	575
16	102	258	078	282	586
15	107	253	073	287	603
14	113	247	067	293	625
13	117	243	063	297	651
12	122	238	058	302	682
11	126	234	054	306	716
10	129	231	051	309	754
09	133	227	047	313	794
08	136	224	044	316	837

From 19° Lat	Northern Hemisphere		Southern Hemisphere		Distance
To Latitude	East	West	East	West	(nm)
29	043	317	137	223	812
28	046	314	134	226	770
27	049	311	131	229	731
26	053	307	127	233	695
25	057	303	123	237	662
24	062	298	118	242	633
23	067	293	113	247	609
22	072	288	108	252	590
21	078	282	102	258	576
20	084	276	096	264	569
19	090	270	090	270	567
18	096	264	084	276	572
17	102	258	078	282	583
16	107	253	073	287	600
15	113	247	067	293	622
14	118	242	002	298	649
13	122	238	058	302	680
12	126	234	054	306	714
11	130	230	050	310	752
10	133	227	047	313	793
09	136	224	044	316	835

From 20° Lat	Northern Hemisphere		Southern Hemisphere		Distance
To Latitude	East	West	East	West	(nm)
30	042	318	138	222	809
29	045	315	135	225	767
28	049	311	131	229	728
27	053	307	127	233	692
26	057	303	123	237	659
25	062	298	118	242	630
24	067	293	113	247	606
23	072	288	108	252	586
22	078	282	102	258	573
21	084	276	096	264	565
20	090	270	090	270	564
19	096	264	084	276	569
18	102	258	078	282	580
17	108	252	072	288	597
16	113	247	067	293	619
15	118	242	062	298	646
14	122	238	058	302	677
13	126	234	054	306	712
12	130	230	050	310	750
11	133	227	047	313	791
10	136	224	044	316	834

From 21° Lat	Northern Hemisphere		Southern Hemisphere		Distance
To Latitude	East	West	East	West	(nm)
31	042	318	138	222	806
30	045	315	135	225	764
29	049	311	131	229	725
28	053	307	127	233	688
27	057	303	123	237	655
26	062	298	118	242	626
25	067	293	113	247	602
24	072	288	108	252	583
23	078	282	102	258	569
22	084	276	096	264	561
21	090	270	090	270	560
20	096	264	084	276	565
19	102	258	078	282	576
18	108	252	072	288	593
17	113	247	067	293	616
16	118	242	062	298	643
15	122	238	058	302	674
14	126	234	054	306	709
13	130	230	050	310	748
12	133	227	047	313	788
11	136	224	044	316	832

From 22° Lat	Northern Hemisphere		Southern Hemisphere		Distance
To Latitude	East	West	East	West	(nm)
32	042	318	138	222	803
31	045	315	135	225	761
30	048	312	132	228	721
29	052	308	128	232	685
28	057	303	123	237	652
27	061	299	119	241	623
26	066	294	114	246	598
25	072	288	108	252	579
24	078	282	102	258	565
23	084	276	096	264	558
22	090	270	090	270	556
21	096	264	084	276	561
20	102	258	078	282	573
19	108	252	072	288	590
18	113	247	067	293	613
17	118	242	062	298	640
16	122	238	058	302	672
15	126	234	054	306	707
14	130	230	050	310	745
13	133	227	047	313	786
12	136	224	044	316	830

From 23° Lat	Northern Hemisphere		Southern Hemisphere		Distance
To Latitude	East	West	East	West	(nm)
33	042	318	138	222	800
32	045	315	135	225	757
31	048	312	132	228	718
30	052	308	128	232	681
29	056	304	124	236	648
28	061	299	119	241	619
27	066	294	114	246	594
26	072	288	108	252	575
25	078	282	102	258	561
24	084	276	096	264	553
23	090	270	090	270	552
22	096	264	084	276	558
21	102	258	078	282	569
20	108	252	072	288	586
19	113	247	067	293	609
18	118	242	062	298	637
17	123	237	057	303	669
16	127	233	053	307	704
15	130	230	050	310	743
14	133	227	047	313	784
13	136	224	044	316	827

From 24° Lat	Northern Hemisphere		Southern Hemisphere		Distance
To Latitude	East	West	East	West	(nm)
34	041	319	13	221	796
33	044	316	136	224	754
32	048	312	132	228	714
31	052	308	128	232	677
30	056	304	124	236	644
29	061	299	119	241	615
28	066	294	114	246	590
27	072	288	108	252	570
26	078	282	102	258	557
25	084	276	096	264	549
24	090	270	090	270	548
23	096	264	084	276	553
22	102	258	078	282	565
21	108	252	072	288	583
20	113	247	067	293	606
19	118	242	062	298	633
18	123	237	057	303	665
17	127	233	053	307	701
16	130	230	050	310	740
15	134	226	046	314	781
14	137	223	043	317	825

From 25° Lat	Northern Hemisphere		Southern Hemisphere		Distance
To Latitude	East	West	East	West	(nm)
35	041	319	139	221	793
34	044	316	136	224	750
33	048	312	132	228	710
32	052	308	128	232	673
31	056	304	124	236	640
30	061	299	119	241	610
29	066	294	114	246	586
28	072	288	108	252	566
27	078	282	102	258	552
26	084	276	096	264	545
25	090	270	090	270	544
24	096	264	084	276	549
23	102	258	078	282	561
22	108	252	072	288	579
21	113	247	067	293	602
20	118	242	062	298	630
19	123	237	057	303	662
18	127	233	053	307	698
17	131	229	049	311	737
16	134	226	046	314	779
15	137	223	043	317	823

From 26° Lat	Northern Hemisphere		Southern Hemisphere		Distance
To Latitude	East	West	East	West	(nm)
36	041	319	139	221	789
35	044	316	136	224	747
34	047	313	133	227	707
33	051	309	129	231	670
32	056	304	124	236	636
31	060	300	120	240	606
30	066	294	114	246	581
29	071	289	109	251	562
28	077	283	103	257	547
27	084	276	096	264	540
26	090	220	090	270	539
25	096	264	084	276	545
24	102	258	078	282	557
23	108	252	072	288	575
22	114	246	066	294	598
21	119	241	061	299	626
20	123	237	057	303	659
19	127	233	053	307	695
18	131	229	049	311	734
17	134	226	046	314	776
16	137	223	043	317	820

From 27° Lat	Northern Hemisphere		Southern Hemisphere		Distance
To Latitude	East	West	East	West	(nm)
37	040	320	140	220	786
36	044	316	136	224	743
35	047	313	133	227	703
34	051	309	129	231	665
33	055	305	125	235	632
32	060	300	120	240	602
31	066	294	114	246	577
30	071	289	109	251	557
29	077	283	103	255	543
28	084	276	096	264	535
27	090	270	090	270	534
26	096	264	084	276	540
25	102	258	078	282	552
24	108	252	072	288	571
23	114	246	066	294	594
22	119	241	063	299	623
21	123	237	057	303	655
20	127	233	053	307	692
19	131	229	049	311	731
18	134	226	046	314	773
17	137	223	043	317	817

From 28° Lat	Northern Hemisphere		Southern Hemisphere		Distance
To Latitude	East	West	East	West	(nm)
38	040	320	140	220	782
37	043	317	137	223	739
36	047	313	133	227	699
35	051	309	129	231	661
34	055	305	125	235	627
33	060	300	120	240	597
32	065	255	115	245	572
31	071	289	109	251	552
30	077	283	103	257	538
29	084	276	096	263	531
28	090	270	090	270	530
27	096	264	084	276	535
26	103	257	077	283	548
25	109	251	071	289	566
24	114	246	066	294	590
23	119	241	061	299	619
22	123	237	057	303	652
21	128	232	052	308	688
20	131	229	049	311	728
19	134	226	046	314	770
18	137	223	043	317	815

From 29° Lat	Northern Hemisphere		Southern Hemisphere		Distance
To Latitude	East	West	East	West	(nm)
39	040	320	140	210	778
38	043	317	137	223	735
37	046	314	134	226	695
36	050	310	130	230	657
35	055	305	125	233	623
34	060	300	120	240	593
33	065	295	115	245	567
32	071	289	109	251	547
31	077	283	103	257	333
30	083	274	109	263	526
29	090	270	090	270	325
28	097	263	083	277	530
27	103	257	077	283	543
26	109	251	071	289	562
25	114	246	066	294	586
24	119	241	061	299	615
23	124	236	056	304	648
22	128	232	052	308	685
21	131	229	049	311	725
20	135	225	045	315	767
19	138	222	042	318	812

From 30° Lat	Northern Hemisphere		Southern Hemisphere		Distance
To Latitude	East	West	East	West	(nm)
40	039	321	141	219	775
39	043	317	137	223	731
38	046	314	134	226	690
37	050	310	130	230	653
36	055	305	125	235	618
35	059	301	121	239	588
34	065	295	115	245	562
33	071	289	109	251	542
32	077	283	103	257	528
31	083	2770	097	263	520
30	090	270	090	270	519
29	096	264	084	276	525
28	103	237	077	283	538
27	109	251	071	289	55
26	114	246	066	294	581
25	119	241	061	299	611
24	124	236	056	304	644
23	128	232	052	308	681
22	132	228	048	312	721
21	135	225	045	315	764
20	138	222	042	318	809

From 31° Lat	Northern Hemisphere		Southern Hemisphere		Distance
To Latitude	East	West	East	West	(nm)
41	039	321	141	219	771
40	042	318	138	222	727
39	046	314	134	226	686
38	050	310	130	230	648
37	054	306	126	234	613
36	059	301	127	239	583
35	065	295	115	245	557
34	071	289	109	231	537
33	077	283	103	257	523
32	083	277	097	263	515
31	090	270	095	270	514
30	097	263	083	277	520
29	103	257	077	283	533
28	109	251	071	289	552
27	115	245	065	295	577
26	120	240	060	300	606
25	124	236	056	304	640
24	128	232	052	308	677
23	132	228	048	312	718
22	135	225	045	315	761
21	138	222	042	318	806

From 32° Lat	Northern Hemisphere		Southern Hemisphere		Distance
To Latitude	East	West	East	West	(nm)
42	039	321	141	219	767
41	042	318	138	222	723
40	045	315	135	225	682
39	049	311	131	229	644
38	054	306	126	234	609
37	059	301	121	239	578
36	064	296	116	244	552
35	070	290	110	250	531
34	077	283	103	257	517
33	083	277	097	263	509
32	090	270	090	270	508
31	097	263	083	277	515
30	103	257	077	283	528
29	109	251	071	289	547
28	115	245	065	295	572
27	120	240	060	300	602
26	124	236	056	304	636
25	128	232	052	308	674
24	132	228	048	312	714
23	135	225	045	315	757
22	138	222	042	318	803

From 33° Lat	Northern Hemisphere		Southern Hemisphere		Distance
To Latitude	East	West	East	West	(nm)
43	038	322	142	218	763
42	042	318	138	222	719
41	045	315	135	225	677
40	049	311	131	229	639
39	054	306	126	234	604
38	059	301	121	239	573
37	064	296	116	244	547
36	070	290	110	250	526
35	077	283	103	257	511
34	083	274	097	263	504
33	090	270	090	270	503
32	097	263	083	277	509
31	103	257	077	283	523
30	109	251	071	289	542
29	115	245	065	295	567
28	120	240	060	300	597
27	125	235	055	305	632
26	129	231	051	309	670
25	132	228	048	312	711
24	136	224	044	316	754
23	138	222	042	318	800

From 34° Lat	Northern Hemisphere		Southern Hemisphere		Distance
To Latitude	East	West	East	West	(nm)
44	038	322	142	218	759
43	041	319	139	221	715
42	045	315	135	225	673
41	049	311	131	229	634
40	053	307	127	233	599
39	058	302	122	238	568
38	064	296	116	244	541
37	070	290	110	250	520
36	076	284	104	256	506
35	083	277	097	263	498
34	090	270	090	270	497
33	097	263	083	277	504
32	103	257	077	283	517
31	110	250	071	289	537
30	115	245	065	295	562
29	120	240	060	300	593
28	125	235	055	305	627
27	129	231	051	309	665
26	133	227	047	313	707
25	136	224	044	316	750
24	139	221	041	319	796

From 35° Lat	Northern Hemisphere		Southern Hemisphere		Distance
To Latitude	East	West	East	West	(nm)
45	038	322	142	218	754
44	041	319	139	221	710
43	044	316	136	224	668
42	048	312	132	228	629
41	053	307	127	233	594
40	058	302	122	238	562
39	064	296	116	244	536
38	070	290	110	250	515
37	076	284	104	256	500
36	083	277	097	263	492
35	090	270	090	270	491
34	097	263	083	277	498
33	104	256	076	283	511
32	110	250	070	290	531
31	115	245	065	295	557
30	121	239	059	301	588
29	125	235	055	305	623
28	129	231	051	309	661
27	133	227	047	333	703
26	136	224	044	316	747
25	139	221	041	319	793

From 36° Lat	Northern Hemisphere		Southern Hemisphere		Distance
To Latitude	East	West	East	West	(nm)
46	037	323	143	217	750
45	040	320	140	220	706
44	044	316	136	224	664
43	048	312	132	228	624
42	052	308	128	232	588
41	058	302	122	238	557
40	063	297	117	243	530
39	069	291	111	249	509
38	076	284	104	256	494
37	083	277	097	263	486
36	090	270	090	270	485
35	097	263	083	277	492
34	104	256	076	284	506
33	110	250	070	293	526
32	116	244	064	296	552
31	121	239	059	301	583
30	126	234	054	306	618
29	130	230	050	310	657
28	133	227	047	313	699
27	136	224	044	316	743
26	139	221	041	319	789

From 37° Lat	Northern Hemisphere		Southern Hemisphere		Distance
To Latitude	East	West	East	West	(nm)
47	037	323	143	217	746
46	040	320	140	220	701
45	043	317	137	223	659
44	048	312	132	228	619
43	052	308	128	232	583
42	057	303	123	237	551
41	063	297	117	243	524
40	069	291	111	249	503
39	076	284	104	256	488
38	083	277	097	263	480
37	090	270	090	270	478
36	097	263	083	277	486
35	104	256	076	284	500
34	110	250	070	290	520
33	116	244	064	296	547
32	121	238	059	301	578
31	126	234	054	306	613
30	130	230	050	310	653
29	134	226	046	314	695
28	137	223	043	317	739
27	140	220	040	320	786

From 38° Lat	Northern Hemisphere		Southern Hemisphere		Distance
To Latitude	East	West	East	West	(nm)
48	036	324	144	216	742
47	039	321	141	219	697
46	043	317	137	223	654
45	047	313	133	227	614
44	052	308	128	232	579
43	057	303	123	237	545
42	063	297	117	243	518
41	069	291	111	249	496
40	076	284	104	256	481
39	083	277	097	263	473
38	090	270	090	270	472
37	097	263	083	277	479
36	104	256	076	284	494
35	110	250	070	290	515
34	116	244	064	296	541
33	122	238	058	302	573
32	126	234	054	306	609
31	130	230	050	310	648
30	134	226	046	314	690
29	137	223	043	317	735
28	140	220	040	320	782

From 39° Lat	Northern Hemisphere		Southern Hemisphere		Distance
To Latitude	East	West	East	West	(nm)
49	036	324	144	216	738
48	039	321	141	219	692
47	043	317	137	223	649
46	047	313	133	227	609
45	051	309	129	231	572
44	056	304	124	236	540
43	062	298	118	242	512
42	069	291	111	249	490
41	075	285	105	255	474
40	083	277	097	263	467
39	090	270	090	270	466
38	097	263	083	277	473
37	104	256	076	284	487
36	111	249	069	291	509
35	117	243	063	297	536
34	122	238	058	302	568
33	127	233	053	307	604
32	131	229	049	311	644
31	134	226	046	314	686
30	137	223	043	317	731
29	140	220	040	320	778

From 40° Lat	Northern Hemisphere		Southern Hemisphere		Distance
To Latitude	East	West	East	West	(nm)
50	035	325	145	215	733
49	039	321	141	219	688
48	042	318	138	222	644
47	046	314	134	226	604
46	051	309	129	231	567
45	056	304	124	236	534
44	062	298	118	242	506
43	068	292	112	248	484
42	075	285	105	255	468
41	083	277	097	263	460
40	090	270	090	270	459
39	097	263	083	277	467
38	104	256	076	284	481
37	111	249	069	291	503
36	117	243	063	297	530
35	122	238	058	302	562
34	127	233	053	301	599
33	131	229	049	311	639
32	135	225	045	315	682
31	138	222	042	318	727
30	141	219	039	321	775

From 41° Lat	Northern Hemisphere		Southern Hemisphere		Distance
To Latitude	East	West	East	West	(nm)
51	03	325	145	215	729
50	038	322	142	218	683
49	042	318	138	222	640
48	046	314	134	226	599
47	050	310	130	230	561
46	056	304	124	236	528
45	061	299	119	241	500
44	068	292	112	248	477
43	075	285	105	255	461
42	082	228	098	262	453
41	090	270	090	270	453
40	098	262	082	278	460
39	105	255	075	285	475
38	111	249	069	291	496
37	117	243	063	297	524
36	123	237	057	303	557
35	127	233	053	307	594
34	131	229	049	311	634
33	13	225	045	315	677
32	138	222	042	318	723
31	141	219	039	321	771

From 42° Lat	Northern Hemisphere		Southern Hemisphere		Distance
To Latitude	East	West	East	West	(nm)
52	034	326	146	214	725
51	038	322	142	218	679
50	041	319	139	221	635
49	045	315	135	225	593
48	050	310	130	230	556
47	055	305	125	235	522
46	061	299	119	241	493
45	068	292	112	248	471
44	075	285	105	255	455
43	082	278	098	262	446
42	090	270	090	270	446
41	098	262	082	278	453
40	105	255	075	285	468
39	112	248	068	292	490
38	118	242	062	298	518
37	123	237	057	303	551
36	128	232	052	308	588
35	132	228	048	312	629
34	135	225	045	315	673
33	139	221	041	319	719
32	141	219	039	321	767

From 43° Lat	Northern Hemisphere		Southern Hemisphere		Distance
To Latitude	East	West	East	West	(nm)
53	034	326	146	214	720
52	037	323	143	217	674
51	041	319	139	221	630
50	045	315	135	225	588
49	049	311	131	229	550
48	055	305	125	235	516
47	061	299	119	241	487
46	067	293	113	247	464
45	075	285	105	255	448
44	082	278	098	262	439
43	090	270	090	270	439
42	098	262	082	278	446
41	105	255	075	285	461
40	112	248	068	292	484
39	118	242	062	298	512
38	123	237	057	303	545
37	128	232	052	308	583
36	132	228	048	312	624
35	136	224	044	316	668
34	139	221	041	319	715
33	142	218	038	322	763

From 44° Lat	Northern Hemisphere		Southern Hemisphere		Distance
To Latitude	East	West	East	West	(nm)
54	031	327	147	213	716
53	037	323	143	217	669
52	040	320	140	220	625
51	044	316	166	224	583
50	049	311	131	229	544
49	054	306	126	234	510
48	060	300	120	240	480
47	067	293	113	247	457
46	074	286	106	254	441
45	082	278	098	262	432
44	090	270	090	270	431
43	098	262	082	278	439
42	105	255	075	285	455
41	112	248	068	292	477
40	118	242	062	298	506
39	124	236	056	304	540
38	128	232	052	308	578
37	133	227	047	313	619
36	136	224	044	316	664
35	139	221	041	319	710
34	142	218	038	322	759

From 45° Lat	Northern Hemisphere		Southern Hemisphere		Distance
To Latitude	East	West	East	West	(nm)
55	033	327	147	213	712
54	036	324	144	216	665
53	039	321	141	219	620
52	044	346	136	224	577
51	048	312	132	228	538
50	054	306	126	234	504
49	060	300	120	240	474
48	067	293	113	247	450
47	074	286	106	254	433
46	082	278	098	262	425
45	090	270	090	270	424
44	098	262	082	278	432
43	106	254	074	286	448
42	112	248	068	292	471
41	119	241	061	299	500
40	124	236	056	304	534
39	129	231	051	309	522
38	133	227	047	313	614
37	137	223	043	317	659
36	140	220	040	320	706
35	142	218	038	322	755

From 46° Lat	Northern Hemisphere		Southern Hemisphere		Distance
To Latitude	East	West	East	West	(nm)
56	032	328	148	212	707
55	035	325	145	215	660
54	039	321	141	219	615
53	043	317	137	223	572
52	048	312	132	228	533
51	053	307	127	233	497
50	059	301	121	239	467
49	066	294	114	246	443
48	074	286	106	254	426
47	082	278	098	262	417
46	090	270	090	270	417
45	098	262	082	278	425
44	106	254	074	286	441
43	113	247	067	293	464
42	119	241	061	299	493
41	125	235	055	305	528
40	129	231	051	309	567
39	133	227	047	313	609
38	137	223	043	317	654
37	140	220	040	320	701
36	143	217	037	323	750

From 47° Lat	Northern Hemisphere		Southern Hemisphere		Distance
To Latitude	East	West	East	West	(nm)
57	032	328	148	212	703
56	035	325	145	215	655
55	038	322	142	218	610
54	042	318	138	222	566
53	047	313	133	227	527
52	053	307	127	233	491
51	059	301	121	239	460
50	066	294	114	246	436
49	073	287	107	253	419
48	082	278	098	262	410
47	090	270	090	270	409
46	098	262	082	278	417
45	106	254	074	286	433
44	113	247	067	293	457
43	119	241	061	299	487
42	125	235	055	305	522
41	130	230	050	310	561
40	134	226	046	314	604
39	138	222	042	318	649
38	141	219	039	321	697
37	143	217	037	323	746

From 48° Lat	Northern Hemisphere		Southern Hemisphere		Distance
To Latitude	East	West	East	West	(nm)
58	031	329	149	211	699
57	034	326	146	214	651
56	038	322	142	218	604
55	042	318	138	222	561
54	047	313	133	227	521
53	052	308	128	232	485
52	058	302	122	238	454
51	065	295	115	245	428
50	073	287	107	253	413
49	081	279	099	261	402
48	090	270	090	270	401
47	098	262	082	278	410
46	106	254	074	286	426
45	114	246	066	294	450
44	120	240	060	300	480
43	125	235	055	305	516
42	130	230	050	310	556
41	134	226	046	314	599
40	138	222	042	318	644
39	141	219	039	321	692
38	144	216	036	324	742

From 49° Lat	Northern Hemisphere		Southern Hemisphere		Distance
To Latitude	East	West	East	West	(nm)
59	031	329	149	211	694
58	034	326	146	214	646
57	037	323	143	217	599
56	041	319	139	221	556
55	046	314	134	226	515
54	051	309	129	231	478
53	058	302	122	238	447
52	065	295	115	245	422
51	073	287	107	253	404
50	081	279	099	261	394
49	090	270	090	270	393
48	099	261	081	279	402
47	107	253	073	287	419
46	114	246	066	294	443
45	120	240	060	300	474
44	126	234	054	306	510
43	131	229	049	311	550
42	135	225	045	315	593
41	138	222	042	318	640
40	142	218	038	322	688
39	144	215	036	324	738

From 50° Lat	Northern Hemisphere		Southern Hemisphere		Distance
To Latitude	East	West	East	West	(nm)
60	030	330	150	210	690
59	033	327	147	213	641
58	036	324	144	216	594
57	040	320	140	220	550
56	045	315	135	225	509
55	051	309	129	231	472
54	057	303	123	237	440
53	064	296	116	244	414
52	072	288	108	252	396
51	081	279	099	261	386
50	090	270	090	270	385
49	099	261	081	279	394
48	107	253	073	287	411
47	114	246	066	294	436
46	121	239	059	301	467
45	126	234	054	306	504
44	131	229	049	311	544
43	135	225	045	315	588
42	139	221	041	319	635
41	142	218	038	322	683
40	145	215	035	325	733

From 51° Lat	Northern Hemisphere		Southern Hemisphere		Distance
To Latitude	East	West	East	West	(nm)
61	029	331	151	209	686
60	032	328	148	212	637
59	036	324	144	126	589
58	040	320	140	220	545
57	045	315	135	225	503
56	050	310	130	230	465
55	057	303	123	237	433
54	064	296	116	244	407
53	072	288	108	252	388
52	081	229	099	261	378
51	090	270	090	270	377
50	099	261	081	279	386
49	107	253	073	287	404
48	115	245	065	295	429
47	121	239	059	301	460
46	127	233	053	307	497
45	132	228	048	312	538
44	136	224	044	316	583
43	140	220	040	320	630
42	143	217	037	323	679
41	145	215	035	325	729

From 52° Lat	Northern Hemisphere		Southern Hemisphere		Distance
To Latitude	East	West	East	West	(nm)
62	029	331	151	209	682
61	032	328	148	212	632
60	035	325	145	215	584
59	039	321	141	219	539
58	044	316	136	224	497
57	049	311	131	229	459
56	056	304	124	236	426
55	063	297	117	243	399
54	072	288	108	252	380
53	081	279	099	261	370
52	090	270	090	270	369
51	099	261	081	279	378
50	108	252	072	288	396
49	115	245	065	295	422
48	122	238	058	302	454
47	128	232	052	308	491
46	132	228	048	312	533
45	137	223	043	317	577
44	140	220	040	320	625
43	143	217	037	323	674
42	146	214	034	326	725

From 53° Lat	Northern Hemisphere		Southern Hemisphere		Distance
To Latitude	East	West	East	West	(nm)
63	028	332	152	208	677
62	031	329	149	211	627
61	034	326	146	214	579
60	038	322	142	218	534
59	043	317	137	223	491
58	049	311	131	229	453
57	055	303	125	235	419
56	063	297	117	243	392
55	071	289	109	251	372
54	081	279	099	261	362
53	090	270	090	270	361
52	099	261	081	279	370
51	108	252	072	288	388
50	116	244	064	296	414
49	122	238	058	302	447
48	128	232	052	308	485
47	133	227	047	313	527
46	137	223	043	317	572
45	141	219	039	321	620
44	144	216	036	324	669
43	146	214	034	326	720

From 54° Lat	Northern Hemisphere		Southern Hemisphere		Distance
To Latitude	East	West	East	West	(nm)
64	027	333	153	207	673
63	030	330	150	210	623
62	034	326	146	214	574
61	038	322	142	218	528
60	042	318	138	222	485
59	048	312	132	228	446
58	055	305	125	235	412
57	062	298	118	242	384
56	071	289	109	251	364
55	080	280	100	260	353
54	090	270	090	270	352
53	100	260	080	280	362
52	108	252	072	288	380
51	116	244	064	296	407
50	123	237	057	303	440
49	129	231	051	309	478
48	134	226	046	314	521
47	138	222	042	318	566
46	141	219	039	321	615
45	144	216	036	324	665
44	147	213	033	327	716

From 55° Lat	Northern Hemisphere		Southern Hemisphere		Distance
To Latitude	East	West	East	West	(nm)
65	027	333	153	207	669
64	030	330	150	210	618
63	033	327	147	213	570
62	037	323	143	217	523
61	042	318	138	222	479
60	047	313	133	227	440
59	054	306	126	234	405
58	062	298	118	242	376
57	070	290	110	250	356
56	080	280	100	260	345
55	090	270	090	270	344¬
54	100	260	080	280	353
53	109	251	071	289	372
52	117	243	063	297	399
51	124	236	056	304	433
50	129	231	051	309	472
49	134	226	046	314	515
48	138	222	042	318	561
47	142	218	038	322	610
46	145	215	035	325	660
45	147	213	033	327	712

From 56° Lat	Northern Hemisphere		Southern Hemisphere		Distance
To Latitude	East	West	East	West	(nm)
66	026	334	154	206	665
65	029	331	151	209	614
64	032	328	148	212	565
63	036	324	144	216	318
62	041	319	139	221	473
61	046	314	134	226	433
60	053	307	127	233	398
59	061	299	119	241	369
58	070	290	110	250	348
57	080	280	100	260	336
56	090	270	090	270	335
55	100	260	080	280	345
54	109	251	071	289	364
53	117	243	063	297	392
52	124	236	056	304	426
51	130	230	050	310	465
50	134	226	046	314	509
49	139	221	041	319	556
48	142	218	038	322	604
47	145	215	035	325	655
46	148	212	032	328	707

From 57° Lat	Northern Hemisphere		Southern Hemisphere		Distance
To Latitude	East	West	East	West	(nm)
67	025	335	155	205	661
66	028	332	152	208	610
65	031	329	149	211	560
64	035	325	145	215	512
63	040	320	140	220	468
62	046	314	134	226	427
61	052	308	128	232	391
60	060	300	120	240	361
59	069	291	111	249	339
58	079	281	101	259	328
57	090	270	090	270	327
56	100	260	080	280	336
55	110	250	070	290	355
54	118	242	062	298	384
53	125	235	055	305	419
52	131	229	049	311	459
51	136	224	044	316	503
50	140	220	040	320	550
49	143	217	037	323	599
48	146	214	034	326	651
47	148	212	032	328	703

From 58° Lat	Northern Hemisphere		Southern Hemisphere		Distance
To Latitude	East	West	East	West	(nm)
68	025	335	155	205	657
67	027	333	153	207	605
66	031	329	149	211	555
65	034	326	146	214	507
64	039	321	141	219	462
63	045	315	135	225	420
62	051	309	129	231	384
61	060	300	120	240	353
60	069	291	111	249	331
59	079	281	101	259	319
58	090	270	090	270	318
57	101	259	079	281	328
56	110	250	070	290	348
55	119	241	061	299	376
54	126	234	054	306	412
53	131	229	049	311	453
52	136	224	044	316	497
51	140	220	040	320	545
50	144	216	036	324	594
49	146	214	034	326	646
48	149	211	031	329	699

From 59° Lat	Northern Hemisphere		Southern Hemisphere		Distance
To Latitude	East	West	East	West	(nm)
69	024	336	156	204	653
68	027	333	153	207	601
67	030	330	150	210	550
66	034	326	146	214	502
65	038	322	142	218	456
64	044	316	136	224	414
63	051	309	129	231	376
62	059	301	121	239	345
61	068	292	112	248	323
60	079	281	101	259	310
59	090	270	090	270	309
58	101	259	079	281	319
57	111	249	069	291	339
56	119	241	061	299	369
55	126	234	054	306	405
54	132	228	048	312	446
53	137	223	043	317	491
52	141	219	039	321	539
51	144	216	036	324	589
50	147	213	033	327	641
49	150	210	030	330	694

From 60° Lat	Northern Hemisphere		Southern Hemisphere		Distance
To Latitude	East	West	East	West	(nm)
70	023	337	157	203	649
69	026	334	154	206	597
68	029	331	151	209	546
67	033	327	147	213	497
66	037	323	143	217	450
65	043	317	137	223	408
64	050	310	130	230	369
63	058	302	122	238	338
62	068	292	112	248	314
61	079	281	101	259	301
60	090	270	090	270	300
59	101	259	079	281	310
58	111	249	069	291	331
57	120	240	060	300	361
56	127	233	053	307	398
55	133	227	047	313	440
54	138	222	042	318	485
53	142	218	038	322	534
52	145	215	035	325	584
51	148	212	032	328	637
50	150	210	030	330	690

From 61° Lat	Northern Hemisphere		Southern Hemisphere		Distance
To Latitude	East	West	East	West	(nm)
71	022	338	158	202	646
70	025	335	155	205	593
69	028	332	152	208	541
68	032	328	148	212	492
67	036	324	144	216	445
66	042	318	138	222	401
65	049	311	131	229	362
64	057	303	123	237	330
63	067	293	113	247	306
62	078	282	102	258	292
61	090	270	090	270	291
60	102	258	078	282	301
59	112	248	068	292	323
58	121	239	059	301	353
57	128	232	052	308	391
56	134	226	046	314	433
55	139	221	041	319	479
54	142	218	038	322	528
53	146	214	034	326	579
52	148	212	032	328	632
51	151	209	029	331	686

From 62° Lat	Northern Hemisphere		Southern Hemisphere		Distance
To Latitude	East	West	East	West	(nm)
72	021	339	159	201	642
71	024	336	156	204	589
70	027	333	153	207	537
69	031	329	149	211	487
68	035	325	145	215	439
67	041	319	139	221	395
66	048	312	132	228	355
65	056	304	124	236	322
64	066	294	114	246	297
63	078	282	102	258	283
62	090	270	090	270	281
61	102	258	078	282	292
60	112	248	068	292	314
59	121	239	059	301	345
58	129	231	051	309	384
57	135	225	045	315	427
56	139	221	041	319	473
55	143	217	037	323	523
54	146	216	034	326	574
53	149	211	031	329	627
52	151	209	029	331	682

From 63° Lat	Northern Hemisphere		Southern Hemisphere		Distance
To Latitude	East	West	East	West	(nm)
73	021	339	159	201	639
72	023	337	157	203	585
71	026	334	154	206	533
70	030	330	150	210	482
69	034	326	146	214	434
68	040	320	140	220	389
67	047	313	133	227	348
66	055	305	125	235	314
65	066	294	114	246	289
64	077	283	103	257	274
63	090	270	090	270	272
62	102	258	078	282	283
61	113	247	067	293	306
60	122	238	058	302	338
59	129	231	051	309	376
58	135	225	045	315	420
57	140	220	040	320	468
56	144	216	036	324	518
55	147	213	033	327	570
54	150	210	030	330	623
53	152	208	028	332	677

From 64° Lat	Northern Hemisphere		Southern Hemisphere		Distance
To Latitude	East	West	East	West	(nm)
73	022	338	158	202	582
72	025	335	155	205	529
71	029	331	151	209	478
70	033	327	147	213	429
69	039	321	141	219	383
68	046	314	134	226	342
67	054	306	126	234	307
66	065	295	115	245	281
65	077	283	103	257	265
64	090	270	090	270	263
63	103	257	077	283	275
62	114	246	066	294	298
61	123	237	057	303	330
60	130	230	050	310	370
59	136	224	044	316	414
58	141	219	039	321	462
57	145	215	035	325	513
56	148	212	032	328	565
55	150	210	030	330	619
54	153	207	027	333	674
0	135	225	045	315	846

From 65° Lat	Northern Hemisphere		Southern Hemisphere		Distance
To Latitude	East	West	East	West	(nm)
74	021	339	159	201	578
73	024	336	156	204	524
72	028	332	152	208	473
71	032	328	148	212	423
70	037	323	143	217	377
69	044	316	136	224	335
68	053	307	127	233	299
67	064	296	116	244	272
66	076	284	104	256	256
65	270	090	270	270	254
64	103	257	077	283	265
63	114	246	066	294	289
62	124	236	056	304	322
61	131	229	049	311	363
60	137	223	043	317	408
59	142	218	038	322	456
58	146	214	034	326	507
57	149	211	031	329	559
56	151	209	029	331	614
55	153	207	027	333	669
01	135	225	045	315	846

Visa Waiver Program

*W*ill a foreign national need a Visa when entering the United States? That depends on their nationality, the purpose of the visit, duration of stay, and many other variables.

Some foreign nationals can bypass the Visa requirement using the Visa Waiver Program, which makes life a lot easier for everyone but requires they travel only on operators approved under the Visa Waiver Program. This used to be the exclusive domain of commercial carriers but 14 CFR 91 operators are now included.

Bear in mind this could impact you as a pilot even if your operator is not on the approved signatory list. If, for example, you fly a foreign national out of the country who entered using the Visa Waiver Program, that person cannot re-enter the United States with you. In fact, that person will have some explaining to do when he or she does re-enter the country, even on an authorized carrier.

Program Summary

[Homeland Security Website] The Visa Waiver Program (VWP), administered by the Department of Homeland Security (DHS) in consultation with the State Department, permits citizens of 38 countries[1] to travel to the United States for business or tourism for stays of up to 90 days without a visa. In return, those 38 countries must permit U.S. citizens and nationals to travel to their countries for a similar length of time without a visa for business or tourism purposes. Since its inception in 1986, the VWP has evolved into a comprehensive security partnership with many of America's closest allies. The VWP utilizes a risk-based, multi-layered approach to detect and prevent terrorists, serious criminals, and other mala fide actors from traveling to the United States. This approach incorporates regular, national-level risk assessments concerning the impact of each program country's participation in the VWP on U.S. national security and law enforcement interests. It also includes comprehensive vetting of individual VWP travelers prior to their departure for the United States, upon arrival at U.S. ports of entry, and during any subsequent air travel within the United States.

Participating Countries

[Homeland Security Website]

Andorra

Australia

Austria

Belgium

Brunei

Chile

Czech Republic

Denmark

Estonia

Finland

France

Germany

Greece

Hungary

Iceland

Ireland

Italy

Japan

Latvia

Liechtenstein

Lithuania

Luxembourg

Malta

Monaco

Netherlands

New Zealand

Norway

Portugal

San Marino

Singapore

Slovakia

Slovenia

South Korea

Spain

Sweden

Switzerland

Taiwan

United Kingdom

Passport Requirements

[Homeland Security Website] Travel under the Visa Waiver Program is restricted to travelers possessing passports with specified security features. Visa Waiver Program requirements are:

- The passport must have a machine-readable zone on the biographic page

- The passport must be an electronic passport with a digital chip containing biometric information about the passport owner.

[Homeland Security Website] All Visa Waiver Program country must issue passports with a digital photograph printed on the data page or their citizens will be required to obtain a visa to travel to the United States. A digital photograph is one that is printed on the page as opposed to a photograph that is glued or laminated into the passport.

Visa Waiver Program Signatory Carriers

[Homeland Security Website] In order to facilitate the arrival of Visa Waiver Program (VWP) passengers, carriers need to be signatory to a current agreement with U.S. Customs and Border Protection (CBP). A carrier is required to be signatory to an agreement in order to transport aliens seeking admission as nonimmigrant visitors under the VWP (Title 8, U.S.C. § 1187(a)(5). The carriers listed below are currently signatory to the VWP and can transport passengers under the program. The date indicates the expiration of the current signed agreement. Agreements are valid for 7 years.

If you transport VWP passengers and are not a signatory carrier, fines will be levied. Use the following link to apply to CBP to become a Signatory Carrier: https://www.cbp.gov/travel/international-visitors/business-pleasure/vwp/signatory-status

The U.S. Customs and Border Protection department maintains a list of VWP Signatory Carriers on their website: http://www.cbp.gov/travel/international-visitors/visa-waiver-program. You need to be on that list to participate as a carrier, even if you are flying strictly 14 CFR 91.

Wake Turbulence

*T*here isn't much difference in wake turbulence regulations across the world, except for a recently added category due to the Airbus A380 "Super."

Categories and Groups

[ICAO Doc 4444, ¶4.9]

Note.— The term "wake turbulence" is used in this context to describe the effect of the rotating air masses generated behind the wing tips of large jet aircraft, in preference to the term "wake vortex" which describes the nature of the air masses. Detailed characteristics of wake vortices and their effect on aircraft are contained in the Air Traffic Services Planning Manual (Doc 9426), Part II, Section 5.

4.9.1 Wake turbulence categories and groups of aircraft

4.9.1.1 Except as provided for in 4.9.1.2, wake turbulence separation minima shall be based on a grouping of aircraft types into four categories according to the maximum certificated take-off mass as follows:

a) SUPER (J) — aircraft types specified as such in ICAO Doc 8643, Aircraft Type Designators;

b) HEAVY (H) — all aircraft types of 136 000 kg or more, with the exception of aircraft types listed in Doc 8643 in the SUPER (J) category;

c) MEDIUM (M) — aircraft types less than 136 000 kg but more than 7 000 kg; and

d) LIGHT (L) — aircraft types of 7 000 kg or less.

Note.— The wake turbulence category for each aircraft type is contained in Doc 8643, Aircraft Type Designators.

4.9.1.2 When approved by the appropriate ATS authority, wake turbulence separation minima may be applied utilizing wake turbulence groups and shall be based on wake generation and resistance characteristics of the aircraft. These depend primarily on maximum certificated take-off mass, wing characteristics and speeds; the group designators are described as follows:

a) GROUP A — aircraft types of 136 000 kg or more, and a wing span less than or equal to 80 m but greater than 74.68 m;

b) GROUP B — aircraft types of 136 000 kg or more, and a wing span less than or equal to 74.68 m but greater than 53.34 m;

c) GROUP C — aircraft types of 136 000 kg or more, and a wing span less than or equal to 53.34 m but greater than 38.1 m;

d) GROUP D — aircraft types less than 136 000 kg but more than 18 600 kg, and a wing span greater than 32 m;

e) GROUP E — aircraft types less than 136 000 kg but more than 18 600 kg, and a wing span less than or equal to 32 m but greater than 27.43 m;

f) GROUP F — aircraft types less than 136 000 kg but more than 18 600 kg, and a wing span less than or equal to 27.43 m;

g) GROUP G — aircraft types of 18 600 kg or less (without wing span criterion).

Note 1. — Information on the wake turbulence group for each aircraft type is contained in Doc 8643 Aircraft Type Designators. Note 2. — Guidance on the implementation of wake turbulence separation between wake turbulence groups can be found in the Manual on Implementation of Wake Turbulence Separation Minima (Doc 10122).

4.9.1.2.1 Essential information, including the wake turbulence group designator as necessary, shall be provided to the controller when separation based on wake turbulence groups is to be applied.

4.9.1.3 Helicopters should be kept well clear of light aircraft when hovering or while air taxiing.

Note 1.— Helicopters produce vortices when in flight and there is some evidence that, per kilogram of gross mass, their vortices are more intense than those of fixed-wing aircraft. When hovering in ground effect or air taxiing, helicopters generate downwash producing high velocity outwash vortices to a distance approximately three times the diameter of the rotor.

Note 2.— The provisions governing wake turbulence separation minima are set forth in Chapter 5, Section 5.8, and Chapter 8, Section 8.7.3.

4.9.2 Indication of super or heavy wake turbulence category

For aircraft in the SUPER or HEAVY wake turbulence categories the word "super" or "heavy" shall be included, as appropriate, immediately after the aircraft call sign in the initial radiotelephony contact between such aircraft and ATS units.

Note 1.— Wake turbulence categories are specified in the instructions for completing Item 9 of the flight plan in Appendix 2.

Note 2.— Wake turbulence Group A is equivalent to the SUPER wake turbulence category, and Groups B and C are equivalent to the HEAVY category.

Time-based Wake Turbulence Longitudinal Separation Minima

Arriving aircraft

[ICAO Doc 4444, ¶5.8.2]

5.8.2.1 Except as provided for in 5.8.1.1 a) and b), the following minima shall be applied to aircraft landing behind a SUPER, a HEAVY or a MEDIUM aircraft:

a) HEAVY aircraft landing behind SUPER aircraft — 2 minutes;

b) MEDIUM aircraft landing behind SUPER aircraft — 3 minutes;

c) MEDIUM aircraft landing behind HEAVY aircraft — 2 minutes;

d) LIGHT aircraft landing behind SUPER aircraft — 4 minutes;

e) LIGHT aircraft landing behind a HEAVY or MEDIUM aircraft — 3 minutes.

Departing aircraft

[ICAO Doc 4444, ¶5.8.3]

5.8.3.1 When using wake turbulence categories contained in Chapter 4, 4.9.1.1 and when the aircraft are using:

a) the same runway;

b) parallel runways separated by less than 760 m (2 500 ft);

c) crossing runways if the projected flight path of the second aircraft will cross the projected flight path of the first aircraft at the same altitude or less than 300 m (1 000 ft) below;

d) parallel runways separated by 760 m (2 500 ft) or more, if the projected flight path of the second aircraft will cross the projected flight path of the first aircraft at the same altitude or less than 300 m (1 000 ft) below.

the following minimum separations shall be applied

1) HEAVY aircraft taking off behind a SUPER aircraft — 2 minutes;

2) LIGHT or MEDIUM aircraft taking off behind a SUPER aircraft — 3 minutes;

3) LIGHT or MEDIUM aircraft taking off behind a HEAVY aircraft — 2 minutes;

4) LIGHT aircraft taking off behind a MEDIUM aircraft — 2 minutes

Separation minima based on ATS surveillance systems

[ICAO Doc 4444, ¶8.7.3]

Aircraft category		
Preceding aircraft	Succeeding aircraft	Distance-based wake turbulence separation minima
SUPER	HEAVY	9.3 km (5.0 NM)
	MEDIUM	13.0 km (7.0 NM)
	LIGHT	14.9 km (8.0 NM)
HEAVY	HEAVY	7.4 km (4.0 NM)
	MEDIUM	9.3 km (5.0 NM)
	LIGHT	11.1 km (6.0 NM)
MEDIUM	LIGHT	9.3 km (5.0 NM)

Chapter 42

Waypoint Symbology

There are various U.S. and international regulations with opinions on how to best annotate your master document, but no one way. Whatever method you choose, you should be able to explain it if an inspector ever comes knocking on your door.

Technique

Here is the method I grew up with, it has served me well for years . . .

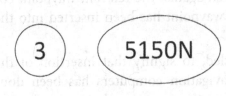

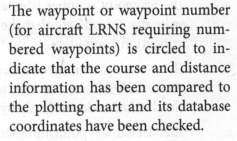

The waypoint or waypoint number (for aircraft LRNS requiring numbered waypoints) is circled to indicate that the course and distance information has been compared to the plotting chart and its database coordinates have been checked.

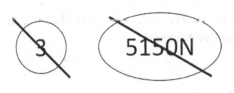

A diagonal line will be drawn through the circled waypoint to show that the course and distance displayed in the FMS has been verified against the master document and plotting or en route chart.

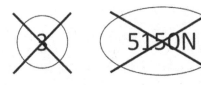

Following acknowledgement of the position report, a second diagonal line will be drawn through the circled waypoint (creating an "X") on the master document to indicate these duties have been completed.

Of course there are other techniques out there . . .

Advisory Circular

[AC 91-70B, ¶6.3.2.7] Adopt an appropriate symbology to indicate the status of each waypoint listed on the master document. For example:

- The first pilot could circle the waypoint, waypoint number, or symbol on the master document to signify that they have independently cross-checked the entry of the coordinates in the navigation computer.

- The second pilot could then tick or diagonally slash the circled waypoint, waypoint number, or symbol to signify having performed the cross-check to include confirming the course and distance information within a specified tolerance (e.g., plus or minus 2° and 2 NM)

North Atlantic

[ICAO NAT Doc 007, ¶ 8.2.7.]

a.   The waypoint number is entered against the relevant waypoint coordinates to indicate that the waypoint has been inserted into the navigation computers.

b.   The waypoint number is circled, to signify that insertion of the correct coordinates in the navigation computers has been double-checked independently by another crew member.

c.   The circled waypoint number is ticked, to signify that the relevant track and distance information has been double-checked.

d.   The circled waypoint number is crossed out, to signify that the aircraft has overflown the waypoint concerned.

Chapter 43

World Geodetic System (WGS-84)

*F*or those pilots who want to avoid all things tech, or understanding all things tech, here is what you need to know about WGS-84 in a nutshell:

- The United States Department of Defense first developed GPS for military uses and that eventually morphed into a worldwide civil system of navigation.

- Various entities around the world started cataloging the positions of things on earth as a way of finding them and, of course, avoiding them. The standard most of us use is known as the World Geodetic System of 1984, or WGS-84.

- If your aircraft and its database uses WGS-84 — and most do — then it is critically important that your navigation and approach charts are based on WGS-84 too.

- Part of your mission planning to international destinations needs to ask this question for every procedure you fly: is this WGS-84 compliant? If not, you should refer to your manufacturer's advice on how to deal with that.

Sphere "Flattening"

The earth is basically round because gravity pulls with equal strength in all directions, tending to smooth variations towards a norm. But it isn't perfectly round, the centrifugal effects of its rotation tends to make it wider in the middle than it is tall. Technically, you would call the basic shape an oblate spheroid.

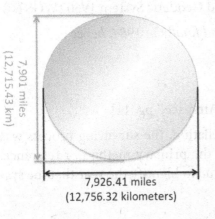

Oblate Spheroid

7,901 miles
(12,715.43 km)

7,926.41 miles
(12,756.32 kilometers)

Sphere versus Geoid

It is helpful to think of the earth's shape as a "geoid," the shape it would most closely resemble figuring the effects of gravity.

[National Geodetic Survey] geoid: The equipotential surface of the Earth's gravity field which best fits, in a least squares sense, global mean sea level.

Even though we adopt a definition, that does not mean we are perfect in the realization of that definition. For example, altimetry is often used to define "mean sea level" in the oceans, but altimetry is not global (missing the near po-lar regions). As such, the fit between "global" mean sea level and the geoid is not entirely confirmable.

The earth doesn't conform to the geoid because the magnetic field isn't uniform and the earth's surface is filled with varying heights of land as well as a sea that does not maintain the same level throughout.

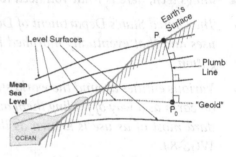

Level Surface = Equipotential Surface
H (Orthometric Height) = Distance along Plumb line (P_0 to P)

Figure: Schematic diagram, from National Geodetic Survey.

Mapping the Earth

[Geodesy for the Layman, Ch. 8] The Department of Defense, in the late 1950's began to develop the needed world system to which geodetic datums could be referred and compatibility established between the coordinates of widely separated sites of interest. Efforts of the Army, Navy and Air Force were combined leading to the DoD World Geodetic System 1960 (WGS 60).

The survey was updated in 1966, 1972, and finally in 1984, hence . . .

Adopting a Standard

["FAQs for Operations in Non WGS 84 Airspace," pg. 11]

With the deployment of the GPS constellation, the surveying process was updated in 1984 to incorporate GPS as the primary method of reference. Therefore, the '84' is appended to the name to identify the year that the system was last updated.

Throughout history, there have been numerous methods to survey the surface of the earth, but the WGS-84 system is the most accurate, having an overall fidelity of less than 1 meter. As an example, the WGS-84 system placed the actual Prime Meridian (0° line of longitude) approximately 100 meters east of where it traditionally lies in Greenwich, UK. This is a prime example of how different methodologies can yield different results.

In 1989, ICAO officially adopted WGS-84 as the standard geodetic reference system for future navigation with respect to international civil aviation. With this policy, virtually all countries use the WGS-84 standard to publish waypoint coordinates for navigation (e.g., airports, runways, navaids, etc.).

Technical Definition

[NIMA, ¶2.1] The WGS 84 Coordinate System is a Conventional Terrestrial Reference System (CTRS). The definition of this coordinate system follows the criteria outlined in the International Earth Rotation Service (IERS) Technical Note 21 [1]. These criteria are repeated below:

- It is geocentric, the center of mass being defined for the whole Earth including oceans and atmosphere

- Its scale is that of the local Earth frame, in the meaning of a relativistic theory of gravitation

- Its orientation was initially given by the Bureau International de l'Heure (BIH) orientation of 1984.0

- Its time evolution in orientation will create no residual global rotation with regards to the crust

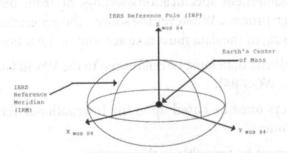

Figure: WGS84 Coordinate System Definition, from NIMA, Figure 2.1

The WGS 84 Coordinate System is a right-handed, Earth-fixed orthogonal coordinate system and is graphically depicted in [the figure].

- Origin = Earth's center of mass

- Z-Axis = The direction of the IERS Reference Pole (IRP). This direction corresponds to the direction of the BIH Conventional Terrestrial Pole (CTP) (epoch 1984.0) with an uncertainty of 0.005

- X-Axis = Intersection of the IERS Reference Meridian (IRM) and the plane passing through the origin and normal to the Z-axis. The IRM is coincident with the BIH Zero Meridian (epoch 1984.0) with an uncertainty of 0.005

- Y-Axis = Completes a right-handed, Earth-Centered Earth-Fixed (ECEF) orthogonal coordinate system

The WGS 84 Coordinate System origin also serves as the geometric center of the WGS 84 Ellipsoid and the Z-axis serves as the rotational axis of this ellipsoid of revolution.

The World Geodetic System 84 is a standard used by most of the world to define exactly where a set of coordinates are on the earth. The issues on using one standard versus another are more than just determining where something is left, right, forward, and aft. Another issue is that the world isn't a perfect sphere, or geoid, and defining where something is can also vary in height above the center of the earth.

ICAO Requirement

[ICAO Doc 9613 ¶3.4] Navigation data may originate from survey observations, from equipment specifications/settings or from the airspace and procedure design process. Whatever the source, the generation and the subsequent processing of the data must take account of the following:

a.   all coordinate data must be referenced to the World Geodetic System — 1984 (WGS-84);

b.   all surveys must be based upon the International Terrestrial Reference Frame;

c.   all data must be traceable to their source;

d.   equipment used for surveys must be adequately calibrated;

e. software tools used for surveys, procedure design or airspace design must be suitably qualified;

f. standard criteria and algorithms must be used in all designs;

g. surveyors and designers must be properly trained;

h. comprehensive verification and validation routines must be used by all data originators;

i. procedures must be subjected to ground validation and, where necessary, flight validation and flight inspection prior to publication. For guidance on the validation process see Doc 9906, Volume 5 — Validation of Instrument Flight Procedures;

j. aeronautical navigation data must be published in a standard format, with an appropriate level of detail and to the required resolution; and

k. all data originators and data processors must implement a quality management process which includes:

   1. i) a requirement to maintain quality records;

   2. ii) a procedure for managing feedback and error reporting from users and other processors in the data chain.

WGS-84 Compliance

You can determine a country's WGS-84 compliance here: https://ww1.jeppesen.com/main/corporate/company/publications/wgs-84.jsp

References

Articles and Books

["FAQs for Operations in Non WGS 84 Airspace"] Honeywell Direct-To, FMS Quarterly Update and Newsletter, December 2011

["Flying to Europe? Think Again"] National Business Aviation Association, April 4, 2005

["Geodesy for the Layman"] Defense Mapping Agency, Building 56 U.S. Naval Observatory DMA TR 80-003, Washington DC 20305, 16 March 1984

[Sobel, Dava] "Longitude: The true story of a long genius who solved the greatest scientific problem of his time," Thomas Allen & Sons Canada Limited, Markham, Ontario, 1995

Canada

[CANPASS] https://www.cbsa-asfc.gc.ca/prog/canpass/privateair-eng.html

[Transport Canada Advisory Circular 700-009] Automatic Dependent Surveillance - Broadcast, 2011-03-11, Transport Canada Standards

[Transport Canada Aeronautical Information Manual] TP 14371, available at: https://tc.canada.ca/en/aviation/publications

Commercial Vendors

[ARINC Handbook] ARINC Voice Services Operating Procedures Handbook, ARINC Headquarters, Aviation Voice Services Support, www.arinc.com, September 27, 2006

[Jeppesen] "Jeppesen" generally refers to the Jeppesen Airway Manual suite of products, including instrument approach plates, en route charts, and text pages. Available at: http://ww1.jeppesen.com/aviation/business/

[PetroValue] Aviation Fuel Handling and Quality Control Procedures Manual, PetroValue Products Canada, Inc., August 2008

EASA / EU

[European Aviation Safety Agency (EASA) Acceptable Means of Compliance (AMC) 20-24] Certification Considerations for the Enhance ATS in Non-Radar Areas using ADS-B Surveillance (ADS-B-NRA) Application via 1090 MHz Extended Squitter, February 5, 2008

[European Aviation Safety Agency (EASA) regulations: http://easa.europa.eu/document-library/regulations#basic-regulation

Hong Kong

[Hong Kong Aeronautical Information Publication, Director-General of Civil Aviaiton, Hong Kong, http://www.ais.gov.hk

International Civil Aviation Organization

[Chicago Convention] "Convention on International Civil Aviation Done at Chicago on the 7th Day of December 1944"

[ICAO Annex 1] Personnel Licensing, International Standards and Recommended Practices, Annex 1 to the Convention on International Civil Aviation, July 2018

[ICAO Annex 2] Rules of the Air, International Standards, Annex 2 to the Convention on International Civil Aviation, July 2005

[ICAO Annex 3] Meteorological Service for International Air Navigation, International Standards and Recommended Practices, Annex 3 to the Convention on International Civil Aviation, July 2018

[ICAO Annex 4] Aeronautical Charts, International Standards and Recommended Practices, Annex 4 to the Convention on International Civil Aviation, July 2009

[ICAO Annex 5] Units of Measurement to be used in Air and Ground Operations, International Standards and Recommended Practices, Annex 5 to the Convention on International Civil Aviation, July 2010

[ICAO Annex 6 Part 1] Operation of Aircraft - Commercial Aircraft, International Standards and Recommended Practices, Annex 6 to the Convention on International Civil Aviation, Part I, July 2018

[ICAO Annex 6 Part 2] Operation of Aircraft - General Aviation, International Standards and Recommended Practices, Annex 6 to the Convention on International Civil Aviation, Part II, July 2018

[ICAO Annex 7] Aircraft Nationality and Registration Marks, International Standards, Annex 7 to the Convention on International Civil Aviation, July 2012

[ICAO Annex 8] Airworthiness of Aircraft, International Standards and Recommended Practices, Annex 8 to the Convention on International Civil Aviation, July 2018

[ICAO Annex 9] Facilitation, International Standards and Recommended Practices, Annex 9 to the Convention on International Civil Aviation, July 2017

[ICAO Annex 10 Vol I] Aeronautical Telecommunications, Radio Navigation Aids, International Standards and Recommended Practices, Annex 10 to the Convention on International Civil Aviation, Vol I, July 2018

[ICAO Annex 10 Vol II] Aeronautical Telecommunications, Communications Procedures, International Standards and Recommended Practices, Annex 10 to the Convention on International Civil Aviation, Vol II, October 2016

[ICAO Annex 10 Vol III] Aeronautical Telecommunications, Communications Systems, International Standards and Recommended Practices, Annex 10 to the Convention on International Civil Aviation, Vol III, July 2007

[ICAO Annex 10 Vol IV] Aeronautical Telecommunications, Surveillance and Collision Avoidance Systems, International Standards and Recommended Practices, Annex 10 to the Convention on International Civil Aviation, Vol IV, July 2014

[ICAO Annex 10 Vol V] Aeronautical Radio Frequency Spectrum Utilization, International Standards and Recommended Practices, Annex 10 to the Convention on International Civil Aviation, Vol V, July 20.31

[ICAO Annex 11] Air Traffic Services, International Standards, Annex 11 to the Convention on International Civil Aviation, July 2018

[ICAO Annex 12] Search and Rescue, International Standards, Annex 12 to the Convention on International Civil Aviation, July 2004

[ICAO Annex 13] Aircraft Accident and Incident Investigation, International Standards, Annex 13 to the Convention on International Civil Aviation, July 2016

[ICAO Annex 14 Vol I] Aerodrome Construction and Design, International Standards and Recommended Practices, Annex 14 to the Convention on International Civil Aviation, Vol I, July 2018

[ICAO Annex 14 Vol II] Heliports, International Standards and Recommended Practices, Annex 14 to the Convention on International Civil Aviation, Vol II, July 2013

[ICAO Annex 15] Aeronautical Information Services, International Standards and Recommended Practices, Annex 15 to the Convention on International Civil Aviation, July 2018

[ICAO Annex 16 Vol I] Environmental Protection - Aircraft Noise, International Standards and Recommended Practices, Annex 16 to the Convention on International Civil Aviation, Vol I, July 2017

[ICAO Annex 16 Vol II] Environmental Protection - Aircraft Engine Emissions, International Standards and Recommended Practices, Annex 16 to the Convention on International Civil Aviation, Vol II, July 2017

[ICAO Annex 17] Security, International Standards and Recommended Practices, Annex 17 to the Convention on International Civil Aviation, March 2017

[ICAO Annex 18] The Safe Transport of Dangerous Goods by Air, International Standards and Recommended Practices, Annex 18 to the Convention on International Civil Aviation, July 2011

[ICAO Doc 4444] Air Traffic Management, Fifteenth Edition, Procedures for Air Navigation Services, International Civil Aviation Organization, 2016

[ICAO Doc 7030] Regional Supplementary Procedures, International Civil Aviation Organization, 2008

[ICAO Doc 7300] Convention on International Civil Aviation, International Civil Aviation Organization, 2009

[ICAO Doc 7910] Location Indentifiers, International Civil Aviation Organization, 2009

[ICAO Doc 8168 Vol I] Aircraft Operations - Flight Procedures, Procedures for Air Navigation Services, International Civil Aviation Organization, 2018

[ICAO Doc 8168 Vol II] Aircraft Operations - Construction of Visual and Instrument Flight Procedures, Procedures for Air Navigation Services, International Civil Aviation Organization, 2014

661

[ICAO Doc 8168] ICAO Abbreviations and Codes, Procedures for Air Navigation Services, International Civil Aviation Organization, 2018

[ICAO Doc 9574] Manual on Implementation of a 300 m (1,000 ft) Vertical Separation Minimum Between FL 290 and FL 410 Inclusive, Second Edition, International Civil Aviation Organization, 2001

[ICAO Doc 9613] Performance Based Navigation (PBN) Manual, International Civil Aviation Organization, 2013

[ICAO Doc 9691] Manual on Volcanic Ash, Radioactive Material and Toxic Chemical Clouds, First Edition, 2001

[ICAO Doc 9859] Safety Management Manual (SMM), International Civil Aviation Organization, 2006

[ICAO Doc 9869] Performance-based Communication and Surveillance (PBCS) Manual, 2017

[ICAO Document 10037] Global Operational Data Link (GOLD) Manual, 2017

[ICAO NAT Doc 001] Guidance and Information Material Concerning Air Navigation in the North Atlantic Region, Seventh Edition, January 2002

[ICAO NAT Doc 003] North Atlantic Operations and Airspace Manual, International Civil Aviation Organization, Edition 2014/2015

[ICAO NAT Doc 007] High Frequency Management Guidance Material for the North Atlantic Region, International Civil Aviation Organization, June 2021

United States

"CFR" Refers to the U.S. Code of Federal Regulations

[14 CFR 1] Title 14 Part 1: Aeronautics and Space, Definitions and Abbreviations, U.S. Department of Transportation

[14 CFR 45] Title 14 Part 45: Aeronautics and Space, Identification and Registration Marking, U.S. Department of Transportation

[14 CFR 61] Title 14 Part 61: Aeronautics and Space, Certification: Pilots, Flight Instructors, and Ground Instructors, Federal Aviation Administration, Department of Transportation

[14 CFR 91] Title 14 Part 91: Aeronautics and Space, General Operating and Flight Rules, U.S. Department of Transportation

[14 CFR 97] Title 14 Part 97: Aeronautics and Space, Standard Instrument Procedures, Federal Aviation Administration, Department of Transportation

[14 CFR 135] Title 14 Part 135: Aeronautics and Space, Operating Requirements: Commuter and On Demand Operations and Rules Governing Persons on Board Such Aircraft, U.S. Department of Transportation

[14 CFR 139] Title 14 Part 139: Aeronautics and Space, Certification of Airports, U.S. Department of Transportation

[19 CFR 122] Title 19 Part 122: Air Commerce Regulations

"AC" refers to U.S. Advisory Circulars

[AC 20-138D] Positioning and Navigation Systems, Change 2, 4/7/16, U.S. Department of Transportation

[AC 20-165B] Airworthiness Approval of Automatic Dependent Surveillance - Broadcast (ADS-B) Out Systems, 12/07/15, U.S. Department of Transportation

[AC 90-96A] Approval of U.S. Operators and Aircraft to Operate Under Instrument Flight Rules (IFR) in European Airspace Designated for Basic Area Navigation (B-RNAV) and Precision Area Navigation (P-RNAV), 1/13/05, U.S. Department of Transportation

[AC 90-100A] U.S. Terminal and En Route Area Navigation (RNAV) Operations, 03/01/07, U.S. Department of Transportation

[AC 90-107] Guidance for Localizer Performance with Vertical Guidance and Localizer Performance without Vertical Guidance Approach Operations in the U.S. National Airspace System, 2/11/11, U.S. Department of Transportation

[AC 90-114B] Automatic Dependent Surveillance-Broadcast (ADS-B) Operations, 12/30/19, U.S. Department of Transportation

[AC 91-70B] Oceanic and International Operations, 10/4/16, U.S. Department of Transportation

[AC 91-85] Authorization of Aircraft and Operators for Flight in Reduced Vertical Separation Minimum Airspace, 8/21/09, U.S. Department of Transportation

[AC 120-42B] Extended Operations (ETOPS and Polar Ops), 6/13/08, U.S. Department of Transportation

[AC 120-47] Survival Equipment for use in Overwater Operations, 6/12/87, U.S. Department of Transportation

[AC 120-61B] In-flight Radiation Exposure, 11/21/14, U.S. Department of Transportation

[AC 120-108] Continuous Descent Final Approach, 1/20/11, U.S. Department of Transportation

[AC 135-42] Extended Operations (ETOPS) and Operations in the North Polar Area, 6/10/08, U.S. Department of Transportation

[AFAIS] Air Force Advanced Instrument School, various presentations, 2009, United States Air Force

[Air Force Manual (AFM) 51-37] Instrument Flying, 1 December 1976, United States Air Force

[Air Force Manual (AFM) 51-40] Air Navigation, Flying Training, 1 July 1973, United States Air Force

[Air Traffic Organization Policy Order JO 7110.65Y] Air Traffic Control, August 15, 2019, U.S. Department of Transportation

[Department of Defense (DoD) Dictionary of Military and Associated Terms] Joint Publication 1-02, 15 November 2013

[ESTA] Electronic System for Travel Authorization, https://www.cbp.gov/travel/international-visitors/esta?_ga=2.58760104.483451993.1615493828-427055092.1615381403

[FAA MMEL Policy Letter] High Frequency (HF) Communications, MMEL Policy Letter (PL)106, Revision 5 GC, June 6, 2014, U.S. Department of Transportation

[FAA-H-8083-15B] Instrument Flying Handbook, U.S. Department of Transportation, 2012

[National Geodetic Survey] https://www.ngs.noaa.gov

[NIMA] World Geodetic System 1984, Department of Defense, National Imagery and Mapping Agency (NIMA), NSN 7643-01-402-0347, NIMA TR8350.2, Third Edition, Amendment 1, 3 Janaury 2000

[Order 8900.1 Vol 3] General Technical Administration, U.S. Department of Transportation

[Order 8900.1 Vol 4] Aircraft Equipment and Operational Authorizations, U.S. Department of Transportation

[United States Aeronautical Information Manual (AIM)] Official Guide to Basic Flight Information and ATC Procedures, U.S. Department of Transportation

[United States Aeronautical Information Publication] Updated by NOTAM, U.S. Department of Transportation

[USGS, Encounters of Aircraft with Volcanic Ash Clouds: A Compilation of Known Incidents, 1953-2009] U.S. Department of the Interior, U.S. Geological Survey, Data Series 545, Version 1.0, 2010

[Visa Waiver Program] https://travel.state.gov/content/travel/en/us-visas/tourism-visit/visa-waiver-program.html

[www.aphis.usda.gov] http://www.aphis.usda.gov/wps/portal/aphis/home]

Index

666

James Albright is an average pilot with average stick and rudder skills, but has an above average desire to learn and instruct. He spent twenty years in the United States Air Force as an aircraft commander, instructor pilot, evaluator pilot, and squadron commander. After retiring as a lieutenant colonel, he went on to fly for several private and commercial operators as an international captain, check airman, and chief pilot. His logbook includes the T-37B, T-38A, KC-135A, Boeing 707, Boeing 747, Challenger 604, and the Gulfstream III, IV, V, 450, and VII.

His website, www.code7700.com attracts nearly five million hits each month and his articles have appeared in several magazines, most notably Business & Commercial Aviation.